Leo Laporte's

2004 Technology Almanac

By Leo Laporte
with Megan Morrone

Contents at a Glance

TechTV Leo Laporte's 2004 Technology Almanac

International Standard Book Number: 0-7357-1404-5

Library of Congress Catalog Card Number: 2003104258

Printed in the United States of America

First printing: September, 2003

08 07 06 05 04 03   7 6 5 4 3 2

Interpretation of the printing code: The rightmost double-digit number is the year of the book's printing; the rightmost single-digit number is the number of the book's printing. For example, the printing code 03-1 shows that the first printing of the book occurred in 2003.

Trademarks

Warning and Disclaimer

Bulk Purchases/Corporate Sales

The publisher offers discounts on this book when ordered in quantity for bulk purchases and special sales. For sales within the U.S., please contact Corporate and Government Sales at (800) 382-3419 or corpsales@pearsontechgroup.com. Outside of the U.S., please contact International Sales at (317) 581-3793 or international@pearsontechgroup.com.

Publisher
Nancy Ruenzel

Associate Publisher
Stephanie Wall

TechTV, Vice President, Strategic Development
Glenn Farrell

Production Manager
Gina Kanouse

TechTV Project Manager
Sasha Zullo

Acquisitions Editor
Wendy Sharp

Development Editor
Carol Person

Project Editor
Jake McFarland

Copy Editor
Krista Hansing

Indexer
Greg Pearson

Composition
Wil Cruz
Jake McFarland

Manufacturing Coordinator
Dan Uhrig

Interior Designer
Alan Clements

Cover Designer
Alan Clements

Cover Photograph
Mark Compton

Media Developer
Jay Payne

Marketing
Scott Cowlin
Tammy Detrich
Hannah Onstad Latham

Publicity
Kim Lombardi

650 Townsend Street
San Francisco, California 94103

Table of Contents

Contents

Contents

Contents

Contents

About the Authors

About the Authors

Leo Laporte is the host of *The Screen Savers* and *Call for Help* on TechTV. He has been a television and radio personality for more than two decades, focusing exclusively on high tech since 1991. He won an Emmy award in 1997 for his work as the virtual character, Dev Null, on MSNBC's *The Site*. Leo lives on a small farm in northern California with his wife, Jennifer, two children, two goats, two sheep, and two cats. The farm is equipped with high-speed wireless networking, but so far none of the animals has shown an interest.

Megan Morrone is a regular contributor, writer, frequent host, and resident Mom of *The Screen Savers* on TechTV. She began her TechTV career as the web producer and shortly after her arrival was forced

kicking and screaming in front of the camera. Megan recently became a real mom herself, but did not (much to the chagrin of fans) actually give birth on television. She lives North of San Francisco with her husband, Marco, and her baby, Annabella. You can see pictures and read all their secrets at www.jumpingmonkeys.com.

About the Contributors

About the Contributors

Mikkel Aaland is a photographer, writer, web producer, and the author of seven books. He is also the co-founder of Tor Productions, a multimedia company founded in 1989, specializing in the use of the still image in new media. He has lectured and taught on that subject at Stanford University, Drexel University, and University of California at Berkeley, as well as speaking at computer graphics conferences around the country.

Phil Allingham is the managing editor for *Call for Help*, working to ensure the accuracy of every tip, story, and article. He started his TechTV (ZDTV) career as the tech wrangler for both *The Screen Savers* and *Call for Help* when the network launched. He also worked as a product analyst for *Fresh Gear* and the technical editor for ZDTV News.

Joshua Brentano is a feature-film screenwriter and currently a segment producer for *The Screen Savers* at TechTV.

Nicole Carrico is a writer, editor, amateur air-hockey champion, and former web producer for *The Screen Savers*. She now leads TechTV's Late Night Web Team in their endless quest for outrageous fun.

Jim Chace is the manager of the PG&E Energy Center in San Francisco.

Roger Chang has been with TechTV since its launch in May 1998. He is currently segment producer for *Call for Help*. He hopes to build and fly his own ultralight and raise llamas by the time he is 60.

Hahn Choi is a technical analyst with TechTV Labs, where he covers mobile computing, wireless, and other technologies.

Sumi Das is the former host of *Fresh Gear*. She now works for MSNBC. Born in Wimbledon, England, Sumi grew up in San Jose, California and graduated from the University of California at Berkeley with a bachelor's in psychology and English.

Dick DeBartolo, known as *MAD Magazine's* maddest writer, has had a story in every issue for the past 35 years. And for the past 20 years, he's also been "The Giz Wiz," showing the latest gizmos and gadgets. If you need more info (and why would you?) go to www.gizwizbiz.com. Oh, okay, go there; it's a fun website.

Liam Deely, associate producer for *Fresh Gear*, joined the *Fresh* crew full time in November 1999. Homegrown in San Francisco, Liam graduated from San Francisco State University with a bachelor's in broadcasting. When he's not engaged in web duties at TechTV or tweaking sound at major-league baseball games, Liam can be found beating drumheads and breaking guitar strings.

Yoshi DeHerrera is a product specialist for *The Screen Savers*. He spends much of his time building wild and wonderful contraptions for the show.

Chris DiBona is the vice president of marketing and co-founder for Damage Studios. Damage is producing the massively multiplayer game, Rekonstruction, set in a post-apocalyptic earth. Chris regularly presents segments on Linux and Open Source–related technologies for TechTV.

Nicole Guilfoyle is the web producer for TechTV's *Call for Help* and *The Screen Savers*. She hopes to have 30 cats by the time she retires.

James Hamilton is TechTV's primetime web producer and despises all things Apple.

Andrew Hawn, labs director and managing editor of product reviews for TechTV, is responsible for establishing TechTV Labs' testing methodologies, mapping out product coverage, and setting editorial tone for each show on the network. He's charged with filtering content to deliver entertaining and insightful programming on news, events, products, and people relevant to both the world of technology and TechTV's loyal viewers.

Robert Heron is a product analyst, a.k.a. lab rat, with TechTV Labs.

Craig Higdon is a production assistant for TechTV's *Call for Help*.

Dan Huard answers your calls on *The Screen Savers* and loves his mother.

Imelda Jimenez is an intern for *Call for Help*.

Jack Karp is a former web producer for TechTV's *Cybercrime* show.

James Kim has been called TechTV's resident tech guru.

Mark Klatte has been a web producer for *The Screen Savers*, *AudioFile*, and various other TechTV shows.

Chris Kraus formerly worked on *Call for Help* and the TechTV information technology team.

Sarah Lane is the senior segment producer on *The Screen Savers*. She also keeps the audience up to date with the world online with weekly Blog Reports, download suggestions, and the latest, best, worst, and weirdest websites.

Brett Larson is our resident Mac evangelist at TechTV, trying his best to inform the world on the wonders of the Mac. He runs a small, self-named website, www.BrettLarson.com, on which he shares his knowledge of the Mac with other TechTV viewers.

Josh Lawrence was a web producer for *The Screen Savers* and has now escaped to TechTV's late night *Outrageous Fun* programming block, concentrating on *Anime Unleashed*, because he can turn himself into a mecha. His own outrageous fun can be found at www.mozomedia.com.

Ed Lee is a former associate web producer for TechTV.

Roman Loyola is a web producer for *The Screen Savers*. His website is at www.romansempire.com.

Fawn Luu is *Call for Help*'s biggest helper.

Lindsay Martell is a segment producer for *Tech Live*. Prior to joining theTechTV team, she field produced for CNBC Business News in Palo Alto,California. Her freelance writing has appeared in *New Moon Magazine* and *Oyster Boy Review*.

Greg Melton spends every working hour at TechTV writing out all of *Call for Help*'s demos and PC tips for the website. When not at work, he spends most of his time surfing, playing in a band, or filming live music and posting clips to his website, www.showpost.com.

Tom Merritt supervisies all content on TechTV.com and helps integrate the web into TechTV's shows.

Rich Migliozzi is a web producer for TechTV's *Unscrewed*.

Dan Mitchell is the line producer on *Call for Help* and one of the original members of *The Screen Savers*.

Bert Monroy is a digital artist and author of *Photoshop Studio with Bert Monroy*. Bert also co-authored the first book ever written on Photoshop. Visit www.bertmonroy.com.

Patrick Norton is a sailor, skateboarder, and all-around good guy. He is the co-host and Alpha Geek on *The Screen Savers*, and he's terribly upset that Leo has yet to send him a check for his contributions to the 2002 and 2003 almanacs.

Gary Nurenberg, leaving his drummer's slot in The Aggressive Duck, became Washington, DC Chapter Chairman of the Worldwide Fairplay for Frogs Committee in the early 70's. A lawyer, Gary is now a television correspondent in DC, where he has failed to convince Martha to name any of their three greyhounds Leo.

Billy Parkinson was the former tech expert on *Call for Help*.

Chris Pirillo is a former TechTV personality. He is also the creator of the world-famous Lockergnome (www.lockergnome.com).

Russ Pitts is a former producer of TechTV's *The Screen Savers*.

David Prager is a producer for TechTV's *The Screen Savers* and claims to be the true genius behind Leo Laporte.

Eileen Rivera has been with TechTV since 2000. Her many TechTV lives include TechTV radio producer and *Tech Live* segment producer. Currently she plays games for a living as a contributor to *X-Play*.

Dave Roos was formerly an associate producer for the website on *The Screen Savers*. Now he lives in Mexico and will always claim to be the true genius behind Leo Laporte.

Kevin Rose, TechTV's "Dark Tipper," is the underground side of *The Screen Savers*. If it has to do with computer security, crazy modding, hacking, or anything a little bit shady—Kevin is our man.

Martin Sargent is a former contributor to *The Screen Savers* and is currently the host of TechTV's late-night program, *Unscrewed*.

Cat Schwartz currently co-hosts *Call For Help* with Leo, where she informs the audience about the latest hot spots on the web. Cat also contributes to www.techtv.com. Her personal site is www.catschwartz.com.

Adam Sessler has been the host of TechTV's *GameSpot*, *Extended Play*, and *X-Play*, which are all the same show with a different name.

David Spark is a comic and writer. His website is www.davidspark.com. Please don't call him Sparkles.

Richard Statter is a former production assistant for *Call for Help*.

David Stevenson is a reporter for *TechLive*.

Alison Strahan has filled myriad roles at TechTV, from reporter to line producer, and is a contributing writer to www.techtv.com. She has acted in film, TV, and theater productions in the USA and her native Australia.

Michelle VonWald is a freelance writer and former producer for TechTV's *Call for Help*. She's currently working on TechTV's *Unscrewed*.

Morgan Webb is the Windows expert on TechTV's *The Screen Savers*. She is also the co-host of TechTV's gaming show, *X-Play*.

Ray Weigel is a former technical analyst to TechTV. You can now find him tinkering away at his own site, www.samuraimind.com.

Wil Wheaton built Wil Wheaton Dot Net, and he writes books. He used to be an actor, and he thinks Morgan Webb is the hottest girl on TV. But please don't tell her. It would make things weird.

Allen Woo is a former lab rat for TechTV.

Darci Wood formerly wrangled products for *The Screen Savers*. You can find her online at www.labmistress.com.

About the Technical Reviewers

These reviewers contributed their considerable hands-on expertise to the entire development process for *TechTV Leo LaPorte's 2004 Technology Almanac*. As the book was being written, these dedicated professionals reviewed all the material for technical content, organization, and flow. Their feedback was critical to ensuring that *TechTV Leo LaPorte's 2004 Technology Almanac* fits our readers' need for the highest-quality technical information.

Robert Blader has worked at the Naval Surface Warfare Center, Dahlgren Division, since 1985. Since 1999 he's worked specifically in computer security and computer forensics. Robert has edited training manuals for SANS and has done technical editing for Sams Publishing (including *Maximum Security* and *Maximum Windows 2000 Security*). He has taught computer forensics at the International Association of Computer Investigative Systems (IACIS) yearly training conference. He graduated from Long Island University with a degree in computer science and earned a certification in computer forensics (Certified Forensics Computer Examiners) from IACIS.

James F. Kelly is co-owner of Those Computer People, Inc., a Houston-based IT consulting company that specializes in networking and hardware/software integration. He has more than nine years of experience in the IT arena, and has MCSE, Network+, Security+, and MCT certifications. When not assisting clients, he can usually be found at Java House Coffee, taking advantage of its wireless network and answering email.

Karen Weinstein is a computer consultant residing in North Potomac, Maryland. She has more than a decade of experience in PC sales and support. Karen has tech edited numerous computer books and online courses on topics including upgrading and repairing PCs, building a PC, high-speed Internet access, MS Office, and MS Visio. In addition to tech editing and tinkering with her own PC, Karen's favorite activities include spending time with her two daughters, her husband Mark, and her beautiful basset hound, Cleo. Karen welcomes comments at kweinst565@aol.com.

Acknowledgments

One man does not an almanac make. We want to acknowledge all our on-air comrades who contributed their hard work and brain power, namely Patrick Norton, Morgan Webb, Cat Schwartz, Kevin Rose, Yoshi Deherrera, Dan Huard, Roger Chang, Sarah Lane, and Martin Sargent. Special thanks goes to those writers you don't see on TV every day: Roman Loyola, Nicole Carrico, Dave Roos, Josh Lawrence, Joshua Brentano, Alison Strahan, Tom Merritt, and our friends from *Call for Help* and the products lab, particularly Michelle Von Wald, Nicole Guilfoyle, and Greg Melton.

And these are just the writers. There are countless others behind the camera without whom there wouldn't be a daily television show or this book.

Finally, we owe so much to the amazing triumvirate of Carol Person, Sasha Zullo, and Wendy Sharp. We thank Carol for her amazing organizational skills. She was able to take the mountain of content we gave her and turn it into something that makes sense. At least, we think it makes sense. Sasha worked late hours coordinating all of our efforts and making sure no digital stone went unturned. And special thanks to our editor, Wendy, for keeping us calm (and always understanding Megan's ultimate challenge of working at home with a newborn).

Foreword

Foreword

The Screen Savers was founded on a fairly simple premise back in 1998: Create a TV clubhouse for people who love to share their knowledge and love of computers with each other, and open the door to everybody. Back then, Windows 98 hadn't yet been released, a PII 500 mHz was state of the art, and no one had ever heard of Napster, MP3s, or USB. Over the next five years, operating systems have come and gone, and our appetites for bandwidth, memory, and processing speed remain insatiable, but *The Screen Savers* has remained a daily can't-miss party for tens of thousands of people. Even with over 1,000 episodes in the logbook, the show continues to amaze, entertain, and inform all of us who help make it. What makes it work? Simple: a very talented group of people doing what they love in front of a live, worldwide audience.

At the center of it all is Leo Laporte, the ringleader, professor, and party host. Leo's ability to make computers fun, to break down and explain technology's complex and confusing quirks, and to leave people with smiles on their faces, is unique.

Patrick Norton, a.k.a. Alpha Geek, is the Yang to Leo's Yin. Whether it's putting a new video board through its paces, building (or breaking) a new computer from scratch, decrying the hype on a new gadget of the month, or just giving advice to a caller on the brink of computer-driven despair, Pat always manages to keep it real.

Yoshi, our Mad Modder; Kevin, the Dark Tipper; Sarah, the super-blogger; Megan, our lady of Macs and downloads; and Jessica, our site finder and utility infielder are more than a supporting cast. These folks really do have to do it all: find, research, pitch, write, produce, and present their own content...and in the most entertaining fashion. The creativity, consistency, and spirit of these up-and-comers is really a delight to watch, both on the air and behind the scenes.

Some highlights over the past year or so: Yoshi built the Y-boxx to revolutionize the way gamers game. Everyone on the show came in mimicking Patrick and wearing kilts. We took apart the real tech of *Star Trek*. Patrick overclocked his computer with liquid nitrogen. The ladies took over for a night. Two geeks got married on the show. Yoshi got "tased." Patrick demolished more than one computer. Kevin Rose showed us how to build a Mac using PC parts and how to take over and unleash the Microsoft Xbox. Kevin Mitnick went online for the first time since he went to jail. We've been visited by Kevin Spacey, Willie Nelson, Woz, Hal Sparks, They Might Be Giants, and a zillion others.

But none of this would have happened without a ton of hard work from people the audience never really notices. The production team, including Ken, Joshua, Heather, David, Dan, Kimberly, Alison, Hanson, Halley, a terrific group of student interns, and a dedicated and talented studio crew, pull the show together every day, setting the stage so the magic can happen. There's a little bit of each of them in this book.

And finally, there's you. *The Screen Savers* has developed a wonderful, loyal core of dedicated fans...and that's for good reason. *The Screen Savers* documents and reflects the movement of technology in and through the world today—and people want to be a part of it. The show rides the forefront of technology the way a surfer rides the front side of a wave. The audience is as much a part of the show as anybody on staff. To that end, *The Screen Savers* isn't the product of a few people's hard work, it's a phenomenon, an ever-changing interaction among friends. It's a mini-movement.

So Leo and the team have gathered the best, most useful, and most sought after tech information from *The Screen Savers* for this book. We hope you have as much fun reading and using it as we have every day working with the cast and crew. Whether you're a user or a fan or just someone who likes to read...Leo's almanac belongs within reach. There's a page of good reading for every day of the year.

Peter Hammersly
Paul Block
Executive Producers

Introduction

Introduction

Welcome to *Tech TV Leo Laporte's 2004 Technology Almanac*. If you're the type to jump right into page one of a book without any idea of what you're getting yourself into, then you probably aren't reading this right now. If you are reading this right now, then I assume you're here for a little guidance, and I aim to please.

If you've enjoyed Leo's past almanacs, then you know that they're always busting at the seams with fresh computer help and generously sprinkled with crazy tech wisdom that's just for fun. It's content that you would normally see on an episode of *The Screen Savers*, but in a format that you can linger over like a good novel. There are two main differences in this year's book. The first is that this year we've included more of the hard work and knowledge of the entire Screen Savers crew; and second, we've organized each month around a single topic.

Let's get to the first difference first. People often ask me if Leo is the same person on and off camera. When it comes to helping people with computers, the answer is yes. I have never seen him refuse to help people with their computer problems, even when he's tired, even when he's busy, even when the cameras are off. And although this year's almanac is more of a group effort, you'll find a bit of Leo in every article. You're not the only one who learns from Leo. Through the years he's influenced everyone on our team in one way or another. He is and has always been the driving force behind *The Screen Savers* on television, on the web, and in print.

That said, this year's almanac includes more of the personality of the entire staff, from Kevin's look at the darker side of tech to Sarah's hip take on the changing face of the web. We've even included work from your favorite past stars of *The Screen Savers*, such as Morgan Webb and Martin Sargent. The content is as varied as an episode of show itself. And as is true for the show, you probably won't agree with all of our opinions on everything, but it wouldn't be very much fun if you did, would it?

Now, a few words on organization. In 2004 we still offer a handful of content for every day of the year (including weekends), but as an added bonus we've organized each month around a single topic. From wireless to gaming to security, and more, you'll find a variety of help and how-to's dedicated to a single subject for each day of each month. On most days we provide one longer piece and a smattering of shorter tips, websites, and polls. The results of the polls come from our website. We're not talking exact science here, but if a hanging chad here and there was good enough for America, then it's good enough for us.

This book also revives a feature from the very first almanac—Laporte Support. One of Leo's greatest gifts is answering tech questions in a way we can all understand. Whenever you see the heading "Laporte Support," you'll find Leo's answers to your questions, with supporting support from Patrick.

But that's not all. In these pages, you'll find a collection of product reviews from our lab. All of these reviews are based on extensive and unbiased testing, with educated opinions from our experienced lab rats, mainly James Kim, Andrew Hawn, and Robert Heron. Although our opinions sometimes differ, we have always stood behind their work.

As in past years, we've made every human effort to make this book as technically accurate as possible. But we're still not at the point where all book publishing is instantaneous. As a result, from the time the manuscript passes from our hands to yours, some URLs may no longer work, prices of products may have gone up or down, and a brand new utility, software update, or service may have made our tips obsolete. We hope you can forgive. And if you can't, we always want to hear about it. You can email any of us with your opinions on our opinions. Most of our email addresses are simply our first name plus @techtv.com (i.e., megan@techtv.com). We don't always have time to respond to all of our mail, but we all read it.

Now, it's up to you. You can read this book one day at a time, devour it all in one night, or use it as a desk reference for many years to come. Whatever you do with it, we hope this book teaches you, amazes you, saves you from disaster, and makes you laugh. But most of all we hope it helps.

Make Your Computer New for the New Year

Megan Morrone

This year, you could resolve to exercise more, quit biting your fingernails, or floss every day. But those resolutions are so mundane, so Dr. Phil. And even if you do quit biting your fingernails, when your hard drive crashes and you haven't backed up your data, I guarantee you'll be gnawing on a cuticle before you can say "Useless New Year's resolution." Flossing might mean that you save your teeth, but who needs teeth when you've lost your precious data. Because few of us can afford to replace our systems as often as we'd like to (or as often as we used to), we thought we'd show you creative ways to upgrade your PC—and I'm not just talking about adding more memory or hard drive space. Each day for the entire month you'll find our best tips for making your computer new for the new year. It won't be hard, but it will take some resolve on your part. Because January is the month for making New Year's resolutions, I'll start you off with my top five.

1. **Back up your data.** When I think of getting burned by not backing up data, the image of a college student losing a prized paper always comes to mind. But now that so many of us own digital cameras, a crashed hard drive could mean more than drinking a Jolt and staying up all night to re-create your brilliant theories on the Russian revolution. How could you ever re-create the photograph you took of your baby's first smile? Read Leo's "Backup Basics" on January 1.

2. **Clear out your files.** January is a perfect time to resolve to get all the garbage off your PC, especially if you're running low on hard drive space. Backing up is good for protecting data, but it's also great for freeing up space. Remember, the space doesn't become available until you empty the recycle bin.

3. **Clean off your desktop.** If your Windows XP desktop is constantly full of random icons, take a minute to use the desktop cleanup utility. If you're using a Mac, move everything out of the finder that you don't use on a daily basis. If you're using OS X, delete the icons that you don't need from the dock and add the programs that you really do use.

4. **Organize your bookmarks.** While you're recovering from New Year's Eve, take some time to organize your Favorites or Bookmark folders. If you haven't already, choose a half-dozen of the sites that you visit every day and drag them right to your toolbar on your browser. A little time now will save you a lot of time later. Get tips for organizing your bookmarks on January 6.

5. **Clean your computer.** It's one thing to delete useless icons off your desktop, but maybe what you need is real physical computer cleaning. Have you taken a good look at your keyboard lately? I've looked at mine, and it's disgusting.

This is just a taste of the tips you'll find to help you make an old computer seem like new again.

Backup Basics

Leo Laporte

Your hard disk will crash. Count on it. It happens to everyone eventually. And when it does, you will be glad you have a backup copy of all your data. You do have an up-to-date backup, don't you? Never fear. Here are the simple rules of data recovery for people who hate to back up.

Where Do I Store Backups and What Should I Use?

I strongly recommend using removable media. If you can't take it with you, it's not a backup. I know an author who lost an entire novel because her backups were stored next to the computer when her house burned to the ground.

Forms of Removable Media

You can back up to floppy disks, but floppies aren't reliable for long-term archival storage. And filling dozens of floppies is so time-consuming that most people put off backing up until it's too late.

Many users want to emulate businesses and back up to tape drives. Tapes are cheap, and their huge capacities make it easy to back up an entire hard drive. But I don't like tape backups because you're never sure whether the data is really there.

I use a CD recorder. These devices cost as little as $75, with blank CDs costing pennies apiece when bought in bulk. Each CD stores 650–700MB, so I can back up all my data monthly for very little cost. CD storage is compact, compatible with nearly every PC on the market, and likely to last for several decades at least. Recordable CDs are as close as you can get to backup nirvana.

CD-RWs (CD rewritables) present another alternative. CD-RWs cost a little bit more per media than CD-Rs, but are well worth it. You can drag and drop directly to the disc, just like when you copy files to a floppy disc.

If portability is more important than storage space, nothing beats a USB thumb drive. These tiny devices are the size of your thumb (hence the name) and can store up to 2GB. I don't recommend one thumb drive over another;

however, the drive you choose should be compatible with the USB mass storage requirement. This means you won't need a driver no matter what operating system you use. Simply plug the thumb drive into any computer with a USB port, and you're good to go.

Older removable storage mediums such as Iomega's Zip (www.iomega.com) are suitable if you already have the required drive. These disks hold 100–250MB—that's plenty of space to back up all your irreplaceable data. However, your money is better spent on a CD-R/RW drive if you don't already own a Zip drive.

Backup Methods

You can also use a second hard drive or create a special partition on your current hard drive to back up data. Programs such as PowerQuest's Drive Image (www.powerquest.com), Norton's Ghost (www.symantecstore.com), and Dantz's Retrospect (www.dantz.com) image all the contents of your hard drive and create a second version. This type of software is ideal only if you have a second hard drive, though. Keep in mind that backing up to a separate partition on the same hard drive isn't going to be recoverable if your hard drive crashes.

Laporte Support

Remote Desktop Connection Client 1.0.1 for Mac

Microsoft has a utility that allows you to connect to a Windows-based computer and work with programs and files on that computer from your Macintosh computer (http:// microsoft.com/ mac/otherproducts/otherproducts.asp+?pid= remotedesktopclient).

Windows XP Built-In System Diagnostic Tools

Patrick Norton

You don't have to go anywhere to get the following tools—they're right there in Windows.

Device Manager

To get to the Device Manager in Windows XP, right-click My Computer, select Properties (or go to the Control Panel and select System), click the Hardware tab, and then click the Device Manager button.

No red X's or yellow exclamation points? Good. Windows didn't find a piece of hardware without a driver. If the device isn't in here, Windows XP can't see it.

Display Properties

Right-click the Desktop. Select Properties and then Settings. You can now tweak your screen resolution and color depth. And if you click the Advanced button and select the Monitor tab, you can jack up your screen's refresh rate. Max it out. Your eyes will thank you.

Click the Adapter tab and then the List All Modes button. You'll get a list of every resolution and refresh rate your card can support

Administrative Tools

Go to the Control Panel and select Administrative Tools to open a folder with a stash of stuff. Performance and Computer Management are most useful for home users.

Click Computer Management, and you get the Swiss army knife of onboard XP tools. The Device Manager is listed. So are all your Local User and Group settings.

What's most important for hardware? The Storage tools. Click Disk Management (under the Storage icon) to see how each drive is partitioned, formatted, and used. You can repartition and format disks here (you'll lose your data). Every disk should be labeled Healthy, which means that the OS can read the format and that nothing's gone wrong with the drive.

How to Clean Out Windows Device Manager

Joshua Brentano

Make your computer perform better by doing some house-cleaning.

Believe it or not, Windows isn't the smartest operating system in the world. Installing and removing hardware can clog the Device Manager with useless devices that may cause your system to perform poorly.

The solution is to delete those garbage items without removing something important.

> *Warning:* These steps are a guide. Your system may have other devices not listed. Deleting the wrong device can cause your system to stop functioning or perform strangely. However, most of the time, deleting a device that is needed will just cause Windows to reload it on the next system boot, so keep your drivers handy.

1. Boot into safe mode.
2. Click Start, go to Settings, click Control Panel, and double-click System. Click on Device Manager.
3. You are looking for duplicate items or items that you know for a fact are not installed in your system. If you find them, choose those duplicates and remove both of them. Windows will reload them the next time the system boots.
4. Do not remove devices that do not have duplicates; chances are, you'll cause more problems than you'll solve.
5. Once you have deleted the devices, reboot the system. Windows will detect any actual devices and will ask you for any needed drivers.

Must-Have System Diagnostic Tools

Patrick Norton

The basic Performance Monitor setup tracks CPU usage (percentage of processor time), physical memory (pages per second), and disk usage (average disk queue length). This tool let's you get a feel for what's creating a bottleneck in your PC or see the difference between running Word, Winamp, and a half-dozen browser windows vs. any recent 3D video game, for example.

PC Pitstop

This website is a kind, gentle, newbie-friendly tool that interprets the data it gets from your system. Leo loves PC Pitstop. The software asks for an email address, but you can test anonymously. Ignore Creating an Account if you don't want to keep logs of your test scores on the PC Pitstop website. Frankly though, if you find problems and try to correct them, the logs can come in handy.

PC Pitstop offers a list of Top Tips and a chart of flags that mark your problem areas. Red is for big problems, yellow is for areas you can improve, and checkered flags signify that everything is OK.

Unfortunately, there are more pop-up ads on the PC Pitstop website, but it's still a very useful tool (www.pcpitstop.com).

SiSoftware Sandra

SiSoftware Sandra has a ton of icons. Each icon launches a different application that either tests your PC or looks at a subsystem in your PC to tell you what exactly is in there. Examples:

- System summary
- Mainboard information
- CPU and BIOS information
- DirectX information
- OpenGL video information, CMOS information

It also offers benchmarks for everything from file systems to cache and memory bandwidth. It even has programs for checking your file types, installed applications, and a performance tuneup wizard.

The performance tuneup wizard gave me a list of about 25 tips for improving performance. There are also less-useful tips, such as, "A mouse with a wheel is recommended for better control" (www.sisoftware.demon.co.uk).

WCPUID

This is my favorite way to get info on a processor and what speed its clock is running. It also lists info on memory, cache, your chipset, and more. Sure, this info is in the other, larger tools, but WCPUID is small and light, and it seems to run faster (www.h-oda.com).

Motherboard Monitor

If your chip and motherboard have the tools to monitor temperatures, this is a fine hunk of software to use to monitor those temps. You can set alarms or even set it to automatically shut down your system when those temps go too high. (See http://mbm.livewiredev.com).

Windows Tips

DLLs to Save Your Windows Machine

Morgan Webb

We've all been there: DLL hell. It's a miserable state in which one or more of your system files (those ending with .dll) have been erroneously overwritten or corrupted, and Windows flails about wildly looking for the information it needs to get itself off the ground.

DLL heaven: In an attempt to help its users, Microsoft has a database of DLL files that you can use to find what DLL is associated with what Windows application. Perhaps a simple reinstall is needed, or you can localize the problem to an Outlook add-on that did more damage than good. Whatever the problem may be, you can get all the DLL information you need from the Microsoft Knowledge base (http://support.microsoft.com). Once there, search for DLL.

Ultimate Data Destruction

Patrick Norton, David Prager, and Roman Loyola

Hard drives grow in storage and shrink in price, so upgrading your hard drive is a no-brainer. But what do you do with that old drive? Chances are, you wipe out the data and donate or sell it. Your data isn't completely gone, however. With a little skill, it can be recovered.

Wipe Out That Drive

The truly paranoid might try to destroy the media with a sledgehammer even after they've wiped the disk with software. The truth is that data can be recovered from physically broken media more easily than from media that's been properly wiped. And if you destroy your drive, they're not likely to take it at the local donation center.

Software Tools

You can use several software tools to wipe out your data. They do a much better job than a simple reformat.

- **Analog X SuperShredder** (www.analogx.com). Free download.
- **LSoft Active@ KillDisk** (www.killdisk.com). Free download. A professional version also is available.
- **Eraser** (www.heidi.ie/eraser/). Free download.
- **AbsoluteShield Internet Eraser** (http://download.internet-track-eraser.com). Free download.
- **OnTrack DataEraser** (www.ontrack.fr/dataeraser/).
- **Tolvanen/Heidi Computers Eraser Available** (www.heidi.ie/eraser). Free download.
- **CyberScrub.** Download the 15-day trial version at https://buy.cyberscrub.com, or go to www.cyberscrub.com to purchase it.
- **Jetico BCWipe.** Visit www.jetico.com for a free 30-day trial, or to purchase.
- **Shred** (www.pcmag.com/). Free download.

- **Multilate File Wiper** (http://home.att.net/~craigchr/mutilate.html). Shareware.
- **Wipe for Linux** (http://wipe.sourceforge.net). Free download.
- **Shredit X for OS X.** Visit www.mireth.com to try it or buy it.
- **Maresware Declasfy** (www.dmares.com). Licensing based on number of users.

Remember, it is not enough just to shred a file. You must destroy the file and the swap file and erase the empty space (or slack space). Zero the whole drive and you'll be safe.

Download of the Day

RegCleaner

Megan Morrone

My computer is a mess. In the last 18 months, I've downloaded and removed more programs than any person has a right to do. So when I threw my old Micron off a cliff a few years ago, it was more mercy killing than murder.

You don't have to take such drastic measures. A free program called RegCleaner (www.vtoy.fi) helps clean out old Registry entries and delete old DLL files.

If the idea of messing with the Registry scares you, don't worry. Jouni Vuorio, author of this program, claims that you don't need to know what the Registry is to use this application. He's basically right, but it still pays to be careful about what you delete. RegCleaner includes an automatic backup feature, just in case your delete finger loses control.

RegCleaner works with Windows 9x, 2000, ME, XP, and NT4. The author warns that support for Windows 95 is limited, and you might have problems running the software on multiprocessor systems.

Organize Your Bookmarks

David Spark

It doesn't take much time or know-how to take control of your bookmarks. Here are some handy tips that will keep you organized.

Bookmarks and Favorites

Internet Explorer saves your web addresses as Favorites, while Netscape, Mozilla, and Safari save them as Bookmarks. Don't be confused—they work the same way. We'll just call them "bookmarks."

There's a difference in the way browsers store bookmarks. Netscape puts all your bookmarks in one file called bookmark.htm. Internet Explorer saves each bookmark as a separate file in your Favorites folder (which is stored in the Windows folder). These Internet shortcut files take up around 100 bytes each.

Check for Dead Links

A website can change its web address, go out of business, or move articles and downloads without informing you. This can leave your bookmarks full of dead links.

Website-Watcher (http://aignes.com/products.htm) is a piece of free software that'll comb through your links and tell you which ones no longer work. Now when you organize your bookmarks, you'll know which links you need to delete right away.

Organize Bookmarks with Freeware

Use the Remark client at MyBookmarks.com (www.mybookmarks.com) to organize your Favorites, Bookmarks, and AOL Favorite Places. It lets you synch all your bookmarks and organize them online.

Put Everything in a Folder

Every time you add a bookmark, give it a home. That way you won't get confused by a long list of bookmarks.

First create and label new folders for all your bookmark categories. When you select File Bookmark from the Bookmark button's pop-up menu, you'll see your list of folders. Just drag and drop your bookmark into the folder of your choosing.

In Internet Explorer, when you add a bookmark, don't click OK. Instead, click the Create In button so you can file the bookmark in a folder.

Branch Your Folders

Nest folders within categories. For example, under Computers, I have one folder for Tech News, one for Software, and one for Tech Support.

Folders Need Not Be Alphabetical

Earlier browsers alphabetized bookmarks. Now you can drag and drop them in the location you prefer.

What's the difference between bookmarks and links on your toolbar? Absolutely nothing, except speed of access. Putting a link on the toolbar makes a site accessible with just one click.

In Netscape, click the Bookmarks button and select Manage Bookmarks. You'll see the Personal Toolbar folder at the top of the list. (It can be moved.) You can edit the Personal Toolbar folder like any other. The only difference is that links in this folder show up on the toolbar.

In Internet Explorer, the toolbar is called Links. You can drag any link from a webpage right onto the Links toolbar in the location you want it. To delete one, just right-click the link and select Delete.

Address: Site of the Day

The Tech Word Spy

Unlock the mysteries of baffling technical jargon and obscure terminology at www.wordspy.com/TechWordSpy.

Top Three Mac-Compatible Mouses

Hahn Choi

Over the years, I've tried to be a dedicated Mac user ("switch" if you prefer Apple's marketing term). But having spent years in a Windows world, I found the differences too great to overcome. Something just didn't feel right, and in the graphical interface world, the mouse is key.

I've grown to love my right-click. Mac's single-button approach made accessing those shortcut menus uncomfortable, and dedicating brain cycles to remembering the awkward Ctrl+click just didn't work for me. Sure, with the right software I could have programmed a two-button mouse. But I'm a software minimalist, especially when it comes to things as basic as the mouse.

With OS X and its native support for two-button mouses, my Mac experience drastically improved. Everything feels as it should, and I look forward to the list of hidden treasures I find with each right-click.

Purchasing a Two-Button Mouse

Don't even consider a ball mouse. They require constant cleaning. Optical mouses or trackballs use light to determine location, so there are no parts to wear out.

Comfort is key. There's a huge selection for righties, but not for lefties. Try one out at a store before purchasing. I prefer the traditional mouse design, but you might feel more comfortable with a trackball or other design.

Look at functions. Beyond the simple two buttons and scroll wheel, many mouses also include extra programmable buttons. You can use them as "back and forward" for surfing the web or "copy and paste" for other applications.

Logitech MouseMan Dual Optical

My favorite mouse is the Logitech MouseMan Dual Optical (www.logitech.com). Dual optical sensors make it fast, especially for online games. It's also comfortable and glides smoothly on most surfaces.

Wireless IntelliMouse Explorer

Microsoft's Wireless IntelliMouse Explorer (www.microsoft.com) isn't cheap, but it's one of the best mouses I've seen. The form-fitting body fits snugly into my hand, but it can be uncomfortable for those with larger hands.

Kensington PocketMouse Pro

With notebooks, I prefer to use a mouse over a track pad or pointing stick. But an external mouse adds to the mess of cables in my bag (power, Ethernet, modem, and so on). The Kensington PocketMouse Pro (www.kensington.com) has a retractable cable. It's an inexpensive and simple two-button optical scroll mouse that does the job.

Laporte Support

Mac OS X NetInfo Manager

If you have a Mac desktop system and a Mac laptop, this tip is for you. Each Mac OS X machine that you log on to saves all of your preferences locally. That means that if you check the same email on your laptop and at home, they never will be synchronized.

Apple's NetInfo Manager allows you to change your home directory to whatever you like, even across your network. For example, you can point your laptop home directory to your home directory at home, or vice versa. This way they share the same information.

Here's how to use NetInfo Manager:

1. Open NetInfo Manager (in Applications, Utilities).

2. Go to the Users section.

3. Choose User. You can change various options here, including your home directory. Just point it across your network.

Modify OS X with .plist Files

Leo Laporte

Mac OS X uses XML for many of its preference files, so it stores preferences in an HTML-like form that you can read and modify. These XML files are stored as Property List (or .plist) files, and you can find them all over your hard drive and inside most application bundles.

You can edit or examine a .plist with any text editor. BBEdit Lite (www.barebones.com) is a good choice, but be careful how you change the file. Any mistakes can render the associated program or even the operating system unusable.

Find the .plists

Open the Library/Preferences folder in your home directory (~/Library/Preferences). Look at all the .plist files! If you've installed the developer tools (free from http://connect.apple.com), double-clicking one of these files opens the PropertyListEditor application.

Otherwise, open them with BBEdit. A good .plist file to edit is com.apple.finder.plist, the Finder's pref file. You'll notice a host of properties and settings inside. The properties are surrounded by the <key> </key> pair. The value follows.

Change Them

Want to change one? Here's how to make a transparent Terminal window:

1. Open ~/Library/Preferences/com.apple.terminal and find the TerminalOpaqueness setting.
2. Change it to 0.85. That's 15% transparency.
3. Save the file (you must be Admin).
4. Open Terminal.

Cool, isn't it?

Another way to modify these files directly is with the Terminal's defaults command. To accomplish the same thing from Terminal, issue the following command:

```
defaults write com.apple.terminal
TerminalOpaqueness '0.85'
```

You can use any setting, from completely transparent, 0, to completely opaque, 1. The freeware System Preference pane TinkerTool (www.bresink.de) does the same thing by modifying the Terminal .plist file for you.

Mac Tips

OS X Secret Keyboard Shortcuts

Leo Laporte

Keyboard Shortcuts with the Dock

Hold down the Option key with menus open to see additional options (for instance, Force Quit in Dock context menu).

Command+Tab switches between applications. You know that already, but keep your finger on Command and tap H to hide the application or Q to quit. Command+Shift reverses direction.

Option+Command+clicking on an application selects that application and hides all others.

Hold Shift and drag the Dock divider to move the Dock up, down, or to the right of the screen.

Hold Option and drag the Dock separator to force the dock to resize.

Other Secret Shortcuts

Command+Option+A opens the Application folder.

Option+Mute brings up System Preferences.

If you hold down Option when you use scrollbars, pages scroll instead of lines.

Modify OS X with .plist Files (continued)

Changing the Time

Let's do something really useful. The following instructions are based on a tip from the awesome Mac OS X Hints website (www.macosxhints.com). Let's change the time format in the menu bar clock. That information is stored in the .GlobalPreferences.plist file in your local preferences folder. It's probably easiest to access this from the Terminal because the Finder can't see filenames that begin with a dot.

1. Open Terminal, cd to ~/Library/ Preferences, and type this:

   ```
   sudo open .GlobalPreferences.plist
   ```

2. After you enter your admin password, the file opens in TextEdit.

3. Find the key named
   NSTimeFormatString %H:%M.

4. You can change this string to anything you like using standard C-style printf codes. The complete list is published in Apple's Developer documentation. For example, to change the menu bar clock to display the date and time, replace the line with this:

   ```
   NSTimeFormatString %a %b %d, %Y
   %I:%M %p
   ```

5. Save the file, and then log out and in again. Your menu bar clock will read something like this:

   ```
   Thu Jul 18, 2002 7:00 p
   ```

I've just scratched the surface of what's possible with .plists. Play around with them, and you'll no doubt find many really useful tricks.

Download of the Day

Folder Size

Megan Morrone

You can speed up your PC by getting rid of excess programs. My favorite tool for uncovering memory hogs is a handy little piece of freeware called Folder Size (www.extech.net).

Simply download and install the program. When you run it, you'll see a window. Choose which drive you want to check. (You'll probably want the C: drive.) Click the Run button.

You can click on the folders to see the sizes of programs in individual folders. When you realize how much space they require, you can make an informed decision about what to keep and what to toss. The only thing missing in this program is the ability to delete folders straight from the Folder Size window.

Windows Tips

Expand Your Folders

Morgan Webb

You can expand all the folders below a parent in a file tree (like the tree you find in the Explorer window or your Registry). Just highlight the parent file and press the asterisk (*) key on the numeric keypad.

You can collapse all the files with the minus (−) key on the numeric keypad. The asterisk and minus keys on the regular keyboard will not have the same effect.

How Do USB Ports Work?

Roger Chang

Your computer probably has at least one USB port, but do you know how to use it?

- How do USB ports work?
- Do USB ports provide power to USB devices?
- Do you have to activate a USB port?

USB stands for Universal Serial Bus, a peripheral bus standard created by Intel. USB ports are what USB devices, such as digital cameras and MP3 players, use to interface with the computer. This interface allows for the transmission not only of data, but also of power for the USB device. It's a plug-and-play technology—just plug in your device, and it's ready to go.

USB 1.1

A USB 1.1 cable consists of four wires. Two are for data, one is for power, and one is a grounding wire. Data speeds are of two types. Low-speed devices run at about 1.5Mbps, and high-speed devices can run at 12Mbps. Power levels in the USB chain reach 500 milliamps, the rated power needed by USB devices that aren't self-powered.

USB 2.0

USB 2.0 increases transmission bandwidth from the 12Mbps of USB 1.1 to 120Mbps, with a possible maximum 480Mbps. USB 2.0 also features enhanced power management and is backward compatible with USB 1.1.

It's meant to be a complement to FireWire (IEEE 1394), with USB taking most consumer peripherals and IEEE 1394 targeting high-end, high-bandwidth devices such as hard drives and digital-video cameras.

USB Hubs

A USB hub, which is a device that expands your number of USB ports, can be powered or unpowered. A powered hub can supply additional power to devices if the power demand exceeds the amount available on the USB chain. This lets you attach several USB devices that use a lot of power. It also means that powered hubs need to be plugged into an electrical outlet. An unpowered hub doesn't need to be plugged in, but it can support only low-power devices such as keyboards and mouses.

Windows Tips

Download Folder

Michelle VonWald

If you're like me, you probably save all of your downloads on your desktop. This can create an unruly mess of icons and random executable files.

Clear up your desktop and organize your downloads into one folder. Simply right-click on the desktop, select New and then select Folder. Name the new folder My Downloads (or whatever name you fancy) and press Enter. The next time you download a program, save it in your Downloads folder.

You don't have to place your new download folder on the desktop. The desktop is a convenient place to access files and folders, though. You might also consider giving every download a name that you'll remember.

Fix Broken Monitors

Patrick Norton

Monitor busted? Just doesn't look right? Here's my checklist of things to try to fix.

Degauss

If you own a recent monitor (last five or six years), it should have a Degauss button. Degaussing is basically the same as demagnetizing. Some monitors automatically degauss the CRT. Degaussing removes improperly aligned magnetic forces that settle in the monitor (usually in the shadow mask) and degrade the signal. Click the button, and it might just fix it. Flat panels don't have this problem.

Cables

Make sure the monitor cables aren't damaged, especially the sensitive pin-filled ends. Using an extra cable or an extra computer to plug your monitor into quickly isolates whether the problem is the monitor or the graphics card and cable. Bad cables cause tons of monitor problems, so make this one of the first things you check.

Setup

Is the monitor set up properly? Tweak the controls until you're satisfied. You can also adjust your monitor using the monitor's bundled software. Monitor diagnostic software helps set everything from brightness and contrast to convergence, and all sorts of other things. Two of our favorites are: DisplayMate for Windows (www.displaymate.com), which contains the most detailed set of monitor tests I've seen, and Nokia Monitor Test (www.construnet.hu/ nokia/Monitors/TEST/monitor_test.html), which is a free monitor test software package by Nokia that has all the basics for setting up your monitor.

Go Inside

Think it's something inside the monitor's case? Go to a pro. Don't go inside your monitor yourself. You can hurt yourself badly by discharging the anode. Take it to a shop with monitor repair experience.

Helpful Links

Tom's hardware guide addresses setting up displays and covers lots you never knew you needed to know at www.tomshardware.com.

You'll find notes on the troubleshooting and repair of computer and video monitors at www.repairfaq.org.

Windows Tips

Speed Up Windows XP

Roman Loyola

Over time, your XP-driven computer can become slower. Want to regain some of that lost speed and maybe make XP faster than before?

Turn off unnecessary services. XP has several services running in the background. But did you know that you don't need all those services turned on? You can turn some of them off for a leaner Windows XP.

Update drivers. Hardware components such as your video card use drivers to work with XP. The latest drivers are often optimized for performance.

Install more RAM. The more RAM you have, the more it can store in this short-term storage area, and the faster your computer runs.

Upgrade your video card. Moving up to the next level of graphic chip will speed up the graphics performance of your computer, which is primarily important for serious gamers.

Optimize your hard drive. When a file is written to your hard drive, it is often scattered among the free sectors. Defragmenting optimizes your hard drive by efficiently reordering the data.

Myths About the Mac

Patrick Norton

Time to debunk some of the myths floating around about the Mac.

File Compatibility

If you're a word processing-jpeg-MP3 kind of user, every one of 'em will work, straight from your Windows PC. It's the obscure stuff that you might have to work to open in OS X. You already checked to see that there's software available to do just that before you bought your Mac, right?

Broadband Connectivity

"My cable/DSL/ISP says they can't connect to Macs." I know people who proved their cable/DSL/ISP wrong on this one. Then the company sent somebody out to learn from said people. The problem isn't the OS.

Available Software

There aren't that many applications for Mac. Ridiculous. Most graphic artists, audio, and video editors claim that the Mac has the superior applications. Unless you're a hard-core gamer, I'd say there are more than enough applications to do just about anything on the Mac.

The exception comes with specific Windows application that can't be substituted. You could run a PC emulator, such as Virtual PC (www.connectix.com), but you'd better have the fastest Mac processor you can find.

Work vs. Home

If my office doesn't use Macs, I can't. Does your office really run any applications that don't have an OS X equivalent?

Affordability

I can't afford a Mac. Well, actually, I teeter on this one. For the price of the cheapest Mac, you can get a PC with a faster processor, a bigger screen, and more memory and hard drive space, not to mention a CD-R burner. A PC with the same specs as the iMac costs a few hundred less.

Will you get the same satisfaction? Therein lies the rub. It's not so hard if you don't have a computer or don't have much invested in a computer. If you have an older printer and a fair number of accessories, and if OS X won't run them, you might have to replace them if you go the Mac route.

Ease of Use

Macs are easier to use. Back in the Windows 3.1 days, sure. Today, I'm not so sure. Any new Mac comes wonderfully set up with a great set of applications. Figuring out the folder metaphors and how to click and drag files? That's pretty much the same on either machine.

Elegance

Macs offer a more elegant and sophisticated environment for computing. Darn tootin'. But, let's face it, not everybody buys a European sedan. There are a lot of pickup trucks and minivans out on the highways.

Mac Tips

What Is Quartz Extreme?

Quartz Extreme is a new feature included with the Jaguar upgrade for Mac OS X. It's a technology that lets the Mac quickly display crisper and cleaner graphics.

The technology doesn't work with all video cards. Quartz Extreme–compatible cards must have one of the following chipsets (your video card must also have at least 16MB of VRAM):

- NVidia GeForce2 MX
- NVidia GeForce3
- NVidia GeForce4 MX
- NVidia GeForce4 Ti
- Any AGP-based ATI Radeon chip

You can't configure Quartz Extreme manually. Jaguar automatically turns it on when it senses a compatible video card.

Add a Second Hard Drive

Greg Melton

If your current hard drive is running out of space or you'd like to speed up those weekly data backups, consider installing a second hard drive.

If you need help opening your computer's case, check the manual. Before you start poking around inside, make sure you're properly grounded. Static electricity can short out the delicate circuitry inside your motherboard. On *The Screen Savers* set we don't have much problem static electricity, but in your home that might not be the case. Ideally, you should set your computer on a grounding mat, but we know that's not practical. Avoid standing on carpet and consider using a wrist strap.

You need an extra space to insert the new drive, an extra spot on the IDE ribbon that's connected to the other hard drive on your system, and an additional four-prong female power supply adapter. Don't forget that you can only have two IDE disks on the same channel.

The IDE ribbon is gray and about 2 inches wide. Sometimes it has a blue or red strip. The ribbon connected to your current hard drive is considered the primary IDE. On the primary IDE ribbon, look for an identical connector like the one connected to your current drive. You use this connector to attach to your new drive.

Follow all the cords coming from the power supply. Find the four-prong female power adapter. Most computers have one or two extras to support additional drives. Use this power adapter to supply power to your new hard drive.

Master or Slave?

When you use more than one hard drive, one drive must be designated a master and the other a slave. *Master* applies to the hard drive your computer boots from, or where the OS is stored. *Slave* refers to any secondary hard drive connected to your system.

You should see a diagram for setting the jumper at the top of your new drive. This diagram should depict different sets of pins with a black box around two of them. Locate the diagram for changing the jumper setting to a slave.

You'll probably need tweezers to change the jumper. Use the tweezers to reposition the jumper between the male prongs and the IDE ribbon connector. To do this correctly, match the settings depicted in the diagram on top of the hard drive.

Most hard drive jumpers are set to master by default, but double-check just to be sure.

To install the new drive, follow these directions:

1. With the power supply still unplugged, place the new drive in its available location.

2. Mount the drive to the computer by screwing two screws on both sides of the chassis.

3. Connect the four-prong power supply to the back of the hard drive.

4. Connect the IDE ribbon to the back of the hard drive.

5. Remove all screwdrivers and additional screws from inside the case and close it.

6. Insert your computer's plug back into its power supply.

When you turn on the computer, it should automatically detect the new drive. Watch as it finds a primary IDE master and another labeled primary IDE slave. You should also see the master and the slave manufacturer's serial number.

If it doesn't recognize the new drive, you'll need to go into the BIOS to designate the new drive as a primary IDE slave. Consult your manual for guidelines on doing this.

Create Restore Points in Windows XP

Greg Melton

System Restore is offered only in Windows XP. If you're familiar with GoBack (www.roxio.com), you might have a good idea of what this feature is all about.

Basically, every time you start your computer, XP automatically creates restore points. A restore point is nothing more than a snapshot of your entire system's settings. If something goes wrong with your machine after a botched installation, you have a way out and won't have to call for help or format your hard drive and start over.

You have the option of creating restore points manually. It's actually a good idea to get into the habit before you load software that's not officially specified by Microsoft to be compatible with XP.

System Restore doesn't affect personal files such as Word documents, browser favorites, or pictures.

Create a Restore Point

To manually set system restore points, follow these steps:

1. Click Start and point to All Programs, Accessories, System Tools, System Restore.

2. In the System Restore Wizard, select the box next to Create a Restore Point, and click the Next button.

3. Type a description for your new restore point. Something like "Before I installed some program that may cause my system major grief" would do just fine, but you don't have to be that descriptive.

4. Click Create.

Okay, so the $20 million question is, how do you restore a point if something bad happens? I'm glad you asked because you can do this one of two ways.

Access Restore Points

During the boot process, you just boot into safe mode (usually by pressing F8) during the post screen. Select the option labeled Last Known Good Configuration (Your Most Recent Settings That Worked) and press Enter. The one drawback to this method is that you don't have the option to select which restore point you'd like to restore. The other method is to boot into basic safe mode and access the System Restore Wizard located in system tools. This method lets you restore based on a calendar of when actual restore points were created and may give you more flexibility in the long run.

Laporte Support

Protect Your Computer with Power Backup

UPS stands for uninterruptible or uninterrupted power supply. It keeps your computer temporarily running if there's a blackout or other electrical disturbance, such as a power sag.

A UPS also acts as a surge suppressor. Most folks buy UPSes that will provide about five minutes of juice after the power goes out. These consumer-level UPSes are little more than batteries in boxes. Businesses tend to invest in massive rack-mount UPS systems that can keep a company's server farm humming until the backup generators take over.

The beefiness of your computer system determines how powerful your UPS should be. The weakest UPS is about 250VA (volt-amperes). Years ago, when everyone had regular Pentium processors and 14-inch monitors, this was fine.

If you have a large 19- or 21-inch monitor and a Pentium II or faster system, not to mention peripherals, you're probably looking at a 400VA to 500VA UPS. Use the calculator at the American Power Conversion Corp. to determine the best UPS for you (www.apcc.com/template/size/apc/rslr/).

Forget Memory Managers

Leo Laporte

No matter how much RAM your computer has, it's never enough. Add the memory requirements of the operating system, your running applications, and all your data, and you're bound to run short of RAM. Yet RAM is where your CPU works on your data and runs your programs.

One of the jobs of your operating system is to juggle applications and data in RAM, swapping or "paging" items in and out of RAM as they're needed. Modern programs are divided into chunks that can be easily swapped in and out.

When a portion of code is no longer needed, it's marked "purgeable," and the operating system can reclaim the memory for other uses. For example, when you print a document, the program loads its printing module. After the job is done, the module is marked "purgeable." Similarly, when a program needs space for data, it asks the OS to claim some from free memory. When it's done with the data, the memory is freed.

Conducting RAM Traffic

As traffic manager, it's the operating system's job to make sure programs get the RAM they need by freeing up space when it's required. If it's absolutely necessary, the operating system can use disk storage as pseudo-RAM. That's what your swap file is for.

The memory manager is one of the most important parts of any operating system. A good memory manager can make a system more efficient and reliable. All modern operating systems, including Linux, Windows XP,

and Mac OS X, have excellent memory managers. However, older versions of Windows and Macintosh didn't do such a good job.

Third-Party Memory Managers

This weakness in older operating systems spawned a slew of programs designed to improve memory management. Are these programs necessary? On any modern system, they're absolutely not needed. And because they take up memory and add to the complexity of the operating system, they actually do more harm than good.

The bottom line: If you're using System 7 on a Macintosh, you need a memory manager. But if you're using a modern OS, such as Windows NT/2000/XP, Mac OS X, or a flavor of UNIX, you should forget that memory manager.

Download of the Day

MacJanitor

Megan Morrone

OS X has a pretty face, but underneath, it's an unwieldy web of UNIX subsystems. These subsystems are designed for machines that run 24×7. To minimize interruption, some important tasks are scheduled for off hours, such as 3 a.m. These subsystems clean up your system and keep it running smoothly. Unfortunately, if you're like most people and occasionally power down your machine, you could interfere with the task schedule and miss out on the benefits.

MacJanitor (http://personalpages.tds.net/ ~brian_hill/macjanitor.html) lets you run these scripts whenever you want. You can't hurt your Mac by running them too often.

Put OpenOffice.org on OS X

Leo Laporte

Recently a viewer wrote:

"I am a poor college student in need of an office suite for my Mac running OS X. I have experience with OpenOffice on Windows, but being new to Mac, the install instructions on their website make me leery. They sound an awful lot like installing an app in Linux, and I would rather have pencils jammed into my eyes than have to install anything in Linux."

Your troubles are over. Install and run OpenOffice.org on Mac OS X.

OpenOffice.org (www.openoffice.org) is the open-source answer to Microsoft Office (and is getting better every day). It includes a word processor, a spreadsheet program, a presentation manager, a formula editor, a drawing program, a data-charting application, and an HTML editor. All the apps can read and write Microsoft Office files and most of its competitors.

The applications are, in nearly every respect, as powerful as the Microsoft equivalent. And why not? OpenOffice.org started with the source code from Sun's excellent Star Office v5. Development is no longer tied to Star Office, and many new features have been added since the two parted company.

Getting It onto a Mac

The biggest difference among Microsoft Office, Star Office, and OpenOffice.org is the price. OpenOffice.org is free. But it used to be that installing it on Mac OS X wasn't easy. You had to manually install X Window because OpenOffice.org is not a native OS X application. It runs under Apple's implementation of FreeBSD, called Darwin, and uses X11 to display on the screen.

But now, thankfully, the OpenOffice.org team has included everything you need, including X Window (Apple or XFree version) in the OpenOffice.org installer. Just download http://porting.openoffice.org and run the installer.

After you install it, you will need to launch OpenOffice.org with the provided Launch OpenOffice app. It will run X Window first and then open OpenOfficeNow, and you're ready to rock and write.

Mac Tips

Find Files Fast in OS X

Leo Laporte

Want to quickly find files in OS X? You can with the UNIX command locate, which is available from the terminal in OS X (it can also be used in any version of UNIX). The command searches a database of files and rapidly comes up with matching entries.

The command uses standard file search wildcards such as * and ?. If no wildcards are used, locate finds every file that contains the provided search text anywhere in the file or folder name.

For example, searching for locate foo nets you results like these: foo.bar pitythefool.txt foolish things/these.txt.

You can make using locate even easier by using the free GUI front end called Locator, which you can download from www.sebastian-krauss.de. Whether you use the command line or the GUI, this method is much faster than the standard Mac search.

Keep It Current

You can also update the file database that locate searches with the accompanying updatedb command, like so:

```
sudo updatedb
```

This should be done regularly—it's a good candidate for a cron entry. What's cron? Well, you can use it to schedule an automatic nightly update to the database, but we can save that for another tip. Or, if you can't wait, you can use Locator's built-in Rebuild Locate Database command to do the same thing.

Change the Logon Message in Windows XP

Morgan Webb

When you disable Fast User Switching in Windows XP and don't use the icon-based logon screen, you log on with the old-school text box, which asks for your username and password.

You can change the text in this box from "Enter a Username and Password That Is Valid for This System" to "Get Your Stinkin' Hands Off My Computer." Or perhaps to something sweeter, such as "Marry Me, Doreen. I'll Get You a New GeForce If You Say Yes."

You could use this trick in a public setting to inform users of the proper policy for logging in, such as, Please See an Attendant for Logon Information. It's a quick Registry hack.

Warning: Hacking the Registry can be dangerous. If you know what you're doing, then just follow these steps:

1. Start the Windows XP Registry. (Go to Start and then Run. Type **regedit**.)

2. Navigate to HKEY_LOCAL_ MACHINE\SOFTWARE\Microsoft\ Windows NT\CurrentVersion\Winlogon.

3. Create a new string value named LogonPrompt and set its value to whatever you want.

Now your computer truly reflects your personality. You can keep the key bookmarked to go back and change it whenever you're feeling particularly creative.

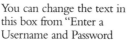

Laporte Support

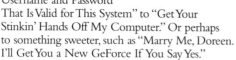

OEM and Refurbished Parts

OEM stands for original equipment manufacturer. OEM parts are usually sold to third-party vendors that resell them to individuals or smaller businesses. OEM parts are available to end users, but you usually get minimal packaging and documentation. Sometimes OEM parts are missing components.

Retail parts are what you typically see on the shelf of your computer store. The parts are nicely packaged and come with complete documentation. They often come with complementary components, such as a fan for a CPU.

A refurbished part is a part that has been returned to the factory, usually because of a physical defect. Some companies label a product refurbished if it has been used and returned but doesn't have a physical problem.

If you can find refurbished products that did not require service, they can be good deals. If you find a refurbished product that has been repaired, be cautious. You're saving money, but you're also investing in a product that is known to have problems.

It's difficult to know if the OEM parts were returned because of defects or simply because the person didn't want the product. You can ask the dealer, but you might not always get an honest answer.

Follow these guidelines when buying OEM products:

1. Make sure your warranty is the same as the original manufacturer's.

2. Buy the most current model.

3. Never buy refurbished hard drives.

17

Drive 10 Disk Utility for OS X

Brett Larson

Drive 10 (www.micromat.com) is an OS X–
based drive utility similar to Norton
SystemWorks. It can be run from a CD and
will even boot your machine so that you can
check startup disks for problems. Remember,
you usually can't run checks on hard drives that
are used for startup. Here's
how to use it:

1. Select the drive from the drop-down
   menu of available drives. Most users will
   see only one. If you have an external drive,
   an added drive in your Power Mac tower,
   or an iPod mounted when running these
   tests, you'll have more than one choice.

2. Click Start Test. The test will take a few
   seconds to a few minutes, depending on
   the size and condition of your disk.

3. You'll get a report of how your drive did,
   as well as explanations of each test performed. If your drive failed any tests, you
   should stop at this point. Back up your
   data before going on with any other tests.

Back up your data! Do not interrupt the optimization process; an interruption could lead to
data loss.

1. Select Optimize Drive from the
   Service menu.

2. Select your drive (yes, again).

3. A quick check is run to show you what
   your drive looks like. Click Start, and away
   it goes.

This can take any length of time, again
depending on the size and condition of
your drive.

Download of the Day

Give Your Mac Trash Can More Oomph

Megan Morrone

I love everything about Mac OS X, except that
the trash can no longer lives on the desktop.
If you'd rather have it close at hand, download
a little tool called Trash X from Northern
Softworks (www.northernsoftworks.com). But
Trash X isn't about aesthetics alone. It also
contains a handful of excellent deleting and
wiping features.

Here's what you can do with Trash X:

- Put the trash on your desktop.

- Bypass the trash and automatically delete
  sensitive items by dragging them to the
  Trash X icon while pressing Command.

- Drag a disk into the Trash X icon to empty
  the trash on that volume.

- Shred sensitive files and folders, as well
  as overwrite them several times for
  extra security.

- Add Trash X to your finder window for
  even easier access.

Trash X is free to try for 30 days and $9.95 to
buy. It requires Mac OS X 10.2.

Warning: If you want to delete an alias, drag it
to the real Trash, not Trash X. If you drag an
alias to Trash X, it will delete the program.
That's not good.

Create a Partition

Roman Loyola

Windows comes with a utility called fdisk that's used to partition a large hard drive into smaller virtual drives. Virtual drives decrease downtime while running applications.

1. To open fdisk, left-click the Start menu, select Run or Hold, and release the Windows button+R.

2. At the command line, type **fdisk** and press Enter. To enable large disk support, select Y and press Enter.

3. Select 5 to set the current fixed disk drive to equal your newly installed drive, and press Enter.

4. Find the number next to your new drive, type it into Enter Fixed Disk Drive Number, and press Enter. (Usually, the second drive number will br 2.) Make sure the current fixed hard drive is equal to the new hard drive. You should see any number other than 1 next to Current Fixed Drive.

5. Select 1 to create a DOS partition or logical DOS drive, and press Enter.

6. Select 1 to create a primary DOS partition, and press Enter.

7. The next screen asks, "Do you wish to use the maximum available size for a Primary DOS partition?" Press Y for one partition or N for multiple partitions. Press Enter.

Create One Partition

1. Press Y. The computer creates the partition and takes you to the beginning screen.

2. Select 4 to inspect the new partition.

Create Multiple Partitions

1. Press N. Enter a value next to Enter Partition Size in Mbytes or Percent of Disk Space to Create a Primary DOS Partition.

For example, to create two 10GB drives on your 20GB hard drive, enter 50% or divide the number of megabytes in half.

2. After entering the partition size, press Enter.

3. Press Esc to return to the new drive's main menu.

4. Select 1 to create a DOS partition or logical DOS drive.

5. To create the extended partition, select 2 from the menu and press Enter.

6. The Enter Partition Size in Mbytes or Percent of Disk Space to Create an Extended DOS Partition dialog appears. If this number is okay, press Enter. For more partitions, lower the number and press Enter.

7. After fdisk creates the partition, press Esc.

8. Select 1 to create a DOS partition or logical DOS drive.

9. Select 3 for a logical DOS drive(s) in the extended DOS partition. Press Enter.

10. The number next to Enter Logical Drive Size in Mbytes or Percentage of Drive should equal the size of of the extended drive.

11. Press Enter to create a logical DOS drive(s) in the extended DOS partition. A new letter for the new partition appears.

12. Press Esc to return to main menu.

Verify That Partitions Were Created Successfully

1. Select 5 to change that current fixed disk drive, and press Enter.

2. All the drives should appear. Press Esc twice to exit fdisk.

3. Restart your computer.

How Durable Are Your CDs and Floppy Disks?

Patrick Norton

What does it take to destroy your media? Your backed-up data—all the stuff you want to save. How safe is it?

What Heat Can Do to Your Media

First we tested a common floppy and a common CD-R. Always store your media in some kind of case to prevent scratching, minimize heat damage (at least at lower temperatures), and absorb the shock if it's dropped.

Both floppies and CD-R media are made of plastic. Plastic, of course, goes rather liquid when heat is applied. That said, don't leave your floppies in the car, either. Online research tells us that on a 78° day, a car parked in the sun can reach 160° in minutes.

Fires, of which my extended family has been through at least two, can melt the aluminum out of a car's intake manifold. CD-Rs and floppy disks will vaporize at those temperatures. Store copies off-site.

We put CD-R disks and floppies through two runs in a home oven. At 150°, CD-R disks begin to curl, even if flat. Oddly enough, a CD-R in a plastic case seems to minimize any damage to the disk. The case itself is unusable and you have to break open the case to free the disk.

Somewhere between 150° and 200° in the oven, our floppy disks turned into little plastic popovers. You might salvage the Mylar disk from inside, but I doubt it.

Lower temperatures such as the dash on a sunny day—say, 120°—didn't appear to have any effect on the disks. Nonetheless, store them in a cool, dry place. And keep copies off-site in case of fire.

What Water Can Do to Your Media

My family has been through floods, too. Floods involve tiny bits and pieces of salt and kelp (ocean floods) or mud (river floods).

CD-Rs laugh at water. Believe me, they laugh at Dr Pepper, too. Just rinse them off and wipe them from the inside out with a soft cloth. Don't scratch them.

Floppies are more complicated. Inside a floppy's plastic case is a Mylar (at least, I've been told it's Mylar) disk. The disk, which has magnetic material bonded to its surface, is sandwiched between two fiber pieces that protect it from rubbing against the case. The question is, has any crud soaked into that filter?

If the answer is "No," let the disk dry out and then copy that data onto a drive. Then I'd burn the data onto something else, such as a CD-R. If the answer is "Yes," then you've got a problem. When the disk dries, it's going to be like glue. That's bad; floppies don't work if they can't spin.

Windows Tips

Defrag from the Command Line in XP

Morgan Webb

It's a good idea to defrag your hard drive on a regular basis. You can set defrag to run from the command prompt in XP:

1. Make sure you have administrator access.

2. Go to Start, Run.

3. Type **cmd**.

4. At the prompt, type **defrag**, followed by the volume letter (**c:**) and then one of these switches:
   - **-a** to analyze your volume
   - **-f** to force the defrag even if your free space is low
   - **-v** to get a verbose output
   - **-b** to optimize your boot files to speed up your boot process

Move Your Mac OS X Swap File with Swap Cop

Roman Loyola
What's a swap file?

All modern operating systems use a swap file, which supplements your computer's memory. The operating system copies as much data as possible into main memory (RAM) and leaves the rest on the swap file, a cache of data on your hard drive. When the computer runs out of memory, it uses a swap file.

Using a swap file means you're using your hard drive, and using your hard drive takes longer than accessing data in memory. To maximize the performance of your swap file, it should be located on your fastest hard drive. By default, the swap file is located on the same hard drive as your OS. If your secondary hard drive is faster than your primary, you'll have to move it.

Moving the swap file to a faster, secondary drive can increase your performance (by as much as 20%, depending on the speed of your drive). When you move the swap file, move it to the first partition of your secondary drive.

Move the Swap File

You can use Swap Cop (www.macupdate.com/info.php/id/7757) to move the Mac OS X swap file. You can move the swap file manually using the Terminal, but why muss and fuss when you can use an application that simplifies the process?

Swap Cop is released under the GNU Public License, which means that you can freely distribute the software as well as customize it. J. Schrier, the creator, gladly accepts donations to help develop new features.

Cut, Copy, and Paste

Call for Help **Staff**
The cut, copy, and paste collection allows you to cut out, replace, or rearrange any highlighted text or data. If you are writing a family newsletter and you want to move the upcoming birthday list from the bottom to the top, highlight the paragraph, cut it, and then paste it at the top of your document.

Simply click Edit in any Windows application and choose the appropriate command, but it's easier to use one of these shortcuts: Control+X cuts any highlighted text or data; Control+C copies any highlighted text or data; Control+V pastes any copied text or data from the Clipboard to any open application. Position your cursor where you want the text to appear.

You can cut and paste any text or data from one Windows application to another. The copied information is held on the Clipboard until you press Paste. After a little practice, you'll be able to cut, copy, and paste with one hand while your other hand remains on the mouse.

Download of the Day

123 Password Recovery 3.01

Megan Morrone
What happens when you forget a password? You could cry, or you could use 123 Password Recovery from iOpus software (www.webattack.com). It's small, it's free, and it works. What more could you ask for?

Download this little app, run it, and then drag the key icon over your password window. Your forgotten password appears in a window. This program works only with passwords for websites that you've already stored so that you don't have to enter them manually. They're the ones hiding behind those little asterisks.

Delete the Scraps and Leftovers on Your Hard Drive

Morgan Webb

RAM, your computer's temporary storage area, loses all stored data when the power is turned off. Your pagefile is extra, RAM-like storage on your hard drive. It maintains its data even when your computer looses power.

The pagefile can contain unencrypted passwords as well as other sensitive data. While the novice user won't be able to see your pagefile while meandering through your computer, it's still a security risk whenever sensitive information exists on your drive. You can tell your computer to clear your pagefile of any information before it shuts down with a simple Registry edit. This tip will protect you from most snoopers, but if you're really paranoid, make sure you use another program to wipe all the unallocated space (see "Ultimate Data Destruction," January 4). Always be sure to back up your Registry before editing it.

1. Go to Start, Run and type **regedit**.
2. Go to HKEY_LOCAL_MACHINE\ SYSTEM\CurrentControlSet\Control\ Session Manager\Memory Management.
3. Modify or add the REG_DWORD entry ClearPageFileAtShutdown and set its value equal to 1.
4. You must restart your computer for the changes to take effect.

Download of the Day

File Scavenger

Nicole Carrico

We at *The Screen Savers* always practice safe computing. We defrag regularly, keep our antivirus software up-to-date, and always, always keep a current system backup. It's unlikely we would ever need to evaluate data-recovery software.

But I have this "friend," see, who isn't quite as cautious as I am. My "friend" called, hysterical over losing some crucial files. Seems the usually dependable PartitionMagic had mutated and devoured her partition data. Then she realized her backup wasn't current and at least a week's worth of work had been lost. I realize this sounds inconceivably stupid, but she's a genuinely bright, responsible girl. She just made a mistake. It could happen to anyone.

If you have any "friends" in this unfortunate position, have them download the free demo of File Scavenger from QueTek Consulting (www.quetek.com). If they're using Windows NT, Windows 2000, or Windows XP and the NTFS file system, they can probably save the day with this sharp little program. Here's a brief list of what makes File Scavenger the best of breed:

- Recovers not only the file, but also the folder path and the creation and modification dates.
- Recovers data deleted from a network share, the Recycle Bin, the DOS command, and Windows Explorer.
- Recovers files from defunct volumes when the original position on disk and the size are unknown.
- Recovers multiple files in one fell swoop.
- Can scan very large volumes.
- Scans damaged partitions and broken striped volumes.

The free File Scavenger demo identifies all your lost files, but recovers only those 32KB or smaller. If you have a larger file that you desperately need, you'll have to pay the full license fee.

Customize Your Mac OS X Terminal

Leo Laporte

It's easy to customize your Mac OS X terminal prompt to make it more informative, more colorful, or just more fun. The tcsh man page is useful, too. Type **man tcsh** at the command prompt.

`set prompt=` is the command to change the prompt.

Type **set prompt="%#"** for the simplest UNIX prompt.

You can use additional variables to add color, time, date, and other informational items to your prompt. Once you have a prompt you like, make it permanent by adding the appropriate `set prompt` command to one of your system startup files. The traditional location is .tcshrc in your home directory, but Apple encourages you to modify the .mine files in the Library/ init/tcsh directory under your home directory instead. The prompt command should be added to environment.mine.

You can use these files to really trick out your system. Look at my files, including my custom prompt, stored in the environment.mine file:

```
set prompt="%{\033[34m%}%M
            (%{\033[31m%}%c3%{\033[0m%})
            %# "
set pager=less
set editor=pico

set time=(8 "\
Time spent in user mode (CPU seconds) :
%Us\
Time spent in kernel mode
(CPU seconds) : %Ss\
Total time
: %Es\
CPU utilisation (percentage) : %P\
Times the process was swapped : %W\
```

```
Times of major page faults : %F\
Times of minor page faults : %R")
set color
set visiblebell
set nobeep
umask 22
mesg y
```

Add this text to the environment.mine file in your Library/init/tcsh folder. It will automatically execute each time you open a new terminal window.

Download of the Day

StuffIt Expander

Megan Morrone

As many of you already know, I'm a Mac person. I'm not uncomfortable with a PC; I just choose to reserve my work computing life to the PC platform and my pleasure computing life to the Mac. And never the two shall meet. Ah, would that were true.

We're constantly forced to open Mac documents with our PCs, and vice versa. Usually it's easy, but sometimes it's not. Some people have trouble opening them with WinZip. I recommended StuffIt Expander, and it worked like a charm.

StuffIt Expander from Aladdin Systems (www.aladdinsys.com) comes with the Mac, but it's a free download for Windows, Linux, and Solaris.

Once you've installed the program, you can drag and drop files into it to unzip them. You can also configure your system to open the files automatically so that whenever you try to open a file that ends in .sit, .cpt, .bin, .sea, or .hqx, StuffIt will jump in and work its magic.

StuffIt Expander is great for unzipping documents, but it won't zip them. You'll need another program for that.

Friday
January 23
2004

Monster Machine: G4/PC Hybrid

Kevin Rose

I love my Mac and I love my PC, but I don't love having two monitors, two keyboards, and two mouses. Switching back and forth has become a royal pain. Why choose sides in the platform war when you can boot both operating systems simultaneously, on the same machine, on the same screen?

Project Goals

- Build a single computer that runs Jaguar and XP natively with one keyboard, one mouse, and one monitor.
- Bonus: Have PIP (picture-in-picture) support so you can launch and view PC and Mac programs on the same monitor.

Inside the Case

- **G4 guts:** I had the homemade G4 running Jaguar from my build-your-own-G4 project.
- **PC guts:** For size considerations, I used the LPC-301 Small FootPrint Powerful Little PC (http://littlepc.com), a miniature PC that fits into a tiny 5 1/4-inch drive bay. I went with the Pentium III 1.2GHz model with FireWire, USB, and DVD player. It runs Linux!

Miracle Monitor

If you're going to build a classy machine, you might as well have a nice view. I chose the Samsung SyncMaster 171MP 17-inch, multifunction LCD monitor (http://samsungusa.com).

Mouses and More

I decided to go wireless with Microsoft's Wireless Desktop Pro keyboard and mouse.

Switching Stuff

I used the Belkin OmniView 4-Port USB KVM Switch with Audio (www.belkin.com) to toggle the keyboard and mouse between the two systems. Not only will this unit switch the keyboard and mouse control, but it also will switch video and audio signals.

To connect the G4 and PC components to the Belkin switch, you need two Belkin KVM cable kits or the equivalent USB and monitor cables.

Assembly Instructions

First, you need to build the homemade G4:

- **CPU:** We used a 1GHz G4 processor from Sonnet (www.sonnettech.com).
- **Logic board:** We used a PowerMac G4 AGP logic board with gigabit Ethernet purchased from MacResQ (www.macresq.com).
- **RAM:** There's nothing really special about the PC133 RAM we bought at Crucial (www.crucial.com).
- **Power supply:** We bought ours on eBay (www.ebay.com). You can also buy power supplies at Nexcomp (www.nexcomp.com).
- **Video card:** We chose an ATI (www.ati.com) video card.
- **Hard drive:** We installed a Western Digital Caviar Special Edition WD800JB (www.westerndigital.com).

Address: Site of the Night

Ruler of the Universe

Enjoy your 15 minutes of fame (or possibly more) at this ego-boosting site, www.davea.org/ruler.htm. Warning: The content of this site changes frequently and may be considered offensive. Surf at your own risk.

Monster Machine: G4/PC Hybrid (continued)

The ports on your motherboard will determine whether you use a USB or ADB keyboard and mouse. There are tons of replacement keyboards and mouses available.

When you're done, you'll have your very own G4. But don't call it a Mac. Only Apple can do that.

1. Installing the Little PC couldn't be easier. Simply slide the Little PC into the 5 1/4-inch drive bay and mount it above the G4's CD-ROM drive.

2. Plug the keyboard, mouse, and monitor into the Belkin switch.

3. Connect the keyboard and monitor cables from the G4 into connector no. 1 on the Belkin. Plug one side of a two-sided USB cable into any of the G4's USB ports on the other side into the Belkin (you don't need a separate mouse cable because the wireless mouse and keyboard are a combo).

4. Do the same with the monitor cable, plugging one side into the G4 and the other into the Belkin. When you set the Belkin to button 1, you'll have full-screen keyboard and mouse control of the G4 machine.

5. Plug a VGA splitter into the Little PC's video card. Plug one end of a two-sided monitor cable into the VGA splitter and the other end into Belkin connector no. 2.

6. Do the same with the keyboard controls, plugging one side of a USB cable into the Little PC's USB port and the other end into Belkin connector no. 2. When you set the Belkin to button 2, you will have full-screen keyboard and mouse control of the PC.

7. Plug a second USB cable from any open USB port on the G4 into Belkin connector no. 3.

8. Plug another monitor cable from the VGA splitter into Belkin connector no. 3.

9. Run an s-video cable from the G4's ATI Radeon graphics card to the video input no. 2 on the Samsung monitor. The s-video cable is the white-tipped cord.

The Results

- Button 1 equals full control of the G4 with full-screen display.

- Button 2 equals full control of the PC with full-screen display.

- Button 3 equals pressing the PIP (picture-in-picture) button on the monitor; you will be able to view both operating systems running at once. You will have control of only the G4, which will run on the smaller screen.

To control the PC in picture-in-picture mode, simply press button 2 again.

Windows Tips

Access Files Quickly in XP and Win 2000

Morgan Webb

Don't you hate it when you open Windows Explorer in Windows 2000 or XP, and you have to sift through all sorts of drives and folders to get to the location you want? Wouldn't it be easier if Windows Explorer automatically opened to that location?

1. Make a shortcut to Windows Explorer on your desktop: Click on the Start menu, and point to Accessories. Right-click Explorer, and drag it (yes, with the right mouse button) to the desktop. Select Make Shortcut Here or Move Here in XP.

2. Now, right-click the shortcut icon and select Properties.

3. You have to add something to the target field. Put a space after the shortcut path and add **/e,/root,path**.

   The "path" is the complete path to the directory you want, including the drive. You will not be able to go up more levels than your specified path. You can have several Explorer shortcuts on your desktop, each opening to a different root directory.

Three-in-One Computer

Patrick Norton

Want to run three different operating systems? Take a look at the Romtec Trio and Trio II devices that allow you to switch among three different hard drives that can each have different operating systems.

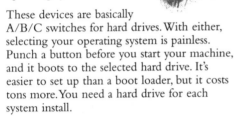

These devices are basically A/B/C switches for hard drives. With either, selecting your operating system is painless. Punch a button before you start your machine, and it boots to the selected hard drive. It's easier to set up than a boot loader, but it costs tons more. You need a hard drive for each system install.

Selector selections include these:

- **Romtec Trios** (www.romtecusa.com)
  - $49.95 (check website for most current pricing)
  - Fits in a 5.25-inch drive bay
  - Three-button front
  - Four rear IDE ports
  - Prevents you from accessing any of the drives attached to it other than the one you're running

- **Romtec Trios II** (www.romtecusa.com)
  - $69.95 (check website for most current pricing)
  - Consists of a tethered remote and a PCI card
  - Controls one drive at a time, or two drives simultaneously
  - Can configure the drives for master/slave configurations

We focused our testing on the drive bay version, the Trios.

Installation was a snap. Figuring out where to mount the drives takes longer than sliding this device into a bay and connecting its IDE cables and power feed. Once configured with the bundled cables (all the cables designated for between the Trios and the hard drives are notched), we picked a button and booted.

We encountered no problems, although when we selected drive 2 during a Control+Alt+Delete reboot, our machine booted into drive 3 anyway. It turns out that you need to turn off the PC to switch to a different drive.

We also became painfully aware that we couldn't access any data on any other drive connected to the Trios. If you regularly transfer files or keep your data on a single drive, you'll want the Trios II or a hard drive that isn't connected to the Trios.

We also noticed that something prevented us from installing a new OS to any drive connected to the Trios after trying to install BSD, Trustix, and Sorcerer Linux. Bypassing the Trios switch and connecting the drive via a regular IDE cable directly to the motherboard was the only way to install a new OS. That might be a security feature for most folks, not a bug.

We didn't test to discover whether the Trios impacted the performance of our drive. For what it's worth, it didn't feel slower, although that's a poor measurement, at best.

The Trios works well at making it simple to boot into multiple operating systems. While $50 sounds cheap, you have to consider the price of the hard drives you use. I'm just lucky I had a stack of 20GB hard drives.

Build a Hard-Drive Switcher

Kevin Rose

The absolute easiest way to run a dual-boot system is to run each operating system on a separate hard drive. With each OS on its own drive, you don't have to worry about partitioning, and it's easier to manage the software.

But, you have to change the master and slave jumpers each time you decide to boot into the OS of choice because the master drive is always the first drive that boots. That means you have to power down your computer, open the case, remove the hard drives (or contort your fingers to reach the jumpers), change the jumper settings, remount the drives, close the case, and power up. Ugh!

Rather than manually change jumpers, I decided to create a flip switch that changes the jumper setting for me. To pick which drive I want to boot, I just flip the switch.

The switch is a single-pull double-throw (SPDT) flip switch from RadioShack. This $3 switch completes the circuit when it's up and stops the circuit when it's down.

You need a Dremel tool and a soldering kit. You also need hard-drive jumpers with wires—not the jumpers you find on hard drives today. Try looking at used computer parts stores, I found mine on an old 286 PC.

1. Place both drives on the same primary IDE channel, and remove all jumpers. It doesn't matter which OS is at the end.

2. Boot the PC. Most drives default to cable select mode when the jumpers are removed. The drives should show up as master and slave. The drive at the end of the chain will be master.

3. Shut down your PC.

4. Place your wired jumpers on each drive. Set the drive at the end of the chain to slave. Set the other drive to master.

5. Solder the other end of the wires to the switch, separating the two wires from each jumper to the two leads on the switch.
   - When the switch is flipped up, the circuit is completed and the jumpers are activated.
   - When the switch is flipped down, the connection is broken and the drives default to the cable select position, as if no jumpers were on the drive.

6. Dremel a hole in a 5.25-inch bay to mount the switch and close your case.

On my PC, I flip the switch up (selects drive 1 as master) to boot into Windows. To boot into Linux, I flip the switch down (selects drive 2 as master).

Laporte Support

What Is Interlace?

Interlace is the method that a monitor uses to display an image. Your display is sectioned into thin lines. An interlaced monitor displays every other line first. When it reaches the bottom, it starts at the top and fills in the rest of the lines.

To display the screen resolution you want, you need to adjust the refresh rate. This will cut down the flicker you see onscreen.

Repair Your Scratched CDs

Roger Chang
Cleaning CDs

Baking Soda toothpaste or any mild abrasive, such as furniture polish, Pledge, or plastic polish, works fine for removing scratches. Use any lint-free cloth, add some of the abrasive to the afflicted area, and wipe. Always wipe from the center of the disc to the rim in a straight line. Never wipe in a circular pattern.

Toothpaste works on only minor scratches, but the results are okay. While it does not fix heavily scratched CDs, it does help light to moderate scratches from skipping.

Use baking soda toothpaste with as few additives as possible. Some gel-based baking soda toothpastes tend to leave a sticky film on the CD, which takes effort to remove.

Car Wax

Unlike polish, waxes fill in the cracks or scratches. Just pour or rub the wax on a scratched area and wipe off with a lint-free cloth from the center to the rim.

Prevent Scratches

Keep your CDs in a safe and scratch-free environment. Always keep CDs in sturdy jewel cases and off the floor, table, or backseat of your car. Clean your CDs with a soft, lint-free cloth and make single swiping motions from the center to its rim. Don't clean in circles as you would a vinyl LP.

Commercial Scratch Removers

SkipDoctor MD (about $30) from Digital Innovations (www.digitalinnovations.com) is a motorized polisher, meaning that it scrubs off the top layer of plastic until the scratches are faint or gone.

My results were mixed. It worked well on minor scratches but had a hard time dealing with deeper, knife-size gashes. While the SkipDoctor brought back my skipping CDs, it's pricey.

I tested Wipe Out! (www.cdrepair.com) from Esprit Development on three scratched discs. The audio disc was your average "been tossed around in the jewel case too long" scratched disc. The two data CDs were scratched with a pocketknife. All still played, although with some major hesitation on the data CDs and a skip on the audio CD.

Initially, it seemed to work, but after closer inspection, I wasn't as impressed. Only after I started rubbing—following the scratch from the center out and with a lot of elbow grease—did the scratch begin to fade. In fact, it worked pretty well and was much better than the SkipDoctor MD on the larger, deeper scratches, although it ties with SkipDoctor on the minor, lighter scratches.

The scratches, however, were not removed 100%, nor should you expect them to be. Both of these products only lessen the severity of scratches so that you can play them again.

I have two complaints with Wipe Out! First, the cloth included with the kit added minor scratches to the face of the disc. Second, the solution is toxic and highly flammable. Warnings state that prolonged eye and skin contact are dangerous. In contrast, the SkipDoctor, which is basically a motorized polishing surface, uses distilled water as a lubricant and poses little, if any, health threat.

For $15, Wipe Out! removes deeper gashes than does the SkipDoctor MD. I recommend Wipe Out! over the SkipDoctor MD, with the caveat that you use it in a responsible fashion, especially around small children and pets.

Save Your Data the Broadband Way

Patrick Norton

Backing up data means keeping it safe. But if you back up your data to something inside your house, it can be stolen, burned in a fire, or simply lost. Huge corporations routinely back up over a network to keep their data safe in a secure location. If you have broadband, it's quick and easy to use a system such as @Backup (www.backup.com) to do the same thing.

What @Backup Does for You

@Backup works only with Windows machines. (Check the website for current pricing.) Once you've set up your account, you download and install a small piece of software. It'll live in your Notification Area (or system tray, the area to the right of the clock on your toolbar). Then you can automatically back up and restore files and folders on your system.

And, hey, broadband's always on, so it might well be faster than archiving your files on disk or CD-R. You won't even have to get up from your chair!

Laporte Support

Making Sense of Hard-Drive Space

Ever bought a 40GB hard drive only to have Windows report that it's only 38GB? Well, this time it's probably not Windows' fault, but the hard drive manufacturer's way of describing the size of the drive. Because it's measured in binary, not decimal standards, 1GB is not exactly a billion bytes. It's actually 2^{30}, or 1,073,741,824 bytes. In addition, manufactures often report the unformatted size of the drive instead of the formatted size, and, of course, you have to format a hard drive to be able to use it. After formatting a drive, you usually lose around 2GB for the table of contents and other elements.

Download of the Day

System Monitoring Toolbar

Megan Morrone

A few months ago, Leo sent me a link to a free Windows system monitor. I've been using the download on my XP system (it should run on any Windows system) that you often see on the show, and I've gotten dozens of emails about it.

The program is called WinBar (www.winbar.nl), and it's simply an unobtrusive toolbar that lets you keep tabs on the workings of your PC, your email, and even the tech news headlines.

Here are the WinBar modules that I've found most useful:

- CPU Usage
- Memory Usage
- Disk Usage
- Google Toolbar
- Slashdot Tracker

If you're a Mac user, take a look at System Manager 1.0 (www.versiontracker.com). This download combines several Mac monitoring programs into one and keeps track of the following:

- CPU usage
- System load levels
- Memory usage
- Network activity

My favorite thing about System Manager 1.0 is that you can keep the program running all the time, and it doesn't hog your system resources. Instead, when you open another program, System Manager makes more CPU power available, using a UNIX utility called renice (www.opengroup.org).

Windows Error Messages

Roger Chang

The best place to find a listing of Windows error codes is the Windows 98 and Windows Me Error Message Resource Center (http://support.microsoft.com).

It May Not Be Windows' Fault

Remember, not all the error codes displayed come from Windows. Some are particular to certain applications. For a description of these error codes, you'll need to contact the developer of that specific application.

An error that occurs in one program can set off a chain of errors in other applications, leading to an inaccurate error message. The error message you receive may be from subsequent crashes, not the initial error.

Most messages are useful only to programmers who are debugging a program. The programmers take the error code and reference it with their source code to sort things out.

Because you usually won't have access to the source code, you really can't do anything about an error except stick your head out the window and yell, "I'm mad as hell and I'm not going to take it anymore!" Then close the window, close all the windows on your PC, and reboot.

Laporte Support

Clear Your Desktop Screen

There are two ways to quickly get to your desktop if your screen is full of open windows in Windows XP:

- If your keyboard has a Windows button, press Windows+D.
- Right-click the toolbar and select Show Desktop to get the desktop, or Show Open Windows to get the windows back.

Windows Tips

Change Recycle Bin Name

Nicole Guilfoyle

Using Regedit, you can change the name of the Recycle Bin to anything you want.

Windows 98 and 95

1. Click the Start menu and select Run.
2. Type **regedit**, and click OK.
3. Double-click HKEY_CLASSES_ROOT.
4. Double-click CLSID.
5. Double-click {645FF040-5081-101B-9F08-00AA002F954E}.
6. In the right window, double-click the (Default) icon.
7. In the Value Data field, enter the new name of your Recycle Bin.
8. Click OK and exit regedit.
9. Reboot your PC.

Windows XP

1. Click the Start menu and select Run.
2. Type **regedit** and click OK.
3. Go to HKEY_CURRENT_USER SOFTWARE MICROSOFT WINDOWS CURRENTVERSION EXPLORER CLSID.
4. Double-click {645FF040-5081-101B-9F0800AA002F954E}.
5. In the right window, double-click the (Default) icon.
6. In the Value Data field, enter the new name of your Recycle Bin.
7. Click OK and exit regedit.
8. Reboot your PC.

Build a Terabyte System

Patrick Norton

What's a terabyte? A terabyte is an awfully big chunk of zeros and ones. Consider this:

- A megabyte is equal to 1,048,576 bytes (2 to the 20th power).

- A gigabyte is equal to 1,024 megabytes. (2 to the 30th power, or 1,073,741,824 bytes).

- A terabyte is 2 to the 40th power. This is approximately 1 trillion bytes (1,099,511,627,776 bytes, to be exact), or 1,024GB.

Put the System Together

Maxtor (www.maxtor.com) was kind enough to loan us eight D540X hard drives. Each packs a whopping 160GB of storage. With only four IDE slots on the motherboard, we had to add additional ATA connectors. A pair of Promise Ultra 133 TX2 ATA cards filled two PCI slots and gave us connections for up to eight more drives. The cards support 48-bit logical block addressing so it supports drives bigger than 137GB. The ATA on the mobo sees only 128GB of the drive, so you lose 30GB. The drives show up as 152.66GB after formatting with the Ultra 133s.

Mounting eight hard drives inside a midtower case is a nightmare. Most cases are designed to pack a pair of drives in a 3.5-inch hard-drive rack, and perhaps two more in empty 5.25-inch drive bays. A full-size case makes it easier; you simply use drive rails to mount the drives in the front of the case in the 5.25-inch drive bays.

You can right-click My Computer, select Manage, and go directly to the Computer Management application. Select Storage/Disk Management for the Disk Management Console.

A huge power supply is a big plus, along with a number of power splitters. A 500-watt power supply is the best solution.

Dynamic Disks

We spanned all eight drives into a single drive that is one drive letter, using the dynamic disk storage in Windows XP Professional (Windows 2000 also supports dynamic disk storage; Windows XP Home doesn't). Instead of loading eight separate drives on our Windows PC, we have two in our terabyte system: the C: drive and a huge "second" drive.

A dynamic disk lets us span multiple drives under a single drive letter. It's not a RAID array, it can't be mirrored, and it's not fault tolerant. If one of the disks goes down, you lose the whole thing. And other operating systems can't use the dynamic disk on your system.

Dynamic disks are easy to create. In the Control Panel, open Administrative Tools (you might need to click on Performance and Maintenance first). Double-click Computer Management, and then click Disk Management to select individual disks and change their status. We partitioned one section of one of the drives to use as a "basic" disk for the boot sector.

Microsoft (www.microsoft.com) has the basic rundown on dynamic storage in Windows XP and a basic how-to. There's also a ton of info in XP's help files.

The $64,000 question is, of course, how long before it takes only one or two drives, instead of eight drives, to get a terabyte of storage? When that time comes, we'll just have to go for a petabyte.

How to Pick a Graphics Card

Patrick Norton

There's no universal answer to the graphics-card question. It all depends on the hardware you already have, the money you're willing to spend, and the games you want to play.

Slow Processors Waste Your Graphics Card

If you're running a processor at under 2GHz and you've got the money, upgrade your processor first! Think 2GHz or faster Pentium 4 or Athlon XP.

The fastest cards will run you $350 to $500, but if you don't have the processor to feed your 3D card, it's wasted money. A new processor might mean a new motherboard and new memory, so think "balance" and make smart choices.

RAM Solves Gaming Problems

That said, if you're playing with lots of folks online—or finding that your games take forever to load and leave (Battlefield 1942 players take note)—it's time to start running 512MB o' RAM in your system.

Says our game-testing maven Robert Heron: "It took us a while to figure out that upping system memory to 512MB solves a lot of problems for many games." Indeed, upping to 512MB might save that 1GHz box from a processor upgrade—at least till the end of the year.

Done all this? Now you can think about getting the new graphics card.

Basic Rules for Your Decision

Here's some expert advice from our Labs:

- If you have a top-of-the-line NVidia GeForce 4 card (the 4600s, for example) or an ATI 9500 or 9700, don't spend the money for a new card yet.
- If you're buying ATI, get a Pro model (www.ati.com).
- If you're buying NVidia, get an Ultra model (www.nvidia.com).

Know When to Hold 'Em

If you're OK playing your fave games with the card you have now, waiting six months—or even two months—means you'll get more 3D power for less money. Sometimes a couple hundred dollars less!

3D-Card Choices if Money Is No Object

- **ATI Radeon 9800 Pro** ($350). This is the current standard for graphics cards, at least if you have the money to buy it.
- **ATI Radeon 9800 Pro 256 MB** ($492). Some games will take advantage of the extra memory to feed gaming at extremely high resolutions. But frankly this is blowing lots and lots o' cash for a feature (an extra 128MB of memory) most games won't use.

For Lots Less Money

- **ATI Radeon 9600 Pro.** This card sells for $160 if you buy it online. Our Labs says this is "the low point of where we'd want to go when buying a new card."
- **ATI Radeon 9500 Pro.** This is a great card if you can find it, and it should cost $130 or so online.
- **NVidia GeForce FX 5200 Ultra.** The Ultra is crucial! This isn't the plain 5200. It can be had for $130 or so online.

Worried about 8X AGP? Don't. We've yet to see it make a difference.

Laporte Support

Moving My Documents

The My Documents folder doesn't have to live on your Windows 98 desktop. You can easily move it wherever you like. Just right-click the My Documents folder and enter the new home of My Documents in the Target Folder Location box.

Games and Entertainment

Megan Morrone

Today you can use the same machine to organize your finances, create a presentation for your boss, and defend the Earth from flesh-eating aliens. But let's be honest: Even with the crazy advances in software, organizing your finances and creating a presentation for your boss are still not half as much fun as defending the Earth from flesh-eating aliens. That's why we've devoted the entire month of February to the noble pursuit of games and entertainment for PCs, Macs, game consoles, and PDAs.

I know what you're thinking. You're thinking that you can skip right over this chapter because you're not a gamer. Gamers are all sweaty, pimpled, 16-year-old boys who lock themselves in their basements sustained only by complex carbohydrates and Mountain Dew for days on end, right? Wrong. Video games aren't just for young boys anymore. Saying you don't like video games is like saying you don't like ice cream or cheese or television or fun. Are you trying to tell me that you don't like fun?

If you watch *The Screen Savers*, you know that each member of our little TV family has a uniquely different interest in games. Morgan loves a good frag fest, whereas Martin's tastes tend toward the bizarre (think frogs in blenders or cow tossing.) Kevin knows how to throw a cutting-edge LAN party, while Joshua and Roger like to kick back with old-school retro game emulators. I like to download free and simple low-res games that you can play on even the dinkiest PC, whereas Patrick prefers to build and rebuild the perfect system for the ultimate gaming experience (see February 13). And leave it to Leo to discover the most unique new gaming experience for the consummate early adopter (see February 1).

This month we review games for all platforms and all personalities, answer your gaming tech support questions, show you where to find the coolest games online, and review all the latest gaming periph-erals. Morgan even shows you how you can cheat at Solitaire. Unfortunately, she doesn't tell you why you'd want to.

From text-based games to high-end virtual-reality 3D graphics, video games let you use your imagination to do something you could never do or be someone you could never be. In the following pages, you can learn how to become Zeus, a caveman, a pirate, or a Jeopardy contestant. You can solve jewel puzzles, drink beer with aliens, placate camels, kill giant insects, escape from evil monsters in the mall, and pull goofy-foot ollies off the rooftop of City Hall.

So, do you still think you're not a gamer? Maybe you just haven't found the right game.

Leo's Pick: The Pyramat PM300

Leo Laporte

Get some comfort to go along with your gaming with the Pyramat PM300 from Pyramat (www.pyramat.com). The Pyramat is a futon with speakers—pardon me, I mean a high-density foam reclining system with sound reinforcement.

Relax and Play

The Pyramat contains a three-speaker sound system and 50-watt amplifier in the headrest, and a handheld wired remote control. When you're ready to play, unroll it, lie down, and pump up the volume. The PM300 is compatible with all video-game consoles, computers, DVD players, MP3 players, and anything else with audio out. Around $150, it's only a little cheaper than my Xbox, but it's a lot cheaper than the recliner I usually sit in to play video games, and it sounds a lot better.

The Pyramat PM300 is one gadget I'll take lying down.

Scary Games

Roman Loyola

If you're looking for an interactive (nonhuman) way to get a good old-fashioned scare, read on:

- **Fatal Frame (PS2)**
  (www.fatalframegame.com). The scariest thing about Fatal Frame is that it looks like Resident Evil meets Pokemon Snap. Its scare factor alone is reason enough to play this game.

- **Aliens vs. Predator 2 (PC)**
  (http://avp2.sierra.com). If you want one of the most entertaining single-player experiences of the year and some solid and original multiplayer fun, it's right here.

- **Eternal Darkness: Sanity's Requiem (GCN)** (http://cube.ign.com). This M-rated title earns its rating not through gratuitous gore or cheap sex, but by presenting a story line that's adult-oriented in its complexity and thought.

- **Bruce Lee: Quest of the Dragon (Xbox)** (www.universalinteractive.com). The only thing scary about this game is that it was made in the first place.

Download of the Day

Maelstrom 3.0.5

Megan Morrone

Save your quarters for laundry. I have an updated version of the ultimate Asteroids clone. And get this: It works on Mac (OS 9 or higher), Windows, Linux, and BeOS.

It's called Maelstron 3.0.5. Ambrosia Software created the original Mac version (shareware, or $15 to purchase) and allowed Sam Lantinga to port it to Linux and Windows for a school project.

Download the file, unzip it, and start playing. Use the Tab key to shoot and the arrow keys to move. If you don't like that setup, press C (or click the C button) when you start up to configure your controls.

Important hints:

- Turn up your speaker volume for the full arcade experience.

- To add a little oomph, try one of the Star Wars or Star Trek sound packages. Both are available along with additional sounds from http://www.devolution.com/~slouken/Maelstrom/add-ons.html.

Maelstrom for Windows and Linux (www.devolution.com).

Maelstrom for Mac (www.AmbrosiaSW.com).

Monday
February 2
2004

Leo's Pick: There

Leo Laporte

Gertrude Stein once said of her childhood home, "There is no there there." But at There (www.there.com), there's plenty of there there. There is an imaginary world that's a lot more fun to visit than are many real-world places I've been.

Five years in the making, There is the brainchild of Will Harvey, a Stanford computer science Ph.D. and game developer, and Jeffrey Ventrella, an expert on artificial life from MIT's Media Lab. The two raised $33 million from a who's who list of techies, including gaming legend Trip Hawkins, Kevin Ryan, and Bruce Leak. Harvey and Ventrella built an elaborate 3D virtual world and invited people to come and play.

You Are There?

There is massively multiplayer, but it's not a game like EverQuest. It's a free-form community. There has clubs, nightly activities, contests, and races, but the chief activity in There is chatting. The avatars are surprisingly lifelike, and you can use gestures and facial expressions to get your point across.

The world of There has its own economy. When you arrive, you're given 10,000 There-bucks. Be careful how you spend them. You can buy a new wardrobe or hairstyle; toys such as paint guns, hover boards, and dune buggies; and even a pet, but everything is expensive. Even a T-shirt can cost hundreds of There-bucks.

You can earn more bucks by selling your There creations, or you can buy more with a credit card. The current exchange rate is around 1,700 There-bucks for each American greenback. The company isn't sure if it'll eventually charge a monthly fee for There, but it'll undoubtedly make a pretty penny on There-bucks. And it's already signed on a number of real-world designers, including Nike and Levi's, to make There items.

There lends itself to community. I rented a clubhouse for 3,000 There-bucks a week and invited my friends to stop by to pet the dog, relax in a hot tub, or play a brisk round of paintball.

I'm ready to rock when There goes public. There's no word from management when that will be, but I'm guessing it can't be too far off.

Address: ## Site of the Day

The Advertising Slogan Generator

Here are some of the slogans this mechanized marketing marvel came up with for *The Screen Savers* (http://thesurrealist.co.uk/slogan):

- Whatever You're into, Get into Martin Sargent.
- Choosy Mothers Choose Martin Sargent.
- There's First Love, and There's Megan Love.
- America's Most Trusted Megan.
- See the Face You Love Light Up with Morgan Webb.
- The Curiously Strong Morgan Webb.
- I am Stuck on Patrick Norton, 'Cause Patrick Norton's Stuck on Me.
- It's Shake 'n' Patrick Norton, and I Helped.
- *The Screen Savers*, the Other White Meat.
- Little. Yellow. Different. *The Screen Savers*.

The All Seeing Eye

Kevin Rose

When I've hosted *The Screen Savers* LAN parties, the no. 1 complaint I get is that players can't find our games online.

Why does this happen? Thousands of online games are taking place at any given time. By the time you download the list of more than 4,000 games, our servers are full.

The solution is called the All Seeing Eye (ASE, www.udpsoft.com/eye). It's a great little shareware application that lets you bypass your slow in-game listing method and replace it with a fast and easy way to find the server of your choice.

Here are some of the ASE's features:

- Knows the geographical location of every server. You can filter out far-away servers without wasting time pinging them.

- Has a buddy tracker that's always up-to-date.

- Uses data compression. On average, it cuts server refresh times by 10%.

- Includes support for dedicated "pingers," which can be set up on your ISP or some close-by server on a fat pipe to do all the server pinging for you.

- Instantaneously applies filters and switches between server lists. You'll never see the hourglass icon.

- Updates itself automatically when a new version is released.

- Draws player names with game font (all games supported).

- Has remote console and admin features for server admins.

- Includes support for helper programs such as QuakeWorld/Quake 2 proxies and Half-Life PunkBuster.

If you play a lot of online games, this will save you hours of time. The application is shareware. If you like it, kick down the $10. It's well worth it.

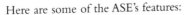

Laporte Support

Internet Game Consoles

Will game consoles that provide Internet access eventually take over PCs as the primary web-access device?

Gaming consoles that provide Internet access, such as the Xbox and the PlayStation 2, are more convenient than PCs, but they have severe limitations. Many technologies that people use on websites—video, MP3s, MIDI, Flash—aren't supported by game consoles. They will support them eventually, but the number of people using a game console for Internet access is so low that developers aren't rushing to adapt their technologies.

For now and the near future, the primary Internet-access device will be the computer. As technology for game consoles evolves, more people will use them for access.

Trick Out Game Boy and Game Boy Advance

Roger Chang

Nintendo's Game Boy and Game Boy Advance represent the pinnacle of handheld video-gaming for many people. They're small and portable, and they sport a relatively long battery life and great games. Thanks to a collection of ambitious programmers and enthusiasts, you can now do more than just play games on the Game Boy. Would you believe you can read books, paint pictures, and even play games created by fans? It's all possible.

Cost

Currently the only way to load software into the Game Boy or Game Boy Advance is via the cartridge slot. Although the software you need is free, the hardware that lets this all happen is not. You'll need a specialized reprogrammable cartridge, and, yes, this miracle of Game Boy innovation comes at a price. What's the rub? About $150.

The Flash Advance Linker is the best-known cartridge, but several similar products are available, including the EZ-Flash that I used.

Is It Legal?

There's a running debate on the legality of these products, mainly because they're advertised as a way to "back up" GBA games. However, Flash Advance Linker also includes the phrase "development device" in its description.

I'm under no illusion. I'm sure piracy is committed under the banner of fair use. But I'm also excited about good, free, and useful apps created by dedicated enthusiasts. In any case, the law is at issue.

How Does It Work?

1. After you purchase one of these flashable game cartridges, install the flashing software and cartridge cradle on your PC.
2. Obtain some Game Boy Advance ROM images. A ROM is a copy of the software usually located in a ROM (read-only memory) device, such as a video game cartridge. In this case, it's the software you want to load onto the flashable cartridge in a GBA-compatible format.

To find ROMs, do a search for PD or public domain ROMs on Google. PD ROMs are free, easy to find, and, most important, legal.

3. When you have the ROMs, launch the flashing application and insert the flash cartridge into the cradle. The application should list the contents of the cartridge. If it's new, there should be nothing on it.
4. Load a boot loader image. This lets the GBA "know" what to do with the cartridge. You can find the boot loader image on the driver disk that accompanied the cartridge. Then click Burn to store the image on the cartridge.
5. Follow the same process for each ROM that you want to load. To delete a ROM, remove the item from the list in the flash app.

GameBoy Book Reader (www.mqp.com), a nifty little application, lets you turn any text into a self-contained e-book that can be read on your GBA. The e-book is rendered out into a GBA ROM file. Install it as you would any other GBA ROM.

1. Run the MakeBook software.
2. Open a text file or document.
3. Select where you want chapter points, title, and author descriptions.

That's it. You now have a handheld gaming device capable of much more than playing games.

Play Video Formats on Your Mac

Roman Loyola

The Internet is littered with thousands (probably millions) of videos that you can download and view on your computer. The problem is that, for every video, there seems to be a different video format. It's disappointing to wait for a video to download on your Mac, only to have it not work.

Video Formats

- **QuickTime** (www.apple.com/quicktime). This is the de facto standard on the Mac. QuickTime 6 plays QuickTime files, of course, but it can also handle MPEG-4, MPEG-2, DVC Pro PAL, and a lot more. You should be able to play most videos using the QuickTime 6 player. You can find a list of video codecs supported by QuickTime at www.apple.com/quicktime/products/qt/specifications.html. Third-party components also are available from companies such as Pulse (www.pulse3d.com) and iPix (www.ipix.com).

- **DivX for Mac OS X** (www.divx.com). The DivX codec is a proprietary technology based on the MPEG-4 compression standard. To play DivX files on your Mac through QuickTime, you need the DivX QuickTime component, which includes a DivX Validator that fixes AVI-based DivX files so they will play in QuickTime.

- **RealMedia** (www.real.com). To play RealMedia files, you need RealPlayer 8 Basic for Mac OS 8.1 or higher or RealOne Player for Mac OS X.

- **Windows Media.** There are two different players for Windows Media. The one you need depends on your OS (see www.microsoft.com/mac/download/ and scroll to the bottom of the page).

Download of the Day

Blobby Volley

Megan Morrone

Daniel Skoraszewsky and Silvio Mummert's 3D German gem consists of two colorful blobs (also known as extraterrestrial jelly babies) playing beach volleyball (see http://home.t-online.de/home/mummertathome/blobby.htm). Use your mouse to control your blob. Right-click to jump.

If you're really adventurous, you can play others online or host your own blobby tourney.

Most of the instructions on the game's splash page are in German, but you can select English Please to switch.

Laporte Support

Wi-Fi for Gaming

Is Wi-Fi fast enough to play games between two computers, and is it fast enough to play games online?

You betcha. It is a bit slower than Ethernet, but I doubt you'll notice. On *The Screen Savers,* we often play Quake online through a Wi-Fi network.

Some of the most addicted gamers at TechTV claim they don't get the best performance out of their gaming systems over Wi-Fi. You'll have problems if you invite 50 of your buddies over to play on your Wi-Fi setup. It can be a problem for Ethernet, too; that's why offices and huge LAN parties segment their networks with routers.

Which Console Should You Get?

Adam Sessler

I'll bet you want one of those new-fangled video-game consoles that all the spiky-haired weirdos on television are yammering on about. While not complete, here's a breakdown of the various consoles' strong points.

Xbox

The Xbox is more an investment in the future. Yes, there are some strong games, especially Halo, but there's little else to distinguish it from other consoles and their equally strong titles. If you want online gaming, this is your best bet.

Some exclusive games help give definition to the system. Primarily, they are the Sega titles, such as Shenmue II, Panzer Dragoon, Gun Valkyrie, and Jet Set Radio Future. Microsoft wants to appeal to the hard-core Sega devotee, so if you were committed to your Dreamcast, it's worth considering (www.microsoft.com/xbox).

GameCube

When you buy the Nintendo GameCube, you buy Nintendo games. That's its undeniable strength. This is the only place you can get Mario, Zelda, Perfect Dark, Star Fox, Donkey Kong, and Conker's. So if those are your favorite games, this is an easy choice.

There are a couple of misconceptions about the GameCube. The big one is the "kiddie console" problem. Kids may like Nintendo games, but that doesn't mean Nintendo games are just for kids. When did bright colors and bloodless gameplay become so unappealing to people? The gameplay in Mario 64 and Banjo-Kazooie is near perfect, and anyone can enjoy it.

That said, Nintendo realized that the N64 lacked the same number of darker games that the PlayStation had, and Eternal Darkness and two exclusive Resident Evil games should be out by the time you read this.

The other misconception is that there will be a shortage of titles. Nintendo has won back the third-party publishers it lost with the N64. The DVD-format is cheaper to produce than the cartridge. Plus, there's good reason to assume that large multiplatform franchises will appear. In addition, developers like the ease of making games for the GameCube (Factor 5 says it took only nine months for Rogue Leader), and this should allow for a far larger library (www.nintendo.com/systems/gcn).

PlayStation 2

You can have confidence in the number and variety of games for the Sony system. Plus, if you want a console with an established library of games, PS2 is the way to go. Some titles now take advantage of the system's power and benefit from longer development cycles.

Yes, the PS2 has been out longer, but it has not been rendered obsolete by the GameCube and Xbox. One look at MGS2 or Ico should lay those anxieties to rest. And, yes, it most likely will be the first console to see a next-gen upgrade, but there's a whole lotta good gaming to be had until then.

If the PlayStation was your primary gaming console and you liked the games, those trends will continue. Don't expect to see the Final Fantasy games and other titles from Square on any other system because Sony bought a significant share in the company. In addition, Sony has managed to produce some impressive first- and second-party titles, such as Gran Turismo 3 A-Spec, Ico, and Twisted Metal Black, making Sony games something you can't get for any other system and a reason to consider purchasing the console (www.playstation.com).

Twisted List: Video Games

Martin Sargent

I'm the kind of guy who loves everything to be brand spanking new. I buy a shiny new Lexus every year, I never wear the same shirt twice unless it's made of a meshlike material, and I still love to dance to the New Kids on the Block at clubs that have just opened. Same goes for the video games I play.

- **Beat Ball** (www.imphenzia.com). A new take on the arcade classic Breakout. It's fresh, exciting, and terribly action-packed! Actually, it's just Breakout set to techno and ambient music, but it's somewhat reminiscent of playing Arkanoid at a rave.

- **Fly or Die** (www.gamedale.com). I love video games with brilliant titles. That's why this one is right up my alley. The object of the game is to fly, or you could die. You've never seen anything like it. Adam Sessler of Extended Play writes, "It will start a revolution in the game space comparable only to the birth of the first-person shooter." I played this game after a particularly intense round of Beat Ball and worked off 15 pounds. I haven't done that since Richard Simmons came out with "Sweating to the Oldies, Part Three." I don't know how Chubby Checker wasn't built like a stick!

- **Pickman-3D** (www.alawar.com). Here's a game with a concept that makes you say, "Why didn't I think of that? I'd be a millionaire!" The concept: Merge the arcade classic Pac-Man with the role-playing game Dungeons & Dragons. That's the crux of the game. It's a whole lot like Pac-Man 3D, except that in the intro it says you're in a fortress full of orcs rather than a maze rife with ghost monsters. I've got an eighth-level awfully good Pickman!

- **Super Methane Brothers** (www.digitalfan.com). You've all heard of Super Mario Brothers, but how about these guys? It's just like the original Super Mario, except with this variation on the old Amiga game: Instead of being a plumber, you're apparently part of a sibling extermination duo that fires methane gas at bugs. It's pretty brilliant.

- **Atomic Superball, the Chicken Edition** (www.tetriscity.com). The game is very similar to Breakout, but with a mind-bending twist: You need to kill a chicken before advancing to the next level.

Talkback

Do Video Games Belong in Gym Class?

Dave Roos

Geeks and gym class do not mix. Mention the words *dodge* and *ball* to any member of *The Screen Savers*, and he's likely to respond with a tragic tale of wedgies past. One school in California has added highly entertaining and mildly aerobic Dance Dance Revolution machines as a substitute for less entertaining exercise options, such as floor hockey and laps.

"My waistline has gone down by 1 inch," one satisfied gamer says. "In, like, two weeks, I've lost 15 pounds," adds another formerly pudgy player.

The machines, which cost $8,000 a pop, are apparently mobbed with students who complain when gym class has to end.

Do video games belong in gym class?

Yes   32%

No   68%

32%
Yes

68%
No

Goodies That Won't Break the Budget

Josh Lawrence

It can be hard to buy cool tech gear on a tight budget. Don't worry, there are plenty of great goodies for less than $50. Here are Megan and Morgan's picks:

- **Unreal Tournament 2003** (www.rockstargames.com). This massively multiplayer first-person shooter has been a favorite of our weekly LAN party fragfests.

- **Grand Theft Auto: Vice City** (www.rockstargames.com). The controversial car-, motorcycle-, plane-, and helicopter-stealing simulation for PlayStation 2 has climbed to the top of most gamers' lists of all-time favorites.

- **Tony Hawk's Pro Skater 4** (www.activisiono2.com). Hop on your board and prove you have the skills to go pro in this game for PlayStation 2, PlayStation, Xbox, and GameCube.

- **Atari 10-in-1** (www.jakkstvgames.com). Want some old school gaming goodness, but don't want a old school bulky console? The Atari 10-in-1 packs 10 Atari 2600 games into a single controller that plugs directly into your TV.

- **Zip Zaps** (http://zipzaps.com). These speed-demon remote-control minicars can be bought in your local Radio Shack. Choose the model you want at the Zip Zaps showroom, and the site can point you to your nearest local store.

- **CDs and DVDs.** Of course, CDs and DVDs are always a good bet for less than $50 as well. For instance, Morgan recommends the Platinum Series Special Extended Edition of *Lord of the Rings: Fellowship of the Ring* DVD set.

Martin's Tips

Top Five Games to Play While Mostly Paralyzed

While vacationing deep within the Amazon River basin over the weekend, I inadvertently infuriated some local savages by wearing a culturally taboo racing-stripe loincloth. This caused the tribal chieftain to blow a poison dart into my neck.

The poison paralyzed my entire body except for two fingers on my right hand, throwing me into a panic. How would I be able to play computer games on my laptop while I lay in the jungle waiting for the paralysis to lift?

Luckily, I had installed five games on my laptop computer that require only simple mouse-clicking to play, on the off chance that just such a situation would arise.

Without further ado, I bring you the top five games you can play if a poison dart paralyzes most of your body in the Amazon:

1. **Spear Toss** (http://games.alentus.com)
2. **Among the Clouds** (www.orisinal.org)
3. **Helicopter** (www.ebaumsworld.com)
4. **Poke the Penguin** (www2.gamesville.lycos.com)
5. **The Mouse Click Game** (www.stupid.com)

How to Cheat at Solitaire

Morgan Webb

We all like to win, but why do we bother when we're competing against ourselves? Man's battle against himself is the noblest form of competition, but it's often debased by our wish for the easy victory. We must ask if it is human nature that makes us revel in this self-deception. We must ask if we merely crave some visceral satisfaction that comes from achieving even a conspicuously empty victory. The moral questions involved, however, are yours alone to answer. I merely give you the tools you need to cheat at Solitaire.

Solitaire Cheat

1. Open Solitaire. Go to Game and then Options, and choose to draw three cards.

2. Any time during gameplay, if you hold down Ctrl+Alt+Shift while you click the deck, you will draw one card rather than three. High scores will be yours every time!

Freecell Cheat

1. When you get stuck in Freecell, hold down Ctrl+Shift+F10.

2. When the user-friendly interface appears, choose Abort.

3. Make any move, and you will automatically win the game!

Bonus: Freecell includes some hidden games. Press F3 or choose Select Game from the Game menu; where it asks you to select a game number between 1 and 32,000, enter **−1** or **−2**. You get two strange new Freecell games to play.

Address: Site of the Day

3D Tetris

The classic puzzle game enters a new dimension of fun. (www.andre-michelle.com/old_studies/tetris3d.htm).

Talkback

Do Video Games Fry the Brain or Sharpen the Senses?

Josh Lawrence

Ever since kids started pumping millions of quarters into Space Invaders stand-up arcade games in the 1970s, worried parents and pundits speculated on whether electronic games were going to turn their brains into action-addicted sludge.

Surprisingly, many have claimed that video games are beneficial to players' brains. Dr. Margaret Chotton suggested in the now out-of-print *Computer Addiction?* that video games increase a player's manual dexterity and hand-eye coordination, and speed up the activity of neural pathways.

So when you or someone you know sits down to play a video game, what do you think is the main effect? Do you believe that brain cells are being challenged and enhanced, or simply being boggled and blasted into stupor?

Do video games fry the brain or sharpen the senses?

Fry the brain   18%

Sharpen the senses   82%

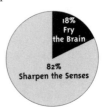

18% Fry the Brain

82% Sharpen the Senses

Classic Arcade Gaming

Ed Lee and Roger Chang

Did you know you can relive part of your childhood in the form of these classic games for free, thanks to the Internet? What's more, these games are downloads—yours to keep and cherish forever.

Emulators and ROMs

Emulators are software programs that essentially duplicate the innards of old video game machines, as well as classic consoles such as the Atari 2600. ROMs are the games themselves, extracted from the source code of the originals and zipped up to be read by the emulators.

If this seems a bit confusing, don't worry. Some excellent sites are devoted to this nostalgic pursuit. At ClassicGaming.com, you can find a variety of emulators and hundreds of ROMs to download.

Mame

By far the most popular type of emulator, according to ClassicGaming.com site director William Cassidy, is Mame (www.mame.net). Mame and its Windows counterpart, Mame32 (www.classicgaming.org/mame32qa), emulate more than 1,500 classic arcade games such as Joust, Centipede, and Pole Position. There's also a Mac version called MacMame (http://macmame.org). Here's how to use Mame:

1. Download Mame. Download the binaries, not the source code, unless you're interested in programming.

2. Download the game ROMs. The legalities involving ROMs are far from resolved, so you'll have to find the ROMs on your own.

3. Install or unzip the Mame file. Notice that in the newly created Mame directory, there's a subfolder called ROMs.

4. Put your downloaded ROM files into the ROM folder in the Mame directory. Do not unzip the ROM files. Mame was created to accept ROM files in zip format.

5. Start Mame. From the File menu, select Show Only Available. If you don't follow this step, Mame will list every supported game, whether you have it or not.

6. You can customize controls within each game's properties. These include sound, game controller, and video settings.

7. Select the game you want to play and click Run. To skip the first warning screens, type **ok**. The game will need to boot up in Mame.

8. Here are your game's controls: 5 and 6 insert quarters into the game; 1 and 2 select one or two players; during the game, adjust specific game settings by hitting the Tab key; Esc exits the settings menu.

Console Emulators

Most other emulators focus on one console, such as the Atari 2600 or the Nintendo Entertainment System (NES). Some of these include Stella (an Atari 2600 emulator), ColEm (ColecoVision), Genecyst (Sega Genesis), and NESticle (NES, www.classicgaming.com). "Virtually all console systems before 1995 or so have been emulated," Cassidy says.

Emulate Multiple Consoles

The only emulator that handles multiple consoles successfully is called Mess (http://mess.emuverse.com). Most people would rather find the emulator that gets their favorite games just right.

Emulators for the Mac

Emulation.net is the one-stop shop for Mac users interested in emulating classic and not-so-classic game machines, including such greats as the Super Nintendo, the Atari 800, and, of course, Mame.

So, this community of enthusiasts has given these games a whole new lease on life with emulator technology. But at this point you might be asking, are these games legal? Isn't someone, somewhere, going to want to be paid?

Games for the Graphically Challenged

Nicole Carrico

You might have the impression that we at *The Screen Savers* are obsessed with finding the latest and greatest in graphical gaming. But that's not entirely true. Granted, we drool over those breathtaking visuals as much as the next geek, but there are plenty of games out there for those who haven't invested in the latest 3D graphics card.

Here are a few of our favorite old-school games. They're all free and fiendishly addictive, and they can all be enjoyed on any computer, no matter how small the screen or how slow the system:

- **Super Collapse** (http://games.yahoo.com). This innocuous little game from Yahoo! comes in the form of a 1.2MB download. The goal is to eliminate the blocks entirely, or to prevent them from stacking to the top before your time runs out. Try it, and you'll discover what every member of *The Screen Savers* team has learned the hard way. We're starting a 12-step group in an attempt to break this horrible addiction, but no one can make it to the meetings: They're too busy playing. This game is free to try and $19.95 to buy.

- **The Land of ZZT** (www.autofish.net). Web producer Josh Lawrence turned me on to these ASCII-based games. Published in 1991, ZZT is a freeware computer game designed by Tim Sweeney with a built-in editor, allowing any user to create new games. Don't let the grainy graphics fool you! You can spend many, many hours in these custom worlds, and you don't need a souped-up system to enjoy them.

- **The Hitchhiker's Guide to the Galaxy** (www.the-underdogs.org). For my money, text-based games don't get any better than Infocom's classic The Hitchhiker's Guide to the Galaxy. It's based on the infamous five-book trilogy by Douglas Adams. I grew up playing this game, and the Solid Gold edition released in 1987 manages to improve the experience without interfering with the original. (Another Infocom favorite is the popular Zork, also at Home of the Underdogs.)

- **Doom** (www.idsoftware.com). Leo would never forgive me if I failed to mention Doom from id Software. This obscenely popular action game offers a fast, simple 3D graphics experience on virtually any system. So load up your shotgun and get ready to shoot some demons! It's free to try.

- **Bejeweled** (www.popcap.com). Last, but certainly not least, Bejeweled is easily one of the most popular free games on the Internet. The 1.6MB download packs quite a punch and earned the title of "Most Popular Game of 2001" from the MS Gaming Zone. If you aren't already hooked on this one, you don't know what you're missing.

Download of the Day

Farnsworth Ferret's Fun Pack for Kids 1.3

Megan Morrone

It's never too early to teach your child how to use your computer. I'm not going to promise that they won't throw up on the keyboard, but I can't promise that about myself these days, either. Morning sickness means my baby's going to be healthy, right?

Farnsworth Ferret's Fun Pack for Kids (http://download.com) is a collection of five games that you can play for free. The games are for kids as young as 4, but because you can change the difficulty level, older kids can have fun too.

Twisted List: Alien Games

Martin Sargent

I know they're out there. In psychotherapy this morning, I uncovered several repressed memories involving a cornfield, a UFO, and several little green men wearing big white coats.

I will never wear a kilt on the farm again.

Anyway, to help me work through the trauma, my therapist suggested I create a list about alien games.

- **Whack an Alien** (http://download.com). This is a new take on the classic Whack a Mole, ingeniously renamed Whack an Alien. I feel kind of guilty because the aliens never even attack. They just wave their heads back and forth and writhe like hippies at a Dead show.

- **PetWings** (http://download.com). How many times can we remake the arcade classic Galaga? Wasn't Galaxian enough? You can remake it at least one too many times, if PetWings is any indication. Again, you feel bad blasting the space critters—they're cute. That is, until you realize that their leaders are giant space bees that shoot fireball stingers at your head. Exterminate!

- **A-Blast 3D** (www.shockwave.com). I wanted to be an astronaut when I was a kid, but then I found out they wouldn't take me because I have 20/400 vision, and if you lose a contact in zero gravity, you're hosed. Not to mention the mess the saline solution would make. A-Blast 3D lets you fly through space and shoot alien vessels. But, it's just not the same as the real thing. I've seen Battlestar Galactica, so I know.

- **Spacebar** (http://download.com). Here's a funny premise for a game. You walk into a brew pub in another galaxy, and aliens offer you cocktails and frosty, delicious, refreshing mugs of beer. Your job? Destroy the drinks with a shotgun. The future has never looked so bleak. Rumor has it that the game was created by a Czechoslovakian company on a government mission to curb teenage drinking and, apparently, to encourage teenage shootings of bars with shotguns.

- **UFO III** (http://download.com). We're so used to defending the Earth from aliens; wouldn't you like to experience the other side? In UFO III, you're the creature in the spaceship attacking Earth using advanced technology. Like most aliens, you mainly want to kill us for no good reason. All of your victims are driving Porsches, however, so you could be alleviating the unequal distribution of wealth in this country— unless you're a believer in Reaganomics and that whole supply-side thing, in which case you're really screwing up our economy.

Download of the Day

Alley Cat

Morgan Webb

Ah, the good old days, when the best sounds you could muster from your PC were blips and bleeps from your internal speaker and 256 colors seemed a dreamlike impossibility.

Now you can relive those simpler, halcyon days with Alley Cat (www.dosgamesarchive.com), a classic (and free!) DOS game written by Bill Williams in 1984.

The object of the game is to leap around the alley of an apartment building, collecting mice and other kitty delicacies while avoiding dogs and other perils of feline street life. Note: This game is definitely abandonware; our research indicates it's freeware, but download at your own risk.

Ultimate Gaming Machine 6.0

Roman Loyola

In case you're not familiar with the Ultimate Gaming Machine (UGM, for short—we pronounce it "ugh-um" on the show), it's a PC we've put together for the best gaming performance and experience.

Core Components

We didn't go for the most expensive, fastest parts. Instead, we considered price as well as performance. Here's a parts list:

- **CPU:** AMD Athlon XP 2800 (www.amd.com)
- **Motherboard:** Asus A7N8X (www.asus.com)
- **RAM:** Corsair (www.corsairmicro.com) XMS 3500 DDR 433 MHz (two 512MB sticks)

Storage

Storage gets more affordable every day, so why hold back? What might seem gluttonous now will be the norm in six months.

- **Hard drive:** Western Digital Caviar 200GB (www.westerndigital.com). A 7,200 rpm drive with an 8MB buffer. You have to partition it to properly use it.
- **CD burner:** Lite-On LTR-52246S (www.liteonit.com.tw). The fastest CD burner in the world: 52X write, 24X rewrite, and 52X read speeds.
- **DVD-ROM:** Toshiba SD-M1612 (http://sdmswb01.config.toshiba.com). 16x DVD playback.

Optional Hardware

Although we didn't include the following items in UGM, we did consider them and had them in for benchmarking:

- **Hard drive:** Fujitsu MAN3367MP (www.buyfcpa.com). A 36.7GB SCSI drive rated at 10,000 rpm.
- **SCSI card:** Adaptec 29160 SCSI card (www.adaptec.com). A single-channel Ultra160 SCSI card that uses a 64-bit PCI interface. This is for our Fujitsu drive, plus future expansion options.

Sound and Input Devices

People often try to save money when buying these components. But because gaming is an interactive activity, it makes better sense to get good input devices and sound components. When sound draws you in and the controls work smoothly, you've got a great gaming experience.

We picked products that offer good price and performance. Picking input devices comes down to how they feel in your hands, so what's comfortable to us might not work for you.

- **Mouse:** Logitech MX700 Cordless Optical Mouse (www.logitech.com). No dirty mouse ball or cable to slow us down.
- **Keyboard:** Logitech Elite USB Keyboard (www.logitech.com). Instant access buttons for quick access.
- **Joystick:** X45 digital joystick and throttle (www.saitekusa.com). For when we feel like flying.
- **Gamepad:** Microsoft Sidewinder Gamepad Pro (www.microsoft.com). It's comfortable and it looks cool.
- **Sound card:** Turtle Beach Santa Cruz (www.turtlebeach.com). Offers six-speaker support.
- **Speakers:** Klipsch ProMedia 5.1 (www.klipsch.com). These are the speakers we used with UGM 5.0. We liked them so much that we decided not to change them.

Video

The video card is a crucial component for the gaming PC's performance. Here's what we picked:

- **Video card:** ATI Radeon 9700 Pro (http://mirror.ati.com/products). According to TechTV Labs, it's the fastest card on the market.
- **Monitor:** Princeton Arcadia AR3.2FTX (www.princetongraphics.com). Combines XGA-computer compatibility, HDTV compatibility, and a built-in NTSC TV tuner in one monitor.

UGM 6.0: Benchmarks

Patrick Norton

How fast is the PC we've put together?

We went for the best numbers we could get on FutureMark's (www.futuremark.com, the benchmark company formerly known as Mad Onion) 3D Mark 2001 SE (build 330), a solid, all-around 3D performance benchmark. We also tested with Unreal Tournament 2003, the most power-hungry game we've seen yet.

Preliminary Benchmarks

Before we built UGM 6.0, Yoshi grabbed the two fastest chips and the two fastest graphics cards, and he came up with these benchmarks (tests run at 1,024×768 screen resolution).

We said Intel's 3.06 PIV ran 3D Mark 2001 a shade faster. It also costs nearly twice the price of the speediest AMD Athlon XP processor. Also, the Athlon XP ran UT2003 faster. Costs less? Runs the real game faster? We went for the AMD Athlon.

UGM Benchmarks

These were the final benchmark numbers on our tweaked but not overclocked UGM 6.0:

3D Mark 2001 SE: 15057

That score is almost identical to the 3.06 PIV we tested. UGM yielded 80 frames per second on Unreal Tournament 2003 Bot Match (full version of the game, not the demo). Not bad.

Frankly, you'll notice nearly no difference in those benchmark results up there.

Behind the Numbers

Is UGM 6.0 that much faster than other top-of-the-line systems out there? Not really. The truth is, most games run in the CPU, memory, and the graphics card. The motherboards that make a healthy difference in performance simply connect those parts better than other motherboards (I'm oversimplifying here).

A faster hard drive helps load games faster. It'll help you change levels faster as your CPU sucks the info off the drive and into main memory. But it's not gonna help many games much (if at all) while you're playing.

The next stop for our UGM? Overclocking, definitely. Then more benchmark tests. Then?

3D Mark 2001	3.06GHz Pentium 4	AMD Athlon XP 2800+
NVidia GeForce Ti 4600	13429	13281
ATI All-In-Wonder 9700 Pro	15054	14756

Numbers are based on Futuremark's 3D Mark 2001 SE benchmark.

Unreal Tournament 2003 Bot Match	3.06GHz Pentium 4	AMD Athlon XP 2800+
NVidia GeForce Ti 4600	73.1	76.44
ATI All-In-Wonder 9700 Pro	75.2	80.77

47

Twisted List: Top Five Free Arcade Games

Martin Sargent

My anthropology Ph.D. thesis advisor, Dr. Kwame Jeyifo, had a theory that you can learn a lot about a nation by looking at the free games the people of that nation download off the Internet. Of course, he was a post-structuralist, and we all know how they are. Regardless, let's see what we can glean about America by inspecting the top five arcade-style games people downloaded from Download.com.

1. In **Natomi Bottle Rockets Extreme** (www.natomic.com), the object is to destroy spaceships using bottle rockets. It's fun, but just remember, kids, that if a bottle rocket can destroy a space vessel from a civilization that's clearly more advanced than our own, just think what a bottle rocket will do if it explodes in your fingers.

2. I can never decide what I like more: foul-mouthed, flatulent schoolboys or Italian-American plumbers who eat magic mushrooms.

   Well, I don't have to decide if I play **South Park Super Mario Bros** (www.gamewizardpro.com), a version of the classic Super Mario Brothers. Instead of Mario or Luigi, you play Kyle or one of the other *South Park* hooligans. But beware—the game is buggy as all get out and tries to mess with your system. I cannot recommend it. There, I said it.

3. Dr. Kwame Jeyifo used to say that people play computer games in part because they can become something they've always wanted to be. A wizard. A god. A fighter pilot. A beer truck driver.

   In **Beer Truck 1.0** (www.mrgoodbeer.com), you steal a beer truck and try to get it back to your trailer without getting nabbed by the fuzz and tossed in the hoosegow. The gameplay is primitive, akin to Spy Hunter after slugging a sixer of Coors Light, chasing each one with some Jaeger. Man, that brings me back to when I lived with my mom.

4. This is a shocker. Apparently, we Americans are pining for a simpler time, unencumbered by the weight of enjoyable video games.

   That's the only possible explanation for why this really crappy version of **Pac-Man** (http://download.com) is on the list. This version came out more than 20 years after the original, yet it is to Pac-Man as Zinjanthropus man is to homo sapien man.

   The only worthwhile twist in this version is that if your Pac-Man drinks a beer, he gets drunk and becomes difficult to control. And believe me, a drunk Pac-Man is messy.

5. The object of **Grand Theft Auto** (www.take2games.com) is to complete missions while car-jacking innocent drivers and smacking into any pedestrian in your path. You actually get points for running over people. It's disgusting.

   I mean, wake up America. Why are you wasting your time on this old version of Grand Theft Auto when there is so much more potential for killing and spilling blood in Grand Theft Auto 3?

Address: Site of the Day

Electrotank Mini Golf

Try your hand at Electrotank Mini Golf (www.electrotank.com), quite possibly the most realistic putt-putt simulator ever created.

Sub-$500 Gaming PC

Patrick Norton

I know that if you already have a PC with an ATX case, a 300-watt (or bigger) power supply, a CD-ROM (or CD-R/RW, DVD, etc.), and a hard drive, I can help you build a kick-ass gaming PC for $362. If you need a case, a power supply, a CD-ROM, and a hard drive, well, it'll cost a whopping $471.

At the core of our cheap gaming PC is an AMD Athlon XP 2100+ CPU, a speedy MSI nForce2 motherboard, 512MB of PC2700 RAM (if you can find PC2700 in 128MB sticks, you can save money by getting 256MB of RAM), and a DirectX 9–ready ATI Radeon 9500 graphics card.

The Parts That Count

Most games live in your processor, main system memory, and graphics card. The hard drive and CD-ROM drive are there to feed those parts the data.

A faster hard drive loads your game levels faster, and a faster CD-ROM drive loads your games onto your hard drive faster.

With this in mind, scrounge! Call every local computer store. Hit Price Watch (www.pricewatch.com). Shop at companies that offer super-cheap or free shipping. Don't order anything overnight. Be patient.

Inventory

- **CPU:** Athlon XP 2100+, $71 (www.amd.com).
- **Motherboard:** MSI K7N2-L, $90 (www.msicomputer.com). The MSI K7N2-L has the NVidia nForce2 IGP chipset, built-in 10/100 Ethernet, audio, five PCI slots, and USB 2.0.

  Want FireWire and the SoundStorm APU surround-sound audio? It'll be a bit more— say, $137 for the Asus A7N8X Deluxe (www.asus.com) or $147 for the MSI K7N2G-L (www.msicomputer.com).
- **Memory:** Two sticks of 256MB PC2700, $65. If you can find 128MB sticks, buy a pair instead. You need two sticks of DDR RAM to take advantage of the nForce2's Dual Channel DDR.

Willing to spend more money? You'll get better performance from the CAS2 PC2700 than the CAS2.5 that comes with most generic DDR RAM.

- **Graphics card:** ATI Radeon 9500 Pro, $136. You could go with an nForce2 motherboard with onboard graphics. The motherboard will cost $30 to $40 more, but newer games, such as Unreal Tournament 2003, will bring the onboard graphics to its knees. ATI's Radeon 9500 is the cheapest DirectX 9 graphics card.
- **Hard drive:** 60GB EIDE drive, $66. On Price Watch, 20GB drives start at $49 and often aren't listed with a brand. 60GB drives start at $66 and are usually Maxtor or Western Digital.
- **CD-ROM drive:** Generic 40X CD-ROM, $25. If you're using the CD-ROM drive only to install games and listen to the occasional audio CD, don't break the bank. If you want faster audio extraction (for making MP3s) and the ability to burn audio discs and data backups, get a CD burner ($50).
- **Case and power supply:** Generic parts on Price Watch, $18. Recycle an old case. Buy a case from a yard sale. Watch for the best power supply you can get.

Small-Time Gaming with Linux

Chris DiBona

PC gaming is getting better for Linux users. Games such as Quake and Unreal Tournament can be played natively on Linux machines. Others, such as Jedi Outcast, can be played via Transgaming Technologies' WineX emulator.

That's all well and good, but what about Tetris, Tetravex, or plain old Solitaire?

These games, while small, are some of the world's greatest diversions. Got a few minutes to kill? A game of Minesweeper is a wonderful distraction. As it turns out, when it comes to small-time time-wasters, Linux users are a lucky lot, with a ton of titles to choose from.

I've listed some of the most addictive little games and a few of the larger time-wasting wonders that come with an installation of Red Hat Linux 8.0 (www.redhat.com).

Tetris Clones

In the Tetris-like game category, we have a number of offerings, including Ksirtet, Ksmiletris, and a fun little twist on Tetris called KfoulEggs. As you can probably tell, I'm concentrating mostly on KDE apps because KDE is what I run.

Mahjongg Mayhem

- Shisen-Sho
- Kmahjongg

Card Sharks

- Patience
- Poker
- Skat

Board Games

- Go and Reversi-style games
- Chinese checkers (Kenolaba)
- Chess
- Backgammon (personal favorite)

More Action

If these games are too slow for you, I suggest some of the faster-paced games included with Red Hat, such as KSpaceduel, which is based on the old SpaceWar games, and Kasteroids, which is an Asteroids clone.

Even More Action

These games are pretty fun, but a few even cooler games come with Red Hat, including Chromium, a space shooter; Tux Racer, a sledding penguin game; and Freeciv, a free version of Civilization.

Find More Games for Linux

Freshmeat.net and Happypenguin.org have even more free games for Linux. Most of these games, including the very addictive Frozen-Bubble, are included on the Knoppix Linux demo CD, so if you don't feel like installing Linux, you can still play all these great games.

Download of the Day

DX-Ball

Megan Morrone

Amiga fans will remember MegaBall, a popular Breakout-like game that ran on just about any Amiga. Now you can download a MegaBall clone called DX-Ball (www.blitwise.com) for free on Windows 9X/NT/2000 or Mac OS 8/9/X. The website doesn't mention XP, but it ran fine on my XP machine.

The game (created by Michael P. Welch) is similar to MegaBall and Breakout. If you've played Hardball for Palm, you'll also see similarities. The object of the game is to hit the ball with your paddle (using your mouse) and knock out the pyramid of blocks. When the ball hits the ground (or the bottom of the screen), you lose a life. The twist to DX-Ball is that not all blocks are created equal. When you first start up the game, you'll see a key to the secrets that each special block contains. Try it. You'll like it.

Help Yourself: Game Peripherals

Eileen Rivera

So you say you got da skills, huh? Well, why not make your gaming experience a little more interesting with some of these peripherals?

VR-1 Virtual Racing Chassis

It's a seat, folks. No steering wheel or pedals, and it's about $300, but it sure is comfortable! It's really designed for the racing game aficionado or someone who has a lot of money to burn. All you do is hook up your steering wheel, and you're ready to go (www.bobearlracing.com).

Nintendo WaveBird

Don't you hate it when people trip over your controller wires when you're playing a game? If you're playing with the GameCube, the WaveBird eliminates that problem. It uses an RF signal, so you can play wirelessly several feet away from the TV. It's a fine investment for every GameCube owner.

Magic Box

Now even after they gave us the S-controller, some people still have problems with their Xbox controller. Well, here's the solution. Plug the Magic Box into your Xbox, and it becomes a conduit, allowing you to use a PS2, Dreamcast, and Saturn controller to play Xbox games. Very cool!

It can be useful for very specific games, primarily fighting games. Bear in mind that Xbox games are designed for the Xbox controller, so you might run into problems if you use your entire library. You'll find the Magic Box only at a video game import store or site, such as www.lik-sang.com or www.levelsix.com.

Airflo

Sometimes after playing for hours on end, you end up sweating all over your controller. Nyko's (www.nyko.com) controller fixes that problem. Inside the handle are fans that blow air and thereby keep your hands nice and cool.

It really doesn't work too well for playing the games, but if you are a really sweaty boy, this might be something to look into.

E-Dimensional 3D Wireless Glasses

These promise a 3D experience right out of your monitor. Well, it's 3D kinda like *Jaws 3D*, and we all know that was a quality film.

Also, if there's any text in this game, it's nearly impossible to read it. You will suffer eyestrain (www.edimensional.com).

Laporte Support

Speed Up a Celeron-Based System for Gaming

Download the Belarc Advisor (www.belarc.com) to find out what CPU and video card you have. You need this information to determine what you can upgrade. With a Celeron-based system, you don't want to get the latest and fastest video cards. Your CPU can't keep up with the processing of GeForce4-type cards. You can probably upgrade to a GeForce2-level card.

You have to open the case to see if you have an AGP slot. If not, you need to get a PCI video card. To get AGP and to be able to use GeForce4-level cards, you'll have to upgrade your motherboard and processor. You need to have at least a 1GHz CPU to take advantage of the GeForce4.

Address: Site of the Day

Adrenaline Vault

This is arguably the best gaming site: www.avault.com. Get the latest reviews, free downloads, and much more.

NVidia GeForce Chips Explained

Patrick Norton

I love the fact that NVidia has pushed the limits on 3D performance (NVidia's drivers aren't bad, either). The company has established its reputation by releasing new products every six months or so. The downside? With new chips coming out and older chips still on the market, that means a lot of NVidia-based boards on the shelves.

TNT2-based boards are cheap; I still see them on shelves for up to $50. Same thing for GeForce 256, the first generation of GeForce processors. For that money, you can get the latest generation of GeForce4 boards, at least the low-cost MX versions.

That said, the GeForce4 MX-based boards might not be the best way to go. Don't get me wrong: Every board listed will play games (especially pre-DirectX 8 games). Read Tom's VGA Charts (www17.tomshardware.com) for a comparison of almost every graphics card sold in the last three or four years. Look closely; you'll see that the GeForce3 and GeForce3 Ti 500 generally outperform the newer GeForce4 MX boards and pretty much trounce them on Aquanox, a DirectX 8 game.

GeForce3 vs. GeForce4

The GeForce3 is actually more advanced technology than the GeForce4 MX, which is essentially a souped-up GeForce2 MX processor. The GeForce4 doesn't contain the nfiniteFX engine (NVidia's vertex shader), which means it doesn't fully support DirectX 8.1. All GeForce3 cards pack this feature. That's one reason the GeForce4 MX is cheaper.

The main differences between the GeForce4 MX and the GeForce2 MX cards are the clock speeds and the GeForce4 MX's Light Speed Memory Architecture II. The GeForce4 MX's implementation of this memory controller has half the segments of the GeForce3 and GeForce4 Ti, and thus considerably less memory bandwidth and performance. While we're going over gadgetry, the GeForce3 boards have a single vertex shader, compared to the GeForce4 Ti's pair of shaders.

For a few dollars more than the GeForce 4Mx 460, you'll get heaps better performance and a longer life with a GeForce4 420Ti board (or, for less money, the late GeForce3 boards), especially if you regularly buy new games. The GeForce4 MX boards are missing those crucial vertex and pixel shaders. That's not a problem with today's Quake, but soon games will demand Direct X 8 or Direct X 9. Avoid the bottom of the barrel GeForce4 MX420; it will barely outperform the GeForce2 MX400.

GeForce Bargains

The best bargains are GeForce3 boards if they're priced under GeForce4 MX cards. The GeForce4 420Ti is the best deal on a top-of-the-line video card. The GeForce4 420Ti is an ideal choice for a middle-of-the-line video card. The GeForce4 MX 440 is a good deal, as long as you pay less than $80 and understand that you'll want to replace it in a year.

If you're running less than a 1GHz processor and already have a GeForce board, you should upgrade the processor first. Or, upgrade the processor and the video card in tandem. Thinking about a top-of-the-line GeForce4 Ti board? You're wasting money if your processor can't feed it, and 1GHz is pretty much the starting point.

Wil Wheaton's Favorite Games

Wil Wheaton, who played Wesley Crusher on *Star Trek: The Next Generation* and Gordie in the film *Stand by Me*, is a gamer as well as an actor, and is a long-time friend of *The Screen Savers*. These classic games delight his inner and outer geek. Be sure to visit Wheaton's site (www.wilwheaton.net).

My Top Five Atari 2600 Games

1. **Kaboom!** (www.geocities.com/elvis8atari). I'd score it higher, but it's just too damn hard on the higher levels.

2. **Combat** (www.atarihq.com). One word: Invisible tank pong with maximum walls. Close your eyes and make the sounds in your head. Now just try to be unhappy.

3. **Circus Atari** (www.atarihq.com). If you don't already have a paddle controller because of Kaboom!, you'll get it for this game.

4. **Pitfall!** (www.thealmightyguru.com), Please tell me I'm not the only person who tried to get to the "end" of this game.

5. **Yar's Revenge** (www.thealmightyguru.com). The best giant-insects-attacking-the-base-while-trying-to-use-the-big-ass-cannon-that-you-can't-fire-from-the-neutral-zone game *ever!*

My Top Five Role-Playing Games

1. **D&D Basic Rules** (www.acaeum.com). Color-them-in-dice, The Keep on the Borderlands module.

2. **GURPS Autoduel**, including all the Uncle Albert's Catalogues (www.sjgames.com).

3. **GURPS Illuminatti**, with a bit of Horror (www.sjgames.com).

4. **D&D 3rd Edition** (www.wizards.com).

5. My friend Terry's **GURPS Space Adventure** (www.sjgames.com), circa 1989, when I got a critical success roll while trying to disguise myself as the president, who I was trying to assassinate. The critical success made my disguise perfectly match the person I was trying to kill, so I totally messed up the entire campaign by walking around firing the president's entire cabinet.

Download of the Day

Age of Mythology Demo

Megan Morrone

This beautiful game is part of the Age of Empires series (www.microsoft.com/games/empires). In the demo, you can play only Zeus. But hey, who's better than Zeus?

This download is a hefty 345MB. If you don't have broadband, go watch *The Two Towers* on DVD; when it's over, the game might be finished downloading.

The Age of Mythology trial version is available at www.microsoft.com/games/ageofmythology/egypt_downloads.asp.

Address: Site of the Day

Rooftop Skater 2.1

Martin Sargent

Dude, there's nothing like jumping on a killer deck and shredding the steps of City Hall pulling goofy-foot ollies and front-side nose-blunt slides. Obviously, I have no idea what I'm talking about. Sure, I like to pretend I'm a skateboarder, but my body is just too delicate, and baggy pants don't flatter me.

To fill the skateboarding void, I play this great game called Rooftop Skater. You can customize your skater, edit rooftop levels, and pull wicked tricks from building to building. It's all the fun of real skating without the brain-scrambling concussions (www.newgrounds.com/portal/view.php?id=30329).

Are Emulators Legal?

Ed Lee and Roger Chang

Emulator ROMs are the code for the games, so they're like individual cartridges for the emulators, which represent the game consoles. The code is converted into binary and fed through a custom-made device into a PC that turns it into an archive. "Often the cartridge reader and software is strictly a homemade affair, so a ROM archivist has to be very technically inclined," William Cassidy of ClassicGaming.com says.

Classic Video Game Sites

- **Mame World** (www.mameworld.net)
- **ClassicGaming.com Hosted Sites** (www.classicgaming.com/sites)
- **Zophar's Domain** (www.zophar.net)
- **Mame.dk** (www.zophar.net)
- **Atari Gaming Headquarters** (www.atarihq.com)
- **ClassicGaming.com Newbie Guide** (www.classicgaming.com/cgng)
- **Intellivision Productions** (www.intellivisionlives.com)
- **Classic Video Games Nexus** (http://home.hiwaay.net/~lkseitz/cvg/nexus/)

The ROM-making community is quite small and, as a result, not nearly as visible as the music file traders. Although the two forms of digital entertainment are quite different, the legal ramifications of sharing intellectual property are similar.

"This is a thorny issue," Cassidy says regarding the legalities of emulators and ROMs. Because emulators are simply reverse-engineered original software that is usually not bundled with ROMs, they are perfectly legal, much like the Gnutella software is considered legal because it only acts as a conduit.

But the ROMs are a different matter. "The program code of a cartridge or arcade machine is the intellectual property of the game's designers or copyright holders," Cassidy points out. Creating a ROM is permissible by the same laws that allow you to make backup copies of software you own—an important caveat being that you cannot then sell the ROMs. "Some people sell ROM packages anyway, but this is almost always illegal. Likewise, you cannot legally download a ROM file unless you own the game in another form," Cassidy explains.

Some intellectual property holders have officially relinquished their rights over their games, and thus these games are considered "free." For the arcade game Robby Roto and the entire library of the long-discontinued Vectrex home console system, the possibility for profit has long since been abandoned, so why make the games available?

"The issue is legality vs. preservation," Cassidy says. "For every game (such as Pac-Man) that is still supported by its owners (Hasbro) and has profit potential, there are hundreds of games that would likely never see the light of day again if it weren't for ROM distribution."

Consoles such as the Amstrad CPC computer, the Bally Professional Arcade console, the Turbografx-16, and hundreds of less famous arcade games might have vanished without the Internet, Cassidy claims. "They would likely disappear forever if people didn't participate in quasi-legal ROM distribution. In these cases, distribution hurts no one's profits (often the companies involved have long since disappeared), so emulation proponents argue, what's the harm?"

When video game companies or intellectual property holders have asked sites to remove the ROMs, they quickly complied. "I am unaware of any legal action being taken against these sites," Cassidy says. "Most of them are perfectly willing to remove the ROMs once they realize that someone actually cares."

It's a sharp contrast to the perceived copyright violations obsessing the music industry. It's most definitely a reflection of the makeup of the different communities and corporations at play.

Warcraft III Strategies and Tips

Dave Roos

Bill Roper and the folks from Blizzard Entertainment (www.blizzard.com) were nice enough to slip us some insider info on how to master their real-time strategy epic Warcraft III: Reign of Chaos. All of these tips (and many more) can be found at Battle.net as part of Marn Thunderhorn's Warcraft III Strategy Guide.

1. Warcraft III is a game of learning. When you lose, you should know why. By knowing why you lost, you can find areas to improve upon on in future games. Watch game replays to figure out where you went wrong, and look at areas in which you can improve. If you are stumped, give replays to your friends and ask them for advice.

2. A hero's skill point should be spent as soon as you get it. Watch the portrait in the top-left corner for the hero's skill points. Don't let them add up. Don't leave them unspent for very long. While in rare situations you might want to save skill points, usually you want to spend them as soon as you get them.

3. Just because your town is gone doesn't mean the game is over. In previous games, a player was eliminated when all of his buildings were destroyed, but in Warcraft III, a team will live on until all buildings from all the team members are destroyed. This means all players should stay in the game until everyone is eliminated.

   Share unit control and fight until the end. Also, you can still get a win if you and your ally are able to beat the enemy. If you manage to win, you both get a win even if all of your (but not your allies') buildings and units were destroyed.

4. Always make sure the worker or hero has a way of getting out when you build a building. If you're not careful, you can end up walling in your worker or hero with buildings or trees. If this happens, you either have to destroy a building, kill the worker, or purchase a Goblin Zeppelin to get them out. You can also kill the unit to free up food.

5. If you have to leave a game and your allies continue playing, open the allies' menu and give all your resources to your ally. Allies will be able to control your buildings and units after you leave the game. This may help them win the game.

Must-Have Games

Adam Sessler

Every home should have these games:

- **The Sims** (PC, http://thesims.ea.com)
- **The Legend of Zelda: Ocarina of Time** (N64, www.zelda.com)
- **Tetris** (NES, www.tetris.com)
- **Ico** (PS2, www.icothegame.com)
- **Rayman 2** (DC, www.rayman2.com)

Download of the Day

Icy Tower

Megan Morrone

Icy Tower (www.freelunchdesign.com) is a fast and free game from Free Lunch Design. You're Harold the Homeboy, and you've found a tower made of ice that you would like to climb. Use the arrow keys to run. Use the spacebar to jump.

The basic version of Icy Tower is small and contains itty-bitty sound files. To listen to the music, download the 2.8MB .dat file or the 6.9MB .dat file and drag it to the C:\games\icytower\data folder.

Twisted List: Dinosaur Games

Martin Sargent

In *Heart of Darkness*, Joseph Conrad taught us that deep within even the most restrained men are primal, prehistoric urges that might some day bubble forth, overtaking and Neanderthalizing any refinement we humans have collectively accumulated through thousands of years of civilization.

Maybe that's why I often make believe that I'm a wooly mammoth. (But in my pretend games the wooly mammoth always beats the Tyrannosaurus Rex, so it's actually a lot cooler than it sounds.) I also fulfill my primal urges by playing these five prehistorically themed computer games.

5. **Dynomite** (http://download.com), also known as Egg Sucker, is like the unbelievably addictive game Snood or the arcade classic Bust-a-Move, but with a dinosaur twist. The object is to line up sets of three like-colored dinosaur eggs, causing the eggs to explode. If you can't destroy the eggs quickly enough, a huge dinosaur stomps on you. Highly recommended.

4. **3D Caveman Rocks** (http://download.com), just as Dynomite was a rip-off of Snood and Bust-a-Move, this is a shameless revision of the arcade classic Donkey Kong. You're a caveman climbing up tilted terrain, jumping over and smashing barrels, trying to reach the top where a big gorilla awaits you. It actually gets a little less Donkey Kong–esque as you advance through the levels, but it never really gets much more fun.

3. **Rampage** (www.shockwave.com) isn't a rip-off of an arcade classic, because it is an arcade classic. In Rampage, you play one of three monsters: a gorilla, a wolf-man, or a dinosaur. The goal is touring the United States and destroying the downtown areas of major cities. The premise of the game wouldn't be so sinister if there were as many Starbucks coffee houses when the game was created as there are now. At least you'd be doing some good when you toppled a building.

2. **Caveman Cards** (http://download.com). I've been playing this a lot since I bought the DVD edition of one of my favorite all-time films, *The Flintstones: Viva Rock Vegas*. In Caveman Cards, you can play a range of casino-style card games, taking on Gar, the dealer. Unfortunately, the game is published by Zapspot, which is notorious for flooding your system with garbage and popping up ads during the game. Unless you want to lose 20 pounds or regrow your hair the herbal way, you might want to avoid Caveman Cards.

1. And no. 1 is **Carnivores** (http://download.com), in which you hunt dinosaurs or get hunted. Some of the dinosaurs are so easy to kill that you occasionally get the feeling that you've just clubbed the equivalent of a baby seal. You'll need to pay for the full version.

Address: Site of the Day

Smilie Games

Find terrific time-wasters right in your browser at www.smiliegames.com.

My Cheating Heart

Morgan Webb

Why not cheat? You'll only be hurting yourself.

When you're stuck in Hearts and you don't know what to do, just take a little peek at everyone else's cards. I won't tell if you won't.

Note: This involves hacking the Window's Registry, which, if you do wrong, can mess things up. If you don't feel comfortable mucking with the Registry, don't do it.

1. Go to Start, Run, and type **regedit**.

2. When you're in the Registry Editor, find the following string: HKEY_CURRENT_USER\Software\Microsoft\Windows\CurrentVersion\Applets\Hearts.

3. Go to Edit, New String Value, and name your new string **ZB**.

4. Type **42** for its value.

5. Open Hearts. Select to be the dealer, and then press F2 to begin a game against the computer.

6. Hold down Shift+Ctrl+Alt+F12 at the same time. Your opponents' cards will be revealed.

7. Hold down the key combo again to hide them.

Note: If you can't find the string for Hearts in your Registry, make sure you've run Hearts at least once on your computer. Quit out of the Registry Editor, run Hearts for a bit, and then exit out of it and start at Step 1 again.

Don't you feel the least bit guilty? I don't know about you, but I sure don't.

Download of the Day

Dink Smallwood

Morgan Webb

Ladies and gentlemen, the adventure games we all miss so much are back. Or maybe they never really left. Dink Smallwood (http://rtsoft.com/dink/index.htm) is an older adventure game that will run on practically any current computer (it runs on 486s and up). The game features a good-natured guy trying to make his way in the Middle Ages (or thereabouts—the exact age is never really specified). You have to talk to people, gather information, and start adventuring in the wide world.

Dink Smallwood was released as freeware by Robinson Technologies for the world to enjoy, so take advantage of it. The graphics aren't stunning and the game is not the most advanced, but the story is good and it is lovingly crafted and maintained. A word of advice: Ctrl is the default select button. Other than that, the game is quite intuitive. Enjoy!

Address: Site of the Day

Map of Middle-Earth

As this *Lord of the Rings* fansite so eloquently puts it, "There is no limit to what a bored nerd can do!" Enjoy the product of one man's freakish obsession (www.taylorcustom.com/localinks/mearth/mearthmap.html).

The Commodore 64 Is Alive

Joshua Brentano

Network your Commodore 64 to your PC and run your favorite old games right off your hard drive.

In 1982, Commodore Business Machines introduced the Commodore 64 home computer. It came with a whopping 64KB of RAM and 20KB of ROM, with built-in Microsoft BASIC, custom sound, and color graphics, all for a mere $600! During 1983, the price of a C64 dropped to $200, and it quickly became one of the best-selling computers of all time, reaching more than 20 million units sold.

And that's when my dad bought us a Commodore 64.

It used a dazzling, beautiful array of 16 colors. We'd never seen anything like it. (It certainly kicked Atari's butt!) Those colors created some of my all-time favorite games, and we quickly amassed a collection of hundreds of games.

Just the other day I stumbled across our C64 carcass, and it prompted me to revisit my favorite games.

We all know that you can download the Mame emulator, load up any C64 ROM you want, and play all those old games in Windows. But I want to run them from my Commodore computer, authentic-like.

Step 1: Hardware

1. Find your Commodore 1541 floppy drive (www.64hdd.com/c64-proj.html).

2. You'll need an XE1541 cable. You can buy one or build one (http://sta.c64.org/xe1541c.html).

3. Sacrifice an older PC to the cause. Because of the internal timings of your C64 and PC, they have difficulty talking to each other. And unfortunately, the newer and faster the PC, the more difficult this becomes. I recommend an old Pentium/486 class PC for this project.

Step 2: Setup

1. Download and unzip 64HDD (www.64hdd.com/c64-proj.html). The trick is getting 64HDD and the ROMs you want copied to the older machine. Many users have successfully set up 64HDD on machines running Windows (details can be found at the 64HDD website). However, I recommend formatting the HD and installing any pre-Windows version of DOS.

2. Download ROMs that you want to play. My favorite site is c64.com. (Note that you need to own the original game to legally use a ROM.) If you download many of them, like I did, break them into smaller subdirectories—say, alphabetically.

3. Burn the 64HDD directory and the ROMs to CD.

4. Copy the 64HDD directory to C:\ (C:\64hdd).

5. Copy the ROMs to C:\ROMS.

6. Connect the C64 to your PC's parallel port using the XE1541 cable.

7. Connect your C64 to a TV and turn it on.

Address: Site of the Night

How to Make Lembas

Megan enters the freaky stage of her *Lord of the Rings* fandom by following this recipe for fictional hotcakes: http://greenbooks.theonering.net/moonletters/recipes/files/r060102_01.html.

The Commodore 64 Is Alive (continued)

Step 3: Running 64HDD

64HDD is a sever that acts like the 1541 floppy drive. It emulates a floppy disk.

The most difficult aspect to this project is getting the software running. Every PC is slightly different and may require a slightly different command-line string.

Be sure to read the documentation included in 64HDD.

To start the 64HDD server, (on your PC at the DOS prompt) type this:

```
64hdd +8 C:\ROMS -rst -xe +lpt 1 -
fastest +p
```

Now the server is running.

To load a ROM, such as ARCHON.T64, (on your C64) type this:

```
LOAD"$",8
```

This loads the current directory that specified on the PC into C64 memory:

```
LOAD"$A",8
```

This loads the A: directory into C64 memory:

```
LIST
```

This lists the contents of the last loaded directory. The ROMs appear in the 8.3 file format, so you might have to rename them to fit that format. The C64 sees those ROMs as any other directory.

```
LOAD"$ARCHON.T64",8
```

This loads the Archon directory:

```
LIST
```

This lists the contents of the Archon ROM. Then load the game just like you did back in the day:

```
LOAD"*",8,1
```

Bring the C64 to Life—Multiple-Disk Games

If your ROM spans multiple disks, it's a trickier process. Included with 64HDD, in the utils directory, is a program for the C64 called MULTIDSK. MULTIDSK defines partitions, to which you assign ROMs that you toggle on the PC as the C64 prompts you for them.

Load MULTIDSK and list the program. You'll see several lines, but you have to change only a few, depending on how many ROMs you need to assign.

Defining partitions:

```
20
OPEN1,DV,15,"$C:/64HDD/DEMOFILE/
DUCKS.D64":CLOSE1
22
OPEN1,DV,15,"$C:/64HDD/DEMOFILE/
DUCKS.D71":CLOSE1
```

Change to:

```
20
OPEN1,DV,15,"$C:/64HDD/DEMOFILE/BARD1.D64":
CLOSE1
22
OPEN1,DV,15,"$C:/64HDD/DEMOFILE/BARD2.D64":
CLOSE1
```

If there are more than two disks, add another set of lines (you'll see what to do when you look at the MULTIDSK program). Tip: Create a partitioning program for each multidisk game.

Run those multidisk games:

1. Start the 64HDD server as normal.
2. Load the partition program and run it.
3. On the PC, F12 toggles between the disks you have defined in the partition.
4. Load the game from the appropriate partition.
5. When the C64 prompts you for the next disk, press F12 on the PC.

There are many other features and tips and tricks to 64HD. So read the manual, read the manual, read the manual. Practice, practice, practice—and good luck!

Hot Wheels

Robert Heron

For modern PC wheels, force-feedback (FF) technologies enhance the driving experience by simulating the texture of road surfaces and gravitational forces. While the overall qualities and support of FF effects are left to game developers to implement, the force-generating hardware within a wheel determines how these effects translate into the user's hands.

All the wheels we looked at utilized Immersion Corporation's (www.immersion.com) TouchSense technology for the FF engine. We tested all wheels and accessories with our AMD test box equipped with an Athlon XP 2800, 512MB DDR memory, Radeon 9700 Pro, and a fully updated installation of Windows XP Pro, including DirectX 9, as well as the latest device drivers.

And the winner is...

Act Labs: Force RS, GPL USB Shifter, and Performance Pedals

The Force RS wheel (Windows) has been TechTV Labs favorite for years because of its heavy-duty design and near-perfect FF response. Despite its rather plain-looking exterior, gripping the leather-wrapped steering wheel imparts the feeling that this isn't a kid's toy.

The Force RS offers seven programmable buttons and a hat-switch on the spokes of the wheel, with three more buttons on the simulated dashboard. An F1-style shifter is integrated just behind the wheel. The included pedals are affixed to a rubber-covered metal base that is slip-free with most floor coverings. The pedals have a limited range of travel compared to the "performance pedals." Act Labs should offer its wheel with a choice of pedal designs.

The GPL USB Shifter and clutch pedal are designed to work with any steering wheel, but software support is another issue. Only NASCAR Racing 2003 Season properly supported simultaneous, multiple controllers—

wheel, clutch/gas/brake, and shifter. Act Labs' racing products support USB as the primary connection, but with three or more USB racing devices connected simultaneously, software developers must incorporate support for "odd" axis assignments as well as specific gear shifting.

Despite the wheel/clutch/shifter support, the Force RS is the most convincing wheel we have ever used. It takes up more space and weighs more than the others, but its LEGO-like toughness and great mounting hardware deliver crisp, precise effects.

Thrustmaster F1 Force Feedback Wheel

Considering its worldwide popularity, F1 racing might as well be the official religion of motor sports. Thrustmaster's F1 Force Feedback (Windows) racing wheel does an admirable job of mimicking its namesake's aesthetic style, but the single-purpose design and unremarkable force feedback engine left us wanting more.

A real F1 steering wheel is a sub-$50,000 custom contraption complete with digital readouts and plenty of controls. Thrustmaster mimics the same "9-3" hand positions with the shifter placed perfectly for fingertip use. Unfortunately, the gas and brake levers, located beneath the shifter mechanism, travel to within less than a half inch of the wheel itself. Drivers with average-size digits had to reposition their hands or stick with the floor pedals.

Even with the force effects set to maximum level, the F1 Force Feedback couldn't match the variety of effects or strength offered by the other wheels.

As the more expensive wheel in this comparison, we expected better FF quality from Thrustmaster's F1 wheel.

Patrick's Favorite Free Games

Patrick Norton

Here at *The Screen Savers*, we love games. Games help us punch through writer's block, fill our copious free time, alienate our spouses/boyfriends/parents, amuse our friends, and provide an easy escape from the terminal condition commonly called life.

The only thing we like better than games? Free games. Here's a list:

- **Grand Theft Auto**
  (www.rockstargames.com/classics/) is free. You know a game company is having a banner year when it repackages the game that started it all—and gives it away. It's a whopping 328MB download. Download it, install the latest version of DirectX, and find out how far Grand Theft Auto has come.

- **Puzzle Pirates** (www.puzzlepirates.com) is brain-frying puzzles, many centered on the classic Tetris stacking style, all in a pirate setting. After playing dozens of hours, I can safely say that this game makes no sense. Empty the bilge, swordfight, navigate, and sail, all by puzzle. It's curiously engaging.

- **FlightGear** (http://flightgear.org) is seriously cool. It's an open-source multi-platform (Linux, OSX, Windows, and more) free flight sim. Very, very cool.

Address: Site of the Night

Overclocked Remix

Martin Sargent

You might not think of chirpy, MIDI-like videogame music as high art, but scores of digital musicians are trying to change that. At Overclocked Remix (http://remix.overclocked.org/index.php), you can find hundreds of videogame sound tracks remixed into jazz, reggae, electronica, classical, and most every other musical genre. There are also tutorials on the site that instruct you how to make your own videogame remixes. Unfortunately, the site is loaded with pop-up ads.

- **Mall Monster** (www.gamehippo.com) is an oddly compelling little game. You're a kid trying to escape the evil monster in the mall. Run too much, the monster hears you, you die. That's just a tiny tidbit of GameHippo.com. This site is heaven for low-budget gamers. No shareware, no demos. All free games, all the time.

Download of the Day

Progress Quest

Morgan Webb

When I was younger, I spent a year playing Phantasy Star 3, and I loved the game because it was a role-playing game, and there was the potential of beating my older brother's scores. All I needed to defeat him was massive amounts of time, and, at that age, I had plenty of it.

Unfortunately, because I have a career, some friends, and my own laundry to do, Phantasy Star, Everquest, and the rest of these role-playing games have fallen by the wayside (though they will always be my first love). Fortunately, I recently discovered Progress Quest (www.progressquest.com). It is a free role-playing game that streamlines your quest.

Slay Monsters, Collect the Gold

You pick your character, roll the dice for your stats, and launch yourself into a world of demons, monsters, and mystical objects. The best part of Progress Quest for a busy woman like me is that the game plays itself.

You slay monsters and collect gold and loot, which you then sell to purchase better loot. You accomplish small tasks (such as "fetch me a sock" or "placate the camels") to accomplish larger tasks and collect experience along the way. The game minimizes to your system tray. Check in once in a while to see how many teenage Fairy Dragons or demon Bacon Giants your great warrior has killed. It's all the adrenaline rush without the commitment.

Xbox Mod Chips

Kevin Rose

Why mod the Xbox? Well, the Xbox is more than just a gaming machine. It's the most powerful computer you can purchase for $199. Under the hood, the Xbox is equipped with a 733-MHz Intel Pentium III processor, an NVidia graphics subsystem, hard drive, Ethernet, and four USB ports. Modding the Xbox turns it from a gaming console into a fully functional PC that can still run games.

Important note: Xbox mods aren't supported by Microsoft and may be illegal under the DMCA. If you mod your Xbox, you're willingly voiding the warranty and potentially breaking the law. If done improperly, modding could damage your Xbox.

Choose a Mod Chip

There are close to a dozen varieties of mod chips, all with different options and features. Rather than bore you with the details on each chip, here are the best mod chips on the market:

- **Xecuter2 Pro v2.2 Plus.** This chip has a parallel interface so you can flash the BIOS directly with your PC. The Pro lacks a BIOS and needs to be manually flashed before using.

- **Xecuter2 Lite v2.2 Plus.** I prefer the Lite chip because it's pre-flashed. Be careful when purchasing your mod chips online. There are lots of shady fly-by-night websites that are just out there to take your money.

Solder the Chips...or Not

Another reason to like the Xecuter Plus chips? Unlike most Xbox mod chips, you don't have to solder the chip to the motherboard. All you have to do is align the chip and screw it down. Once you've screwed the chip into place, boot your Xbox. You should see the Xecuter logo instead of Microsoft's. If you see this, it means you installed the chip correctly and it's functioning.

I've found that Xbox-Scene (www.xbox-scene.com) is the best resource for Xbox tutorials on the web. Other good site are The Console Corner (www.modchip.ca) and www.xbox-modchips.com.

The Mess over Mod Chips

Dave Roos

Lik Sang International (www.lik-sang.com) used to be one of the most popular sites to purchase mod chips for Sony's PlayStation 2, Microsoft's Xbox, and Nintendo's GameCube, but it was forced to halt sales of its mod chips due to a lawsuit filed by Sony, Microsoft, and Nintendo.

In the United States, the best argument for keeping mod chips legal is that they let gamers play backup copies of their own games. This is the same argument that's used in the fight against strict copy protection of CDs. Many gamers and music fans believe they should be allowed to make copies of their property according to common "fair use" guidelines.

Should mod chips be stopped? Do most gamers use mod chips to play pirated software? Does Lik Sang have a chance against the "big three" of gaming?

Should mod chips be illegal?

Yes   14%

No   86%

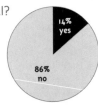

Yahoo! Games (http://games.yahoo.com)

This site is responsible for single-handedly sucking more productivity out of *The Screen Savers* staffers than anything else, except maybe UT2003 (www.unrealtournament2003.com).

Stay Safe Online

Megan Morrone

Here on *The Screen Savers*, we like to joke that the only way to keep your computer safe is to never connect it to the Internet. Although infallible, that's not exactly practical.

In the pages that follow, you'll discover dozens of tips on surfing safely for kids, making secure purchases online, and protecting your important documents from prying eyes. But even the most advanced encryption techniques and expensive firewalls won't do a lick of good unless you choose smart passwords.

Here are my top ten password tips:

1. Never use dictionary words. You already know not to use obvious words such as your child's name, but any dictionary word is insecure in the face of sophisticated dictionary password crackers.

2. Use a combination of letters and numbers. Replacing the letter O with the number 0 in a common word increases your security, but even this isn't totally safe if you're still using dictionary words.

3. Think of a sentence you'll remember, and create a password from the first letter of each word. For example, the password StWOCaaT stands for "Saving the World, One Computer at a Time."

4. Never keep your passwords in a text file on your computer. If you must save passwords on your computer, use one of the encryption tools that Kevin recommends on March 10.

5. Change your passwords often. It's a good idea to go back to sites and change old passwords, especially if they're insecure.

6. Use several different passwords. So, you've come up with the perfect password and it's so perfect that you want to use it for everything. It just stopped being perfect. The more passwords you have, the better.

7. If passwords are case sensitive, use upper- and lowercase letters.

8. The longer the password, the better.

9. Never use a known alphabetical sequence (tuvwxyz) or keyboard sequence (qwerty).

10. Never give away your password. If you must give your password to a friend, you must change it afterward. Also, a reputable website will never ask you to send your password. Scammers commonly send emails that appear to come from eBay, PayPal, or other commerce sites asking for your password for "routine maintenance." Never give it to them.

Firewalls in Mac OS X

Leo Laporte

Mac OS X comes with an industrial-strength built-in firewall called IPFW. Like many applications hidden in OS X, IPFW is part of Darwin, the FreeBSD UNIX foundation upon which OS X is built. OS X 10.2 and higher provides easy access to the built-in firewall through Sharing (in the System Preference pane). Although OS X is generally secure as shipped, the firewall is not enabled. It should be if you use your Mac on the Internet.

If you want even more complete coverage, download a front end to IPFW. There's a good shareware choice available: Brian R. Hill's BrickHouse (http://personalpages.tds.net/~brian_hill/brickhouse.html).

I recommend and use BrickHouse. For most users, BrickHouse is the simplest way to go. You can try it for free, although Hill requests $25 if you like the software.

BrickHouse walks you through a series of choices about the protection you want. In general, it's best to block all incoming and outgoing traffic except for the services you know you want, such as HTTP (for the web) and FTP (for file transfer). BrickHouse can also create rules blocking well-known attacks such as Back Orifice and Netbus. Based on your decisions, BrickHouse creates a configuration script for IPFW and optionally installs a startup script that turns on IPFW each time you boot. The latest version of BrickHouse can enable IPFW's built-in Internet connection sharing.

You don't have to use BrickHouse. You can configure IPFW by hand, but it's tricky. A misconfigured firewall is worse than no firewall at all, so I recommend hand configuration for network experts only.

If you want to understand what IPFW is doing, I recommend an excellent discussion of BSD security and IPFW on the FreeBSD website (www.freebsd.org/handbook/firewalls.html). Keep in mind that OS X does things a little differently than FreeBSD, so some of the instructions don't apply. Or read the manual by opening the Terminal application and typing **man ipfw**.

Test Your Firewall

When your firewall is running, try ShieldsUp (www.grc.com), which scans your system for open ports. With IPFW running, ShieldsUp should give you a clean bill of health.

Another way to check for open ports is to run Nmap, a command-line port scanner free from Insecure.org (www.insecure.org). Nmap compiles and runs without hassle on OS X, and it's a good tool to have around. Nmap comes with most Linux distros so you can use your Linux box to scan your Mac.

Running Nmap or ShieldsUp should reassure you that your system is fully secure. You won't need to run BrickHouse again unless you want to change your configuration.

Remember, no firewall offers 100% protection. Any time you're on the Net, you're vulnerable. Keep your system software up-to-date, run an antivirus program, and never, ever, open attachments. Although most nasty exploits are designed for Windows systems, even Macs can be attacked. The UNIX under the hood of OS X offers built-in protection, but it also puts Mac users in the mainstream, which means that the bad guys will be waiting.

Windows Tips

File and Print Sharing

Windows 98 makes it nearly as easy as it is in Windows XP to initiate file and print sharing. Simply open the Control Panel, open the Network control panel, click File and Print Sharing and check both boxes.

Protect Your Identity Online

Identity theft is one of the leading consumer complaints logged by the Federal Trade Commission (FTC). What's worse, there will likely be more, thanks to a growing number of websites that put a price tag on your personal information. This list of tips might help prevent someone from stealing your identity.

Identity Theft Prevention Tips

- **Check your security.** When surfing the web, make sure your web browser indicates that you are on a secure server. If the padlock icon in the corner of the window is locked, you can be reasonably sure that you're safe.

- **Check your credit card statement.** On a fairly frequent basis, see what's being charged to your account.

- **Check your credit report.** This is a good way to find out who's inquiring about your credit or who might be setting up accounts using your identity.

- **Use a different email address for different people.** Have one email for close family, one for business associates, and one for throwaways. When you sign up for services online, use your throwaway address so you can separate unwanted email and spot viruses easier.

- **Do a vanity search.** Use a search engine, such as Google, to find out what pops up when you enter your name or contact information.

- **Use a credit card.** When making an online purchase, always use a credit card. If the product doesn't arrive or isn't what you thought you were paying for, you can cancel the charge. Furthermore, use only one of your cards for online purchases.

Identity Theft Resources on the Web

- **Identity Theft Resource Center** (www.idtheftcenter.org). Watchdog site run by the Privacy Rights Clearinghouse (www.privacyrights.org), a nonprofit consumer protection organization.

- **Identity Theft.org** (www.identitytheft.org). Identity theft survival and prevention guide written by author and attorney Mari Frank.

- **AARP Identity Theft** (www.aarp.org). Common ways your identity can be stolen.

Laporte Support

Windows XP Security Hole

Windows XP has a security hole (which our own Kevin Rose uncovered) that can be exploited to make unwanted messages pop up on your desktop. Fortunately, it can be easily disabled. This is all you have to do:

- Right-click My Computer.
- Select Manager (you must be logged in as Administrator).
- In the console that pops up, double-click Services and Applications.
- Double-click Services.
- Scroll and select Messenger.
- Turn off Messenger Service (You only need Messenger Service if there are problems with your corporate network).
- Set the Startup Type for Message Service to Disabled.

Now you'll never get an annoying message asking you to pay $10 to keep annoying messages from appearing.

File-Sharing Tips and Tricks

The Screen Savers **Staff**

Many file-sharing programs are available online. Whether you choose WinMX (www.winmax.com), KaZaA (www.kazaa.com), Morpheus (www.musicity.com), or a program from our file-sharing software guide, these tips will help you maximize your download capabilities.

Servers

Your file-sharing program might allow you to add other servers to its list of searchable servers. If so, go to Navigator and add some, or all if you want to totally maximize your searches. With every server you add, your chances of finding what you want increase dramatically.

Searching

The key to finding what you want lies in the way you search. We've found that searching by the artist or song name might not give you all the results out there. If you can't find what you want searching by artist, try searching for the name of the album without the artist's name. Or, if you are looking for a full album, search for "album."

Downloading

When you have the results, it's time to download. The first step is to download the same file from a bunch of different people. Keep the connection that downloads the fastest, and delete the others.

When you find someone you can share a fast connection with, browse the files on that person's machine, and download everything you want.

Repeat these steps until you are downloading the maximum amount your connection will allow.

Upload

Download speeds for broadband connections tend to decrease as your upload speed increases. Although this tip goes against the very nature of file sharing, throttle back the maximum speed at which people can grab your files. Try knocking back the speed to 1–2Kbps.

Some programs also allow you to limit the number of people who can download files from you. Keep this number to a minimum, to help maintain your download speed.

Many programs assign sharing privileges to a folder on your system. Often this folder is the same folder used as the destination for your downloads. Create a new, empty folder as your shared folder. That way, you aren't showing shared files, and people can't download anything from your computer. It's a selfish thing to do, but if you're trying to download as much as possible, you want as much bandwidth as possible.

Watch What You Share

This tip has nothing to do with speed, but has everything to do with privacy. Make sure the folder you designate as your shared folder does not contain files you want kept private, such as your tax returns, journal, photos, school papers, and so on. File-sharing programs can see different file types, not just MP3s, which means many of the files on your computer are vulnerable.

Ensure your privacy by checking your shared folder every time you go online for a file-sharing session. If you can, use a separate drive other than your C: drive. Using file-sharing can open your system to hack attack, so if you must turn on file-sharing, share as little as possible. Never share an entire drive. Share a single folder instead. Windows XP creates a "shared document" folder in My Computer just for this purpose.

Mind Your Manners

Cat Schwartz

Remember when your mother nagged you to mind your manners? Thanks to the web, you now have no excuse for bad behavior.

If you're going on a date, you need good manners. I was once on a date with a guy who had horrible manners. He was so cute, funny, and sweet, but we were finished once I saw him with his elbows on the table, chew with his mouth open, not hold doors open, and not put his napkin on his lap.

Please take this advice and follow these links to get some pointers on good manners. If you do, you'll be able to ask that special someone out for a second date with confidence.

The most interactive guide to manners I could find is Manners International (www.ryangrpinc.com). This site informs readers on many areas of etiquette, from using manners in the home and dealing with guests to using manners in the workplace and following social graces. There's a lovely Flash animation demonstrating how to correctly set a table, and a number of videos showing how to be a gem in many social situations. Feel free to ask questions. You might get an email response.

Although Manners International is a great site, the official maven of manners is Emily Post (www.emilypost.com). Her eponymous Institute has released a book called *Etiquette in Society, in Business, in Politics, and at Home*. For a free look at this guide to being a perfect person, flip through the book online (www.bartleby.com/95/index.html).

For online etiquette information, take the Miss Manners online quiz (www.thirdage.com/cgi-bin/squiz.cgi?/www/docs/tech/web/manners/+quiz).

Now that cell phones have become so popular, you need to be considerate of others while you're communicating. To find out what's proper and what's rude, dial into the CellManners.com site (www.cellmanners.com).

For an old-school approach to manners for girls, and for a few good laughs, take a peek at *Manners and Conduct in School and Out* (www.uoregon.edu/~joe/digilib/). Written by the Deans of Girls in Chicago High Schools, it offers a look into the past and at how girls were expected to behave in 1921.

Download of the Day

Purge IE

Megan Morrone

You already know that cookies are bad. They're the tools that websites use to track your visits to their site and what you do while you're there. Although most of these cookies are not connected to your personal information, they might still violate your privacy.

You can delete them manually, but it's a temporary fix because they'll grow back the next time you go to that site. You could set IE to not accept cookies, but then you'll be without access to some of the web's best sites. Plus, cookies can be useful for storing passwords so you don't have to re-enter them.

I have a solution to your cookie woes. It's called PurgeIE (www.purgeie.com). This utility lets you purge the cookies you don't need and keep the ones you do. It also lets you clear your cache to make IE run more efficiently.

To get the most out of this program, read the PurgeIE FAQ. Purge IE is free to try. If you like it, pay the registration fee.

TiVo Web Access

Leo Laporte

My Series 1 TiVo barely resembles the weak-ling Sony SAT-T60 I purchased over a year ago. I upgraded the stock 30GB hard drive to two drives totaling 200GB. (That's about 190 hours of recording capacity.) I also installed a TurboNet card that puts my TiVo on my local area network and eliminates the need for a phone line for the daily call.

When the TiVo was visible on my home network, I enabled Telnet functionality using a script from JS Productions (www.jsprod.net). This required removing the drive from the TiVo and mounting it on my PC. It's not hard, but it's a pain. Fortunately, when Telnet is working and you can log on to the TiVo from your PC, you shouldn't have to disassemble your TiVo again. You can download software and modify your TiVo system directly from a terminal window on your computer.

One of the first hacks I installed was Tivo Web (http://tivo.lightn.org). This open-source web server written in TCL gives you web-based access to all the standard TiVo functions. Installing it is as simple as downloading the software using this command from the bash shell (all on one line, of course):

```
http_get -T 0 -C 0 -D /var/hack -U
http://199.240.141.102:80/TiVoweb-tcl-
1.9.4.tar.gz
```

After you download the file, untar it and run the install script. Read the installation details at http://tivo.lightn.org. I modified my /etc/rc.d/rc.sysinit file so that TiVo Web starts up automatically whenever I reboot my TiVo.

I can use Tivo Web to browse the entire channel guide, perform searches, and schedule and delete recordings from any web browser on my home network. If you're willing to expose your TiVo to the world, you can do all this from anywhere on the Net, too.

TiVo Web supports password protection, but, as its documentation says, a password doesn't guarantee security.

Kevin's Tips

KaZaA Lite

When it comes to file sharing, why do so many people use KaZaA? Because, chances are, you can find what you need. KaZaA has hundreds of millions of files available for download. (Now, the legality of some of those files is a different story altogether.)

I love KaZaA but there is a major problem with the software. KaZaA is riddled with adware and spyware. Nobody wants annoying pop-ups.

To ditch the spyware and adware, you have to ditch KaZaA. File sharing no more? No. Replace KaZaA with its spyware- and adware-free software sibling, KaZaA Lite (www.k-lite.tk). It's free, but donations are gladly accepted.

After you've downloaded KaZaA Lite, here's how to properly install it:

1. Uninstall KaZaA. This should remove all that unwanted spyware and adware.

2. You might want to install and run Ad-aware (www.lavasoftusa.com) to make sure the unwanted wares are removed.

3. Install KaZaA Lite. No more adware and spyware. KaZaA Lite seems to perform faster than the fully released version.

Clean Out Your PC

Roman Loyola

With hard drives getting bigger and cheaper, and with tons of freeware, shareware, and other downloads available, no one thinks twice about installing and trying new stuff. However, sooner or later, all the applications, the *Lord of the Rings* fonts, and the movie trailers add up, clogging your hard drive and slowing your computer. Here's what Leo and Patrick suggest to get rid of the mess.

Delete temporary items. Your computer often uses items that aren't supposed to stay on your computer permanently. These are often used by installers, but they can be used by other applications.

Launch Windows Explorer and open the Windows folder. Open a folder named Temp (your temporary directory) and delete most of the contents. Make sure no applications are running that might be using items in the Temp folder. You can't delete items that are in use.

Clear the Internet cache. Those graphics on your favorite webpages are downloaded to a directory on your hard drive and then used by the web browser. Web browsers often download files to your Internet cache for quick access. You can empty the cache easily through the browser's options. To keep the cache from getting too big, adjust its size in the browser's options. We suggest setting it to about 10MB; if it fills up, your browser will empty it.

Delete fonts. Fancy fonts look cool and it's tempting to install them, but when was the last time you used Candy Bits (www.fontpool.com)? Some applications, such as word processors, can also slow down because of too many fonts.

Defragment your hard drive after you've deleted files (also called optimizing).

Use Norton SystemWorks (www.symantec.com). This software has tools you can use to keep your system tidy. Norton Utilities can fix problems and optimize your hard drive.

Norton CleanSweep removes unnecessary files. Web Tools cleans up after you spend time on the Internet.

Clean the Registry. It's not enough to just dump files. Those applications you just uninstalled sometimes leave behind Registry entries. Use Reg-Cleaner (http://www.jv16.org/) to manage your Registry.

Download of the Day

IZArc

Roger Chang

Every self-respecting Windows user has a good Zip archiver in his or her software library. Sure, Windows XP has one, but you don't want to use its primitive interface and capabilities for an extended period of time. The time-honored WinZip is a perennial favorite among many new and experienced users. That said, unless you pay for WinZip, you encounter the ever-present nag screen. So today I present to you, our favored frugal readers, a free alternative that matches, and in some ways surpasses, WinZip.

IZArc (www.webattack.com/get/izarc.shtml) is like many other Zip applications; you can open zipped files as well as create your own. It goes one step further by supporting a myriad of other compression formats, such as ACE, RAR, TAR (for you Unix types), and dozens of others, allowing you to open a number of different compression archival formats without installing additional programs.

Other nice features allow you to convert one compression format to another (i.e. *.zip to *.ace) and span multiple files. Get this, it also includes a built-in password hacker to go along with its password encrypter. Not bad, eh?

If you want a good zipping application and you're just a tad bit short on cash, give IZArc a try. The only thing it'll cost you is a few minutes of time.

Lifting Laptops

James Hamilton

With literally hundreds of laptops being stolen every day, more laptops are getting ripped off than ever. One group targeted by thieves, not surprisingly, is business travelers at airports and hotels. The following links to products, services, and tips can help you keep tabs on your laptop when you're away from home.

Laptop Antitheft Software

A variety of antitheft software packages are available on the market. Most of these programs automatically send the computer's IP address and other information to an online service every time the computer logs on to the Internet. When a computer is stolen, the service tracks down the physical location of the computer using this information. The antitheft service usually works in conjunction with law enforcement to retrieve your laptop. Here are the most popular products currently available:

- **zTracehttp** (www.ztrace.com). This invisible software security application traces the location of missing laptops for recovery. If the laptop is reported missing, the zTrace recovery team identifies the computer's exact physical location.

- **The CyberAngel** (www.sentryinc.com). This program automatically transmits the calling location ID—whether there's a telephone or network connection—when the password entry system is violated. Using public databases, the service identifies the street address where the stolen laptop is being used.

- **ComputracePlus** (www.computrace.com). Built for corporate users, this program contacts an online monitoring center on a regular basis with IP address and phone number.

Tips on How to Protect Your Laptop

Travel safety consultant Kevin Coffey has an informative site on travel safety and security. Visit these sites, recommended by Coffey and other Internet sources, to get tips on how to protect your computer:

- **Laptop Theft, Know Before You Go** (www.corporatetravelsafety.com). Coffey offers tips on keeping your laptop computer safe when on the road.

- **Tips for Preventing Laptop Computer Theft** (http://mpdc.dc.gov/info/consumer/laptop_theft.shtm). Get the Washington D.C. Police Department guidelines on keeping your computer safe.

- **Laptop Theft** (http://rr.sans.org/homeoffice/laptop_theft.php). Read a paper from the SANS Institute that examines methods and scams used to steal laptops.

Laptop Loss Statistics

Loss Statistics Charts. Here's a list of computer theft statistics, organized by model. It's compiled by Safeware (www.safeware.com/losscharts.htm).

Stolen Computer Databases

Many manufacturers, consumer groups, and individuals around the world have set up stolen laptop databases. If your computer is stolen, register it with one or more of these groups. If your laptop is recovered by law enforcement, officials can easily find you if you're registered with one of these databases:

- **Stolen Computer Registry** (www.stolencomputers.org). Formed by an industry consortium in 1992 to foil hardware theft and foster confidence in the purchase of used computers. The Registry does not charge for its services.

- **theRegistry** (www.pcid.com). An independently run database of computer systems, household and business items, and other assorted property that increases the odds of getting back an item that was lost or stolen.

Always on, Always Vulnerable?

James Hamilton

Think your broadband-enabled home computer is secure? Don't be so sure. Cable modems and DSL lines might give your computer blazing speed and an always-on connection, but if left unprotected, they also give hackers uninterrupted, high-speed access to your system.

If you use a cable modem or DSL hub at home, don't despair. By installing a firewall, properly configuring your file-sharing options, and following some basic guidelines when using your computer online, you can keep most hackers out of your home system.

File-Sharing Configurations

If you have a DSL or cable modem connection and run Windows 95/98/Me, the best way to ensure that File and Print Sharing can't be used by hackers is to disable your file- and print-sharing options—or, at the very least, make sure all shared files and folders are password-protected.

Security Guidelines

There's no single solution for securing your computer from a hacker trying to attack multiple vulnerabilities in a system. Here you'll find links to checklists and guides to make sure your entire system is as secure as possible:

- **Home Network Security** (www.cert.org). An overview for home users of the security risks and countermeasures from CERT.
- **The Home Computer Security Centre** (www.lockdown.co.uk/). Security information and free advice for home computer users.

Laporte Support

Recover Lost Passwords

Internet Explorer's Content Advisor lets you say what you feel comfortable seeing on the Internet. For example, you can adjust the settings if you want to see nudity, partial nudity, or no nudity. Here's how to activate it:

1. Click Tools, Internet Options, and go to the Content tab. Under Content Advisor, click the Enable button.

2. Set your preferences on the Ratings tab. Go to the General tab to set a master password so the kids can't change anything.

If you lose the password, you'll need to delete it from the registry and delete the file. To change the registry:

1. Click Start, Run, type **regedit**, and click OK.

2. Go to HKEY_LOCAL_MACHINE\ Software\ Microsoft\Windows\ CurrentVersion\\Policies\Ratings.

3. You'll see two entries: Default and Ratings. Delete Ratings. Don't do anything with Default.

Now search your C: drive for the Ratings.pol file and delete it. To start your search, click Start, Find, and type **ratings.pol** in the Name box. Make sure the C: drive appears in the Look In field and press Enter.

Freeware can help you recover your lost web and Windows passwords. Here are some options: 123 Password Recovery (www.webattack.com); Protected Storage PassView (http://nirsoft.multiservers.com); LC4, the latest version of L0phtcrack (www.atstake.com/research/lc/); and NT Password & Registry Editor (http://home.eunet.no/~pnordahl/ntpasswd/).

Windows XP User Accounts and Permissions

Leo Laporte

In Windows XP, everyone who uses the computer must have a user account. When you first install XP, it automatically creates an Administrator account. If you haven't created any additional user accounts, you're probably running the machine using that original Administrator account. Don't. It's not safe for you or for the Internet.

The Administrator, like the root account in UNIX, is all-powerful. Admins can examine and delete any file on the hard drive. Only they can install and remove software. And the computer's administrator has access to other features of XP, such as raw sockets, which can be dangerous in the wrong hands.

Most users like the power and convenience of running as Administrator. After all, that's what we're used to. In Windows 95, 98, and Me, every user had full Administrator powers. It's not a good idea to always run as Administrator. If you become infected with a virus or Trojan horse, that malicious program inherits your power and can do things you won't like. Even more important, a Trojan horse running on your system as Administrator can launch attacks against other computers on the Internet without your knowledge.

For your own safety, and the safety of the Internet, you should not routinely log on to your computer as Administrator. Create a limited user account for day-to-day operations. Log on as Administrator only when it's necessary for system maintenance.

Even if you're the only person using your computer, it's important to create a limited user account for day-to-day operations. If many people use the same computer, user accounts offer security and privacy for each user. For those of us who are used to the all-powerful control of Windows 95, 98, and Me, using a limited account takes a little getting used to, but it's the safest way to operate a computer.

Download of the Day

Window Washer

Call for Help Staff

Many people are unaware that Internet browsers and Windows store information, including pictures you have viewed, documents used, websites visited, and many other activities performed on your computer. It's possible for anyone to turn on your computer and trace your steps. However, there is a way to cover your tracks.

Window Washer (www.webroot.com) gives you the peace of mind of having a clean PC by eliminating all traces of your Internet and PC activity. This incredible program not only covers up your web-surfing tracks, but it also cleans your cache, history, drop-down address bar, recently viewed pictures, downloaded program files, Recycle Bin, recently opened documents list, and much more.

Keep your computer activities private and remove telltale files.

Windows Tips

Restore Registry Defaults in XP and 2000

Morgan Webb

If you are a Windows 2000 or XP user, there is a special string of the Registry from which all new user settings are taken. The purpose of this string is to keep a healthy version of the Registry around for the new users, regardless of the damage and general havoc the old users caused.

This default version is found at HKEY_USERS\.DEFAULT. What good is it?

- It's a reference point for all you compulsive Reg-hackers out there (to find the default setting after you've changed it 30-odd times).

- It's the key to press if you're an admin and want to change an entry for all the subsequent new users on a machine.

Top Ten Ways to Secure Your PC

Kevin Rose

While you're enjoying that broadband connection, downloading files, watching web videos, flipping from webpage to webpage, your computer is sitting there, ripe for the picking by hackers looking for fresh victims. Before you get hacked, protect yourself. Here are my top ten ways to secure your computer:

1. **Turn off file sharing.** File sharing is one of the first things a hacker looks for to access your computer. Turn off file sharing in Windows 98 or Windows XP. Set file sharing preferences for Mac OS X.

2. **Install a firewall.** Try ZoneAlarm (www.zonelabs.com), BlackICE (http://blackice.iss.net/index.php), or Mac OS X firewalls (http://personalpages.tds.net/~brian_hill/brickhouse.html). Even the built-in Windows XP firewall is better than nothing.

3. **Scan for spyware.** Kill that spyware and adware with my two favorites: Ad-aware (www.lavasoftusa.com) and Spybot—Search & Destroy (http://security.kolla.de).

4. **Scan for viruses.** My favorite antivirus program is Norton AntiVirus (www.symantec.com). If you want to save cash, try the free AVG Anti-Virus (www.grisoft.com).

5. **Update OS.** Update your operating system frequently. Always run the latest patches and drivers for your system. Windows update: http://windowsupdate.microsoft.com. Mac OS X updates: www.info.apple.com. For Linux, visit the website for your distribution.

6. **Security scanner.** Run some type of outside security scanner on your machine. I recommend the demo version of Retina (www.eeye.com/html/Products/Retina/) or the Microsoft Baseline Security Analyzer (www.microsoft.com).

7. **Secure instant messengers.** Keep IM conversations private with Trillian Pro (www.trillian.cc) for 128-bit encrypted AIM and ICQ conversations.

8. **Secure email.** Hotmail get hacked again? Try Hushmail (www.hushmail.com). Hushmail uses 2048-bit encryption to keep your email safe and sound. Hushmail has been around for ages and I've heard many great things about it.

9. **Secure your files.** Get PGP Disk (www.pgp.com/products/personal) to encrypt all your sensitive files. Store your files in the ThumbDrive Touch (www.thumbdrive.com/touch.htm), a USB drive that uses a built-in fingerprint reader to protect your data.

10. **Safe passwords.** Keep your passwords safe, secure and uncrackable with Personal Vault (www.soft1st.com).

Talkback

Do Kids Deserve Online Privacy?

Dave Roos

Public school students have been notoriously exempt from civil liberties since the days of dunce caps and paddles. Random drug testing, locker searches, dress codes—it's all kosher. School officials are supposed to act in loco parentis, but often they engage in tactics that not even the most "loco" parent would approve.

When you monitor adults, it's called "snooping," but when you monitor kids, it's just part of growing up. Is this right? Do kids really not deserve any privacy online?

Do kids deserve privacy online?

Yes   45%

No   55%

Password-Protect Your Website

Leo Laporte

For the past year, my daughter has been pestering me to create a password-protected website for her. She wants to put things online that only her friends can see. I'd like to do that, too. I use my website to back up files and private stuff I don't want anyone else to download. Having a password-protected directory would add to my peace of mind.

You can add a password to a webpage in all kinds of ways. If your website is running on an Apache web server (most websites are), you can use Apache's built-in file access commands. The Apache config file, httpd.conf, contains information about each directory on your site. You can modify this file, but you must restart Apache each time you change the configuration.

You might need to modify your httpd.conf file once to enable this directory-level control. Ask your system administrator to enable .htaccess files, or, if you have access to the configuration file yourself, add the following line to the directories where your .html files are stored:

```
AllowOverride AuthConfig
```

Because Apache reads in the access control file each time the directory is accessed, it's best to enable this for only the directory or directories you want to password-protect. I added a block in my httpd.conf file that reads as follows:

```
<Directory "/home/leoville/public_html">
AllowOverride AuthConfig
</Directory>
```

Then I restarted Apache. This tells the server to check the directory public_html and all its subdirectories for an access control file each time it reads the directory. The default name for the access control file is .htaccess. It's a plain text file that I created in the subdirectory that I wanted to protect. The file reads like so:

```
AuthUserFile "/home/leoville/.htpasswd"
AuthGroupFile /dev/null
```

```
AuthName "Leo's Private Files"
AuthType Basic
require valid-user
```

Use `valid-user` to allow anyone in the .htpasswd file to log on. Or, for even more security, require an actual user name—`require leo`. You'll want to modify the `AuthUserFile` to point to your password file (I'll tell you how to create that in a second) and change `AuthName` to an appropriate string for the password prompt. Make sure to make the .htaccess file world-readable by typing this:

```
chmod ugo+r .htaccess
```

Finally, you'll need to create the password file, .htpassword. It's best to put this in a directory above your HTML directory. You can use the htpasswd program to create the file by navigating to your safe directory and typing this:

```
htpasswd -c .htpasswd username
```

You're prompted for a password for the name. Add more names with this command:

```
Htpasswd .htpasswd username
```

Delete users by editing the .htpasswd file with any text editor. Now try to access the directory. You should be prompted for a logon and password. If it doesn't work, check the error_log file. On my system, here's what I type:

```
tail /etc/httpd/logs/error_log - leave
   space after tail
```

This lets you read the last ten lines of the error log. You should be able to tell what's wrong from that. All this is well-documented in the Apache manual (http://apache-server.com).

That's the trickiest but most secure way to add a password to a website. Other web servers have similar techniques. Read the documentation for details. For users of Microsoft's IIS server, read the Microsoft technical note at http://support.microsoft.com for information on migrating .htaccess type control files to IIS.

Macro Security

Morgan Webb

A macro is a tiny little program you make in an Office document to automate a task. For example, if you often apply certain formatting to a Word document or the same multistep calculation in Excel, you can create a macro to turn that repetitive task into a simple click of a button. Macros can be as complicated or as simple as you need them to be.

The Dark Side of Macros

Unfortunately, macros aren't all fun and games. They can be used to infect your computer with a virus. Macros can include malicious Active X instructions or other harmful pieces of code that find their way onto your computer through a seemingly harmless Word document. Your Office programs offer security settings to protect you from executing macros from a foreign document, and you can manage these security settings to your liking.

Macro Security

If you have trouble opening an Office document, it might be because your macro security setting is set too high. Office is trying to protect you, but if your document comes from a trusted source, go to Tools, Macros, Security and lower your security setting. If you set it to Medium, you're asked what you want to do when an unsigned macro attempts to run. If you agree to run the macro, that document's source is added to your future safe list and you're not prompted again. Setting your security level to Low runs all macros, but you won't be protected.

If you have an antivirus program running that's compatible with your version of Office, it should scan the document for harmful macros either when the document is loaded onto your computer or when it's opened. If you keep your virus definitions up-to-date, you should be safe from harmful macros even if your macro security setting is Low.

Windows Tips

Password-Protect Your Office 2002 Files

Morgan Webb

Office 2002 has built-in file encryption to protect your files from being opened by anyone but you. Here's how to use it:

- Open a document.
- Go to Tools, Options, Security.
- Enter a password to protect your document.
- Write down or remember this password. You will not be able to read your document if you lose it.

Your document is stored as an encrypted file. You can open it in other applications, such as Notepad or DOS Edit, but you cannot read the information it contains. You can also use the same menu to require a password from anybody wanting to modify the document. Keep those sneaky souls out of your work!

Megan's Tips

Privacy Report

If you have privacy concerns with cookies, use Internet Explorer's privacy report.

1. In Internet Explorer, click View.
2. Select Privacy Report.
3. Choose Setting and adjust the slider as you see fit.

Hidden Files on a Shared Network

David Prager

Windows 98 contains a number of files that you don't want to delete or accidentally change. As a safety feature, these files are hidden.

For example, the desktop is stored in the folder C:\Windows\Desktop, but if you open My Computer, the C: drive, and then the Windows folder, you won't find the desktop.

View Hidden Files and Folders

1. Choose Start, Settings, Folder Options.
2. Click the View tab in the Folder Options dialog.
3. Click Show All Files, then click OK.

When Windows shows hidden files and folders, their icons appear as ghostly images. To hide them again, repeat the preceding procedure. In step 3, select Do Not Show Hidden or System Files.

Hide a File

1. Select the file or folder.
2. Click Properties on the toolbar.
3. Right-click the file or folder, and choose Properties from the shortcut menu.
4. If it is not already selected, click the General tab. Near the bottom of the General tab is a list of attributes, one of which is Hidden. Check Hidden.
5. Click Apply and OK to close the Properties dialog.

Hide Files or Folders from the Start Menu

1. Right-click Start and select Explore.
2. Right-click the desired folder, program, or file.
3. Click the check box next to Hidden.
4. Click Apply and OK to close the Properties dialog.

Caution: A hidden file or folder should not be considered secure. The Find command can still find a hidden file or folder if its name is entered properly in the search string. Anyone who finds the file can open it directly from the Find window without knowing that you intended to hide the file.

If you don't want other people who use your computer to find particular files, you should either encrypt the files, password-protect them, or move them to another secure location.

Talkback

My PC Is Killing Me

Dave Roos

I can't feel my pinkies. After a full day of pointing, clicking, scrolling, and typing, the tips of my most extreme extremities are freezing cold and numb as a wooden leg. This is not good.

I consulted an ergonomic expert who raised my chair, lowered my keyboard, propped up my monitor, and repositioned my mouse, but it hasn't done a lick of good. The clear culprit is my computer, in front of which I sit for nearly nine hours a day. But what's a web slave to do? Quit?

Does your computer make you sick? Have you tried various tactics to relieve aches, pains, and assorted PC symptoms? Have any of them worked? Do you think employees deserve compensation for computer-related injuries?

Does your computer make you sick?

Yes   34%

No   66%

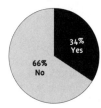

Favorite Free Utilities

Leo Laporte, Patrick Norton, and Dave Roos
Why are you reading this ridiculous intro paragraph? In the seconds you've wasted perusing these meaningless sentences, you could have been downloading the greatest list of free PC and Mac utilities this puny world has ever seen.

Leo's Five Favorite Free Windows Utilities

1. **Stuffit Expander** (www.alladinsys.com). WinZip is still the best for making ZIP files, but for unpacking them, you can't beat this free alternative.

2. **Webshots Desktop** (www.webshots.com). Everyone needs a little nature now and then. Download hundreds of free desktops and rotate them on your screen.

3. **Windows Power Toys** (www.microsoft.com). TweakUI is a must-have utility for customizing your system. There are other helpful tools here, too—all free from Microsoft.

4. **PGP** (www.pgp.com). The best way to protect your data is to encrypt it. PGP is back—and free. When the open-source Gnu Privacy Guard (www.gnupg.org) gets easier to use, I'll recommend that instead.

5. **AVG** Antivirus (www.grisoft.com). You must have an antivirus program. This one is free, and Grisoft keeps it up-to-date.

Leo's Five Favorite Free Mac OS X Utilities

1. **Launchbar** (www.obdev.at). Run, do not walk, to download this must-have launcher for the Mac. Access any file in a couple of keystrokes. This is a shareware program, but you can use it free for up to seven different items, which is enough for most people.

2. **Konfabulator** (www.konfabulator.com). This very cool widget factory makes it possible for anyone to write useful little desktop utilities. It's shareware, but it works fine even if you don't pay the measley $25.

3. **Locator** (www.sebastian-krauss.de). Find files fast. Did I mention it's free?

4. **Weatherpop** (http://glu.com). Put the weather in your toolbar (where it belongs). It's free, but you'll end up paying $8 for the advanced features.

5. **Fink** (http://fink.sourceforge.net). A whole world of free UNIX software awaits you with Fink. Download and install the command-line version, or use the free GUI Fink Commander. It's the easiest way to find and install UNIX programs on OS X.

Patrick's Picks

- **Mozilla** (http://mozilla.org). Mozilla is my browser of choice on the PC. Camino, a Mozilla variation, is what I mostly use on the Mac. Okay, I keep Internet Explorer around for those really gnarly sites with ASP scripting that won't run on anything but IE. But this browser is more convenient, feels faster, and offers better security.

- **Smoothwall** (http://smoothwall.org) and **IPCop** (http://ipcop.org). Smoothwall and IPCop cost nothing, and they turn an old PC into a firewall/router/DHCP server. How's that for saving moolah?

- **SiSoft Sandra** (www.sisoftware.net). Want to know something about your system? SiSoft Sandra is very, very cool, even though many features aren't enabled in the free version. The free version could tell me my motherboard model, processor, and memory type, but I had to pay for the feature that detects my ACM/ACPI compatibility.

- **Winamp** (www.winamp.com) and Musicmatch (www.musicmatch.com). This is my favorite standalone MP3 player and my favorite free MP3 encoder (up to 320Kbps!).

- **IMovie 3** (www.apple.com). Got OS X? Wanna make movies? This program absolutely kicks it and might well be what pulled me onto the Mac and OS X full-time!

- **Nero Burning** ROM 5.5 (www.nero.com). Okay, it's not free. But Ahead Software's Nero Burning ROM 5.5 is great CD-R/DVD burning software. With a free 30-day trial, it's worth your time.

Top Five Ways to Detect Spyware

Megan Morrone

Spyware is nasty. Spyware (also called "adware") is usually free software that comes bundled with little bits of code that sneak into your system to collect information about you and pass it on to another source without your knowledge or permission.

Here are the top five ways you can protect yourself from software spies:

1. **Spy Chaser** (http://camtech2000.net/Pages/SpyChaser.html). Spy Chaser is simply a database of known spyware. Before you download anything, type the name of the program in the window on top. If it is spyware, the program shows up in the box on the right. You also can scroll through the box on the left to see if you can find the program you are considering downloading.

2. **Spychecker** (www.spychecker.com). Spychecker is similar to Spy Chaser, but it has a larger database, which it claims to update daily. This program is a bit easier to use. With a click of the mouse, you can check to see if software is spyware, or report your experiences with invasive free software. If you don't want to download the program, simply bookmark the Spychecker website and enter your query there.

3. **SpywareInfo** (www.spywareinfo.com). If you're concerned about your online privacy, bookmark this resource right now. The SpywareInfo website will keep you updated on the latest news about suspicious software as well as government surveillance. You'll also get links to the newest downloads and software updates, to help you get rid of any bad stuff already on your PC.

4. **Silencer** (www.spychecker.com/silencer.html). If the program you plan to download shows up in a spyware database but you still really want it, you can use a program such as Silencer, which disables communication between your PC and the company collecting information. Note: If you use this program, you could be violating your EULA (end-user license agreement).

5. **Ad-aware** (www.lavasoftusa.com). I have yet to find a program that is more effective than Ad-aware at checking and removing spyware from your system. Ad-aware scans your memory, Registry, and hard drive for invasive software and lets you easily remove offenders. You can continue to use some programs after removing the spyware, but other programs will cease to work.

Download of the Day

Anti-Mal

Megan Morrone

Anti-Mal (www.thaiware.com/software/util/UL00724.htm) was designed and developed by Saranyou Punyaratanabunbhu in Bangkok, Thailand, to protect PCs from mosquitoes, rats, and roaches by emitting sound waves at a certain frequency. We tried it with our pet rat, Taco. Not only did it not repel him from the PC, but he seemed drawn to it.

Warning: Some PC users have complained of headaches resulting from the sound waves.

Much of the download site is written in Thai. Don't panic! The Download button is easily identifiable, and the key points are all translated to English, for your convenience.

Netcam Motion Detection

Greg Melton

Did you know it's possible to use a netcam to monitor your home, office, kids, pets, or anything else imaginable while you're away?

For starters, you need a netcam and some software. Any USB netcam will work and should cost somewhere between $25 and $100. Then you need to determine if you want to use your netcam to stream live video, snap still images, or capture pictures when it detects motion.

Home Surveillance

Netcam surveillance software packages run the gamut from single-camera setups to multiple remote-control cameras equipped with motion detectors, and the average computer user can set them up.

The basic netcam surveillance packages include support for one camera that snaps a picture every few seconds with a timestamp and then posts it to the web for viewing. Some mid-level packages use a video camera connected to your PC and also include motion detection that will notify you by email anytime movement is recorded. Advanced features include live streaming, support for more than one camera, creation of video clips when motion is detected, and control of pan-tilt-zoom cameras.

Software packages

The HomeWatcher (www.homewatcher.com/products.htm) is a free surveillance solution is limited, but it works fine for one netcam. Snapshots remain on your PC and are viewable through a custom webpage on your hard drive. The complete program ($25) supports up to nine cameras, video creation when motion is detected, and automatic image uploading to an FTP site. It also will send snapshots to unlimited email addresses.

The Gotcha! ($69.95, www.gotchanow.com/text/g30f.html) surveillance system comes with the same features as HomeWather as well as surveillance scheduling, a "Dynamic Profile" recording mode (for recording events over long periods of time), a password-protected and inconspicuous system tray icon, and pager alerts when your hard drive space is running low.

Place your netcam on the TrackerPod ($150, www.trackerpod.com) robotic stand. The software instructs it to swivel and follow motion. It's compatible with your existing netcamming software.

Yes, X10's (www.x10.com/products/) pop-up ads are annoying, but it supports a wireless system of multiple netcams. You can set up a pseudo-CCTV security system by placing a cam on your front door, in your garage, and in your backyard.

Motion Detection

Netcam motion detecting is built into the software. The software snaps a picture every few seconds and then compares the most recent picture with the picture that was taken before it. If nothing has changed, the new picture is discarded. But if the most recent picture is different, it's automatically saved as having detected motion.

With a timestamp recorded onto every picture, you have a detailed log in chronological order of every movement captured. More expensive surveillance software will actually record a movie file as well as the pictures.

Live Streaming

With TeVeo (www.teveo.com) you register with the company website and choose whether you'd like your netcam to be public or private. It's that easy. Once you sign up, you can view a live stream from inside your home on the website. The best thing is the site is free.

iVista Personal Edition ($49.99, wwws.inetcam.com/secured/download_personal.html) comes complete with your own webpage hosted on Inetcam.com, where you can view live video transmitted from your home computer. It also features a scheduler, wireless ability, recording, and a 30-day free trial support.

Remove Ads from XP's Messenger

Morgan Webb

Ads are everywhere. Why tolerate them in Windows XP Messenger? In just a couple of short steps, you can be ad-free forever.

First, get rid of the little Messenger men in the background of your buddy list. You can turn the semi-transparent Messenger logo into a picture of anything you want. I used a picture of myself, but vanity is by no means a prerequisite for this little project.

1. Open the Messenger program folder and locate lvback.gif, or search your computer.

2. You can modify this picture to whatever you want, or you can save a different picture in its place. The new picture doesn't even have to be the same size!

3. Exit Messenger and restart it.

4. Your new picture should be ready.

Now, if you are one of the unlucky people who has rotating ads on the bottom of your buddy list, follow these steps to kill them dead:

1. Exit MSN Messenger completely.

2. Locate the file links.txt. It should be in your C:\Documents and Settings\User\Local Settings\Temp directory, but if you search your hard drive for links.txt, it should be the only file to appear.

3. Open the file in Notepad.

4. Highlight and erase the entire contents of the file. The file should contain links. Save the file.

5. Right-click the file and choose Properties.

6. Check Read-Only so MSN Messenger cannot write new links to the file.

7. Now when you open MSN Messenger, there will be one basic MSN logo in the buddy list instead of rotating logos.

8. This basic logo is stored on your computer in the Messenger program folder as logo.gif. You can rename logo.gif to logobak.gif (or delete it altogether), and the normal ad space will appear blank.

9. You can change logo.gif into whatever picture you choose. Need some suggestions? Perhaps use a picture of your favorite feline companion. If you're feeling practical, you can create a little note reminding you to get back to work. The choice is yours.

There's no need to stare at those ads anymore. Go forth and chat ad-free!

Laporte Support

Reputable Internet Businesses

Want to know how to find out whether an Internet business is reputable?

I recommend the following resources:

- **Better Business Bureau** (www.bbb.org). Information on whether a company has received complaints.

- **ResellerRatings.com** (http://resellerratings.com). Consumer comments and satisfaction indices.

- **Epinions** (www.epinions.com) Consumer reviews.

- **ConsumerReview** (www.consumerreview.com). Community of sites offering aficionado reviews for various product categories.

- **Federal Trade Commission** (www.ftc.gov). Body that enforces a variety of federal antitrust and consumer protection laws. Check the Formal Actions, Opinions, and Activities (www.ftc.gov/ftc/formal.htm) section for questionable behavior.

Secure Your Wi-Fi

Patrick Norton

Thinking about dragging a cheap base station into your corporate office to use your notebook wirelessly in the conference room? Wi-Fi is a cheap solution, but that doesn't make it a good idea. Your IT department would probably beat you with a stick, because you can easily compromise the security of the entire network.

Don't need a secure wireless network at home? Imagine the neighbor kid using your DSL or cable bandwidth to download warez and porn, or to launch a slightly sleazy cracking session online.

Don't assume you can just whip that wireless access point (WAP) out of the cardboard and Styrofoam, plug it in, and start networking. It'll probably work, but you won't be secure at all.

That said, don't panic.

The Answer

The Wired Equivalent Privacy (WEP) algorithm, which is part of the 802.11 standard, isn't the complete answer. WEP is compromised.

That said, it's good to practice good security habits:

- Don't use Wi-Fi in places you don't want to share your network connection.
- Turn off beaconing. Beaconing sends a signal with your service set identifier (SSID), and anybody can match up to it. If you disable it, the SSID in the client must match the SSID of the base station. This makes it harder for strangers to find your system and log on.
- Change the stock SSID.
- Lock down your WAP using MAC addresses.

- Getting serious? Put the WAP outside your firewall and create a virtual private network (VPN) that connects through it.
- Change your passwords on a frequent basis.
- Even though it's not completely secure, turn on WEP. It's one more thing to put in the way of the baddies.

Download of the Day

WatchCat

Megan Morrone

If you're anything like me, over the years you've had to develop an elaborate ruse to prevent your boss from catching you playing Tetris.

Sometimes it was enough to just close the window really fast, but then you lost your game. Next you learned to minimize, but then you had that one really nosey boss who would get up right behind you and check the minimized windows at the bottom of your screen, and you were caught.

Finally, there's WatchCat (www.geocities.com/ vassili_bourdo/software/wcat/download.html), a tiny application that lets you make offending windows disappear at the stroke of a user-defined keystroke. The programs will still run, and you can get them back as soon as your boss leaves you alone.

Good for Less Sneaky People, Too

Even if you don't have a nasty Tetris addiction like I do, you can use WatchCat to keep your desktop tidy or to keep things slightly secure by password-protecting windows.

I say "slightly secure" because any hacker worth his weight in stolen passwords will figure out how to make your windows come back if he or she can see that icon.

Stay Anonymous Online

Kevin Rose

When you're surfing the web at work, there's a good chance that someone's watching you. It's easy to snoop on websites, email messages, and instant-messaging conversations.

Many "hackers" and work surfers get caught because they don't understand the inner workings of the Internet. When you understand how people get caught, you'll find it easier to avoid getting caught.

Joe Worker

Joe's obsessed with sports, so much so that he spends a good amount of his work day checking scores and player stats.

What Joe doesn't know is that his employer monitors all incoming and outgoing web traffic though the company's switch. Every time Joe connects to a website, the packets of information are being recorded by packet-sniffing software such as Iris (`www.eeye.com/html/Products/Iris/`).

Joe's boss approaches him about the sites he has been visiting, presenting him with a stack of printouts showing the requested information and websites being sent to his computer.

Joe's busted.

Avoid the Bust

Here's what Joe's computer setup and Internet connection looks like:

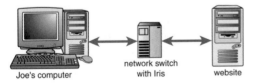

Joe's computer   network switch   website
                        with Iris

The network switch uses Iris to capture all of Joe's unencrypted web traffic.

By using a proxy, Joe could have kept his boss from busting him. A proxy is a server that requests a webpage on your behalf and then delivers it to your machine. A standard proxy wouldn't have helped Joe because Iris still would have captured the unencrypted webpage.

Joe needs to use an encrypted proxy. An encrypted proxy makes network data indecipherable to packet-capturing software such as Iris.

I highly recommend Anonymizer.com (`www.anonymizer.com`), which has a free service. Its pay service has many added features and is much faster. Another great tool is NetSpy (`http://netspy.ukrpack.net`), which lists and rates free anonymous proxy servers.

When using a service such as Anonymizer, your Internet connection changes:

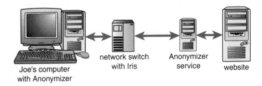

Joe's computer   network switch   Anonymizer
with Anonymizer   with Iris   service   website

Joe sends an encrypted request for his sports site, which then contacts Anonymizer.com. Anonymizer.com then encrypts the webpage and sends it back to his computer, which decrypts it in real time. Iris captured all of this, but because the data is encrypted, none of it is legible.

Don't Hack with It

For surfing from work, Anonymizer works great, but don't even consider it for hacking. Never break the law. And hack for knowledge, not for destruction.

The Screen Savers' Site-O-Rama

Leo Laporte, Sarah Lane, Kevin Rose, and Yoshi DeHerrera

You know what's the best thing about the Internet? Websites. For the 20th consecutive year. Server hardware, assorted cables, and mouse-clicking are all tied for a distant second place. We recently did some site searching and came up with our personal picks of the best the Net has to offer.

Leo's Top Three Programming Sites

1. **Perl Monks** (http://perlmonks.com). Perl is one of those programming languages that really lends itself to obscure but brilliant short programs. This website is a rich repository of such code wizardry. Inside the Monastery gates, Perl adepts offer the best magic incantations for all sorts of programs. Better yet, you can post your questions and bugs and get personal answers.

2. **Stepwise** (www.stepwise.com/). Mac OS X programs are written in C++ using the Cocoa frameworks. Cocoa is powerful, but it can be tough to learn. Stepwise is hosted by Scott Anguish, co-author of *Cocoa Programming*, published by Sams and the best Cocoa book out there. Stepwise is also home to Bill Cheeseman's famous book *Vermont Recipes* (Peachpit).

3. **O'Reilly** (http://oreilly.com). Not only does O'Reilly publish some of the best programming books out there, but it also has an incredibly useful site for programmers in any language. Check out the resource centers for Python, Java, Perl, C, .NET, Wireless, Bioinformatics, Mac OS X, and on and on.

Sarah's Picks

1. **Craigslist** (www.craigslist.org). The "Best of Craigslist" section is worth a whole afternoon.

2. **Cat of the Day** (www.catoftheday.com). You might laugh, but I visit this site every day for a smile.

3. **Dr. Weil** (www.drweil.com). I love Dr. Weil. I think he's the best doctor around. I love this site for the recipes, the health message boards, and his daily advice.

Kevin's Top Five Sites

1. **Astalavista** (www.astalavista.com). Astalavista Security Group is a great underground search engine for information on hacking, encryption, security, and more.

2. **MacRumors** (www.macrumors.com). This is my favorite site for Mac rumors. Find out about what Apple is up to before release.

3. **Kaliber10000** (www.k10k.net). Here's my favorite graphic-design website. Top-notch designers showcase their works here.

4. **Kevinrose.com** (www.kevinrose.com). You'll find dark tips, hacking, encryption, security, and more here.

5. **Olsen Twins Countdown** (www.olsentwinscountdown.com). This handy site counts down the days, hours, and minutes remaining until the Olsen twins turn 18. Disclaimer: Uh, this site is kind of disturbing—funny, but disturbing.

Yoshi's Furious Five for Modders

1. **[H]ard|Forum** (www.hardforum.com). This is a great forum for hardware and modding advice from experts.

2. **VHForums.net** (www.vhforums.net/upload). The tag line says it all: "Where the Mawd Gawds Hang Out!"

3. **Pheaton Forums** (www.pheatonforums.com/phpBB2/). Here's yet another great bulletin board for modders, by modders.

4. **Overclockers.com** (www.overclockers.com) Anyone looking to overclock the CPU should visit this site.

5. **Electronics Information Online** (www.eio.com). When you figure out what you need, this is the place to find great deals on hardware.

Spybot—Search & Destroy

Dan Mitchell and Roger Chang

Who's watching your computer? In this age of data insecurity and unscrupulous online spyware, Spybot has made a name for itself as the premier ad and spyware killer. Much to the delight of its followers, Spybot creator Patrick Kolla has released an update (http://security.kolla.de). Most adware programs are also spyware—they report back to the "mother ship" about your surfing habits. Many of these advertising companies claim that the information is anonymous or specifically used to target ads, but do you really want to take that chance with your privacy? We didn't think so.

Eliminate Spyware

Spybot—Search & Destroy (Spybot—S&D) finds and removes adware and spyware modules on your hard drive. The first time you run the program, you'll be shocked at how much spyware is on your hard drive. Detecting and removing spyware is only one of the many things this program can do for you. It also detects key loggers, some Trojans, Internet dialers, browser hijackers, and several other nasties you might have picked up in your travels through cyberspace

Here's how to get rid of all the information this stuff's been gathering:

1. Launch the program, click Search & Destroy, and click Check for Problems. Spybot scours your system.

2. Peruse the list and uncheck anything you want to keep on your system. Entries in red are most dangerous.

3. Click Fix Selected Problems.

When these modules are removed, the related programs could stop working. No worries. Spybot—S&D lets you restore the programs with its Recovery tool. You can also use the new Exclude feature to exclude specific programs, files, and cookies. It's great if you have spyware you need to keep to use a program, as is the case with KaZaA.

Previously, you needed to regularly check for spies. The Immunize feature included in this version reduces the number of intruders you'll find. It acts like a vaccine, preventing known spyware agents from installing themselves on your system.

Erase Your Tracks

As if that weren't enough, Spybot—S&D also cleans your tracks:

1. Select Usage Tracks Check Only from the Fix Sets drop-down list.

2. Click Fix the Selected Problems.

Not just the usual Internet browser stuff. Sure, it'll let you clear cookies, URL history, and Temp files. But it'll also let you clear stuff in individual programs, including lists of recently viewed photos in your favorite imaging program and text in Word. And, it can also find and fix invalid Registry entries.

Spybot—S&D also lets you permanently and securely remove files you no longer want or need. Just click Tools and choose Secure Shredder.

The Tools area also has a host of new utilities to help you manage your system and delete documents completely, including these:

- **Host file.** The standard browser host file is a list of known websites and IP addresses that you actively want to block. Spybot lets you add its list of known spyware proliferators to the host file.

- **Process list.** This is a list of actively running applications on your PC.

- **System startup.** This is a list of programs that launch when Windows loads.

Click Online to find another group of utilities designed to keep Spybot current. It includes an update feature, a bug report feature, and a spam opt-out email list. Spybot—S&D does it all.

Windows XP Password-Recovery Disk

Greg Melton

Thanks to XP's Forgotten Password Wizard, your conscience will be free and clear if your mind happens to accidentally misplace your user password. Here's how to launch the Forgotten Password Wizard to create your password-recovery disk:

1. Click Start, Control Panel, User Accounts.

2. Click your user account name.

3. Under Related Tasks on the left, click Prevent Forgotten Password to launch the wizard.

Now that you've launched the wizard, let it walk you through creating the recovery disk. Make sure the disk you use is formatted and in the drive. After it's finished creating the disk, label it and stash it away for an emergency.

If you forget your password, just click your user icon at the logon screen. Even though you don't have your password, go ahead and click the green arrow. This launches a little yellow dialog box directing you to use your password-recovery disk. Don't lose the disk or change your password after creating the disk or you're out of luck.

Megan's Tips

Windows Hibernate

Windows has a feature called hibernate. It shuts down your computer and saves everything the way you left it. It even bypasses the startup for quicker entry in Windows. Here's how to do it on Windows XP:

1. Click Start, then select Shut Down.

2. Press Shift and Standby changes to Hibernate.

For this to work, you must have hibernate enabled in the power options of the Control Panel.

Windows Tips

XP Run Box Shortcuts

Morgan Webb

You want what you want when you want it—and usually, you want it immediately. That's what being a power user is all about, right? Here are 12 handy shortcuts you can type into your XP Run menu to get the utilities you want and need. Note: Some of these work only in XP Pro.

control	Control Panel access
clipbrd	Clipboard Viewer access
wordpad	Access to a handy text editor
compmgmt.msc	Computer management
devmgmt.msc	Device manager
diskmgmt.msc	Disk management
dfrg.msc	Disk defrag
eventvwr.msc	Event viewer
fsmgmt.msc	Shared folders
gpedit.msc	Group policies
lusrmgr.msc	Local users and groups
perfmon.msc	Performance monitor
rsop.msc	Resultant set of policies
secpol.msc	Local security settings
services.msc	Services

ZoneAlarm

Robert Heron and Nicole Guilfoyle

Hackers have a variety of programs to poke and prod any computer connected to the Internet. Most users are unaware of any attempts to gain access to their systems until it's too late. ZoneAlarm (www.zonelabs.com) is free for personal use and is a must-have for the growing community of "always-on" Internet users. This great piece of software provides excellent security and flexibility while remaining easy to use. It monitors and tracks all incoming and outgoing Internet traffic, blocking access when necessary.

How ZoneAlarm Works

ZoneAlarm provides firewall protection from outside intrusions, along with an Application Control feature that can intercept any rogue outbound traffic, such as information stolen by a Trojan horse or "spyware" attack.

Configure ZoneAlarm

The first time you launch ZoneAlarm, you're walked through the installation and setup wizard that determines how you'll use the program. The questions it asks are based on the type of connection you specify.

- Do you want ZoneAlarm to notify you when it blocks Internet traffic, or do you want it to protect in silence?

- Do you want ZoneAlarm to configure your browser's security settings right away or the first time you launch your browser? It's safe for most users to do this right away. Advanced users will want to customize access and server permissions. Novice users should stay away from the Advanced options.

When setup is complete, you can customize more settings.

- Overview quickly shows how much traffic ZoneAlarm has blocked, which programs have attempted to go online, and how many email attachments are quarantined.

- Go to Product Info to get version, licensing, and registration information, as well as product updates and help.

- Preferences contains ZoneAlarm's display properties.

- Firewall settings are broken into two categories: Internet Zone Security and Trusted Zone Security.

- The Internet Zone Security option includes all computers on the web. Trusted Zone Security lets you share files with other "trusted" users.

- Use the Advanced button to tweak security settings by blocking specific types of incoming and outgoing traffic.

- Go to Zones to add computers to your Trusted Zone.

- It's recommended that you keep Program Control on the Medium setting so that each program requests permission to access the Net. You can also access the Program Wizard if you want to change any of the original options you chose during setup.

- Automatic Lock shuts off Internet access after a period of inactivity. Click Custom to specify what amount of time determines "inactivity," or choose to have it activate when the screen saver comes on. You can also block all Internet traffic or grant permission to pass-lock programs.

- Go to Programs and left-click one of the symbols next to a program's name to change its access: Allow, Block, or Ask.

- Alerts and logs. Specify whether you want to get alert pop-up messages for things that are not programs. The Log Viewer lets you look over all the alerts you've received.

- Turn MailSafe on and off. This feature spots questionable email attachments.

It's easy to minimize ZoneAlarm's screen. To turn off the program, right-click the icon in your system tray and choose Shutdown ZoneAlarm.

SlimBrowser

Sarah Lane

Nobody wants to like Microsoft, but many of us depend on it. But that alone makes me mad. I love to rebel, or at least subvert. That's why I love SlimBrowser (www.flashpeak.com/sbrowser/sbrowser.htm).

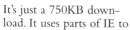

It's just a 750KB download. It uses parts of IE to bring you a cleaner, faster browser—what Internet Explorer should be. When you're up and running, SlimBrowser displays your pages just as IE would. For example, I'm having a problem viewing my blog (www.sarahlane.com) in Netscape and Safari, but SlimBrowser displays it like it's IE.

Besides being cool and different, SlimBrowser is just better than IE. I personally love tabbed windows. Peruse the drop-down menus to see what else it can do.

Here are the top ten reasons SlimBrowser is better than stupid, lame IE:

1. It runs Popup Killer automatically (unless you disable it). I haven't had a pop-up since I installed SlimBrowser. What I get instead is a little beep indicating that SlimBrowser has squashed another pop-up. You can choose to view the pop-ups if you want. But why would you want?

2. It comes with a handful of skins that make it look like Windows XP, Red Hat, ColdFusion, and so on.

3. You can hide sites that you don't want people to know you're looking at. Choose to view them again when the coast is clear.

4. Upon download completion, SlimBrowser automatically imports all your IE bookmarks and chosen homepage. It even keeps your current Internet options.

5. The Languages tab lets you translate pages or text using Google or Babelfish. SlimBrowser also has a built-in dictionary.

6. If you enjoy viewing certain sites together, you can create site "groups" that open all at once. For example, I like viewing my news sites simultaneously in the morning. Now I can click once and open everything in individual windows!

7. The shortcuts menu jumps you over to your Desktop, Control Panel, and Recycle Bin. I find this menu easier to use than my Start menu.

8. The Tools menu has nifty options such as Clean Trace, which erases cookies, history, cached files, or all three in one fell swoop!

9. It gives me no slowdown or funny crashes, as I get with many other programs.

10. It subverts Microsoft! Fight the power!

Give it a shot. I think you'll like it. Besides, it's time we all stopped fearing change. Hell, I might cut off all my hair in appreciation!

Laporte Support

Windows 95 Logon

The Windows 95 logon is useless. If you press Cancel or Esc, you can skip the logon and get to any files on the computer. Unfortunately, there's no way to change this in Windows 95 or Windows 98. This is one of the advantages of Windows 2000 and Windows XP. They have real logons that protect the computers.

You'll have to download some third-party software to make Windows 95 and Windows 98 computers secure. Go to Download.com and do a search on "95 security" or "secure logon." Any of the results that have a rating of 75 percent or more are safe bets, but you'll probably have to pay for them.

Crack Windows Passwords

Kevin Rose

Ever tried logging into a Windows computer and realize that you forgot the password? There's a way to crack the password, and it doesn't involve reformatting and reinstalling Windows.

The solution is called @stake LC4 (formerly L0phtCrack, www.atstake.com/research/lc). LC4 attacks your Windows machine with a combination of dictionary and brute force attacks. LC4 can crack almost all common passwords in seconds. More advanced passwords with numbers and characters take longer.

How It Works

Windows NT, 2000, and XP passwords are stored as encrypted hash marks. LC4 attacks these hash marks with hundreds of passwords per minute. Eventually, the correct password is sent and then displayed to the screen.

Good Intentions

- System administrators can find weak passwords within minutes. Sys admins can then change the passwords to make them more secure.
- LC4 can be used to access computers of users who have forgotten passwords.
- In companies, it can be used to access PCs of employees who have left the company.

Bad Intentions

- Hackers can use LC4 to sniff passwords over networks.
- Hackers can install this application onto a primary domain controller and steal hundreds of passwords within minutes.

Laporte Support

Safe Surfing

These sites and products help you create a child-safe surfing environment for your kids:

- **CyberPatrol** (www.cyberpatrol.com)
- **ChildSoft Children's Desktop and Browser** (www.childrensdesktop.com)
- **ChiBrow**, the Children's Browser (www.chibrow.com)
- **Yahooligans!** (www.yahooligans.com/parents)
- **Google SafeSearch** Filtering (www.google.com)
- **AOL Parental Controls** (www.aol.com/info/parentcontrol.html)
- **Internet Explorer Security Zones** (www.microsoft.com/windows/ie/using/howto/security/setup.asp)

I believe that the most important thing is a parent's involvement in a child's online activities. I recommend spending time talking with kids about online safety. Consider a contract with your kids. For more information, visit NetSmartz (www.netsmartz.org).

Address: Site of the Day

TheFreeSite.com

Welcome to the Fort Knox of free downloads and utilities, www.thefreesite.com.

Secret Data Stash

Kevin Rose

Sooner or later, it'll happen to you. You have some valuable data on a disk—passwords, warez, personal finances, journals, incriminating JPEGs of your ex—that you want to put in a safe, hidden place. Maybe you even have some valuable hardware such as Xbox Mod chips that you want to keep out of sight (since Microsoft is sure to hunt you down). It's time to find a good hiding place for your goods.

Stuffing items in a box and stashing it in the dark crevasses of my closet wasn't enough. Safe deposit box? Too much of a hassle. Renting a storage space is expensive, and I just don't trust my friends enough to let them keep my stuff for me (but I still love you all).

It's time to think creatively. I'm going to show you how to build inexpensive and effective hidden data storage. All these hiding places involve items you see almost every day. The catch is that you wouldn't think that there are hidden items in them. Sneaky, huh?

If the Shoe Fits

A shoe can hold more than your foot. With a little bit of handiwork, you can turn that old shoe that you never wear anymore into a home for your hard drive. (Face it, by the time elevator boots are back in style, you'll be using a walker.)

Tools and supplies: Dremel tool, the largest shoe in your closet, Velcro, and a hard drive.

Instructions:

1. You're going to create a cavity for the hard drive in the shoe. Hollow out the underside of the large shoe with the Dremel tool. Try a variety of different Dremel bits and see which one works best for hollowing out the shoe.

2. Slide in the hard drive and align it properly with the level of the sole of the shoe. If something doesn't fit quite right, use the Dremel to make adjustments.

3. Apply Velcro to the back of the shoe flat. This will conceal the large hole you created with the Dremel.

4. Back up your data. Hide the shoe in the back of your closet, and no one will suspect a thing.

Can It, Bud

Thieves will never suspect that your giant can of Dinty Moore Beef Stew has your floppy disk backups of your taxes from the past four years.

Tools and supplies: Food can (how big is up to you; depends on how hungry you are), Oxo Smooth Edge can opener, newspaper or other stuffing material, and Super Glue.

Instructions:

1. Open the can with the Smooth Edge Can opener. Eat the contents, or feed them to your dog. (Don't toss out the food! Didn't your mother teach you not to waste food?)

2. Wash the can. Be careful not to damage the label. Keep it looking new.

3. Dry the can. You don't want your goods to get wet. That would suck.

4. Fill the can—hard drive, mini CDRs, oregano, anything you want.

5. After you've filled the can with stuff, add some newspaper to prevent the things from moving around.

6. Seal the can with Super Glue. This prevents the can from opening and ensures a realistic look and feel.

Secret Data Stash (continued)

Opportunity Knocks

Doors are everywhere in your house, most likely in a doorway. If you're still living at home with your parents, get their permission to install a new door. That shoe with the hard drive can make for a pretty painful whuppin' from an angry dad.

Tools and supplies: Dremel tool, a hollow door ($20 at hardware store), extra wood, extra screws, and flat white paint.

Instructions:

1. Drill through the side of the door and start hollowing out a pocket with your Dremel tool.

2. Measure your newly created hole and determine the dimensions of your hidden door insert.

3. Build out the hidden door with the extra wood, and test for a snug fit. A snug fit is essential so that the hidden door does not move when being opened or closed. This will prevent it from being detected.

4. Create a flush cover for your hidden door and paint it flat white.

Picture This

One of the most overlooked hidden storage places in the house is a picture frame. Deep picture frames can be easily modified to hold CDs, hard drives, and more. Placed it in a well-arranged group of pictures, and it will never be detected.

Tools and supplies: Dremel tool and a deep picture frame.

Instructions:

1. Open the back of the frame, and find an area on the frame for a cavity that's the same size as your item.

2. Use the Dremel tool to hollow out the space on the frame.

3. Fit the item into the cavity. Make adjustments with your Dremel tool as necessary.

Talkback

That's Not Me!

Dave Roos

We've been using the Internet so long that it's easy to forget two basic rules of web safety:

- Don't give out personal information.

- Don't post your picture in a public forum, unless you want the whole world to see it and snatch it.

Even though the web seems to be getting safer, it's still wildly unregulated. Plenty of eager "entrepreneurs" will hijack your personal information for their devious profit.

Has your personal information been hijacked online?

Yes   17%

No   83%

Windows Tips

One-Click Lockdown

Morgan Webb

If you work in a public area, you should lock your computer whenever you leave it. Make a shortcut on your desktop or Quick Launch bar to quickly secure your computer:

- Right-click your desktop.

- Choose New, Shortcut.

- Paste **rundll32.exe user32.dll, LockWorkStation** (without the quotes) into the target area.

- Click OK.

- Click your new shortcut to keep secure.

It's a Router; It's a Firewall

Patrick Norton

It shares Internet access with all the PCs on your network, and—will you look at that—it's an Internet proxy as well. Heck, it's everything you've ever wanted between your home systems and the big bad Internet. It's SmoothWall (www.smoothwall.org)!

Okay, granted, it sounds a lot like my first Linksys Etherfast Cable/DSL Router. Except it's free! Or, it's free if you have an old beater system (a 486 or better will do nicely), a couple of NICs, and the ability to burn a CD. Plus, it's open source, so lots of eyes are making it better every day.

Things to Like About SmoothWall

- It recycles a system that might otherwise get tossed into a landfill.
- It's a quick install from its 22MB ISO image.
- It can talk directly to many USB DSL modems.
- It can act as an Internet proxy, storing oft-hit web information locally.
- It has a simple web-based interface.
- It's got some excellent documentation.

And it keeps things simple for us non-IT maven types. If you set up your cable or DSL modem, you can set up this.

You administer your network in three basic areas, defined as Red, Green and Orange. The Orange area acts like a DMZ, so your web servers and email servers are quarantined. The Green interface is your safe, protected area, while the Red zone is your connection to the Big Bad Internet. In fact, the hardest part of the install for me was figuring out which Ethernet card gets associated with which zone.

Get that straightened out, and you've got a fairly well-protected system. The whole process took less than an hour to set up. You've got a ton of options, so definitely read the FAQs and the manuals for details. Feeling adventurous? You can try SmoothWall 2.0 beta. It uses the Linux 2.4 kernel (which makes for better NIC support), a new file system, and IP tables instead of IP chains, not to mention a new interface. It also has the promise of better VPN support. Beta means it's not finished yet, but it will probably be shipping by the time you read this. Of course, you could say the same thing for my first Linksys Etherfast Cable/DSL Router. It was getting major updates to the firmware for months after it came out.

Download of the Day

Wizmo

Megan Morrone

You've probably heard of Steve Gibson of the Gibson Research Corporation (http://grc.com) and SpinRite. He's a security expert known for exposing flaws in many popular Microsoft products and helping you protect yourself from PC intruders. Steve has developed a clever little tool designed to speed up the processes you use most. Wizmo (www.atstake.com/research/lc) is a tiny executable you can configure for tasks such as turning off your monitor, exiting Windows, or shutting down your system in one click.

How to Use Wizmo

1. Download the program, and move it to C:\Windows\System directory. (Be sure you actually move it. Don't just create a shortcut.)

2. Create a shortcut on your desktop (or any other place you find handy).

3. Right-click the shortcut and choose Properties. In the Target box after the directory path, add a space and type the command you'd like to execute. Check the list of Wizmo vocabulary for commands at http://grc.com/wizmo/wizmo.htm.

4. Change the icon so you can differentiate your shortcuts.

You can make as many shortcuts as you have commands.

Safeguard Your Passwords

Kevin Rose

If you're like me, you have a dozen or so passwords for various websites, applications, networks, and so on. You need someplace to store them—safely.

I've found two great password safehouses for your downloading pleasure.

Password Safe

This is an open-source project, a database that encrypts each individual password (www.counterpane.com/passsafe.html).

Pros

- Because it's an open-source project, anyone can look at the source code of the application (there are no hidden back doors).
- It's based on strong Blowfish encryption.
- It autogenerates strong passwords.
- It's free.

Cons

- The interface needs work.

Personal Vault

It's shareware and has the features and ease of use I want (www.soft1st.com).

Pros

- It has an awesome, easy-to-use interface.
- It minimizes nicely in the Windows system tray.
- It encrypts each password.
- It autogenerates strong passwords.

Cons

- No source code is available.

Windows Tips

Check Your Certificates

Morgan Webb

Whenever you enter a secure area of a website, a small padlock appears at the bottom of your IE browser window. You can double-click this padlock to see who verifies the identity of the remote computer and issues the SSL keys. You can even see who verifies the the verifying computer. Do some certificate snooping:

1. To explore the certificate information, go to www.paypal.com and click to log on as a member (you won't need an account).
2. Double-click the padlock at the bottom of your browser window to view the certificate information for this site.
3. VeriSign verifies PayPal's identity, but you'll also see other popular certificate authorities.
4. Click Details to learn what version of the software the site is using, the certificate's expiration date, and more.

This system is not foolproof, however.

Laporte Support

2.4GHz Interference

Can a wireless phone that runs at the 2.4GHz frequency "listen in" to a CPU that runs at the 2.4GHz frequency band?

Perhaps, but it's highly unlikely. Theoretically, it makes sense that someone could intercept the Wi-Fi signals and read the data, but it takes a lot of work to do it. A wireless phone could cause some interference with Wi-Fi (and vice versa), but the phone looks for available channels to avoid interference with other signals.

Secure Public Wi-Fi

Patrick Norton

A viewer writes:

> "I have a laptop and a Wi-Fi card. I'd like to use the public wireless access points at places such as Starbucks, but I don't want the guy at the next table sniffing my passwords and watching my surfing habits. What is a good way to encrypt my wireless transmissions on a public network? Can I encrypt if the access point does not have WEP (Wired Equivalent Privacy) or any security enabled?"

You can secure a Wi-Fi connection at the local coffee shop, but only if you're willing to work for it. Forget about using WEP. It's supposed to make Wi-Fi as secure as Ethernet, except it's too easy to crack.

Adding a firewall will help protect your computer, but it won't keep crackers from sniffing your wireless connections and getting your private info.

Starbucks uses T-Mobile's HotSpot (www.t-mobile.com/hotspot). The network is accessible for Starbucks customers with a wire-less-ready notebook computer or Pocket PC. To connect, customers need a T-Mobile HotSpot account and Wi-Fi capability for their wireless device. Although T-Mobile recommends that you secure your Wi-Fi connection, it doesn't offer any security services.

Service Providers

What you need is a virtual private network (VPN). It's a sort of protected tunnel between your machine and a safe spot out somewhere in the Internet. National wireless provider Boingo (www.boingo.com) offers VPN connections for $30 a year.

T-Mobile HotSpots (www.t-mobile.com) is honest (at least halfway) about its security policy. It tells you clearly that responsibility for security is on you. Before you drop the cash, find out whether your office already has a VPN, or build one into your setup at home.

Windows Tips

Troubleshoot Your Startup

Morgan Webb

We've all been there, fuming as our computer pummels us with meaningless error messages, beeps, and blips.

Was it the new antivirus you just installed? The virtual plant you downloaded that grows if you water it and shrivels if you don't? Who knows what it could be, but there is a tool to help troubleshoot your problems:

1. Open msconfig by going to Start, Run (or pressing Windows+R) and typing **msconfig**.

2. Click the Services tab.

3. Below the list of services, check the box titled Hide All Microsoft Services. Microsoft's default services disappear, and you are left with those of foreign parties. Third-party services are necessary, especially for antivirus software, but you can temporarily uncheck Services to see if a certain application is the culprit in your Windows woes.

4. Remember to recheck Services when you're finished troubleshooting because some applications need them to function properly.

Web Tips

Mozilla Pop-Up Blocker

Mozilla is nice enough to bundle a pop-up blocker in its browser. To enable it, go to Edit and click Preferences. Double-click Advanced, and select Scripts and Plug-Ins. Uncheck Open Unrequested Windows and click OK. Now you're free of pop-ups!

Control Access to Your Internet Options

Morgan Webb

Someone can do a bit of damage to Internet Explorer's settings if given five minutes and a curiosity to "see what this setting does." In a shared-access situation, you might not want people to mess with IE's settings at all.

In Windows 98, you can disable certain tabs of the Internet Options dialog (Tools, Internet Options) or disable the dialog entirely. It involves a little regedit. Note: If this is your first time editing the Windows Registry, please note that you can accidentally damage your system, so be careful. Read up on the Registry at www.annoyances.org/exec/ show/registry.

1. Open the Registry Editor (go to Start, Run, type **regedit**, and press Return).

2. Navigate to HKEY_CURRENT_USER\ Software\Policies\Microsoft\ Internet Explorer\Control Panel.

3. To make a specific tab disappear, locate the appropriate entry, such as ProgramsTab, ContentTab, SecurityTab, or AdvancedTab, and set the corresponding value to 1. If you want the tab back, set the value back to 0.

4. If you're missing an entry, add it as a DWORD value and set it equal to 1. If you set every tab to 1, you won't be able to access Internet Options until you change one or all values back to 0.

5. These changes take place immediately, but can also be immediately reversed.

6. Keep a copy of this article in your records so you know where to find it if and when you want your tabs back.

This Registry edit is a good tool for maintaining your settings in a public environment. Just make sure you know how to get your tabs back.

Talkback

Has Technology Made Us Safer?

Dave Roos

Some insist that the events of September 11, 2001, were undetectable and unstoppable, the coolly calculated act of a group of hateful individuals. Others believe we must share some of the blame, citing lapses in security—by both human intelligence and technological surveillance—for missing the telltale signs.

Those who hold the latter view have turned to technology for solace. They believe that by requiring million-dollar explosive detection systems (EDS) in all U.S. airports and installing biometric face-recognition cameras on street corners, we can thwart further terrorist assaults.

Do you derive any comfort from antiterrorist tech? Can any technology prevent such unthinkable acts?

Has technology made you feel safer?

Yes   11%

No   89%

Web Tips

Bypass Security Notices

Nicole Guilfoyle

Do you really need to be notified every time you leave or enter a secure site? Here's how to turn off the notice:

1. In Internet Explorer, click Tools.

2. Select Internet Options.

3. Click Advanced, and scroll down to Security.

4. Uncheck Warn if Changing from Secure to Nonsecure Mode.

Manage Your Life Online

Megan Morrone

I don't know about where you come from, but here in San Francisco, where we tape *The Screen Savers*, April showers are a myth. April begins San Francisco's hot season. The Winter rains are gone, the summer fog has yet to appear, and the sun even shines for a very brief period. It makes us all feel like we live in Hawaii.

Don't worry, those sunny days don't keep us outside and away from our computers for long. As soon as March draws to a close, we are busy devising our April Fool's Day pranks. On the set of *The Screen Savers*, we're known for the practical jokes we play on one another. Removing someone's mouse ball is a perennial favorite, but with the rise of the optical mouse, we've had to become more creative.

One year I took a screen shot of the desktop on Martin's computer, removed all the icons, and then made the screen shot his desktop wallpaper. That meant that every time he tried to click on an icon, nothing happened. Man, that was rich.

I once changed Morgan's cell phone so that everything was displayed in French. Boy, was she sorry she majored in Italian at Berkeley. Another year, I almost had Patrick convinced that Microsoft had bought Mozilla. You should have seen him steam.

A few years ago, I even tried to convince you viewers that Leo was leaving *The Screen Savers* for a new gig hosting *Survivor*. Wow, did I got an inbox full of angry emails. Here's a tip: Never joke about Leo leaving *The Screen Savers*.

And, of course, who can forget the year that my favorite online store, ThinkGeek, offered the $129.99 Megan Morrone Download of the Day Internet Appliance/Doll for sale on April 1. You wouldn't believe how many people fell for this prank. My parents tried to order a dozen.

Only Leo seems to be immune to my pranks. When I send him fake files that appear to delete his C: drive, he never opens the attachment. When I leave messages on his voice mail pretending to be Steve Jobs wanting his opinion on the new iBook, he always recognizes my voice. And when I hack the GPS in his car, he still manages to find his way home. Mark my words, people. Someday I'll fool him. Someday.

T.S. Eliot wrote that April is the cruelest month, and I believe this has something to do with the fact that the joy of April Fool's day leads to the trauma of filing our taxes two weeks later. Thankfully, Easter falls in there somewhere, and we can ease the pain with chocolate.

Create a FileMaker Database

Leo Laporte

If you have a collection, whether snow globes or Furbies, you can use your computer to catalog it. A computer catalog is also called a database, but don't be put off by the comp-sci terminology. It's easy to create and maintain a database with the right software.

Various organizations and companies, from banks to *The Screen Saver*'s website, use high-end databases such as Oracle, Sybase, and SQL Server. You don't need anything that powerful or difficult to use. Numerous database packages are designed for simple single-users. Some are commercial; some are shareware. Many free open-source database engines are available, too.

SourceForge (www.sourceforge.net) lists 399 active projects. WebAttack (www.webattack.com) lists hundreds of free and shareware database programs, including db Organizer, an approximately $65 shareware program for Windows. I prefer to use a commercial program.

FileMaker

Even though it's not the cheapest database engine out there (it's $300), I use FileMaker Pro (www.filemaker.com) for all my databasing needs. It's easy to design, it's easy to use, it runs on Mac and Windows, and it has all the power I need. You can try it free for 30 days.

I used FileMaker to create a simple database to keep track of my movie collection. You can start with the built-in FileMaker templates, or you can design from scratch.

Start by designing your database on paper. All databases contain records, one record for each unique item. I created a new record for each item in my collection. If I have two copies of a movie, one on DVD and one on VHS, I have two records. In some cases, you might prefer to have one record for each movie, with information about each format.

Every database record contains a number of fields describing that record. I created the following fields:

- Movie Title
- Director
- Cast
- Year
- Genre
- Running Time
- Format
- Date Acquired
- Location
- Cover

Think about the fields you want to keep track of, but don't worry if you leave something out. FileMaker makes it easy to add fields later.

Use FileMaker's Define Fields command to add the fields to your database. You can choose the data types for each fields. You can also create drop-down menus to make it easy to fill in your forms. I created a drop-down for Format, which includes VHS, DVD, and Laserdisc. You can also configure FileMaker to automatically enter today's date into the Date Acquired field.

FileMaker has two modes. Use the Layout mode to design how the database looks, and use the Browse mode to browse and search the collection. After you define the fields, use Layout mode to create a data entry form. You might also want to create a list form. Look at the templates to get design ideas.

FileMaker is particularly well suited for my movie collection because I can change the design whenever I need to. Many database programs won't let you do that. It can also create labels and other reports.

Safety Tips for Booking Trips Online

Jack Karp

Here are some guidelines to help you make it from keyboard to paradise:

- Always check and read all terms of use, privacy standards, user agreements, and payment policies on any travel website before making a purchase.

- Never book anything through a website unless you can find a telephone number for that company. And make sure you have the company's phone number with you when you travel. You probably won't have web access at an airport or hotel.

- Pay by credit card. Paying by credit card gives you the opportunity to cancel or dispute charges.

- Read the fine print. You might get a cheap airfare but end up paying extremely high fees or service charges.

- Print everything. Print all cancellation and refund policies, itineraries, and receipts. When the fare on a trip expires, the web-page that describes it usually does, too.

- Always call to verify reservations. A confirmation number or itinerary does not necessarily mean you have a seat or a room.

- Know the agency's cancellation policy. Not all online travel agencies guarantee compensation or travel alternatives if a flight is delayed or cancelled.

- Be careful of charter flights. A charter company can legally cancel flights, change schedules, or delay flights for up to 48 hours with no compensation or alternative transportation arrangements. And charter flights do not have reciprocity agreements with other airlines.

- Don't be rushed. Phrases such as "last day to book" and "offer expires at midnight" are usually high-pressure advertising tactics. Be wary of any deals that require you to "act immediately."

- Beware of scams. Emails promising cheap or even free trips, advertisements offering discount fares in exchange for listening to timeshare presentations, and travel clubs that require join-up fees in exchange for special discounts, are all common travel scams. Be careful, and check all deals with a legitimate travel agent.

April

2

Windows Tips

Clear Recently Opened Documents

You can disable Windows XP's feature that lists the documents you recently modified:

1. Right-click the taskbar and choose Properties.
2. Click the Start menu tab.
3. Click Customize.
4. Click the Advanced tab.
5. Uncheck List My Recently Opened Documents.

Address: **Site of the Night**

Minutes-N-Motion

Research what your elected officials are doing at www.minutes-n-motion.com.

Talking GPS Devices

Leo Laporte

I get lost a lot, and I hate asking for directions. From these two facts, you can deduce a third: I drive my wife absolutely crazy. But something has changed that syllogism forever.

Satellite Guidance

GPS, the Global Positioning System, relies on 24 satellites that circle the Earth twice a day. By locking into three of those satellites, a GPS receiver calculates its position to within 15 meters. Combine that information with a mapping system, and you have a great way to navigate the streets and highways of America. And you have several million happy wives.

We checked out three GPS-based car navigation systems. All three offer automatic route calculation, real-time mapping as you drive, and talking prompts that tell you when to turn.

The Magellan 750M

The Magellan ($1,700 street, www.magellangps.com) is identical to the Hertz NeverLost system (www.hertz.com). The friendly female voice is soothing and reassuring, even when it says you're off-course.

You have to select letters and numbers with a wheel. But the system remembers previous destinations, so you have to enter each one only once. It did a decent job plotting my course to and from work, although, like most computer-mapping software, it seldom picked the optimum route. When I went off-route, the Magellan recalculated new driving directions, and the nice lady in the box got me back on track.

The chief drawback is the cost. You can buy a lot of paper maps for that kind of dough.

The Garmin StreetPilot III Deluxe

Priced around $800, the Garmin (www.garmin.com) is similar in functionality to the Magellan, but it was a little easier to enter locations. The Garmin maps were more accurate in my informal testing, but the nice lady who tells you when to turn isn't quite as nice.

The Garmin can access only part of the United States at any given time. You download the areas you want into the proprietary data card via a USB connection. This is a little more cumbersome and requires some planning, but it does mean that the maps can be updated and improved.

The Pharos Pocket Navigator

If you own a Pocket PC device, consider the Pharos Pocket GPS Navigator (www.pharosgps.com). It consists of a CF-slot GPS receiver and Ostia mapping software. You can add it to your existing Pocket PC device for around $230. Get the full kit, which includes an external GPS antenna for the dash and a cigarette lighter power adapter.

Data entry is the easiest because you use the Pocket PC's onscreen keyboard. It can also pull destinations directly from your address book. You get spoken turn-by-turn directions via the Pocket PC's speaker, automatic rerouting, and maps for the entire United States. You can't load the entire map, however. Each region is about 16MB, so you need some free space in RAM. If you have an additional memory slot (the CF slot is occupied by the GPS receiver), you can store maps there, too. Unlike the other devices, the Pharos tracks your trip for later playback, so you'll know exactly where you went.

If you already have the Pocket PC PDA, the Pharos is the least expensive way to add talking navigation. It's not as polished at the dedicated units from Garmin and Magellan, but it does the job. My wife likes it so much that I'm considering giving her one. It's not the most romantic gift, but it sure does wonders for a marriage.

ReplayTV Takes on TiVo

Andrew Hawn and *The Screen Savers* Staff
TechTV Labs helps you decide which personal
video recorder is best for your TV-watching needs.

Geek's Choice: ReplayTV 5000

Like earlier ReplayTV 4000 and 4500 series
PVRs, the ReplayTV 5000 series won't appeal
to everyone, although its usability and price are
definite improvements. If you have access to a
speedy Internet connection, as many corporations do, then waiting an hour or two to send
or receive high-quality content might not be
such a big deal. One day, when everyone has
access to a T3 or OC3 in their home, we'll
finally catch up to ReplayTV. For now, it's still
an innovative idea packaged in a good but not
great PVR.

Company: Digital Networks North America
(www.replaytv.com)
Price: $300 to $900
Category: Personal video recorder

Megan's Tips

Automating Net Connections in Windows

When you're on the road, you probably use a
laptop with dialup Internet access. When you're
at home, you probably use your laptop on a
broadband connection. Here's an easy way to
automate switching between these connections:

1. Go to the Control Panel and open
   Internet Options.

2. Click on the Connections tab and then
   turn on Dial Whenever a Network
   Connection Is Not Present.

Couch potato paradise: TiVo Series2

The Philips DSR6000 combines TiVo
functionality—it records up to 35 hours of
television onto a large hard drive—with a
DirecTV receiver. Compared with the
ReplayTV 5000, the TiVo Series2 has a better
remote and a slightly more intuitive interface.
In Andrew's opinion, TiVo is still the safest
PVR choice for the average couch potato.

Company: TiVo (www.tivo.com)
Product: TiVo Series2
Price: Starting at $199 for hardware

Windows Tips

Record Comments in MS Word

Morgan Webb
You can record an audio comment on your
document or on someone else's document in
Microsoft Word.

Say it loud, say it proud:

1. Open Word, go to the Insert menu, and
   choose Comment.

2. In Office XP, click the little picture of the
   cassette tape on the new toolbar that
   appears. In other versions of Office, click
   the little picture of the tape in the new
   bottom window.

3. You'll get a new window to record a sound
   object. Hook up your microphone and click
   the record button. If you don't have a PC
   microphone, you can use any microphone
   that will plug into your sound card, or you
   can purchase one for under $5.

4. When you're finished recording, click Stop.

You now have a sound object associated with
your document. When you want to replay it,
just click the little speaker icon.

Favorites: Ten for X

Megan Morrone

There is virtually no way I can present my latest Mac find without sounding like one of those Ginsu knife hawkers. "Now, how much would you pay?"

Aladdin System's Ten for X Utilities (www.aladdinsys.com) is a great deal, and the list of apps is impressive. You get ten pieces of software for $50. Of course, some of the programs are more useful than others, and some functionality seems to overlap, but there's not a totally lame app in the bunch. If you bought each utility individually, you'd pay $150.

The suite of utilities includes LaunchBar, a personal favorite of Leo's. This program lets you quick-start your commonly used apps with shortcut keys. Ten for X also includes the pro version of LimeWire, which means no spyware and no ads. And if you're an OS X user pining for the pop-up window days of OS 9, try Window Shades. Ten for X includes the following:

- **Alarm Clock S.E. 2.4.** Add your music or Flash files to alarms.
- **Fruit Menu 2.0.** Hack menus.
- **iClean 5.0.** Clean out cookies, cache, trash, and more.
- **IdeaSpiral 1.0.3.** Use a note-taking tool, for creative types.
- **LaunchBar 3.2.2.** Launch your favorite apps fast.
- **LimeWire Pro 2.4.6.** Share, search for, and download files.
- **piPop 2.0.** Find files fast.
- **PrintMagic X 1.1.** Speed up printing.
- **Pseudo 1.2.** Easily modify programs in administrator mode.
- **WindowShade X 2.0.** Get back that retro OS 9 window-shade feel.

Bonus app: Xounds 1.2—Play sounds when you navigate OS X.

Megan's Tips

Free Web Hosting

Megan Morrone

The days of free web hosting are not over. The following sites let you post your website for free:

- **101 Hosting** (www.101h.com). 10MB of space. You can sign up for more accounts as long as you have additional email addresses.
- **ESmartStart.com** (www.esmartsart.com). 20MB of space.
- **1st Host Web** (www.1sthostweb.com). 25MB of space.

Another Option: Spymac

A site called Spymac (www.spymac.com) is a great alternative to the Mac service. Sign up for free registration, and you get access to forums, a 25MB email account, and the capability to upload and store photos in the Spymac gallery. You don't need a Mac to use this service, but the site is optimized for the Mac. Warning: Always keep a copy of your webpage on your hard drive. I can't promise that any of these free sites will be around for the long haul.

Laporte Support

Extend Laptop Battery Life

You can do a few things to extend the battery life of a Windows XP laptop.

- Turn down the brightness on the monitor.
- Adjust the power setting to Max Battery so the laptop turns off everything that doesn't need to be running, including the screen savers.
- Turn off unneeded background applications sitting in the system tray.

Definitive Guide to Windows Shortcuts

Greg Melton

Have you ever wanted to speed through tasks in Windows like a pro? Thanks to shortcuts, you can. We've compiled the ultimate list of secret keyboard shortcuts. Put these secrets to use, and geek status is all yours.

Top Ten Keyboard Shortcuts

Function	Key Combination
Help	F1
Open Start menu	Ctrl+Esc
Switch between open programs	Alt+Tab
Quit program	Alt+F4
Delete items permanently	Shift+Delete
Highlight items in window	Ctrl+A
Copy	Ctrl+C
Cut	Ctrl+X
Paste	Ctrl+V
Undo	Ctrl+Z

General Keyboard-Only Commands

F1: Start Windows Help.

F10: Activate menu bar options.

Shift+F10: Open a context menu for the selected item. The same as right-clicking an object.

Ctrl+Esc: Open the Start menu. Use the arrow keys to select an item.

Alt+down arrow: Open a drop-down list box.

Alt+Tab: Switch to another running application. Hold down Alt and press Tab to view the task-switching window.

Shift: Press and hold Shift while you insert a CD-ROM to bypass the autorun feature.

Alt+space: Display the main window's System menu. From the System menu, you can restore, move, resize, minimize, maximize, or close the window.

Alt+-: Display the Multiple Document Interface (MDI) child window's System menu. From the MDI child window's System menu, you can restore, move, resize, minimize, maximize, or close the child window.

Ctrl+Tab: Switch to the next child window of a MDI application.

Alt+underlined letters in menu: Open the corresponding menu.

Alt+F4: Close the current window.

Alt+down arrow: Open a drop-down list box.

Ctrl+F4: Close the current multiple document interface (MDI) window.

Alt+F6: Switch between multiple windows in the same program. For example, when the Notepad Find dialog is displayed, Alt+F6 switches between the Find dialog and the main Notepad window.

Microsoft Natural Keyboard Keys

Windows: Open the Start menu.

Windows+R: Open the Run dialog box.

Windows+M: Minimize all.

Shift+Windows+M: Undo the minimize all.

Windows+F1: Open help.

Windows+E: Open Windows Explorer.

Windows+F: Find files or folders.

Windows+D: Minimize all open windows.

Ctrl+Windows+F: Find a computer.

Ctrl+Windows+Tab: Move focus from Start to Quick Launch bar, to system tray. Use the right or left arrows to move focus to items on the Quick Launch bar and the system tray.

Windows+Tab: Cycle through taskbar buttons.

Windows+Break: Open the System Properties dialog.

Application key: Display a context menu for the selected item.

Microsoft Natural Keyboard with IntelliType

Windows+L: Log off Windows.

Windows+P: Open the Print Manager.

Windows+C: Open the Control Panel.

Windows+V: Open the Clipboard.

Windows+K: Open the Keyboard Properties dialog.

Windows+I: Open the Mouse Properties dialog.

Windows+A: Open Accessibility Options (if installed).

Windows+spacebar: Display the list of IntelliType hot keys.

Windows+S: Toggle the Caps Lock key on and off.

Dialog Box Keyboard Commands

Tab: Move to the next control in the dialog.

Shift+Tab: Move to the previous control in the dialog.

Spacebar: If the current control is a button, this clicks the button. If the current control is a check box, this toggles the check box. If the current control is an option button, this selects the option.

Enter: Equivalent to clicking the selected button (the button with the outline).

Esc: Equivalent to clicking Cancel.

Alt+underlined letter in dialog item: Move to the corresponding item.

Four Fun Gadgets for Power to Go

Hahn Choi

A device's portability ultimately hinges on battery life, not on the simple fact that it fits in a pocket or small bag. To overcome the limitations of power-hungry mobile devices, here are a few solutions that will keep you on the road longer. But there are trade-offs....

- **Electrovaya's PowerPad 160**
(www.electrovaya.com). You can buy extra batteries, but then you have to charge them. Electrovaya's PowerPad 160, which can be charged simultaneously with your notebook, adds more than 12 hours of computing time. But it adds 2.4 pounds and costs $500.

- **Electric Fuel's Instant Power**
(www.instant-power.com). When you're in a pinch and need power, Instant Power zinc-air batteries provide a boost. Zinc-air batteries aren't rechargeable, but they provide instant power. Unlike rechargeable batteries, zinc-air batteries have a shelf life of around three years. The batteries cost $10–$20, plus the cost of the cable.

- **Solar Dynamics' The Cub**
(www.solar-dynamics.com). Power up pretty much anything with The Cub. It's battery equipped, with a 75-watt AC inverter, DC outputs, and a DC socket adapter. A solar panel recharges the battery, although you can use an optional AC or car adapter. All the components are tucked in a carrying case complete with shoulder straps. According to Solar Dynamics, the battery is sufficient to power a notebook for 2.6 hours. Although the concept is novel, the hefty 13-pounds and $340 price provide little payoff for relatively low battery life.

- **ICP Global Technologies' iSun BattPak**
(www.isunpower.com). The BattPak ($35 with four batteries or $30 without) is one of the most unique and versatile battery chargers we've seen. The BattPak charges up to ten AA or AAA NiMH or NiCD batteries, and includes an integrated DC accessory socket and power output jack for powering devices with the charged batteries. To charge the batteries, the BattPak connects to the optional $80 iSun solar panel, but solar charging takes far too long for today's fast-paced world. The batteries can also be charged with the included car adapter or through an AC outlet.

Patrick's Tips

Be a Civil Cell Phone User

Cell phones go off in restaurants, in movie theaters, and just about everywhere. It's annoying! I have a request: Use your cell phone or pager's vibrate mode.

When your cell phone or pager is in vibrate mode, it physically vibrates instead of ringing. It's a nice balance between turning off your cell phone (which you should do in restaurants and movies) and letting it ring and annoying the universe.

The vibrate mode can still annoy people around you. The device rattles if placed on a table, which is just as bad as ringing.

I'm convinced that vibrate mode uses more battery life than a regular cell phone ring, but it's not enough to make a huge impact.

Be a civil cell phone user. Don't let your cell phone howl in a place where it will annoy everyone around you.

Address: Site of the Night

furfuri.com

Morgan's a fan of this quirky Japanese design site: www.furifuri.com.

Planes, PDAs, and Cell Phones

Patrick Norton

Cell phones and airplanes just don't mix. What happens when I am between Los Angeles and New York City, and I quickly check my PDA? Doesn't it activate the cell phone? Am I interfering with the pilots doing their job because I need an address?

According to the folks at the FAA (www.faa.gov), nothing that is an "intentional emitter"—any portable electronic device that emits a signal—can be used for the duration of the flight.

That category includes your cell phone, the PDA features built into your cell phone, your PDA with a built-in cell phone, and pretty much any personal electronic device that is designed to send a signal out to an antenna and get a signal back. That includes those spiffy two-way pagers, too. Playing a Game Boy is okay, but connecting two for head-to-head battles emits signals, which is a can't do.

Unless you can pull the wireless card out of your PDA or it has a special "airplane mode," such as the latest Samsung phones that turn off the cell phone/wireless parts, the FAA says you're legally required to keep the gadget off for the duration of the flight.

Is the ban really scientific? I'm not going into that debate, which has pilots, engineers, and lots of business travelers taking both pro- and anti-wireless stances on flights. Nor am I going to bring up the separate FCC ban on cell phone usage in flight (it claims this louses up ground-to-ground reception).

The FAA says no accident or major incident has ever been attributed to cell phone usage in flight. I'd hate to be the dude talking to the office that they could prove caused the first one, though. Really, can't you wait until the plane gets on the ground to get that address?

Talkback

When Will You Upgrade Your Cell Phone?

Josh Lawrence

Everyone wants the newest and fanciest. Cell phone manufacturers have saturated the market (you can tell by the number of phones that ring in a movie theater), but they're hoping people will ditch their old phones for new, shinier versions.

Are the new bells and whistles enough to make you upgrade? Enough that you're going to get a new phone this month? Or are you happy as long as it's functioning, bells and whistles be damned?

When will you upgrade your cell phone?

This month   19%

Six months   16%

Two years   11%

When the old one dies   54%

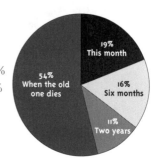

Address: Site of the Night

Virtual Om

Turn up your speakers and open your mind for an enlightening and entertaining online experience at www.virtualom.com.

Sumi's Top Five Products for Less Than $20

Sumi Das

You're finally ready to get organized, but you don't know where to start. Or perhaps you're worried that simplifying your life will complicate your finances. Don't worry. I found five bargains—each less than $20—that'll start you on the path to serenity.

1. Retractable phone cords are compact, coiled cords that give you several extra feet of play. So, even if the phone is across the room, you can still kick up your feet while you connect to the Internet. Targus (www.targus.com) sells an 8-foot version for about $10 (for twice that, you get a luxurious 20 feet) and includes a male-to-male RJ-11 adapter, letting you daisy-chain phone lines. If you tend to stay at hip and high-tech hotels, look for a retractable Ethernet cord instead.

2. Surge protectors are an absolute necessity, especially when traveling abroad. At best, a power surge could erase hours of unsaved work. At worst, it could fry your laptop, rendering it useless. Belkin's MasterCube (www.belkin.com) defends your PC from nasty electrical spikes. And it's not a one-trick pony. The MasterCube also protects your laptop from spikes that might be carried through the current in phone lines.

3. Better surfing. Quick, name the no. 1 nuisance on the Net. Did you say "pop-up ads?" So do most people. If you've spent time hunting for the "close window" button, download Free Surfer (www.emsproject.com). The tiny freeware program sits quietly in your system tray, killing those pesky pop-ups before they appear. Open the Free Surfer window to view a counter in the lower-right corner. It'll give you the satisfaction of knowing exactly how many pop-up ads you didn't have to suffer through. And make use of the Snapshot feature. It offers five presets that save your open browsers, letting you quickly launch them for future use. (I created one with all my favorite news destinations and one with my top travel sites.)

4. Image editing. Can't spare $600 for a beefy image-editing tool such as Photoshop? Bring in The GIMP (www.gimp.org)! The GNU Image Manipulation Program is pretty powerful. A palette of tools lets you paint, erase, and smudge your digital pics, but The GIMP really flexes its muscles with plug-ins. A few words of caution: The GIMP is full of bugs. Every time I tried to use the Clone tool, it unceremoniously shut down. But cut it some slack. It's free. I ran the program in Windows, but I've heard it's more stable in Linux. Finding the right file to download is also confusing. I ended up with a patch that helps The GIMP work with GIF files, but there's no need to follow in my footsteps. You can find the installer page at www.gimp.org/download.html.

5. LED flashlight. Old-school flashlights eat through batteries and burn through bulbs. Their smarter LED siblings (www.zbattery.com) shine brighter and last longer. Princeton makes several small torches as well as a key-chain version. Beat the dead battery blues, and keep one in your glove compartment for road-side emergencies.

Laporte Support

Streaming Audio

You can broadcast your music on the Internet using a couple of services:

- **ShoutCast** (www.shoutcast.com)
- **Live365** (www.live365.com)

Track Your Phone Usage

Patrick Norton

How many minutes have you used this month? I'll show you how to track your phone usage. You might think that the usage tracker feature on your phone is going to be a big help. It will tell you exactly how much time you spent on the phone. As a matter of fact, the phone we used on the show tracks the following:

- Length of the call.
- Total calls. This includes the total number of calls you have on the phone and the total minutes or hours you've used (or, at least, the number used since you last reset the phone).
- Total outgoing time.
- Total incoming time.
- Clear function.
- A "minute minder" feature that beeps every 60 seconds while you're on the phone.

Unfortunately, it doesn't track peak and off-peak minutes. Most people I know have a lot fewer peak or business minutes compared to weekend and night minutes. I have yet to see a phone that breaks down time or rounds up the minutes the way providers bill. (For example, a call that is 2 minutes and 20 seconds becomes 3 minutes.)

Sound frustrating? A writer for *The Wall Street Journal* found that getting minutes remaining from your service provider can be a trying experience. I'm lucky—if I dial ★4 on my phone, I get an announcement that tells me how many off-peak and peak minutes I have left. But it took three listens to figure it out because the computerized voice wasn't clear.

Oddly, it was completely clear when it told me that SprintPCS plans to charge airtime usage every time I press ★4. No wonder the message went on and on after they gave me the information I was looking for.

It could be worse. The same writer for *The Wall Street Journal* discovered that AT&T doesn't even have the information unless you subscribe to certain plans.

Patrick's Tips

Travel Tips for Your Laptop

I take my laptop with me almost everywhere, which means I travel with it frequently. Here are a few things to keep in mind when traveling with a laptop computer.

X-Rays

Every engineer I've asked or have seen quoted in print says that the x-ray machine doesn't hurt your laptop. I've carried laptops through x-ray machines on a couple of continents over the last ten years, and I have yet to have a problem.

Pack 'Em In

Some travelers pack their laptops in suitcases that they check at the gate. This is very risky to the health of the laptop.

I use my laptop for everything. It's always on the plane with me. You never know what might happen to your bags after they're checked.

If you must check your laptop, pack it well. Nestle it in the center of the luggage, padded by clothing. If you can, pack it in a well-padded, hard-shell case designed for computers, such as the Pelican 1490 provided by our friends at Man of Rubber (www.manofrubber.com).

While you're at it, label the box "Mutant Tissue Samples." Marking it as a computer is just asking someone to steal it. Think of your computer as you would a passport on an international trip. Try to keep it with you at all times.

Address: Site of the Night

Community Weblogs

See what happens when longitude and latitude collide. See http://confluence.org.

Kennolyn Camp

Cat Schwartz

I took a wonderful walk down memory lane. I went to the Santa Cruz mountains, where I met my younger cousins, and we went to the very best summer camp in the whole wide world, Kennolyn.

I had not been to Kennolyn in about 13 years. I can distinctly remember saying goodbye to the love of my life, Steven Caldwell. Eventually, I got over my relationship with Steven, but I never got over my passion for spending a few weeks of the summer being dirty from head to toe and sitting around a campfire at night singing camp songs.

I understand that not everyone can get to Kennolyn Camp, but lots of other great camps are available. I believe that it's every kid's right to spend a few weeks at a camp somewhere in the world, to let loose.

Address: Site of the Night

Trapping Hackers

Megan Morrone

Ever wanted to trap a hacker in their own sticky web? The folks who work on the Honeynet Project (www.project.honeynet.org) do just that. The project is a non-profit group of volunteer security professionals deploying fake networks for hackers to attack. They use these honeynets to track blackhat hacker activity and learn how the hackers operate.

The Honeynet Project uses the old roach motel technique. According to Honeynet Project founder Lance Spitzer, Honeynets use firewalls that let any traffic come in, but they don't let it go out. The Honeynet Project is a completely open source organization, and they share all the information they collect with the public. If you want to donate money or computer systems to the project, go to www.project.honeynet.org/funds/ donate.html.

To help you and your family find the camp of your dreams, go to Camp Search (www.campsearch.com). Use its search engine to find a camp that's right for you. To find out what other people think about the camp, visit Epinions (www.epinions.com).

Laporte Support

Nielsen Ratings

How does Nielsen (www.nielsenmedia.com) get its rating for TV and radio? Is Nielsen spying through a VCR?

Nielsen isn't spying on anyone who hasn't given consent. Nielsen uses an old polling practice called sampling. Using math, you can figure out how many people you need to query for a survey, without asking everyone in the population. For example (this example isn't accurate—it's merely used to explain sampling), to poll a group of 100,000 people, you can figure that you need to ask a sample group of only 5,000 people within the 100,000 people to get relatively accurate results.

Nielsen finds people who are willing to be a part of the sample. They are given boxes that attach to their TV to track their viewing habits. The results are sent through the Internet to Nielsen, which uses the data to get ratings.

As for ratings, a viewer sent this email:

> "The Arbitron (www.arbitron.com) company sends out diaries to each member of a selected family. You fill out the diary with the stations you've listened to and the times you listened. The diary usually runs for a one-week period."

Nielsen can't get any information from your VCR. Your VCR isn't connected to the Internet, and it doesn't transmit a broadcast signal—only the signal to your TV.

Become a Laptop DJ

James Kim and Greg Melton

Q: I want to become a laptop DJ and mix my own music or MP3s and WAVs I've downloaded. I've heard of programs such as Virtual Turntables, but I can't seem to find them.

A: Several programs allow you to mix your music files. Most of them attempt to simulate real turntables and mixers by adding key DJ'ing elements, such as pitch control, cue points, and even scratching. Of course, there's nothing like a couple of Technics, a mixer, and some dope vinyl.

The following programs, however, are reasonable digital substitutes and allow anybody with the desire—and a decent collection of MP3s—to become a DJ. Best of all, the only thing you need to bring to the party is a laptop.

The easiest way is to download a shareware program called Virtual Turntables, by Carrot Innovations (www.carrotinnovations.com). Modeled after Panasonic CD-decks, the robust interface comes complete with mouse-controlled jog dials and a crossfader.

Don't be fooled by its simplicity. Virtual Turntables allows real-time mixing, volume and pitch control, play lists with AutoDJ functionality, and a number of user-definable special effects, such as scratching and backspins. Perhaps its coolest feature is the automatic pitch-matching system, which helps calculate a track's beats per minute (BPM).

This powerful program was the first of its kind. With a library of MP3s (you can also rip tracks from CDs) and a little practice, you can tear up any dance floor. Furthermore, Virtual Turntables supports Winamp plug-ins. This program is free to try and $42 to keep.

If you want the best MP3 mixing software available, look no further than PCDJ Red (http://pcdj.com/Products/Red.asp), from a company called Visiosonic. It's loaded with features aimed at professionals. These include exact cueing to a fraction of a millisecond, instant start, back cueing, 20 independent cue memories per track, ripping, recording, looping, turntable brake, automatic pitch matching, and auto-BPM detection. The interface is a DJ's fantasy, featuring a host of tweakable controls and a convenient "record bag." Of course, the software will set you back about $200.

Don't have the cash? Check out Visiosonic's PCDJ Silver (http://pcdj.com/Products/Silver.asp). It lets you set two cue points per track and makes beat matching a breeze with an 8% pitch control on each player. It's basically the bare-bones version of PCDJ Red. Best of all, it's free.

In addition, Visiosonic has a product called PCDJ Blue (http://pcdj.com/Products/blue.asp). It costs about $100, and is a beefed-up version of PCDJ Silver and a stripped-down version of PCDJ Red.

Besides a large hard drive (to hold all your music), a fast system and two sound cards are necessities for optimal functionality (one sound card for master sound, the other for headphone cueing). The PCDJ Red requires a 350MHz Pentium II or AMD Athlon, 64MB RAM, and a DirectX-supported sound card.

Web Tips

Fix the Alt+Enter Problem

Sometimes the Alt+Enter shortcut for wrapping domain names mysteriously stops working. Here's how to fix it:

1. In Internet Explorer, click on the Tools menu, select Internet Options, and click the Content tab.

2. Click Auto Complete and check Web Addresses.

Eavesdropping on the Womb

Megan Morrone

The first milestone in my pregnancy was hearing the baby's heartbeat at my doctor's office. It was music. It was art. It was beautiful. And as with any good drug, I wanted more. I found cheap versions of the fetal doppler that doctors use and tested them all in my second trimester. The later you are in your pregnancy, the more likely you are to hear heartbeat sounds.

Consult your doctor before you use any of these devices:

- **Munchkins' Wombsong** (http://store.babycenter.com). It's tough to find the heartbeat with this device, but you can hear other sounds. These sounds might be your digestion, or they might be your baby's movement. I prefer to think they're the latter. Your doctor probably used a gel to amplify the sounds of your baby, but don't try this with the Wombsong: It will destroy the microphone.

  The Wombsong (about $50) also lets you play music or talk to your baby through a microphone. It comes with headphones and a Mozart CD. Doctors say the best time to start playing music for your baby is the third trimester.

- **BébéSounds Prenatal Heart Listener** (www.unisar.com). I never managed to find a heartbeat with the BébéSounds device (about $40).

  I did find other soothing sounds with this device. The controls are easy to use, which prevents you from blowing out your eardrums every time you move the amplifier. BébéSounds also comes with two headphones.

- **BabyBeat Doppler** (www.babybeat.com). These fetal dopplers (about $500 or $30 per month) are what the doctors use, which explains the high price. Finding and listening to the heartbeat is very cool, but the novelty wears off pretty quickly. Plus, when you find the heartbeat once and then have trouble finding it again, you're bound to get nervous.

  The BabyBeat has speakers in addition to a headphone jack, so you can entertain a whole room with your baby's sounds.

- **BabyBeat Display Doppler** (www.babybeat.com). The only difference with this BabyBeat device (about $625 or $49 per month) is that it measures and displays your baby's heartbeat. Don't be afraid if the heart rate seems abnormally low. Quite a few times, I picked up my own heartbeat instead of the baby's.

  Both BabyBeat devices come with an aloe vera ultrasound cream that helps magnify the sound waves.

Windows Tips

Address: Site of the Night

Population Clock

The U.S. Population Clock calculates the gradual rise and fall of the total U.S. population—person by person, second by second. See www.census.gov/cgi-bin/popclock.

Increase Type Size

Make Microsoft Word easier on your eyes. But remember that this doesn't affect your printouts:

1. Click View from the toolbar and then click Zoom.

2. Select 200%.

Games for Girls and Boys

Megan Morrone

Here are three popular games for kids:

- **Zoombinis**, The Learning Company (www.zoombinis.com)
- **Harry Potter and the Chamber of Secrets**, Electronic Arts (www.ea.com)
- **SpongeBob SquarePants**, THQ (www.thq.com)

John Weston reviews games for Gamers.com. These are the games he thinks kids like:

- **The Sonic Mega Collection**, GameCube
- **Sonic Adventure 2 Battle**, GameCube
- **Animal Crossing**, GameCube
- **Star Fox Dinosaur Planet**, GameCube
- **Pikmin**, GameCube

Laporte Support

Gig for the Tyke

A viewer wants to buy an Apple PowerBook for his 20-month-old child to run educational software. The iBook he's looking at has 512MB of RAM, and Apple wants another $300 to upgrade it to 1GB of RAM. Is it worth it?

A PowerBook is a sophisticated piece of technology for a 20-month-old, but if you're willing to pay the money, more power to you. As for the RAM, educational software doesn't demand much in resources. You're fine with 512MB of RAM.

If your 20-month-old plans to do video editing, digital art, or anything that involves large files, you'll want the 1GB of RAM. You don't have to buy your RAM from Apple, however, you can buy it at a computer store.

You might want to consider paying a technician to install the RAM, because laptop RAM is a bit trickier to install than is desktop RAM. However, it's easy to do it on your own.

Download of the Day

Labor Day 1.0

Megan Morrone

As soon as the world learned I was pregnant, I started getting emails from friends recommending Labor Day. It's a free contraction timer program solely for OS X. It was the perfect recommendation. Not only is it for pregnant women, but it's for my favorite operating system.

If Then Software's (www.ifthensoft.com) Labor Day helps you time the length of your contractions, as well as the time between them. When you feel the first sensation, click the Begin Timing button. When the contraction stops, click End Contraction. When one begins again, click Start Contraction. The program creates a chart that you can easily email to your doctor or anyone else.

When I told Leo about this download, he said he wrote a similar program in HyperCard (www.apple.com/hypercard) before his daughter was born. It didn't work because his wife's contractions were so irregular. Plus, he thinks that timing contractions is just busywork to keep one's mind off all that pain.

Either way, Labor Day is a handy program, but don't forget to have a stopwatch for backup. Also, you should probably install this program on a PowerBook or an iBook; I don't think you want to lug your desktop to the hospital.

Labor Day 1.0 is available at www.macupdate.com. Contraction Timer 2.12 is a similar program for Palm (www.palmgear.com). If you use Windows, try Cindi's Contraction Timer (www.simtel.net).

Best Camcorders for Less Than $800

James Kim

Prices for digital camcorders (both MiniDV and Digital8) are coming down. We looked at five camcorders selling for less than $800 and rated them based on optics and video quality (lens, zoom, and image stabilization), design and ease of use, and extra features.

Don't forget the older Digital8 format. It's a bona fide alternative if you're looking for affordable digital video. One of our top five camcorders is a top-of-the-line Digital8 camera available for $700.

Sony DCR-TRV18

The TRV18 is Sony's most affordable MiniDV camcorder at $800, but it includes most of the features you'll find in more expensive models. It looks good, it feels good, and it's very easy to operate (www.sony.com).

A quality 10x optical Carl Zeiss lens provides the best video quality in this roundup.

Sony includes an 8MB MemoryStick for capturing 640×480 stills or short MPEG movies, and the list of extra features (such as digital effects and night shot) goes on and on. This is a great camera for beginners and advanced users who want a compact secondary camera.

Canon ZR45MC

Canon raised the bar and lowered the price on consumer digital video cameras. Canon's $700 ZR45 combines a unique and compact body design with excellent optics and a powerful 18x optical zoom for a great "on-the-go" MiniDV camcorder (www.canon.com/cusa/).

The camera has large and easy-to-operate buttons. The zoom mechanism could be better. The ZR45MC ships with an 8MB MMC memory card (also compatible with SD), so you can shoot low-quality still photos directly to the card. We recommend the ZR45MC for its size, impressive zoom, and full set of features.

Panasonic PV-DV102

Panasonic's newest inexpensive DV camera is chock-full of features, but are they worth it? The DV102 might not have the best lens or the prettiest design, but it delivers good video quality for $700. However, the video from the 700x digital zoom is pixilated beyond recognition (www.panasonic.com).

You can also shoot still images up to an interpolated 1280×960, or shoot compressed MPEG movies, which are stored on an SD or MMC memory card (not included). Throw in some digital effects, a zooming microphone, and built-in light, and it's a solid MiniDV camcorder.

The Canon is probably a better choice for the same price.

JVC GRDVL-120U

The JVC 120U is a little rough around the edges, but if you want a MiniDV for less than $600, this is it (www.jvc.com).

The largest MiniDV camera in this roundup, the JVC 120U deserves consideration for its rock-bottom price. Although its interface needs work (the power switch is difficult to turn), the 16x optical zoom and decent video quality should suffice for those who need a utilitarian camera.

There's no memory card slot to store still pictures, but you get a night shot feature, some basic digital effects, and limited manual control. The JVC is best for parents who want their child to get started on the digital video path.

Sony DCR-TRV340

The TRV340 is one of the most advanced high-end Digital8 camcorders on the market. It has a $700 price tag and features galore, including a 25x optical zoom, night shot, and a range of manual features. The camera is best for novices and users who don't necessarily value size (www.sony.com).

Best Camcorders for Less Than $800 (continued)

Comparison Chart

Camcorder	Canon ZR45MC	JVC GRDVL-120U	Panasonic PV-DV102	Sony DCR-TRV18	Sony DCR-TRV340*
Price	$699	$599	$699	$799	$699
Optical Zoom	18x	16x	10x	10x	25x
Digital Zoom	360x	700x	700x	120x	700x
LCD	2.5-inch	2.5-inch	2.5-inch	2.5-inch	2.5-inch
Optical Viewfinder	Color	Black and white	Black and white	Color, black and white	Storage card
Yes	No	Yes	Yes	Yes	Memory
SD/MMC (included)	—	SD/MMC	Memory Stick (included)	Memory Stick (included)	Weight
Weight	1.1 pounds	1.4 pounds	1.3 pounds	1.4 pounds	2 pounds

*Digital8

Performance Chart

Performance ratings are based on a scale of 1 to 5, with 5 being the highest possible score.

Camcorder	Canon ZR45MC	JVC GRDVL-120U	Panasonic PV-DV102	Sony DCR-TRV18	Sony DCR-TRV340*
Video Quality	4	2	3	5	4
Interface/Design	4	3	4	5	4
Ease of use	5	3	4	5	4
Features	4	2	3	4	4
Value	4	4	3	4	4
Overall score	4	3	3	5	4

*Digital8

Recycle Your Old Computer

Steve Wyatt and Michelle VonWald

More than two million PCs are thrown into landfills each month, and in five years that will reach five million. Computer recycling is a better option.

Your PC's parts are probably not worth saving. Most will be useless in a newer machine. Instead, donate your intact computer and peripherals to a nonprofit recycling organization. Even if you can't use the stuff, thousands of schools, families, and nonprofit educational programs can. You can probably purchase a computer that's twice as powerful for less than half the cost of your two-year old machine. The money you save in taxes with a charitable tax-deductible receipt might pay for the new PC.

Three types of programs will take your computer:

- **Nonprofit charitable programs.** The Computer Recycling Center (www.crc.org) is one example. It reuses parts, and its computers and education program donates systems to schools and community programs. There are locations throughout North America. Local schools, churches, and community programs can usually give you a tax-deductible thank-you letter. Sometimes they have levels of machines they will accept and nothing less. They might not be capable of taking what they can't use.

- **State government websites.** Go to your state government website and look for publications listing places and programs in your state. Look at the website of your state Environmental Protection Agency office.

- **Federal agencies.** The federal government has several agencies that list information for recycling electronic products. The National Safety Council and the EPA host a conference each year focusing on electronic product recovery. National and international companies and organizations with strong commitments to recycling and reuse are listed as participants by these agencies.

What to Donate

Erase your personal files, but leave the programs. Tape the software licenses to the case. Here's what most places will take:

- Clean keyboards. (Use spray-on, wipe-off cleansers if yours is dirty.)
- Working VGA or SVGA color monitors.
- Inkjets and late-model laser printers.
- Software, packaged and sealed.

Here's where to donate your computer gear:

- **Computer Recycling Center**, San Francisco/Northern California, (www.crc.org)
- **Resources for Parents, Educators, and Publishers National Directory of Computer Recycling Programs** (www.microweb.com/pepsite/Recycle/recycle_index.html)
- **Share the Technology**, national (www.sharetechnology.org)
- **BBB Wise Giving Alliance**, for help choosing a charity (www.give.org)
- **National Cristina Foundation** (www.cristina.org)
- **A list of other donation programs** (www.cascade-assets.com/charity/nationaldonation.htm)

Address: **Site of the Night**

Baby Names Index

Megan Morrone

Everyone had an opinion about what to name our baby girl. We had some names in mind, but were always ready to hear suggestions. The Social Security Administration website (www.ssa.gov/OACT/babynames) tracks the popularity of names by year or by state. You can even view the most popular American names all the way back to the 1800s.

Who Needs Paper?

Roger Chang

You can see your bills, bank statements, documents, and webpages on your computer screen. So why are you still printing all that stuff? Here are some simple ways to reduce the amount of paper you use.

Online Banking and Bill Pay

Most large banks offer some sort of electronic bill pay. You tell the bank what bills you want to pay (power, water, heat, credit cards) and when. When the time comes, the bank pays the appropriate business or company with funds from your checking account. It saves time, worry, and, most important, paper. If your bank doesn't offer the service, consider Yahoo! Bill Pay (finance.yahoo.com/bp).

Email

Why are you still mailing letters, unofficial documents, and pamphlets? Email whenever possible. It's faster, it's cheaper, and uses a lot less paper.

Electronic Filing Cabinet

Unless it's your tax return or an official document, you can get by with saving most documents electronically. Store your files on your PC, or burn them to CD (or a similar archival medium) for backup. Still stuck on floppies? One 3.5-inch 1.44MB floppy disk can hold the equivalent of 750 sheets of paper. That's a stack of paper 5 inches tall.

Print Smart

Saving paper isn't about not printing. It's about reducing the amount of paper you use when you do print. Many of you print documents, read them over, and make changes on your screen. Stop! Cut back on the number of forests felled for printer paper by editing onscreen and using the spell- and grammar-checking features in your word processor before you print. If you absolutely need to print a draft, use scrap paper. When both sides of the scrap paper are filled, throw it in the recycling bin.

Adjust your margins and print setup options to eliminate blank spaces on the page. This also keeps you from printing blank pages at the beginning or end of a print job. Put any blank pieces of paper back in the paper tray.

April

18

Talkback

Something to Hide?

Dave Roos

In the back of every serious web surfer's mind is the nagging fear that one day, when he least expects it, his brief (or not so brief) online improprieties will come back and bite him. Perhaps his girlfriend will stumble onto a forgotten stash deep within the C: drive, or his mom will browse through some suspicious cookies and find a digital paper trail that would make Pete Townshend blush.

Is there anything on your hard drive that could get you into trouble? Not necessarily with the police, heaven forbid, but with family members, room-mates, significant others, etc.

42% No

58% Yes

Yes 58%

No 42%

Patrick-Proof Notebooks

Patrick Norton

Are rugged notebooks "Patrick-proof?" If you're thinking a direct hit from a 12-pound sledgehammer to the middle of the screen, I think the answer would be a decided "no"— even with a Mil-Spec-801-F certified notebook. (And to all you supergeeks out there thinking, "Which part of 801-F?" chill out. I don't know the spec numbers for functional shock. Or for humidity, salt flog, altitude, or acidic atmosphere! You can look 'em up at www.environlab.com/mil_Std_810.htm.)

The notebooks I looked at call themselves rugged, but they aren't designed for sledge-hammer-type abuse. A 10-inch drop while running? Okay. A sledgehammer to the screen or keyboard? Not any notebook I've seen.

I've broken only one notebook: a Gateway that slipped from my grip and tumbled down a flight of concrete stairs. I'm sure the iTronix GoBook II (1.8GHz Mobile Pentium 4 processor; $4,845, www.itronix.com) or the Panasonic Toughbook CF-28 (1GHz Pentium III-M processor; $3,700, www.panasonic.com) would've survived that awful 4-foot fall to the first step, as well as the end-over-end bouncing down the concrete stairwell and the landing on the concrete floor. These notebooks are heavily armored, especially around the corners.

That's the idea of a ruggedized notebook. It's designed to survive things that would kill other notebooks. They're the Hummers of portable computing—they're big, heavy, and heavily reinforced. They have rubber flaps to plug every port and keyboards that shed water. The most serious ruggedized notebooks are certified under Mil-Spec-801-F, a collection of military standards for environmental testing.

The GoBook II and Toughbook CF-28 claim to meet military specifications. I'm not sure if that means they're certified by the military to meet that specification. The spec says a notebook must be capable of surviving a variety of situations, such as drops onto plywood over concrete, rain, sandstorms, and temperature extremes. As with other good technical specs, I found the tests to be random, and the extremes often varied depending on whether the notebook was on or off.

But if I ever want a computer that can survive being steam-cleaned after a biohazard threat, I know where to look for the spec.

Does my one major notebook accident make me a candidate for either of these 8-pound (minimum) wonders? I don't think so, and I'm an ultraportable kind o' geek. I haven't carried a computer that weighed more than 5 pounds in years.

If you compute in serious places—the deserts of Iraq or your average construction site, for example—or if you have 150 service crews getting their information over notebooks that have to survive a van full of parts and tools, ruggedized notebooks start to look attractive.

Megan's Tips

Safely Power Down

Using the power button to turn off your computer is not healthy for your PC. Here's a better way:

1. Right-click on the Desktop and choose Properties.
2. Select the Screen Savers tab and click Power.
3. Click the Advanced tab.

In Windows XP, you can configure your PC to shut down with the power button.

Healthy Dose of Sites

Jessica Corbin

All right, my lovely 'Savers, it's time to pump you up! Normally we just pump you up on the latest technologies. But I want to tell you about some very effective websites that help you get jazzed and savvy about your health.

Before you begin any workout program, consult a physician. After you see your doc, you should record your weight, inches, and body mass index (BMI).

Your BMI is calculated by dividing your weight by your height, and it will tell you if your health is at risk. There's a thorough explanation and BMI calculator at RealAge (www.realage.com). BMI calculators are all over the web, but RealAge has other assessment tools you can use to get further into your newly found commitment to health.

Now it's time to put your boo-tay into action! FreeTrainers.com gives you a great workout catered to your profile and goals. You can have your workouts customized for a gym or your home. I recommend trying the free option and spending the money if you find it's working for you. If you want to work out in the privacy of your home, visit Half.com and purchase workout videos for really cheap.

Eating Right

Even though you're working out, you still need to watch what you eat. Don't rationalize another piece of cheesecake because you worked out on the stair-climber for 20 minutes. For nutritional guidance, go to Ask the Dietitian (www.dietitian.com). It has an extensive index of nutrition topics and questions answered by a registered dietitian.

Food logs

I think a food log is the best way to become aware of what you're consuming. A great log can be found at FitDay.com. This is an online diet and fitness journal that tallies your calories, carbs, fat, and protein. It even breaks down what you've eaten and converts the results into a pie chart.

To tabulate your food intake, go to FITteen.com. It's intended for teens, but anyone can use its log. Print out a bunch, keep them in a journal, and watch your progress unfold.

Taking the food log one step further, you can track your calories, sugars, fat, protein, and more by using a program on CalorieKing.com. I downloaded onto my Palm a program that has a food database of 20,000 items! No matter where I go—or what I eat—I can always keep tabs with a program like this.

More Health-Enhancing Sites

Here are a few other sites that will support your health endeavors:

- **Thinkarete.com** is a staple for me. It helps me stay focused and motivated to take care of myself and lead an energetic and positive life.

- **AllStarHealth.com** has the best prices for vitamins and a good selection.

- **Active.com** is a registration database where you can find sporting events in your area, such as 5K runs, triathlons, baseball tournaments, and of course bowling scrambles.

I'm giving you no excuses to start taking care of your health! Everything is free, or at the very least has a free trial and a minimal upgrade charge. All you need is access to the Internet and a willingness to try.

Address: Site of the Night

Sheep Game

Herd your virtual flock using the fun Flash game Sheep Game, at www.electrogamer.com.

Government Goodies

Cat Schwartz

The U.S. government's well-designed and totally functioning website FirstGov (www.firstgov.gov) is the place to go for information about the government, both state and federal. It's awesome. Martin Sargent likes it so much that he wants to rename it FirstGov.LUV.

This site amazes me. You can get so much stuff done. Check on your immigration case, apply for Social Security or a government job, change your address, and even pay your parking tickets. It has an information section for businesses that need answers to common questions. You can also download forms, find contact information for any government agency, and find links to every .gov site.

For example, start at www.ssa.gov/top10.html if you want to apply for Social Security benefits. Click the first link on the page to go to the instruction page. Fill out the appropriate forms.

Renewing your driver's license is just as easy. Go to www.firstgov.com/Topics/Motor_Vehicles.shtml, pick your state, find a link to your state's online service, and follow the instructions. This is also where you'll find the option to pay your parking tickets online.

Are you a little low on funds? Before heading out to look for a second job, find out if the government owes you money. FirstGov provides links (www.firstgov.gov/Citizen/Topics/Money_Owed.shtml) where you can see if you have assets waiting for you. These assets could come from failed banks, credit unions, pension funds, mortgage refunds, tax refunds, and unclaimed property.

Download of the Day

Hotbidz 1.0

Sarah Lane

Whether you've been using eBay for years or you're just starting out, Hotbidz 1.0 (www.code9software.com) will give you an idea of what stuff sells for. Start the bidding too high, and you won't get any bites. Start it too low, and you won't get maximum cash. And I know you want the cash!

You can search through Hot Items (categories and subcategories), although not all categories are available in the demo version. However, you can choose to search through all of the categories one at a time by typing in the category number for each. With the demo version, you get one page of results. With the full version, you get unlimited results.

I did a few searches just to find out what I could get for various things in my house:

- Epson Stylus C82 Printer, 18 bids at $66.
- Wingback chair with ottoman: five bids at $36 (darn).
- X-Box, anywhere between $50 to $150: depending on the condition.

It's not for every eBay lurker, but if you're planning to sell, why not see which bids have already been successful?

Have fun, and happy selling.

Moving Made Simple

Cat Schwartz

Living in a big city has many perks, like walking down the block to eat out, easily catching a late-night movie, taking the bus to work, and constant entertainment nearby.

The only issue I've found with all of these is the cost. Eating out every night, catching a flick, going to bars and clubs...it all added up for me and left me with credit card bills and no money. When worse came to worse, my parents gave me a welcoming pat on the back and helped me move back home.

That's right. I am now a statistic that's also a sign of these tough times. I'm 25, single, working, and living back at the house I swore never to live in again. It's not half-bad.

Although my parents made it easy for me to move back, the whole process has to be one of the most grueling I've ever encountered. To help alleviate some of the stress around completing the move, I've found the ultimate resource on the web for moving at Moving.com (www.moving.com).

The most useful tool on Moving.com changes your address. Once you've signed up with your old address and new address, you're logged in as a user. For $1.50, the site registers your address change with the Postal Service.

You can even change various utilities and services. Choose from a list, including gas, cable, banks, and phone. Enter in your account information and it's done. It's so easy! If you do decide to use this service, I would suggest double-checking to make sure the requests were completed.

If you're wondering about demographic information in the area you're moving to, the site has a very useful tool under the Neighborhood tab. Here, you can enter in the ZIP code of your new abode, and the site charts out such information as crime rates, male-to-female ratio, age average, cost of living, and more.

Use the site to find a real estate agent, find a mortgage and calculate your payments, find cool entertainment in your new 'hood, and even find where to store the stuff that won't fit in your new house.

So if you're moving, I definitely suggest you visit this site to ease your relocation woes.

Personal Screen Saver

Greg Melton

In the past it was darn near impossible to create a personal screen saver using your own photo collection. You had to track down a third-party application and sloppily piece together your pictures. The engineers at Microsoft must have realized they hated third-party applications and decided enough was enough. You can take the pictures stored in your My Pictures folder and display them in random order as a screen saver in XP.

To make a personal screen saver in XP, follow these directions:

1. Right-click an empty spot on your desktop and choose Properties.

2. Click the Screen Saver tab inside the Display Properties dialog.

3. In the Screen Saver pull-down menu, choose My Pictures Slideshow.

4. Underneath the Screen Saver pull-down menu, adjust the time of inactivity before Windows will initiate your screen saver.

5. Click Settings to make additional adjustments. You'll be able to adjust transition effects between pictures, how frequently they change, what size the pictures should be, and more.

6. Click OK when you're done tweaking the settings adjustments.

7. Click the Preview button to see what your screen saver looks like.

8. If everything is to your liking, click Apply.

Speed School

Patrick Norton and Yoshi DeHerrera

It's not a pretty sight to see grown men drool. But that's exactly what happens when you let two card-carrying car freaks get within 5 feet of a cherry-red Formula Dodge racer. The roar of the engine, the smell of the tires, the feel of the wheel in your hands....

As the bad boys of *The Screen Savers*, we headed south to take a crash course (pun obviously intended) at the world-famous Skip Barber Racing School (www.skipbarber.com) at the Mazda Raceway at Laguna Seca.

Computer Car

At each Skip Barber school (there are 20), one special racer is designated the "computer car." This vehicle is equipped with a state-of-the-art software package called the Pi Video Indexed Data System (Pi VIDS). The Pi VIDS System (www.piresearch.com) collects two crucial pieces of data:

- Video footage of the driver in the cockpit.
- Specific vehicle information, such as how much pressure the driver applies to the brake pedal and how many G forces are created during turns.

The two forms of data are played back on a synchronous display. Instructors and students study the results to determine whether a particular head movement contributes to slow shift time or whether the driver has a habit of picking his nose while passing.

Download of the Day

Print Window

Back in ye olde days of Mac OS 9 and earlier, it was easy to print Finder windows. You simply chose Print Window from the File menu. For some reason this feature doesn't exists in OS X. Scott from SearchWare Solutions (www.swssoftware.com) created a small utility that makes printing Finder windows easy again.

Joshua's Tips

Online Car Resources

Whenever my Mercedes Benz SLK600 or Shelby Cobra needs repairing, you can literally hear the local auto mechanics drooling and aching for a chance to gouge me for hundreds and hundreds of dollars. It's not that tough to work on your car—all you gotta do is learn where to look for the answers.

- **Autos.msn.com** has news, prices, classified ads, and more.
- **Alldatadiy.com** is a mere $25 per year, per vehicle. You get factory recall and technical service bulletins, illustrated diagnosis and repair procedures, OEM part numbers, diagnostic charts and trouble codes, component locations and diagrams, factory maintenance schedules, and so on.
- **Alldata.com** also has a page you can check for factory recall and technical service bulletins. It's free, so you don't have to spend a dime. Note: Manufacturers such as BMW, Honda, and others do not allow this service.
- **Car Talk** (www.cartalk.com) is a wonderful site, jam-packed with articles about automobile repair, from general repair guides to specific make and model questions.
- Visit **Helminc.com** to buy the factory shop manuals that your mechanic uses: Ford, GM, Honda, Isuzu, Suzuki, and KIA. For other manuals, just search on Google.

Buying and Selling

- To determine the value of a car you're selling or buying, don't forget these old favorites: Kelley Blue Book (www.kbb.com) and AutoTrader (www.autotrader.com).
- Check your local newspaper classifieds, or visit AutoTrader (www.autotrader.com) and TraderOnline (www.traderonline.com).

Do Cell Phones and Gas Stations Mix?

Patrick Norton

Before you start to worry about talking on the cell phone while loading up on unleaded, don't panic. The Petroleum Equipment Institute (PEI) has documented "over 150 refueling fires that appear to be caused by a discharge of static electricity." They estimate that Americans pump gas into vehicles between 16 billion and 18 billion times per year without incident. The concerns over static? A "sharp increase of incidents that could not be attributed to a running engine or cigarette smoking, the leading known causes of such fires."

From every source we consulted by phone and online, there appear to be no confirmed incidents of cell phones starting fires while refueling. (I wonder if that's because many gas stations post signs banning the use of cell phones while refueling.)

According to the Society of Petroleum Engineers, the American Petroleum Institute (API) has no confirmed reports of static electricity incidents in the United States or elsewhere caused by using cell phones while fueling.

Hang It Up While You Fill 'Er Up

The API suggests that it is a good safety practice "to simply avoid being distracted by doing other things, such as talking on the cell phone" while refueling.

The Naval Safety Center consulted with the National Fire Protection Association to get its answers on cell phones and refueling. It points out that cell phones simply aren't designed "for use in an environment where an ignitable atmosphere might exist." Still, the PEI and the API are much more concerned about static electricity while refueling your car. The basic rules? The PEI's Stop Static program says these are the keys:

- Turn off the car's engine.
- Don't smoke.
- Never re-enter your vehicle while the car is fueling.

That last one? Static buildup on cool, dry days, most likely caused by clothes slipping across car seats, is the prime suspect in 150 gas fires while refueling. When you get out of the car on a crisp October morning to fill the tank, stay out of the car until it's full.

Patrick's Tips

Recycle Your Cell Phone

Can you recycle a cell phone? You can, and you should. Generally, phones are refurbished, reused, or ground up so that valuable metals can be extracted and recycled.

Your cell phone provider probably prefers that you drop off your phone at any cell phone retail location. The provider will collect the phone and recycle it. Unfortunately, word on the street is that many places simply trash the phone. Ask the store where and how it recycles it. If they don't have a good answer, go somewhere else.

Earth 911 (www.earth911.org) is a great online resource that lists local places where you can drop off your phone for recycling, along with nationwide charities that either redistribute your phone or turn it over to raise funds. Earth 911 even has information on recycling your PC.

If you have rechargeable batteries that you want to recycle, go to the Rechargeable Battery Recycling Corporation (www.rbrc.org).

Web Tips

Fill Out Forms

Save time when filling out forms on the web. Instead of retyping the same word, highlight the word and drag it where you want it to go.

Pay Bills Online

Cat Schwartz

At least four bills show up in my mailbox each month. I used to put all my bills in a pile, get out my checkbook, pay the bill, mail it, and file the transaction information for my records. Then Leo turned me on to Paytrust (www.paytrust.com).

I love Paytrust. Just sign up for an account, pay a small monthly fee, and the service handles all your payments. It offers several levels of service:

- Complete Bill Management lets you receive, review, pay, and organize your bills through a simple online interface. (Receiving a bill and paying a bill are separate transactions.)

- Plan 1 costs $4.95 per month and charges $0.50 per transaction

- Plan 2 costs $12.95 per month for 30 free transactions. After that, it's $0.50 for each additional transaction.

- Bill Pay Plus is $2.95 per month and $0.50 per payment. You can make payments with an online checkbook and use Paytrust's SmartBalance and reporting features.

- Paytrust Small Business Edition is $19.95 per month and $0.75 cents per payment.

Many banks offer online bill-payment service, but Paytrust is better. Here are a few benefits:

- With the bank's system, bills are still sent to your address. With Paytrust, you no longer deal with paper! Your bills are directly mailed to Paytrust and scanned into your Paytrust file. You can access your file any time and can schedule automatic deductions.

- You're always aware of what's going on with your account, regardless of when you visit the Paytrust site. Paytrust emails you when bills arrive, when payments are made, and when a bill is about to be overdue.

- Great customer service.

- You're not limited to services that accept only online payments. The "pay anyone" features lets you send a check to anyone, such as the babysitter.

- Paytrust can integrate with Quicken and Microsoft Money and Excel.

Your financial records are available online for a year, and you can opt to receive a CD-ROM with all your transaction records at the end of each year. That's great for doing your taxes!

If you still can't live without a paper copy, you can receive your bills at home and still use Paytrust. Just sign up for a plan that suits your needs.

If you're ready to jump into online bill payment, try Paytrust. Leo and I both love it.

Laporte Support

Track Your Cash

Banks offering online banking give you free money-management software. You can also download simple templates for your spreadsheet program, such as Microsoft Excel, to manage your finances. These programs aren't sophisticated, but they do the trick for many folks:

- **AceMoney** (www.mechcad.net/products/acemoney/) is an inexpensive $20 shareware option. The free trial has no limitations, but it'll nag you.

- **Checkbook for Excel** (www.djicomputer.com/Checkbook.htm) has a 30-day free trial. Pay $15 to keep it.

- If you need more, download **Moneydance** (http://moneydance.com). The shareware is $30, it's free of ads, and you can use it free for up to 100 transactions. Moneydance works on all platforms.

- If you have your own website with PHP and MySQL installed, you can use a free web-based finance program called **Personal Finance 1.0** (http://crudmuffin.com/downloads.php).

Tech Support Survival Guide

Patrick Norton

It's great being computer-savvy. Sometimes you're the envy of your family and friends. But it also means that everyone asks you for help.

Top Tips

Here are the most frequent computer situations I'm asked about. The solutions are pretty basic, but when you're bombarded with questions, it's easy to get frazzled and lose focus.

- Save all the boxes. If you need to send the computer out for repair or need to return it, you'll need all the original bits, pieces, cardboard, and foam. Pack up everything and hide 'em so Dad doesn't pitch 'em or your sister doesn't use 'em to flame that picture of her ex.

- "It doesn't work," "It won't turn on," or "I can't hear sound":
  - Make sure everything is plugged in.
  - Check the power. Is there a light switch that shuts off the outlet?
  - Check the speaker volume.
  - Check the cables. If they're color-coded, make sure the cable's colors match the colors of the plugs.
  - After you've checked the cables, have somebody else check the cables.

- Read the manual. I'm an alpha geek, and you have no idea how much it hurts me to say, "Read the manual."

- Connect the digital camera. If you plug the camera into your PC/Mac via a USB or FireWire cable, or if you plug a digital still camera's memory into a USB/ FireWire adapter, you might need drivers and software that either came in the box or need to be downloaded over the Internet. Check the manual. Lots of cameras need their drivers and software loaded first to run properly.

- When installing hardware, don't rush in and tear up your PC. Here's a simple rule of thumb: If you've never done it, read up before you start pulling things out of your PC. Ask the nearest geek, or go to our website and read an article. Or read the manual. Or, and this really pains me to say it, take it to a computer store and pay them to install it. And back up your data.

- Can't connect to the Internet? Is the modem plugged into the wall? Quit snickering, this happens. If it's plugged in, is someone on the other line calling Aunt Gertie? Have you set up an account with an Internet service provider? Have you loaded your PPPoE or other software to make the cable or DSL modem work?

- Put the mouse on the Start button and click. It's a metaphor, darn it. Put the mouse on the table or desktop. Move it around. Notice the little white squiggle on the screen? That's the pointer. The mouse moves the pointer. Hover the pointer over something on the screen. Quickly click the button (or the left button if you have more than one button on your mouse) twice, and watch the fun.

Jessica's Tips

Post codes

If your PC beeps, you're probably getting a post code. Your computer uses beeps to tell you that there might be a hardware problem. Check your manual to find out what the codes mean.

Find Health Sites You Can Trust

Call for Help **Staff**

No website has a Ph.D. or license to practice medicine, yet we're all tempted to go online to try to fix whatever's ailing us. Ingrid Driscoll, project manager for the Internet Services Group at Kaiser Permanente (www.kp.org), tells you how to use common-sense criteria and buyer-beware scrutiny to determine which health sites you can trust. She also has some guidelines on how to use them.

Here are a few things to look for as you try to separate sites with good information from those with an agenda:

- The site must have an About Us section.
- The site should disclose its editorial policy. Articles should be sourced and dated.
- Don't trust sites that ask for too much personal information. If you decide to share any of your personal information, make sure the site has a solid privacy policy.
- Is a site focused on diagnosing illness? Never use websites for self-diagnosis. Online medical information should be used to help you formulate questions to ask your doctor.
- Buyer beware. If the site focuses on selling drugs and herbal remedies, watch out.

Also, sites sponsored by drug companies aren't necessarily bad. For example, OncoLink (http://oncolink.com) is a great cancer resource sponsored by Bristol-Myers Squibb.

Sites You Can Trust

When you need information about an illness, you probably don't want to spend a ton of time researching websites. Here are a couple resources that have done all the legwork for you:

- **Healthfinder** (www.healthfinder.gov). The U.S. Department of Health and Human Services and other federal agencies developed Healthfinder as a portal to reputable sites, self-help groups, and information. Here's how to use the site:
    - Search an alphabetical list of organizations, or use Search at the top of the page to find a specific term.
    - The health library is packed with information about prescription drugs, alternative medicine, disease prevention, and more.

- Go to the Just for You area (www.healthfinder.gov/justforyou) to find information targeted at men, women, teens, infants, parents, seniors, or health professionals. You can also find information about health issues affecting specific ethnicities.
- Need more information about doctors, dentists, nursing care, or other types of caregiving? Visit the Health Care section (www.healthfinder.gov/healthcare).

- **VitalSeek** (www.vitalseek.com). The VitalSeek search engine finds information on sites accredited by the American Accreditation HealthCare Commission, also known as the URAC (www.urac.org). You can enter your search term in the primary search or use the advanced search to filter information. You can filter as much or as little information as you want with an advanced search that includes topic, URAC accreditation, type of website (.com, .org, .edu), viewpoint (traditional or alternative), credibility, and more.

Although a Google search is cheaper than a doctor's visit, websites should be used only as research tools. Do not delay seeking treatment for possibly serious illness.

Address: **Site of the Night**

Google Answers

For a small fee, Google's gaggle of search engine experts will answer your most pressing questions. See https://answers.google.com/.

Print Custom Envelopes and Labels

Greg Melton

If you use Microsoft Office, you can print customized envelopes directly from Word. It's relatively easy and is a great way to send personalized greetings. You only need a printer, envelopes, or standard Avery mailing labels available at any office supply store.

1. Open Word, go to File, and select a New document.

2. On the new document, click Tools.

3. Select Envelopes and Labels. If you have Office XP, mouse over Letters and Mailing, and select Envelopes and Labels to open the dialog.

4. Go to the Envelopes tab or the Labels tab, depending on what you want to do.

Delivery and Return Address

1. Enter the delivery instructions in the Delivery Address field. Use a different line for name, street, and city/state/ZIP code.

2. For envelopes, enter the return instructions in the Return Address field. Use a different line for name, street, and city/state/ZIP code. To leave this field blank, check Omit.

3. If you want a return address on your labels, check Use Return Address and enter the information.

Change Envelope Size and Printing Options

To change the envelope size to anything other than the default size (4 1/8 by 9 1/2 inches) or choose the correct way to orient envelopes for printing, follow these directions:

1. Click Options on the Envelopes and Labels dialog.

2. The Envelopes options should be open. Select the Envelopes Options tab, if it isn't already selected.

3. Under Envelope Size, select the correct envelope size.

4. Click the Print Option tab.

5. Choose the option that best illustrates the way your printer handles envelopes.

6. Press OK when you've finished making all your adjustments.

Add to Document

The last step before customizing is to click Add to Document on the Envelopes and Labels dialog. You should see a dialog asking if you'd like to make the return address your default setting.

Start Customizing

You should now see a template of an envelope or label with the information you entered in the Envelopes and Labels dialog.

Change fonts by highlighting the text, and then choose a font from the font toolbar.

To insert a picture or clip art on the envelope, click Insert, mouse over Picture, and select From File. Navigate to the image you'd like to add on your hard drive, and click Insert Image. Place images on the left side of envelopes, to avoid processing problems at the post office.

Start Printing

Place an envelope or Avery labels in the printer, and click Print in Word (or Ctrl+P). It might take a couple of times before you orient envelopes correctly in the printer. Keep trying. If you don't get it right the first time, you will eventually.

April
28

123

Timesaving Tips for Word 2000 and XP

Martin Sargent

If you spend as much time using Microsoft Word as I do, you should master all the timesaving tricks you can. These time-savers will shave precious seconds off my hectic workday. And they work in Word 2000 and XP!

Collect and Paste and Spike

A rosy feature that made its debut in Word 2000 and continues to wow in Word XP is Collect and Paste. You can copy or cut more than one object or block of text to the Clipboard. The Clipboard can hold up to a dozen items, and you can paste them all in one spot, in order, in one fell swoop. This is a real time-saver if you're trying to consolidate blocks of text in one location.

The feature works automatically. Just copy more than one thing, and the Clipboard appears. To paste everything on the Clipboard, click Paste All on the Clipboard toolbar.

Spike It

Spike does essentially the same thing. To use Spike, select the block of text or graphic you want to move and press Ctrl+F3. Do this for as many items as you want to cram onto the Spike. When you're ready to empty the Spike's contents into a document, position the insertion point appropriately and press Ctrl+Shift+F3.

Unlike Collect and Paste, there's apparently no limit to the number of text blocks or graphics you can place on the Spike.

Squint a Bit and Save a Tree

This is the perfect feature for environmentalists with good vision. In Word 2000/XP, you can print up to 16 pages of text on a single page. Select File and Print as you normally would—but before you click Print, go into the Zoom section of the Print dialog and select the number of pages of text you want crammed onto one sheet.

In addition to saving precious print time and paper, this is a handy way to store a lot of information on one piece of paper that can fit easily in your pocket or day planner.

Click and Type

In Word 97, you press Tab, Enter, and that king of all keys, the spacebar, over and over again to move the cursor to where you'd like to start typing. Not so in Word 2000 or XP. All you have to do is double-click where you'd like to start typing and, well, start typing. For some stupid reason, though, this doesn't work in Normal view. You need to switch to Print Layout view or Web Layout view.

If Click and Type still doesn't work, you might need to turn on the feature. Select Tools and Options, and click the Edit tab. Make sure the Click and Type check box is selected.

Also note that Click and Type isn't available in multiple columns, in bulleted and numbered lists, to the right and left of pictures with top and bottom text wrapping, or to the left and right of indents. (Alas, these are some of the places where it'd be handy.)

Timesaving Tips for Word 2000 and XP (continued)

Give Your Page Some Color

I'm not really sure if this is a time-saving tip, but I think it's somewhat cool. In previous versions of Word, you had a limited number of text and background colors to choose from. In Word 2000/XP, you have a 16 million-in-attendance festival of hues and shades that we in the business refer to as 24-bit color.

To color your text, choose Format, Font, and click the Font Color drop-down list. Choose More Colors and click Custom. Use the sliders to reach the color you want, click the Color field, or enter values between 0 and 255 for Red, Green, and Blue, or for Hue, Saturation, and Luminance.

Quick Scroll

If you've ever tried to scroll through a Word document that's rife with graphics, you know it can take a while and be disorienting, especially if your computer doesn't have much RAM. For those of you with too little RAM, it's easy to hide a document's graphics while you're working on that document. Choose Tools, Options, and click the View tab. Check the Picture Placeholders check box under Show.

Instead of graphics, you should now see only placeholders, which your memory should be capable of handling with aplomb.

Express Yourself

You could find synonyms using the Thesaurus feature in Word 97, but finding synonyms is much more convenient in Word 2000/XP. Just click the boring word that your meager mind came up with and then right-click. When the pop-up menu appears, choose Synonyms. Word displays a list of alternative words.

This simple feature comes in handy, especially if you tend to make frequent trips, journeys, expeditions, or treks to the thesaurus.

Download of the Day

Three Little PC Downloads

Megan Morrone

It's the little things that make the difference. FreewareWeb.com (www.freewareweb.com) is a site that features little downloads that let you tweak your system. Here are my three favorite utilities:

- **TitleBarClock.** This simple download displays the date, time, and percent of free physical memory in your system.

- **FileDrag V 3.0.** Don't know what to use to open a file? Drag and drop it into the FileDrag window, and it'll tell you.

- **A_ShutDown.** You could configure your system for a one-click shutdown, but why bother when you can do it with a download? This utility also lets you set your computer to shut down at a scheduled time.

Windows Tips

Clone Text and Graphics in Microsoft Word

Nicole Guilfoyle

Here's a way to copy and paste blocks of text or images in Microsoft Word documents in fewer steps than you thought possible:

1. Highlight the text or graphic you want to copy.

2. Hold down the Ctrl key.

3. Use your mouse to drag the selected text or graphic to a new location.

This drag-and-drop copy trick will save tons of time if you need to create a border or repeat text in several places. It's more fun than using the copy-and-paste shortcuts or going through the Edit menu. Enjoy!

Merry Month of May

Megan Morrone

I use file-sharing programs to download music from the Internet. Statistics show that you do, too. In the past I've offered all kinds of rationalizations that make it okay. I still buy CDs, sampling music means I buy more CDs, etc., etc. But my favorite rationalization has always been that technology is ahead of the record companies, and until they catch up, I'm going to keep on downloading.

If you've got a Mac, technology is about to catch up. Apple's iTunes 4 Music Store (www.apple.com/music/store) lets you download single tracks for only a dollar. IMHO, that's a deal.

I took a sneak peek into Leo's hard drive, and in the short time that the Music Store has been open, he's already downloaded and purchased these songs (and more):

- "Be My Yoko Ono," The Barenaked Ladies, *All Their Greatest Hits (1991–2001)*
- "Emerald Eyes," Fleetwood Mac, *Mystery to Me*
- "Drunken Angel," Lucinda Williams, *Car Wheels on a Gravel Road*
- "Space Oddity," Natalie Merchant, *Live in Concert*
- "Don't Know Why," Norah Jones, *Come Away with Me*
- "Ancient Voices (Nhmamusasa)," Paul Winter, *Common Ground*
- "I Will Remember You," Sarah McLachlan, *Mirrorball*
- "Psycho Killer," Talking Heads, *Talking Heads 77*
- "Warm Beer and Cold Women," Tom Waits, *Nighthawks at the Diner*
- "Pride (In the Name of Love)," U2, *The Best of 1980–1990*
- "Pot Kettle Black," Wilco, *Yankee Hotel Foxtrot*
- "A Change Would Do You Good," Sheryl Crow, *Sheryl Crow*
- "Mea Culpa," Enigma, *MCMXC A.D.*
- "Suffragette City," David Bowie, *The Rise and Fall of Ziggy Stardust and the Spiders from Mars*

Leo's iPod Essentials

Leo Laporte & James Kim
My name is Leo and I'm an MP3 junky.

I've converted every CD in my collection into MP3 files. I personally own five portable MP3 players: a Diamond Rio 500, Apple iPod, Phillips Expanium MP3 CD player, Sony CLIE 760, and an HP Jornada 565, plus an Apex DVD player capable of MP3 playback. I have well over 10GB of MP3 music and spoken word files stored on my computers and burned on CD-R. For me, MP3 represents a revolution in the way I listen to music. And my favorite MP3 player of all is the Apple iPod. It's MP3 perfection.

Fast and Fat

The iPod is a hard-disk-based player. The original edition sported an 8GB drive; the newest iPod more than triples that capacity. My iPod has become my personal radio station. I put my 1,000 favorite tunes on it, put it into shuffle mode, and just listen away. No commercials, no DJs, no fluff—just pure, high-quality, digital music.

The iPod is compact (about the size and weight of a pack of cards), sounds great, and with its FireWire interface it can copy a song in a second from your system to its hard drive. It took me about 20 minutes to fill the 5GB drive. That's about 20 times faster than USB equipped MP3 players.

A New Generation

Now Apple has come even closer to perfection with a thinner and lighter design, a new user interface, a better screen, and a few key firmware improvements. With all these features, plus bigger hard drives and a more competitive price, the iPod has never been a more attractive purchase. The iPod also serves as one of the critical elements of the iTunes Music Store.

Here are the new iPod features:

- **Three sizes at competitive prices.** 10GB, 15GB, and 30GB (7,500 songs) versions for $299, $399, and $499, respectively.
- **Sleeker design.** At just 0.62 inches thick and 5.6 ounces light, these iPods are the smallest ever. Apple added four touch-sensitive buttons dedicated to player controls and menu. These buttons light up in an amazing reddish-orange hue in the dark.
- **Playlists on the fly.** Finally, Apple added the capability to create playlists without a computer. The implementation is seamless. Simply click a track for a couple seconds, and it blinks, indicating that it has been added to a new playlist.
- **Customizable menu.** Lets you select which features appear on the top menu page. For example, I can now easily configure an iPod to show off only Songs, Clock (including the new alarm), Settings, and Games on the top menu screen.
- **One version.** The days of separate Windows and Mac versions are over. The new iPod is compatible with USB 2.0. Windows users can purchase an extra USB 2.0 cable, which includes a FireWire subcable and power adapter.
- **Docking cradle.** The 15GB and 30GB versions ship with a docking cradle, which allows for synching with iTunes, using the iPod as a hard drive, and recharging (the iPod's communication port has been moved to the bottom of the device). There's even a head-phone jack/line-out built into the cradle.

The new touch-screen interface, menu customization, and playlist-on-the-go feature should make the iPod the best and most sensible digital audio player available.

Leo's iPod Essentials (continued)

Little-Known facts

For one thing, it contains a game of breakout. No kidding. Go to Settings and select the About screen (it's called "Legal" in the latest version of the iPod firmware). Then press the middle button for a few seconds and there it is. You can even continue to listen to music while you play. This is more than a curiosity, however. It plays up the fact that the iPod is really a computer with a hard drive, so it's possible to extend its capabilities almost infinitely.

Apple did just that with the release 1.1 of the iPod firmware. Apple has added an equalizer to match the equalizer already in iTunes (don't worry, your iTunes EQ settings will automatically transfer over to the iPod) and the ability to copy contacts from Microsoft Entourage, the Palm Desktop, and the Mac OS X Address Book.

This is the first step toward turning the iPod into a full-fledged PDA. The new firmware is well worth downloading for any iPod user (www.apple.com/ipod/download/).

To prevent music piracy, the iPod will only synch with one computer's music library at a time. This keeps you from bringing your iPod to your friend's house and copying all the stored songs onto her hard drive. It also keeps people who own multiple Macs from legally sharing the iPod and its files with other systems.

Fortunately, there are many free add-on programs that make it possible to move files to and from the iPod without iTunes. I recommend an $8 utility called PodMaster 1000 (www.macupdate.com/info.php/id/6791) from Flying Mouse Ware, but a search of VersionTracker (www.versiontracker.com), my favorite Mac download site, will turn up dozens of other programs.

Ear Essentials

You might also want to consider buying better headphones for your iPod. The little white earbuds that come with the device are OK, but the iPod's amp can handle better phones than that. I use a $70 pair of Grado SR60 (www.gradolabs.com) headphones and love the sound quality.

If you prefer something a little more portable and stylish, try the Bang and Olufsen (www.bang-olufsen.com) A8 Earphones for $170. My friends at Apple love 'em (even if they don't take them to work).

The iPod's elegant design, portability, speed, and sound quality make it one of my most cherished gadgets. I hope these few little tips help you enjoy it as much as I do.

 Laporte Support

How Do You Get Volume Control to Appear and Work in the Taskbar?

To make volume control appear in the taskbar:

1. Open the Control Panel.
2. Open the Sounds and Audio Devices control panel.
3. Click on the Volume tab.
4. Check the box with the option to place the volume control in the taskbar.

If you get an error, try reinstalling the sound card's driver and bundled software. XP is looking for the card's mixer and it can't find it.

May
2

Home Theater PC

Yoshi De Herrera

Hooking up your PC to your home theater system isn't a complicated process and can be done at a minimum expense. Think about the equipment you have and how you'll use the system. If you plan to use your PC primarily for games and music, you can hook it up to any stereo system. Just plug the output from your audio card into the AUX input on your stereo.

To watch DVDs and hear the full glory of Dolby Digital surround sound, you need a receiver that can decode Dolby digital sound. Generally, you need a sound card or DVD decoder board that offers digital output compatible with your receiver or decoder.

Receivers

You can use a variety of products for your home theater system, from all-in-one systems that cost a few hundred dollars to components that cost thousands each. Chances are, just connecting your PC to your home stereo will improve audio quality.

For surround sound, your receiver needs to support Dolby Digital 5.1 channels sound—five satellite speakers (left, right, center, two rear speakers, and a subwoofer). Some high-end receivers support 7.1 channels, but they are expensive.

Sound Cards for the Budget-Minded

The Diamond Multimedia MX300 supports a daughter card to output Dolby Digital 5.1 sound. Although it is no longer produced by Diamond/S3, you can still buy it. Both cards cost about $35 each. It uses the Aureal vortex 2 chipset.

If you want a more mainstream card, use the Creative Sound Blaster Audigy Platinum (www.soundblaster.com). It's a little more expensive (around $200), but it has some features not available with the MX300.

Graphic Cards

Depending on the room size and your budget, you might want a large computer monitor (go for one at least 19 inches) instead of your TV. The picture quality is much better on a monitor, but the cost of a 27- or 30-inch monitor is prohibitive.

If your monitor doesn't accept VGA output, you'll need something that can output the NTSC video that your TV needs. ATI's Radeon line of cards offers awesome DVD video decoding and has great 3D gaming performance, to boot. You could also purchase a dedicated DVD decoder card (the Hollywood Plus [www.sigmadesigns.com] DVD decoder card costs around $50) that has both an NTSC composite or S-video output and a digital audio output.

If you have a PC with at least a 350MHz Pentium II or a Macintosh G4, you could decode the DVD video in software such as Intervideo's WinDVD (www.intervideo.com). The faster your system, the better-looking the output. Don't expect to do much while this is running; your processor will be carrying a serious load to decode in software mode.

So You Wanna Be an iPod

James Kim

The iPod MP3 (www.apple.com) player raised the bar for design, features, and quality. It was an immediate success, and competitors scrambled to come up with similar products before the portable MP3 market belonged solely to the iPod.

Creative Nomad Jukebox Zen

The Nomad Jukebox Zen holds 20GB (about 4,000 MP3s) and connects to a PC through USB or FireWire. Creative is banking on a fresh look, excellent audio quality, and an impressive $300 price (after $50 rebate). To keep costs down, Creative uses a 2.5-inch notebook drive; the iPod has a 1.8-inch Toshiba drive (www.nomadworld.com).

Hard drive: 20GB
OS: Windows, Mac
Supported formats: WMA, WAV, MP3
Transfer: USB 2.0, FireWire
Pros: Awesome sound quality, excellent value
Cons: LCD too small, confusing interface

Neuros Digital Audio Computer

This futuristic digital audio player from Digital Innovations includes an FM tuner and a built-in FM transmitter that lets you broadcast the audio up to 20 feet. The 128MB (or 20GB, around $400) player can also record FM radio, voice, or an external audio source into MP3, and the Hear It See It button can sample 30 seconds of any song you're listening to on the radio (www.neurosaudio.com).

Hard drive: 128MB Flash or 20GB hard drive
OS: Windows
Supported formats: MP3
Transfer: USB 1.1
Pros: FM transmission, FM tuner, customizable interface
Cons: Large size

Samsung Yepp YP-900

Although it's not as intuitive and elegant as the iPod, the $400 YP-900's versatility makes it a legitimate competitor. The YP-900 has 10GB and can play both WMA and MP3 files. USB 2.0, on-the-fly MP3 encoding, and FM transmission make the Yepp a great choice. Whereas other player/recorders can encode CDs directly into MP3, the Yepp actually remembers the original CD, so it automatically fills in the ID3 tag information when it's connected to a computer (www.samsung.com).

Hard drive: 10GB
Supported formats: WMA, MP3
Transfer: USB 2.0
Pros: FM transmission, FM tuner, CD info
Cons: Not as elegant as iPod

Other MP3 players

- **Bantam BA1000** (www.bantamusa.com). Buy directly from Bantam.
- **Toshiba Mobilphile** (www.toshiba.com).
- **Sonicblue Rio Riot** (www.rioaudio.com).

Address: Site of the Night

Video Game Music Archive
Download memorable MIDI music from your favorite classic games at www.vgmusic.com.

What to Look for in a DVD Player

Roger Chang

Now that the DVD standard has successfully penetrated the home video market, it can be extremely intimidating to choose the right DVD player.

DVD Video Quality

Video quality between DVD players tends to vary. The first thing you need to look at is the back panel. It should have some combination of the following types of DVD input/output connectors:

- RCA composite jacks, for basic video output, are usually yellow. Almost all TVs support this type of input, and all DVD players have them. This type of output signal offers relatively low quality.
- S-Video, or Super Video, connection is a step up from RCA composite jacks. S-Video isolates the luminance (brightness) and chrominance (color) signals from each other for better picture clarity. S-Video is usually a multipin, mini-DIN style connector that's usually black.
- Component video, or component color connection, is one of the best methods for connecting a DVD player to a TV. It separates the chrominance and various luminance levels into three separate channels and maintains a higher level of data integrity. Also written as Y'Pb'Pr', this applies to the way component color video separates color signals. Y' (luminance) is the brightness and darkness of the signal connector. Pb' is blue minus the luminance signal connector. Pr' is red minus the luminance signal connector.

Most consumer-level DVD players come with these connections. A DVD player should at least possess an S-Video and composite connection. S-Video provides a far superior picture to composite, while component offers the best.

To use an S-Video or component video connection, you need a television capable of accepting these signals. S-Video TVs, however, are cheaper and more available than component color–capable TVs, which are usually either wide-screen TVs, video monitors (such as a professional TV studio would have), or HDTV.

Progressive Scan/Line Doubler

Progressive scan draws an image onscreen from top to bottom at one time. The result is a clear, sharp image compared to a standard interlaced TV image.

If you can get a progressive-scan DVD player at an affordable price, go for it, but like S-Video and component video, the progressive-scan capability needs a compatible digital TV or video monitor to be utilized.

DVD players with integrated progressive scan are generally not as capable as separate external progressive scan boxes. If you want the ultimate home theater setup, skip the integrated progressive-scan DVD player and go with an external unit.

Laporte Support

Leo's Pick: The Gruvstick

The Gruvstick, from CenDyne (www.cendyne.com), is a USB Memory Stick MP3 player that comes with LCD readout, MP3 voice recording, and an optional FM radio transmitter so you can listen to your Gruvstick on your car stereo.

The Gruvstick is small and convenient. Because it plugs into your USB port, you don't need cables or special software to copy music. On the other hand, it doesn't work with the Mac, and it's a little pricey, at about $180 for 128MB (enough for two CDs) or $130 for 64MB.

For mass MP3 listening, I still like my iPod best, but the Gruvstick is a great companion for my workouts.

What to Look for in a DVD Player (continued)

DVD Audio Quality

The other half of a DVD experience is sound. Like video, DVD audio has several standards:

- Dolby Digital, a surround-sound audio-compression technology from Dolby Labs, allows for discrete multichannel sound through a multispeaker setup. It's capable of 1 to 5.1 channels of sound.

- PCM (pulse-code modulation) audio is uncompressed digital sound similar to what's used on CDs. It can provide one to eight channels of sound, but you'll hear a loss in audio quality when it's set to anything above two channels.

- MPEG-2 audio is a compressed multi-channel sound format based on PCM audio and is capable of 1 to 5.1–7.1 channels. Don't confuse MPEG with MP3 audio, which is a different digital audio format. Only DVD players that specifically support MP3 files will play them.

- DTS (digital theatre system) is a competing surround-sound audio-compression technology that allows multichannel sound through a multispeaker setup. This is an option on some DVD players and is capable of 1 to 7.1 channels of sound.

Both Dolby Digital and DTS require a decoder box and a stereo amplifier. And both DTS and Dolby Digital connect to an amplifier in one of two ways:

- RCA-style connector, colored orange (referred to as an S/PDIF connector)

- Square-style connector (referred to as a TOSlink)

Your decoder must accept a digital output signal and the same style connector to use the Dolby Digital or DTS technology.

Some DVD players incorporate a Dolby Digital or DTS decoder. The back of a DVD player should have six RCA-style audio output jacks. These still require a surround-sound capable amplifier or A/V receiver.

Finally, you might find THX sound. THX (Tomlinson Holman Experiment) sound is not a specific technology, per se. It is a group of technology-quality standards from Lucasfilms. Equipment labeled THX is certified by Lucasfilms to meet certain criteria in sound and acoustics.

What Does DVD Mean?

Roger Chang

DVD, or digital versatile disc, is a technology standard that stores data on optical discs. Like the CD (compact disc), a DVD holds information in a digital format as pits on the surface of the disc denoting ones and zeros.

The DVD standard covers several different uses:

- **DVD-Video.** The standard for encoding and storing video on a DVD disc. You need a DVD-Video–capable player to play a DVD-video disc.

- **DVD-Audio.** The standard for encoding and storing high-fidelity audio on a DVD disc. You need a DVD-Audio–capable player to play a DVD-audio disc.

- **DVD-ROM.** The standard for encoding and storing computer files on a DVD disc. You need a computer equipped with a DVD-ROM drive to play a DVD-ROM.

Rip CDs to MP3s

Greg Melton and Ron White

Converting or ripping audio CD tracks into MP3s is a hassle-free process if you have the right tools.

Get the Software

To convert audio CDs, you need a ripper. The term *ripper* applies to a program that rips or encodes .cda audio tracks from a CD and turns them into MP3s. A ripper compresses the original audio track to one-tenth its file size.

Download and install the best ripper/player/burner out there. It's called Musicmatch Jukebox (www.musicmatch.com), and it's free. Or, try a program such as Cdex (www.cdex.n3.net). Or, search Hotfiles.com or Download.com for the term "ripper," and you'll find heaps of them.

After installing Musicmatch, you need to make three decisions:

1. What track-naming convention will you use? Musicmatch lets you select up to seven different fields to be included with every CD file you encode. Selecting Artist, Album, Track Number, and Track Title should be enough to get your collection started.

   All of the track characteristics are referred to as MP3's ID3 tags. Quite a few ID3-tag editors are available. To modify the order of the track fields in Musicmatch, click Options, Settings, and then select Music Library tab.

2. What bit rate will you use to encode files? Bit rate is the average number of bits that one second of audio data will consume, and it has a direct relationship to the quality of an MP3. For near-CD quality, the bit rate can be 96Kbps. However, for CD quality, encode all CDs at 128Kbps or 160Kbps.

   As the bit rate number increases, the MP3's file size increases. Remember that as your MP3 collection gets larger, available hard-drive storage space gets smaller.

To change the bit rate settings in Musicmatch, click Options, mouse over Recorder, and select Settings. If you have the hard-drive space, leave it at 128Kbps.

3. Where will you place the songs after they've been ripped? Musicmatch's default directory is MyDocuments\MyMusic\. Remember this so you'll know where to access your songs later.

   To modify where Musicmatch places MP3s after they're ripped, click Options, mouse over Recorder, and select Settings. Select Songs Directory and select the folder where you want to place the MP3s.

Check Your CD-ROM

Musicmatch automatically checks the CD-ROM drive to see if it's capable of digital-audio extraction. If you bought the drive in the last year or so, chances are, it is.

If the CD drive doesn't handle digital audio extraction, you can still rip songs, but the process will take as long as it takes to play the songs.

Rip CDs Using Musicmatch:

1. Open Musicmatch, and insert a CD into the CD-ROM.

2. Connect to the Internet. Musicmatch automatically recognizes that an audio CD is inserted and initiates the Recorder to begin searching the online CDDB (CD database). If it finds a match for your CD, Musicmatch fills in all the artist and album information. You might need to type in the track listings if it doesn't return a match.

3. After the CDDB returns a match, or after you've completed inputting artist and album names and the track titles, click Record on the recorder.

4. Depending on the speed of your PC, the CD should be fully ripped in less than 10 minutes.

MP3 Jukebox Software

Patrick Norton

Here's what a jukebox can do:

- Play digital audio files and CDs.
- Rip and encode CDs into MP3s (or WMAs or other file formats).
- Browse your collection.
- Stack tunes into playlists.
- Provide CDDB (CD Database) access to label CDs and other files.
- Sometimes burns files onto an audio CD.
- Play visualizations while you listen.

Some jukeboxes can play video or control a TV tuner.

If you don't want a jukebox to take over (darn near) every multimedia playback function, don't do an express install. Choose a custom install so you can pick which media type (MP3, WMA, and so on) will automatically play.

Now to the pros and cons of each package.

Musicmatch

This is the standard, the one we generally recommend. It's free in the basic version (www.musicmatch.com).

Pros

- Free MP3 encoding up to 320Kbps.
- Tons of recording options; a tweaker's paradise.

Cons

- Is the interface getting uglier?
- Some interface confusion.
- Easy to get lost in the features if you don't spend time with the manual.

Windows Media Player

I like this one more than I thought (www.microsoft.com/windows/windowsmedia).

Pros

- Simple interface with big, labeled buttons— once you get past the weird disappearing/ reappearing window that hides things.
- Not packed with options—not necessarily a bad thing, especially when recording music.
- The max, 192Kbps, WMA encoding was excellent and more than a third smaller than maxed-out 320Kbps MP3 files.

Cons

- The native WMA setting, 64Kbps, sounds weak (128Kbps sounded fab).
- The Options and Copy Music settings are hard to find.
- Does Skin Chooser really need a huge tab?
- You can't install WMP 9.

Media Jukebox (www.mediajukebox.com)

Pros

- Easy to navigate to open files; big buttons show where to rip and burn CDs.
- Options for TV tuner.
- Natively set to use WMA at 128Kbps.
- Sounds better than Windows Media Player, until you reset to 128Kbps.
- Tons of options for encoding MP3, Ogg Vorbis, and Monkey's Audio. Plus it's fast.

Cons

- Not the prettiest skins.
- Need to download codecs separately.
- Costs $25 after free 30-day trial expires.

RealOne Player

RealJukebox integrated into the RealOne Player. If you're a dedicated Real fanatic, it's okay. Otherwise, I'd avoid it (www.real.com).

Give Windows XP a Creative Boost

Cat Schwartz

The modern operating system does more than simply let you use your computer. It provides a creative wonderland for you to browse and edit photos, make movies, and listen to music while visualizations gyrate to the beat. Microsoft takes your ability to be creative with Windows XP to the next level with Microsoft Plus! Digital Media Edition ($20, www.microsoft.com/windows/plus), a collection of simple but powerful applications designed with the digital media enthusiast in mind.

Here are the numerous elements that make up Plus! Digital Media Edition. Some are great, some not so great.

Photo Story

Photo Story is what makes this a worthy purchase. It lets you enjoy and share your photo collection by combining digital photos with music and narration. Apply zooms or pans, or let the computer take over. Add some commentary over the music. Finally, compress the file and email to family and friends. It's an entertaining way to show off your pics in story form.

Party Mode

This feature essentially turns your PC into an impenetrable full-screen jukebox using Windows Media Player. While it's in Party Mode, your files and personal info are protected from anyone trying to access the computer. Quitting Party Mode takes you to the Windows logon screen and makes the perpetrator the death of the party. There's also an interactive guest book that displays messages on the screen ticker style. When you're ready to quit, Windows even asks, "Is the party over?" It's a feature every computer should have.

Analog Recorder

Analog Recorder lets you record analog sources (such as cassettes or vinyl records) using the sound card's line-in jack, a feature that Musicmatch and RealOne have had for a while. The silver lining is that Analog Recorder includes automatic hiss and pop reduction, track splitting, and other editing features. A wizard for beginners guides the user through selecting a sound device and an input channel, and setting proper sound levels.

Dancer

We've all seen media players with a variety of visualizations (from the swirling psychedelic variety to spectacular 3D animations) that synch up to the beat of any media player. Dancer introduces 11 realistic dancers to Windows Media Player. From hip-hop Amanda to break-dancing Seth, the amazingly lifelike characters dance to any beat on your desktop. You can resize them, move them around the desktop, and select dance styles such as disco, salsa, and hip-hop. More dancers will soon be available for download.

CD Label Maker

Another feature seen in other media players. This application automatically adds artist, track, and album information to customizable CD labels, inserts, and booklets.

Synch & Go

This application will help you transfer audio and video content from Windows Media Player and other content providers to your Pocket PC PDA. It works a lot like AvantGo (http://avantgo.com); just synch and watch and listen to news clips and trailers on the go.

Other Features

- Audio Converter converts your digital audio files from one format to another.
- Effects & Transitions adds 50 new video transitions and effects to the new and improved Windows Movie Maker.
- Alarm Clock turns your computer into a fully programmable alarm clock, complete with a snooze button and sleep timer.
- And there's a whole new set of Skins for your Windows Media Player.

DVD Region Coding

***The Screen Savers* Staff**

All DVD players and discs have region codes. A DVD player and disc must have the same region, or the disc will be rendered inoperable. This is not a concern for most of North America—almost all first-run movies are released here first.

If you want to watch movies from other countries, you need a multiregion DVD player. Because TV standards differ, you might also need a specialized NTSC/SECAM/PAL TV or a DVD player that can output any signal to an NTSC signal. The United States, Canada, Mexico, and Japan use NTSC. Europe and South America use a combination of PAL and SECAM.

Other DVD Features to Consider

- **MP3 decoding.** With the popularity of MP3s, many DVD players incorporate playback of MP3s written to CD-Rs.

- **Carousel.** A carousel lets you rotate between movies without getting off your duff. Think CD carousel, except with DVDs.

Use reviews to help you narrow the field, but the final selection is up to you. Take a DVD title that you know well to your local electronics store. Test each of the DVD players using your DVD. If you want good DVD-player reviews written exclusively by people who have purchased them, visit Audio Review (www.audioreview.com).

If you still have questions and you'd like to learn more, visit DVD Demystified (www.dvddemystified.com).

Laporte Support

DVD Longevity

How long will DVDs last?

Every digital medium is eventually replaced by a medium that offers more storage capacity, better longevity and reliability, and increased portability. That said, DVDs have a lot to offer in those areas, which is why they're so widely accepted.

DVDs will eventually be replaced, but when is hard to tell. The next generation, called blue-laser DVDs, is on the horizon but is at least a couple of years away for the general public. And you can bet that efforts will be made to make blue-laser DVD drives compatible with the current DVDs.

We think the current DVD disc will be around for at least a decade—maybe longer. DVD set-top players are cheap, so there's no reason not to buy one now. Don't worry about the medium being obsolete. Its popularity almost guarantees compatibility in the future.

Windows Tips

Change Startup Sounds

Customize Windows event sounds with the WAV file of your choice.

1. Click Start, Settings, Control Panel (Start, Control Panel in XP).

2. Double-click Sounds (Sounds and Audio Devices in XP).

3. Under Events, select Start Windows.

4. Under Sounds, click Browse, find the file you want to use, and click OK.

5. Click Apply and OK.

Can Bad MP3s Be Saved?

Patrick Norton

Pennywise (www.pennywisdom.com), one of my favorite bands, did something very cool. It picked up a stack of unauthorized bootleg concert CDs, turned them into MP3s, and made them available on their website.

Making audio CDs from MP3s is easy. I made a playlist in Nero and clicked Burn. The results sounded awful, though. Was it Nero, or was it the Pennywise MP3s I downloaded? My quest: Make the Pennywise MP3 CDs (and CDs I make from my MP3 collection) sound better.

No Tweaks Available

I burned CD audio discs from the Pennywise MP3s and some MP3s made from my CD collection at rates from 128Kbps to 320Kbps. I used Musicmatch, Media Jukebox, Nero, iTunes, and a few random downloads.

You can change the space between songs, or you can render the MP3s to a WAV file separately from the burning process, but that's about it.

The full version of Musicmatch lets you apply digital audio effects to the file you burn.

What You Can Do

You can render your MP3 file to a WAV file and use audio software to try to filter and improve that sound. But that didn't clean up the sound of the cymbals on the Pennywise tracks.

There's an old phrase in data processing: "Garbage in, garbage out." It's still true, whether you're talking video, audio, or scanning in photos. If you're burning MP3s to CDs, use the best-quality MP3 files you can get.

With that in mind…

Dear Pennywise,

You're an unbelievably cool band. Is there any chance you might offer your collection of unauthorized live bootleg CDs in a slightly higher MP3 format? Say, 192Kbps? Please?

Patrick

Download of the Day

The GodFather

Craig Higdon

Like any good godfather, this MP3 ID3 tag editor is full of options. Unfortunately, it's kinda hard to understand. If you make a mistake, you might end up swimming with the fishes (more on this later).

The GodFather (http://users.otenet.gr/ ~jtcliper/tgf/) is, first and foremost, an ID3 tag editor, but it also lets you organize, sort, and otherwise manhandle your MP3s. It lays everything out for you, telling you a file's bit rate, sample rate, file size, and duration, and it lets you change a bunch of ID3 tags all at once. This feature is pretty handy when you have a bunch of files, but it's also where I ran into trouble. I clicked the Apply button, thinking it would apply all my changes. Instead, it applied my current changes to all the MP3s. My bad. Now all my files are apparently "undone" by Weezer. So be careful.

The GodFather has plenty of features that are great if you want to take the time to learn them, but as an MP3 player, this program might as well be at the bottom of the lake with Fredo. If you just want to play MP3s, use something like Winamp instead.

MP3 Explained

The Screen Savers Staff

MP3s are audio files compressed to a small size. Compression makes them easy to transfer either over the Internet or from a hard drive to a disc or CD-R.

Portable MP3 players such as the Diamond Rio 500 let you create a portable personal jukebox with a higher sound quality than a cassette. You can also obtain MP3s on the Internet and listen to music right off the hard drive.

How Do They Work?

MP3 files use the third audio layer of the MPEG (Moving Picture Experts Group) compression standard.

A CD provides high-quality music by reproducing sound fairly faithfully. MP3s work by getting rid of inaudible or barely audible parts of the music, dramatically reducing the size of the file.

Your computer can't represent the sound exactly—that's too much data. Instead, the computer samples the music, assigning a unique number to each sound. To sample, the computer listens to a sound a certain number of times per second.

For CD-quality sound, this could be 44,100 times per second. For example, for every 44 thousandths of a second, the computer decides what number to assign based on the sound's sine wave. The sound parts are glued together to approximate the smooth curve of the actual sound. The human ear can't easily tell the difference.

MP3 Separate Applications

Patrick Norton

You don't need no stinking jukebox? Fine with me. Here are some kickin' tools for making, playing, and burning digital audio files:

- **Winamp** (www.winamp.com). I use this player to play all the digital audio on my home system.

- **LAME** (www.mp3dev.org). "Lame Ain't an MP3 Encoder." Uh, okay, it's source code. But lots of people think the LAME code makes the best standalone software for ripping and encoding MP3s. Read the list of software that runs LAME (www.mp3dev.org/mp3/links.html), download one, and give it a try. You might not go back to a jukebox.

Burning audio CDs from your digital music collection? Leo has finally convinced me that Nero is the way to go. And you can try it free (www.nero.com).

Download of the Day

The Screen Savers Theme Song

Megan Morrone

I don't know about you, but I can't get our opening theme out of my head. Last week I woke up in the middle of the night humming it. I guess that means it's catchy. Either that or I'm crazy.

You can now download it at http://cache.techtv.com/binaries/2002/tss_theme.mp3. Play it. Mix with it. Write lyrics to it. Dance to it. Make music videos with it. Whatever.

Music Machines: Elektron's Machinedrum and Propellerhead's Reason 2.0

James Kim

These two electronic music tools represent some of the best hardware and software on the market.

Elektron Machinedrum SPS-1

(www.machinedrum.com)

- **Dimensions:** 13.4 by 6.9 by 2.7 inches.
- **Weight:** 6.2 pounds.
- **Bottom line:** In our opinion, this is the world's most advanced drum machine.

Software is all the rage in electronic music production. It's affordable, and it runs on your desktop. So why did Sweden's Elektron (creators of the wacky SidStation) develop and distribute a new hardware drum machine that costs more than $1,000?

One evening with the Machinedrum is all it takes.

- The Machinedrum has real buttons and knobs and comes in a dedicated case, which makes programming, sequencing, and using it much more enjoyable than manipulating virtual knobs and buttons with a mouse.
- It comes with a limitless array of cutting-edge (and classic) built-in sounds.
- The Machinedrum has a look and feel of a classic.

You can't import sounds, but then again, who needs to import when you have an advanced synth engine with dual waveform LFOs, a collection of mind-numbing effects, and some of the best preset kits and patterns I've ever heard.

Propellerhead's Reason 2.0

(www.propellerheads.se/)

- **Platform:** Windows/Mac.
- **Bottom line:** For less than $400, you get the software equivalent of thousands of dollars of hardware.

The team at Sweden's Propellerhead Software deserves a huge hug for creating what is, in my opinion, the coolest, most enabling music software on the planet. The team has managed to cram audio interfaces, mixers, drum machines, samplers, sequencers, and synths—all of which work splendidly together—into a $400 application.

Every type of instrument works and sounds like its hardware equivalent, although it's a bit more difficult to manipulate knobs and buttons using a mouse (unless you have a MIDI controller).

Version 2.0 includes two new instruments:

- **Malstrom.** A granular polysynthesizer that can create unusual undulating tones.
- **NN-XT Advanced Sampler.** This tool lets you manipulate sampled loops with ease and precision.

Other improvements include a detachable sequencer window, a new sound library, and full Mac OS X support.

Mac Tips

LeanStream

Brett Larson

Looking for a free and easy way to stream your favorite audio content? LeanStream (www.melonsoft.com/products/leanstream), from Melonsoft, works with both OS X and OS 9, and is quick to set up.

First, put together a playlist. Select the + key to add files to your playlist. Use the file browser to find your .mp3 files. When in your playlist, check your settings to make sure you've set a reasonable number of listeners and a port number.

Open iTunes. Select Advanced, Open Stream, and type in your IP number plus the port in the previous step. You'll enjoy everything in your playlist in the same order.

MusicMatch Tips

Patrick Norton

MusicMatch (www.music-match.com) is one of my favorite applications. It can do a lot, including burn audio CDs. Best of all, MusicMatch is free.

Don't just hit Record. Go to Options, Settings, and select the Recorder tab. Start with the Recording Format drop-down list in the Recording Quality dialog. I usually encode in MP3 format; if you click Custom Quality, you'll find the slider set to 160Kbps. That's great for small portables, but 192Kbps is better. For hard-drive MP3 players, I crank it up to 320Kbps.

Got more than one CD-R drive? Want to record an old tape through your line-in jack on your sound card? Use the Recording Source drop-down to select the source of the music.

The whole point of legally ripping MP3s is to get the best audio quality possible. Make sure you check Digital in the CD Recording Mode box. Notice that Error Correction check box? Error Correction tries to filter out noise and fix the problems created by scratches on the disc. It increases recording time, so compare the results with Error Correction turned on and off.

The Tracks Directory button brings up a dialog that controls where your new MP3s are stored and what information is stored in the name of the file. Some MP3 players won't stack an album's songs in the correct order unless the track number is included in the MP3's file-name. If this is the case with your player, check Track Number in the Name Track File box.

Finally, the trick stuff is hidden in the Advanced Recording Options dialog. Just click Advanced Recording Options.

Download of the Day

Musical Screen Savers

Megan Morrone

Musical screen savers provide a novel way to torment your co-workers. They also deliver an invigorating surprise in a silent room. (Adjust the time settings and volume accordingly.)

Several options await the screen saver lover in you. We've found a few of the best.

Britney Spears (www.winsite.com). Winsite's download includes a wallpaper utility that will have you singing "I'm not that innocent" all day.

LeAnn Rimes (www.celebrityscreensavers.com). With rotating pictures and annoying MIDI music versions of LeAnn Rimes's favorites, you'll have your co-workers in a tizzy in no time. It's a snap to download, at 3.8MB.

Pete Yorn (http://download.com). Pete Yorn happens to be a favorite of mine. Download this free program and enjoy the sweet sounds of this indie musician. He's not too hard on the eyes, either. There's an easy Sound Off/On Button in case your co-workers get really annoyed.

Elvis (http://download.com). We've managed to narrow our Elvis selections to two. Both feature the King in his later years. Both contain a montage of photos to a musical track. Unfortunately, there are no vocals on either program.

Bouncing Beethoven (http://download.com.). For the classical lovers, here's Bouncing Beethoven, which features spinning and bouncing busts of you-know-who.

Louis Armstrong Tribute Screen Saver (http://download.com). This excellent Satchmo saver features music, photos, and quotes from Louis Armstrong.

Sopranoland (www.sopranoland.com). Enjoy images of your favorite Mafia family while the theme song from the HBO series plays.

Saturday
May 15
2004

Standalone MP3 Player

Patrick Norton and Joshua Brentano

Want to dedicate an older machine to playing MP3s? No problem. You need at least a Pentium 100. Forget about 386-class systems and anything below a 486DX100 is tough. Frankly, if you raid your parts closet or hit a few garage sales, you can put together a system to play MP3s for really cheap.

The Basics: Linux

It'd be nice if somebody built a Linux install that fits on a floppy, autodetects your sound-card, and pops up a (TV-friendly) GUI that you can browse from across the room. If there is one, I can't find it.

You need a 486-class machine. Find at least a Pentium—anything less than DX100, and you're better off building an old-fashioned DOS boot disk, right down to the audio drivers and downloading DAMP (www.damp-mp3.co.uk) or MPXPlay (http://maxplay.tripod.com). You say you're a Windows type? Windows only? The only Windows-based MP3 player I had any luck playing MP3s—even of weak quality without skipping—is Soritong's Sonique.

Stick with a basic SoundBlaster sound card, to keep your DOS/ISA configuration woes to a minimum. I picked up a wireless mouse (just under $20 at CompUSA) to control this box from the living room coffee table.

The Basics: Windows

With a Pentium 90/100 or better, you can use Win95/98. Winamp (www.winamp.com) works. Demo Andromeda (www.turnstyle.com/andromeda), works too. You won't be doing anything else on that machine but playing MP3s.

PCI slot? You can use a SoundBlaster Live sound card, or, for better audio on the cheap, TurtleBeach's Santa Cruz.

The Basics: Faster PC

Using a PC faster than a Pentium 100? Use any software you want. Winamp is our fave. Turning up the font size in the Preferences helps.

Feeling aggressive? Put together a home entertainment box with a DVD player and a spiffy wireless (and mousepad free) mouse.

When it comes to the sound card, go with a high-end card, such as Digital Audio Lab's CardD (www.digitalaudio.com).

DAMP and others offer extensions to show ID3 tag information on an LCD display, but be forewarned that browsing for files this way is tough.

Want to use the TV in the rumpus room to display your files? You'll need a graphics card with a TV output.

Keyboard and Mouse

Because you'll be sitting on your couch, you need a wireless keyboard and mouse. Be sure to get a radio frequency (RF) device; infrared (IR) will severely limit the distance you can be from the MP3 player. There are many wireless RF keyboards; here are a couple we found:

- **Gyration Gyro Remote and Wireless RF Keyboard** (www.gyration.com)
- **Focus Electronics FK-730 Radio Wireless Keyboard** (www.focustaipei.com)

Playlists

Playlists are your friends. Make up playlists to follow your mood or to keep a party pumping. Then you won't have to sit down and drag 'n' drop together a playlist before you start listening.

The easy route: Use dedicated hardware MP3 player, such as the Sonicblue Rio Receiver (www.rioaudio.com).

Leo and Patrick's Portable MP3 Player Picks

Leo Laporte

Are you looking for an MP3 player but you don't know what to buy?

Like Patrick, I still own and use my classic Sonicblue Rio 500 (www.rioaudio.com). That's right, not the more recent Rio 600 or Rio 800. The 500 is a model of form and function that exactly suits my needs.

I added a 64MB memory card to give the Rio 500 about two hours of playing time. That's starting to look meager compared to more recent MP3 players, but for rock-solid performance in a tiny player, the Rio 500 can't be beat.

As runners-up in this category, I'd like to mention my Sony CLIE (www.sonystyle.com) Palm OS PDA and my HP Jornada (http://hp-at-home.com) 565 Pocket PC 2002 PDA. I've added 128MB of solid-state memory to both, so they equal the playing capacity of the Rio 500. The PDA devices are much bigger, but they make up for the added size by adding functionality, not only as PDAs but also with better MP3 players. I use my Jornada every day for audio books from Audible.com.

MP3/CD Players

I was sure the MP3/CD player would revolutionize the MP3 player market. Its capacity—650MB of MP3s per disc (more than 100 songs, or roughly 10 audio CDs)—is huge. Bring 10 MP3 CDs with you, and you've got enough music for several days without repeating. These babies sport good battery life and infinite capacity at a very reasonable price. And if you have a CD burner, it's the easiest way to make a MP3 collection permanently portable.

The drawbacks are that they're bigger than the other MP3 players, and the small LCD screens make them less than ideal for track information. I'm not sure why, but CD/MP3 players just haven't taken off. I've owned several. For my money, the Sonicblue RioVolt SP90 (www.rioaudio.com) is the most functional and delivers the best sound.

Hard-Drive Players

Patrick has always touted the hard drive–based MP3 player. Sure, it has huge capacity, but it's the most expensive solution and it's big, heavy, and offers lousy battery life.

Then came the Apple iPod (www.apple.com/ipod). Apple's second-generation hard drive–based player is a marvel of engineering. It's so cool to have 1,000 songs in a package that's not much bigger than my Rio 500. The software functionality is excellent, and it gets better with each release. And the battery life is 10 hours, comparable to my other players. The price is still exorbitant, but the iPod is a beautiful piece of technology that has quickly become my all-time favorite MP3 player.

Talkback

Who Wants 3D TV?

Dave Roos

I've seen a lot of 3D movies, and each one stunk in its own special way. I don't blame the 3D technology; I blame the context in which it's used—everything from Epcot Center's infamous Michael Jackson-in-space flick *Captain EO* to the IMAX supermovies that frequently inspire nausea rather than awe.

Yet, despite the fact that 3D technology has not evolved beyond mere gimmickry in every medium from cinema to PC video games, a stubborn few believe 3D is the future of TV, much like color was the inevitable future of black-and-white.

Would you pay for special hardware and software to watch 3D movies at home? Is this just another high-tech fad?

Just a gimmick   51%

Future of TV   49%

How to Burn an Audio CD

Mark Klatte

When you burn a CD, you write data, such as audio files or program data, and to a CD-R (compact disc, recordable) or CD-RW (compact disc, rewritable). A CD-R disc holds 72 to 80 minutes of music, or 640MB to 700MB of data, and can be used only once. A CD-RW is rewritable and a bit more expensive than a CD-R.

CD-R and CD-RW drives come in a wide price range, with many configurations and speeds. The higher the speed, the quicker the burn.

For a CD-burning program, we chose Roxio's Easy CD & DVD Creator (www.roxio.com). It's a good, basic, intuitive, easy-to-use program, and it's found on many Windows-based CD-burning setups.

Preparation and Procedure

Close all your programs and turn off the screen saver. It's a good idea to start with a freshly booted computer. You don't want to crash and be stuck with a "coaster" just because someone sent you an instant message in the middle of things.

1. Open your program files folder and double-click Creatr32. You'll see a Welcome window and a choice of Data CD or Audio CD. Select Audio CD, and click Next.

2. Select the songs you want to add. There's a mini-window to help you locate the folder that contains your files. Double-click the file to open it, and you should see the contents of the file folder—the song title, file size, and file type for each file.

3. You can preview any song by double-clicking on it. The Preview window has play, pause, and stop functions. Preview mode is great for putting together a set list or just deciding which files you want to use.

4. Click on a song once to select it. Click Add Now to add it to the queue. The queue is represented by a horizontal bar.

You should see the song in the queue and in the main Easy CD Creator window. Repeat the process to add more songs. When you're finished adding songs, click Next. You can also add the disc title and artist name to the CD. When you're finished, click Next.

5. You can close the session or keep it open. If you leave it open, you can edit the session or add songs later. You can't play the CD until the session is closed, so click Close the Session, and click Next.

6. The Test page gives you the option of "testing" or simulating the entire writing process. If the burn goes well the first time, you probably need to do the test only if your burner hiccups later. Choose either Perform the Test or Do Not Perform the Test and click Next.

7. You'll see the Ready to Create CD page. If you're ready to burn the CD, click Create CD Now and then click Finish. Otherwise, click Create CD Later, and click Finish to save as a CD layout file that you can burn at any time.

Laporte Support

Disc at Once and Track at Once

Ever burn an audio CD-R or CD-RW and find a nasty gap of silence between each track? It's especially vicious if you're trying to keep the "live" flow of a CD going. The opening to a song can get cut off with a two-second delay before the rest of the song starts. Or, your 80 minutes of hypnotic ambient music can get broken up by annoying gaps. This is called "track at once" recording.

For audio CDs, use "disc at once" recording to eliminate the gaps.

Image Browser Arctic

Roger Chang

We always bring you the best free image viewers, file format converters, resizing tools, thumbnail viewers—and you still want more.

Well, you're in luck, because today I have a freeware gem called Image Browser Arctic (www.uticasoft.com/intro.htm) that allows you to do everything I mentioned above, plus create musical slide shows from your digital images. Here's how it works:

1. Launch IBA. Click Tools and Slide Show (or press Ctrl + F1). You are now in the Slide Show Editor.

2. Click the + symbol at the top to add pictures (JPEGs or BMPs) to your slide-show queue. You should see a list of your images.

3. To change the image title to something a little more recognizable, right-click the image, select Title, and edit the text.

4. Use the Changing Slide Method drop-down menu on the left to choose how you want to advance the slides: Mouse Click, Automate, or Synch with Audio.
   - **Mouse Click.** Advance each slide with a left-click.
   - **Automate.** Advance each slide after a set time. To set the time, highlight an image and select a time from the Set Timer drop-down menu. Don't use the shortest time setting if you plan to use transition effects. The image will not completely reveal itself.
   - **Synch With Audio.** Synch slide show advancement with your MP3 music.

5. If you want to add a transition, highlight an image and select an effect from the Transition drop-down menu.

6. Below the main window is a button titled "More Options." Click it to select your MP3 music and author splash screen.

7. Click Compile to create a stand-alone slide show executable.

Transfer Tape to CD

Greg Melton

First, you need to connect a tape player to your sound card's line-in terminal with a 1/8-inch mini-jack and record the contents of a tape as a WAV file. We recommend using the free version of Musicmatch. Just set Musicmatch to record the line-in channel, press Play on your tape deck, and press Record on Musicmatch Jukebox.

After you've done that, you'll be converting the analog sound on the tape into digital audio, breaking it down into numbers. Welcome to the world of digitizing.

After you've recorded a WAV file, it's easy to make an audio CD-R. We recommend a program called Spin Doctor from Roxio (www.roxio.com). It's part of Roxio's Easy CD & DVD Creator 6. You also need a CD-R drive, of course. When you've gathered all the necessary hardware and software, read "How to Burn an Audio CD," on May 17.

Before you create the CDs, you might want to transfer the WAV files to an editing studio. Pro Tools (www.digidesign.com), Sound Forge (www.sonicfoundry.com), and Cool Edit Pro (www.syntrillium.com) work just fine. Let your budget determine which one you get.

Personalize and Organize Your MP3s

Nicole Guilfoyle

Imagine trying to keep your MP3s organized without knowing the names of the songs and artists or the track information. Programmers ran into this problem when they first started converting CD audio to MP3. Then came the ID3 tagging system.

ID3 tags let you keep track of the audio information, including a song's title, album information, artist, genre, cover art, lyrics, and even the mood you associate with a song.

Add ID3 Tags to MP3s

Most desktop MP3 players let you manipulate ID3 tags to organize and personalize music. Let's use Musicmatch Jukebox (www.musicmatch.com) as an example.

To edit an MP3 ID3 tag in Musicmatch Jukebox, follow these directions:

1. Open Musicmatch Jukebox and make sure the track you want to edit isn't playing when you edit the MP3 information.

2. Click the My Library tab.

3. Open the Tag Songs screen by high-lighting a song. Click Tag at the top of the Music Library window. Or right-click a track and select Edit Track Tag.

4. Select information from drop-down menus or specify your information. You can even put a URL and email address in the Notes and Bios section.

Your new tags will appear in the Track Info screen.

Your MP3 player can also display a picture while you play a song:

1. Download or scan a CD album cover, for example, and save it as a .bmp or .jpg in the Musicmatch Jukebox file or subdirectory.

2. Click Edit Track Tags.

3. Click Find Art File.

4. Find the file in the Art box, and click OK.

We like Musicmatch Jukebox (www.musicmatch.com), TagMaster from AnalogX (www.analogx.com), and mp3Trim (www.logiccell.com) for editing ID3 tags.

Talkback

Did Downloading Die with Napster?

Dave Roos

Napster was more than a popular piece of software. It was a religion. When users logged on, they stayed on, sometimes foregoing sleep and sustenance for one more song. Back in 2000, you could say (with a straight face) that you were part of the file-sharing "community." You opened your hard drive to the music-hungry masses, and it felt like a revolution, not grand theft.

But when Napster died, so did the "MP3 revolution." With the rash of post-Napster clones and the ensuing lawsuits, file sharing began to feel less like a community and more like a crime.

Did your file-sharing fanaticism die with Napster? Has your MP3 experience been cheapened by the explosion of file-sharing sites and the constant lawsuits?

Are you downloading more music post-Napster?

Yes   70%

No   30%

Reset the Apple iPod

Patrick Norton

I feel like a small child who has whacked his Tonka truck one too many times. Except I swear I haven't whacked my iPod. It's just been bouncing around in my backpack. And, in defense of the iPod, I have yet to keep any hard-drive player in my backpack for more than a few months without it needing a rebuild.

How do you know the iPod is dead? It won't fire up when you press a button. You've tried to reset by pressing the Play and Menu buttons down at the same time. The iPod logo should appear. The regular iPod menu should show up. Instead, mine shows a file folder with a little tiny triangle over one corner. Inside is a little tiny exclamation point. That's a bad sign; it means the iPod can't find its software.

Here are the links to rebuild it:

- IPod software updater 1.1 (`www.apple.com/ipod/download`). This software updates the software on the iPod. Duh. You need it to update the iPod or to restore it.

- How to update the iPod (`www.apple.com/support/ipod`). Updating the software just loads the latest software and firmware onto the iPod.

- How to restore the iPod (`www.apple.com\support/ipod`). If updating doesn't revive it, you'll need to restore the iPod. That completely erases the disk; you will lose all your data. That might be the only way to bring your iPod back to life. Hope you backed up.

- IPod hacks (`www.apple.com/support/ipod`). Go ahead. I dare you. You know how to restore it.

- IPod Diagnostic Mode (`http://ipoding.com`). This doesn't work for version 1.04 of the iPod, but it works fine for early and later versions. (The iPod has a two-finger and a three-finger salute! Who knew?) Props to the folks at iPoding for having the information up. Don't enter this mode without reading up first. (Unfortunately, it tells me my iPod's hard drive is dead. Urg.)

Morgan's Tips

Mute

Not getting any sound from your computer? Maybe you have mute turned on. Here's how you can check:

1. Open the Control Panel.
2. Select Sounds and Audio Devices.
3. Click Volume.
4. Make sure Mute is unchecked.

Download of the Day

Smoke

Megan Morrone

In the past, I've shown you a program called Dremples (`www.geisswerks.com/drempels`) and a program called Geiss (`www.geisswerks.com/geiss`). Both are funky visualizations for the PC created by Ryan Geiss. Now Ryan has a new Winamp plug-in called Smoke (`www.nullsoft.com/free/smoke/`). Like Geiss, it creates colorful patterns to go along with your music. The new twist is that it simulates fluid dynamics, the branch of science that has to do with the movement of gas and liquids.

System requirements:

- Windows 98 or higher
- Video card with 3D support
- Winamp
- 500MHz processor or higher

Where Can I Find and Download MP3s?

Greg Melton

Where can an honest person go to find MP3s?

P2P Applications

- **Gnutella** (www.gnutella.com). Developed by the same team that brought the world Winamp, Gnutella is similar to Napster, but it doesn't use a centralized server to facilitate transfers.

- **Audiogalaxy** (www.audiogalaxy.com). Use Audiogalaxy to select which songs to download from other members, and then watch the client software facilitate the file transfer. It works best with Internet Explorer.

- **KaZaA** (www.kazaa.com). This peer-to-peer file-sharing program is similar to Gnutella. One selling point: KaZaA finds the fastest download.

- **BearShare** (www.bearshare.com). BearShare lets you search for, download, and share files with everyone on Gnutella's global peer-to-peer network. After a quick download, the Connection Setup Wizard makes it easy to start downloading. Give this client a try, and you'll see why thousands are switching to BearShare.

- **Napigator** (www.napigator.com). Napigator is a tiny download that acts as a front-end launcher for Napster and essentially gives you control over what server you download from.

- **Zeropaid** (www.zeropaid.com). Use this portal to stay up-to-date on the latest and greatest P2P applications.

Real-Time Chat Trading

You can trade MP3 files using the file transfer feature of popular chat clients such as ICQ (http://web.icq.com), mIRC (www.mirc.com), and Aimster (www.aimster.co.uk).

FTP

FTP (File Transfer Protocol) sites are excellent sources for MP3s. Use a FTP program such as CuteFTP (www.cuteftp.com), which has a built-in search engine.

Newsgroups

Newsgroups present another way to collect MP3s, but using this method requires a little extra work.

Websites

The easiest way to download an MP3 from the Internet is to right-click on the link that points to the file and select Save Target As or Save File As (depending on your browser). Then select a directory for the song to be saved in, rename the song (if you choose), and click Save.

Here are some popular websites for listening to, searching for, and downloading MP3s:

- **MP3.com** (www.mp3.com)
- **MP3Board** (www.mp3board.com)
- **Lycos** (http://music.lycos.com/downloads)
- **Audiophilez** (www.audiophilez.com)

Download of the Day

365 Days

Megan Morrone

The promise of dotcom riches is gone. Napster is but a pleasant memory. You can't see your email through all that spam. The government doesn't respect your privacy, and every day you're bombarded with another security threat. Is the Internet good for anything anymore?

Yes.

Thanks to independent artists and musicians such as Otis Fodder, the web is still rich with obscure gems that can delight even the most callused Net cynic. 365 Days (www.otisfodder.com/365days.html) is Fodder's current project to post a free and legal MP3 for every day of the year. The files are primarily obscure and often out-of-print music, with the occasional spoken-word piece thrown in here and there.

Build Your Own Headphone Amp

Patrick Norton

Can you turn a $30 pile of parts into a headphone amplifier? Sure. Will it beat out a $200 headphone amp? Not quite. But if you're willing to work with a soldering iron, you can have a portable headphone amp and get outstanding sound from your portable audio player.

Props and thanks go to a viewer who sent me a headphone amp that he built into a mint tin, based on a design by Chu Moy (www.gradolabs.com). It's one of many projects Moy has posted on an excellent do-it-yourself website called HeadWize (http://headwize.powerpill.org).

Why You Need an Amp

I spend a lot of time listening to music over headphones. Headphones don't bother the neighbors when I'm jamming at 4:00 in the morning. I own three pairs of Grado Labs (www.gradolabs.com) headphones, and my favorite pair is my Prestige Series model SR225. It's epic sound for rock, ska, jazz, whatever.

The 225s suffer when connected directly to most portable players. I have a HeadRoom Little (www.headphone.com) amp for use at home. Awesome sound. There are also portable amps such as the HeadRoom Airhead (about $120) and HeadRoom Total Airhead (about $200).

Make Your Own

With $30 a soldering iron, you can build your own portable headphone amp.

Moy's original plans call for a pair of Burr-Brown OPA134 opamps ($2.10 each from Digi-Key [www.digikey.com], part number OPA134PA-ND [http://focus.ti.com]), one for each channel of stereo.

A viewer built his around a single Burr-Brown OPA2134 ($2.63, also from Digi-Key, part number OPA2134PA-ND). The 2134 is essentially a stereo OPA134; it packs two OPA134s into a single 8-pin chip. You can pack two 9-volt batteries for a tad more power on tap.

For the complete plans to building your own headphone amp, read about the pocket headphone amplifier project at HeadWize.

Phone Call to MP3

Greg Melton

If you have a fax/voice modem, you have the capability to connect your telephone to your PC. Just install Phone Dialer from your Windows disk, and you're almost ready to record. Consult your manual if you need help connecting your phone to your modem.

1. Left-click Start, mouse over Settings, and select Control Panel.

2. In the Control Panel, double-click Add/Remove Programs, and click Windows Setup.

3. In the Components list, click Communications, then click Details.

4. In the Communications dialog, click Phone Dialer, then click OK.

5. Insert the Windows disk to finish installing Phone Dialer.

To start Phone Dialer and make a call, follow these steps:

1. Click Start and point to Programs, Accessories, Communications. Then click Phone Dialer.

2. In the Phone Dialer dialog, type a telephone number using either the keyboard or the Phone Dialer numeric keypad.

3. Click Dial.

If you don't have a fax/modem, here are some other options:

- **Recorder Telephone Pickup** (www.radioshack.com)
- **RL-100** (www.ahernstore.com)
- **Deluxe Recorder Control** (www.radioshack.com)
- **ACS Telephone Recording Jack** (works with PBX systems, www.ahernstore.com)
- **Voice Path** (www.jkaudio.com)

High Criteria makes the Call Recording Director 110 (about $90, www.highcriteria.com). It does a good job sending audio from an analog phone line directly to your sound card to use with any sound-recording software.

A better value is DynaMetric's TMP-636 (about $80, www.dynametric.com), which is compatible with analog and digital phone lines and can play back any audio over the phone line. DynaMetric has other adapters that don't play back audio and cost even less.

TT Systems (www.ttsystems.com) has the TR-50 and TR-70. Although they don't say anything about being used through the line-in or microphone-in of a computer sound card, they'll operate that way. The TR-70 works with both phone lines, and can play back audio over the phone (is not automated to switch between playback and recording).

All require connecting the device to the sound card's line-in or microphone jacks. Remember which jack you plug the peripheral device into so you can configure Musicmatch correctly.

Software

You can use Dictation Buddy from High Criteria (about $32, www.highcriteria.com) for dictation and phone conversation or for transcription purposes. It can encode into MP3. One of its best features is the capability to bookmark, for import, important points in the recording, and to add descriptive text notes.

The ModemSpy (www.modemspy.com) is a tricky piece of software that does exactly what its name says: spy. It can automatically record, in stealth, every single call from a given phone line. Calls can also be automatically labeled with times and caller ID information.

Phone Call to MP3 (continued)

If you're using a fax/voice modem, go ahead and try making a call with Phone Dialer. If you're using a peripheral device, try picking up the phone to detect a dial tone. Do you hear anything? Make sure everything is connected correctly and that nothing is muted inside the Volume Control panel.

To access the Volume Control panel, left-click the Start menu and mouse over Programs, Accessories, Entertainment. Choose Volume Control.

Configure Musicmatch

To configure Musicmatch to record an MP3, follow these directions:

1. Open Musicmatch.
2. Mouse over Options, Recorder, Quality, and select MP3 (128Kbps).

Musicmatch can be configured to receive an audio signal in four ways: line-in, microphone, system mixer, or CD-ROM. For a fax/voice modem, set the recording source to the system mixer. For a peripheral device, set it to the jack (line-in or microphone); it's connected to your sound card.

Mouse over Options, Recorder, Source, and choose the option that's right for you to set Musicmatch's recording source.

It's Time to Begin Recording

If everything has been set up and configured correctly, it's time to start recording. Open Musicmatch's Recording dialog.

1. Go to View and select Recorder.
2. Before you start, highlight Edit Track Name Here Before Beginning, and change the name.
3. When everything checks OK, press REC on the recorder.

Unless you've changed the default recording path, the program automatically places all recorded files inside C:\My Documents\My Music\Artists\Album. Look for the track name you labeled, and double-click it to play it back.

Build an MP3 Player

Patrick Norton

I'm going to use the PJRC High Capacity MP3 Player (www.pjrc.com/tech/mp3) to build an MP3 player. This isn't the first time I've tried. I would have shown the kit before, but I melted the power inverter for the monitor's backlight. I should point out that my PJRC MP3 player never stopped working it just works erratically. What else could you expect from a project that has had folks developing its firmware in fits and starts for years?

My PJRC History

Let's fill in the backstory: It's September 16, 2000, when the only hard drive–based MP3 player around, the PJB100 (www.pjbox.com), cost a whopping $700.

The PJRC High Capacity MP3 Player Board costs less than $150. There's no display, but compared to the $700 PJB100, I can live without one. I immediately bought one before the supply was sold out. (I know how well I solder, so I bought the finished board.)

Then and now, you build a case and provide the hard drive and a power supply. The board includes a 72-pin SIMM slot, connectors for 3.5- and 2.5-inch hard drives, and power inputs for 12-volt adapters or AA batteries. It also packs buttons for Next File, Play/Pause, Previous File, Random Mode, Volume Up, and Volume Down.

Even finished, the board was decidedly a work in progress. Back then, the firmware couldn't access the DRAM. If memory serves, Random Mode didn't work and the volume buttons were sketchy.

I was thrilled. I added a spare notebook hard drive, a 12-volt car lighter adapter, and my car cassette adapter. I had hours of MP3s.

Back to the Future

Now you can pick up a back-lit display for about $77. The main board costs about $150 assembled. Hard drives are cheaper, and you still provide a case.

Considering the cost, it's not exactly a bargain. A 10GB iPod or 20GB Creative Nomad Jukebox Zen are about $300. Neither requires you to Telnet in firmware updates over a serial cable or transfer files to the hard drive by connecting it to your home system.

Neither lets you design your own case with a giant blue display, either.

That's the fun of the PRJC MP3 kit. It remains a work in progress, especially the firmware. Support for browsing folders and .M3U playlists looms on the PJRC's horizon. All the buttons now work, and the board can access the SIMM, which caches MP3s, saving battery life.

You can access regular snapshots of the PRJC MP3 Firmware at www.davidgillham.com/tech/pjrc/.

The PJRC Homebrew MP3 Player Discussion site (http://groups.yahoo.com/group/pjrcmp3/) has an active forum to troubleshoot and offer ideas for the software. The group talks about everything from USB access to the hard drive, to plans for adding an IR remote.

I Did It

Do-it-yourself projects are not for the faint of heart, especially when you're creating a power supply. I know this; I've broken my share of parts. When I finally build this into the dashboard of my truck, or build an aluminum case and stack it in my home stereo, well, I know it'll be a lot more fun than simply hitting the plastic on an assembled MP3 player. Of course, that could take three years less of waiting.

Alcohol 120%

Kevin Rose

When I purchased my first CD-R drive (1x speed), the standard for burning CD-Rs was Easy CD Creator. Somewhere between the launch of Windows 2000 and the launch of Windows XP, Easy CD's market share started to give way to Nero's market share. Today Nero is my CD-burning software of choice. It's rock-solid, it's easy-to-use, and it works great for burning and backing up data and music CDs. But it can't handle copy-protected data CDs, such as games.

Most new games released in the United States have some form of copy protection. If you stick a new game in the CD-ROM drive, put a blank in the CD-R, and click Copy, you'll probably get errors and the copied disc won't work. The solution: Alcohol 120%.

Copy Protection

Several CD copy-protection solutions are out there, including SafeDisc (www.macrovision.com), StarForce (www.star-force.com), and SecuRom (www.securom.com). Most of these solutions work by duplicating errors. When it's created, a copy-protected data disc is burned with unique errors or physical flaws. Under normal usage, these errors are ignored. But when you try to copy the disc, the CD-burning software tries to correct the errors. After receiving the first few errors, the burning software decides that the disc is damaged and aborts the burn.

Alcohol 120% (www.alcohol-software.com) can duplicate the errors on new CD-Rs using a different backup method for each type of copy protection. Backing up your games is a two-step process:

1. You must identify the type of copy protection used on your games. But how? Use the Internet.

2. Fire up Alcohol 120% and select Copy Wizard.

3. Under Data Type, choose the copy protection of your game.

4. Click Next and begin your burn.

Hard-Drive Backup

You can also back up and run games on your hard drive:

1. Choose the Image Making Wizard in Alcohol 120%.

2. Choose Data Type.

3. Select the copy protection of your game.

4. Click Backup to create a duplicate CD image on your hard drive.

When you have the image on the hard drive, you can mount it as a virtual CD drive and run the game directly from the hard drive. This saves you from swapping out CDs, and runs the game up to 200 times faster.

Download of the Day

CDex CD Ripper

Morgan Webb

CDex (http://cdex.sourceforge.net) has long been my favorite CD ripper, for several reasons:

- It's easy to use.
- It's freeware.
- It's open source (which always makes me feel more confident about software).
- It uses the high-quality LAME encoder (which is also open source).

CDex rips the digital data straight off your CD. Other programs turn the digital signal into analog as it runs through the sound card, and then turn it back to digital to encode it to MP3.

CDex also has access to CDDB (the Compact Disk Data Base) built into it, so if you have an Internet connection, you don't have to type the song names.

iTunes Tour

Leo Laporte

In my day, when I wanted to take my music with me, I dubbed it, in real time, from a vinyl record to a cassette. The shelves for my music collection took up most of a good-size apartment wall.

I had a little velvet-covered pad called a Discwasher for buffing my LPs before I played them. Back then, pops, clicks, and hisses were a fact of life.

The more you played a record, the worse it sounded. Of course, in my day, Debbie Boone had the no. 1 record in the land and people thought Bob Dylan was pretty radical.

That's so old school, and I couldn't be happier about it. In transforming vinyl LPs and cassette tapes to bits and bytes on a hard drive, the digital revolution revitalized the art of music. And the business of music is going along, kicking and screaming.

With digital technology, nearly anyone can create music without spending a king's ransom for Sun Studios, and no polycarbons are necessary to get that music to listeners. The bits can flow nearly seamlessly from a musician's instrument to your ears. Fans can share music and transport it anywhere, easily.

Digital Revolution

MP3 and Napster started the digital music revolution. Now, as it has done so often with other technologies, Apple has reinvented the music player in a most elegant, attractive, and useful form.

The new holy trinity of digital music is the iPod, iTunes, and the iTunes Music Store. Taken together, they let me buy my favorite albums, copy them to my computer, and carry them wherever I go. I can share my music with any computer in my house and with friends anywhere on the Internet. If I feel nostalgic, I can even burn them to a CD.

Create MP3 Playlists

Nicole Guilfoyle

Creating an MP3 playlist in Windows Media Player is not easy, nor is it intuitive. Usually you need to search your hard drive for media, find the MP3 you want, and add each song to the playlist one by one. Here's a simple and quick way to organize your MP3s without the hassle:

1. Open Windows Media Player and go to the media library.

2. Create a new playlist or double-click the icon for the playlist you'd like to use.

3. Open the folder where you store your MP3s on your hard drive.

4. Select the songs in your playlist. Hold down the Ctrl key to choose multiple MP3s.

5. Drag the MP3s into the right pane of your playlist.

Laporte Support

Edit MP3s

To trim the blank space in MP3 files, use mp3Trim (www.logiccell.com/~mp3trim). The free version lets you cut the blank space at the beginning and end of your MP3s. It also can normalize the files to play at the same volume.

When you edit an MP3, the editor reads the file as the number of frames. In your typical audio editor, sound data is seen as a wave. Most MP3 editors, such as mp3Trim, display the MP3s in frames.

Music Mayhem

Brett Larson

The latest version of iTunes lets you encode your songs as several different types of music files, including AIFF, MP3, and AAC. But which should you choose? Today I explain the different formats and how to use iTunes to get those music tracks onto your PC.

To start encoding files in iTunes 4, open Preferences, select Import, and pick your file format. Here are your options:

- AIFF files are as big as CD files, but they also offer CD quality. ITunes gives you options to set sample rate, sample size, and channels. Each change will affect quality of the finished product. It's best to leave it on Auto.

- MP3 is an old favorite. They're small files, can sound almost as good as CDs at the right data rate, and you can use them on portable players. ITunes gives you tons of options for encoding to MP3, including stereo bit rate, sample rate, channels, and stereo mode (joint or normal). You can also choose Variable Bit Rate (VBR) encoding, which picks the bit rate as it goes for the best sound. These files can get big, so be warned.

- AAC files are smaller than MP3s and are of higher quality! However, your encoding options are a little more limited. You can pick bit rate, sample rate, and channels (stereo or mono). The default is fine and sounds great.

If you want to share high-quality files with Windows users, consider the WAV format. The files are as big as AIFF files, but work better with Windows.

Must-Have CD-Burning Software

Roman Loyola

Make your own CDs. Everyone is doing it. They're making everything from custom music mixes to data backups and archives.

Must-Have Tools

Here are Leo and Patrick's recommendations for CD burning:

- **Music CDs:** Musicmatch Jukebox (www.musicmatch.com). Use the free version to make music CDs. You pay about $19 to get a boatload of music-management features. What a deal.

- **ISOs and archiving:** Nero (www.nero.com). When we're downloading Linux ISOs, we turn to Nero.

- **Packet writing:** InstantCD/DVD (www.vob.de). This software comes with support for Universal Disk Format.

- **Bit-for-bit copies:** Blindwrite Suite (www.vso-software.com). This copies exact images of your CDs to your hard drive.

- **Advanced burns:** CDRWin (www.goldenhawk.com). When you need complete control over the disc layout and track spacing, look here.

- **So easy your grandparents can use it:** Roxio Easy CD & DVD Creator (www.roxio.com). A great all-purpose CD-burning package.

May

28

155

MP3 vs. MiniDisc

Roger Chang

MiniDisc technology was developed from Sony's experience in magneto-optical (MO) drives. The MO drive tried to combine the best qualities of CDs and floppy disks. Like CDs, MO discs hold large amounts of data and write or delete data the same as with a floppy disk. With MO, a laser head is located above the disc, and a magnetic head is located below it. First, the laser reads the data from the disc. Second, the disc is heated to allow data to be written to the magneto-optic film.

This technology allows the MiniDisc player to write and erase information from a MiniDisc. However, a MiniDisc holds 160MB of data vs. the CD's 650MB. To compensate for the lack of storage capacity, MiniDisc uses a technology called ATRAC (Adaptive Transform Acoustic Coding).

ATRAC Compression

ATRAC is a "lossy" compression technology, meaning that to reduce data size, information deemed superfluous is removed. The standard ATRAC bit rate is 285.3Kbps. MP3 allows for near–CD-quality music files that can be played on any multimedia PC.

Encoding

Both formats use a form of "lossy" compression, so neither format sounds exactly like the CD it was recorded from. Although some audio engineers say the average person won't notice the "missing" frequencies, tests show that individuals notice things have changed but cannot pinpoint an exact flaw.

Pop, rock, or hip hop tend to be heavily produced with effects filters and sound compressors, and most people won't notice anything. You will notice that MiniDisc has a slight edge in music that has greater dynamic range, such as classical or jazz.

Storage

You're limited to the size of the MiniDisc medium (either 74- or 80-minute discs). Using additional compression via the LP modes on newer MiniDisc players will almost quadruple your storage.

Hard-drive MP3 players offer a seemingly endless amount of space, with 6GB and up to 20GB on some models. Flash-memory MP3 players are the most limiting, with the highest

CF media card at 1GB. The best solution is the CD/MP3 hybrid players that allow MP3s to be burned onto a CD-R/W disc. CD/MP3 hybrids can play regular audio CDs as well.

Hardware

Many MiniDisc players let you record from a variety of line-in sources, including a microphone. MP3 players usually hook up directly to a computer to transfer music or delete files. To use an MP3 player, you need a computer; a MiniDisc requires only a CD player, a home stereo, or a microphone.

Music Sharing

To prevent unauthorized copying, SCMS (Serial Copy Management System) is encoded on a MiniDisc any time you copy from a digital source. SCMS thwarts transferring music from one MiniDisc to another digital source, such as DAT or another MiniDisc. The only way to get around SCMS is to use more sophisticated and expensive home- and professional-grade MiniDisc decks, plus a digital format converter that removes the SCMS signal.

If you own a PC and want a lot of music, get an MP3 player. MP3 has no copy protection, so you'll be able to trade without loss in sound quality.

However, if you regularly listen to music that requires higher fidelity, get a MiniDisc player. The format is close to sounding like a CD, and it's lighter and more convenient.

Autocopy Files in iPhoto and iTunes

Brett Larson

When you drag a file into iPhoto or iTunes, the program makes a copy of the file. Here's how to stop the madness.

You can set up iTunes to keep track of your music files in an XML database instead of copying the files into your iTunes Music folder. Here's how:

1. Open the iTunes preferences.

2. Click on Advanced.

3. At the bottom of the window, uncheck Copy Files to the iTunes Music Library.

Now files won't be copied.

Why would you want to copy files? Well, it's great when you're ripping your CDs, because iTunes organizes them in the Music folder. But if you've got a folder of music in, say, your Documents folder, there's no reason to have them duplicated.

Unfortunately, in iPhoto there's no way to stop the unnecessary copying of files. Your files are coming off your camera, and iPhoto wants to make sure it puts them in a safe place on your hard drive. When you've successfully copied photos into your iPhoto library, burn them to CD and discard the original files scattered throughout your computer.

If you check Keep iTunes Music Library Organized, iTunes finds all the matched sets of music (such as all your REM songs) and puts them in easy-to-navigate folders organized by artist.

Download of the Day

Automatically Rename MP3 Files

Dan Mitchell

If you download an album as one file and then split it up, you have to name each individual song and enter in the ID3 tag information by hand. Or worse, if you download songs one at a time from various sources, you have to rename each song. But thanks to this free file, you'll never again have to manually enter another MP3 filename or ID3 tag.

PsychicMP3 (`www.medic.dk/index.htm`) uses FreeDB to look up track and ID3 information. Simply select the proper folder and click the Query button. The program will then offer a list of possible albums (it nails it almost every time). Once you pick the right album it'll display the new filenames. Click the Rename Files button and PsychicMP3 will automatically rename every file in the folder. It's that easy.

So do yourself a favor: Download PsychicMP3, stop manually entering track titles, and give your carpal tunnel a break. If you already use a file renaming program, get rid of it. I doubt it's in the same ballpark as PsychicMP3.

May

30

MP3Gain

Richard Statter and Craig Higdon

Your television's volume seems to get 10dB louder when a program breaks into a commercial. Who knows why TV networks let that slide. Now we've noticed a similar thing happening with MP3s.

MP3s can be ripped at different volume settings, and they retain this information as they're swapped from PC to PC. To listen to your MP3s at the same volume, you need to calibrate, or "normalize," the recording levels. MP3Gain is a great program to get the job done.

1. Open MP3Gain (www.geocities.com/ mp3gain) and click the Add File(s) button.

2. Find the files you want to convert, select them, and click Open. Continue adding files until all the MP3s you want to normalize are in the File List.

3. Set your target volume in decibels (dB) in the Target "Normal" Volume field. You can also choose to leave the level at the default 89dB setting.

4. Click the Radio Analysis button. MP3Gain analyzes the files to report the current volume level and the change required to meet the target volume.

5. Select the files that don't meet the Target "Normal" Volume. Make note of the MP3's original volume level (the value under the Volume column) if you want to modify the volume setting back to its original value.

6. Click the Radio Gain button to modify the files with the volume settings you chose for Target "Normal" Volume.

7. Listen to your new MP3s. If they sound too loud or too quiet, adjust the Target Volume setting and click Radio Gain again.

It seems like a lot of steps, but MP3Gain does most of the work for you. The hardest part is finding the files you want to normalize. As long as you know where your MP3s are stored on your hard drive, you'll love MP3Gain.

Windows Tips

Make CDs Autoload in Windows 98

1. In the Control Panel, double-click System.
2. Choose Device Manager.
3. Expand the CD-ROM branch and double-click on the drive.
4. Select Setting.
5. Check Auto Insert Notification.

Download of the Day

Media Library

Brett Larson

Want to organize everything in your life? Whether or not your media is digital, I have a freeware solution for you. Media Library (www.tiff-tools.com) makes a library out of your media, whatever it may be.

Quickly enter new records into the database, including information such as box number, customer name, description, and CD number. Once you've filled in your information, search your inventory for any of these criteria.

I found only one downside in this free file: a banner ad. Granted, you're getting a pretty useful tool for organizing your never-ending collection of CDs, DVDs, home videos, or recordings of your favorite mac tips.

June 2004

Weird and Wonderful World Wide Web

Megan Morrone

Since its humble beginnings, the web has been a lot of things—laboratory, library, red-light district, and artistic forum, to name just a smattering. These days, the web is still all of the above and a lot more. This month we have lists of our favorite sites and tips that will help enhance your web-surfing experience. You'll also find that many pages in this chapter are devoted to our favorite new online phenomenon, the weblog.

Like the web itself, weblogs (also called blogs) can be many different things. They're personal diaries, public journals, news sources, and communities organized around a specific interest. Weblogs are young. They haven't truly defined themselves yet. However, two characteristics unite all weblogs: They're updated regularly, and anyone can create one.

In the three years since I started keeping my weblog (www.jumpingmonkeys.com) I've made enough mistakes and received enough feedback to offer you my tips on starting your own:

1. **Have something to say.** Always consider your audience. Unless you're Jennifer Aniston, Scott Peterson, or someone living in Iraq, most people probably aren't interested in the mundane details of your life. They may, however, be interested in your personal take on those details.

2. **Write well.** You don't have to be Shakespeare, but you should have a grasp of proper grammar and punctuation. The fewer errors you have in your work, the more people will take your ideas seriously. Remember, most people don't like to read long paragraphs on the web. Get your ideas across succinctly, and you'll have more readers.

3. **Provide links.** Use your medium. The beauty of the web is that you can use links to easily elaborate. Most weblog programs make it easy to create hyperlinks, even if you don't know HTML. If you find an interesting link on someone else's weblog, don't forget to give that person credit.

4. **Add photos.** The web is a visual medium. Illustrate your entries with photos, but be kind to your visitors and don't overdo it. Keep the resolution low, or create a thumbnail or text link to the image. It's best to use photos and images of your own. If you find an image on another website, be sure to ask permission of the copyright owner before you use it.

5. **Never forget that anyone can (and probably will) read what you write.** If you're not interested in having anyone read what you write, then don't publish it on the Net. I encourage you to be honest in your weblog, but before you publish anything, think to yourself, "Do I want my mother to read this?" If the answer is no, then don't publish it. So, have I scared you away from starting your own weblog? I didn't mean to, but if I did, don't worry. Even if you're not into blogs, this month you'll still find tons of cool sites to browse and tips on navigating the rest of the weird and wonderful world of the web.

Browserless Blogs

Leo Laporte

Does anyone remember Pointcast? People used it to build newspapers by downloading content from different online sources. At many companies, Pointcast was so popular that Internet access ground to a halt at 9:05 a.m. as everyone tried to download Dave Barry's latest column.

Fast-forward to the 21st century. People are once again aggregating their news, this time with RSS. RSS stands for Really Simple Syndication or Rich Site Summary (depending on who you're talking to). Either way, it's an XML standard for syndicating content via the Internet. A site with an RSS URL offers its content in XML so that programs other than web browsers can fetch and format it.

Without RSS, there wouldn't be newsreaders such as NetNewsWire (http://ranchero.com/netnewswire) for Mac OS X and Wildgrape's truly wonderful NewsDesk (www.wildgrape.net) for Windows. These programs let you read news, blog entries, and the like without being cluttered by a general-purpose browser. I use them all the time to check news headlines. They do much the same thing as Pointcast did, but with many more content choices and without clogging the network.

If you want to create a newspaper with the content you want, download an RSS reader. And if you run a site with content that you want other folks to read, make sure you support RSS.

Download of the Day

The Safari Toolkit

Megan Morrone

I've been using Safari (www.apple.com/safari/download) for a while, so it must be time to tweak it. Thanks to a viewer for recommending ScifienceStudios (www.scifience.net), which offers a way to change the brushed-metal appearance of Safari, get rid of underlines in links, and enable hidden debugging features.

Download the program and double-click the drive icon that appears on your desktop. Double-click the tweaks you want to install. You might have to drag the Enable Debug Menu.sh file into the terminal to make it work. ScifienceStudios includes easy uninstallers, just in case you want to go back to your pretweaked state.

Now if only they could find a way to add tabs to Safari, I might completely convert from Chimera (www.mozilla.org/projects/chimera).

You can download the Safari Toolkit at www.scifience.net. After you've installed the Make Safari Aqua package, run Safari from your Applications folder, not from the Dock. You might have to take Safari out of your Dock and put it back to make it work. Like Safari itself, this program still has a few kinks. If you're still having trouble, try Safari Enhancer 2.0.1 (www.macupdate.com/info.php/id/10482).

Of course, these are tweaks that you can do yourself if you have a little time on your hands. I don't. Do you? If you're looking for other ways to enhance your Safari experience, check out the offerings at Version Tracker (www.versiontracker.com).

Find Out How to Speed up Your Web Surfing

Patrick Norton

When you look at a webpage, you download files, such as the code and image files for that page. Look at the same page every day? Chances are, you're downloading the same files over and over again. It's not that big a deal if you have broadband. But if you're on a dialup, why waste precious bandwidth?

Caching in Your Browser

Check your browser to see how much space you have to store temporary Internet files. Internet Explorer uses space on your hard drive to store the files that make up webpages. Storing these files can speed up browsing, because you're not downloading every element every time you look at that page. If you use Windows 98 or higher, the files are stored in a Temporary Internet Files folder that's found within your Windows folder. Remember, if you're using Windows XP, each user has a Temporary Internet Files folder.

In Internet Explorer, if you open Tools, Internet Options, General tab and click the Settings button under Temporary Internet Files, you can change the amount of drive space used to check pages. You can also set IE to automatically check for newer versions of stored pages when you start IE, or when you go to that page by selecting the Every Visit to the Page option. Mozilla, Netscape, and Opera should have similar settings.

Sharing the Cache

Turning on a cache in a browser works fine for individual users. But if several people browse from a small network of computers, the solution is a central cache of files served from the same proxy server that serves the Internet to all the machines on the network. The files downloaded (and cached) for any computer on the network are available to every computer on the network.

Unfortunately, Microsoft Internet Connection Sharing and AnalogX Proxy Server don't cache files. Neither do most hardware routers between the network and the broadband or dialup account.

What you need is a proxy that can cache websites. If you're a Linux maven, use Squid to cache and proxy the Internet. If you're not into Linux, you'll need to either download a program or build a dedicated server. I especially like SmoothWall. Not only does it act as a cache, but it can talk to modems and PPPoE, and it connects to USB cable modems.

Download Faster

Roger Chang and Nicole Guilfoyle

A lot of products and services promise faster download speeds, but not many deliver. Don't worry. We have three practical tips that actually work.

Upgrade to Broadband

The best way to speed up your downloads is to stop using a dialup connection. Sure it's the least expensive Internet option, but it's slow! If your time is money, seriously consider an upgrade. Here are some numbers we crunched:

- The 97.7MB Unreal Tournament download takes about 3 hours and 58 minutes on a 56Kbps modem. The download takes about 20 minutes on a high-speed line.

- Your friend's band put its new songs online as MP3s. A 5MB download takes about 12 minutes on dialup. That's assuming that you're not disconnected halfway through. If you're rocking the broadband, it'll take you a paltry five or six minutes.

Convinced? After you upgrade, use these tips to optimize your connection.

Don't Download from the Source

A lot of people download from a developer's site, overwhelming its server with requests. If you want a faster response, look for alternative places to download. Mirror sites offer the exact same files at a fraction of the download time. Geographic proximity to a server can affect download speed. Try to find a mirror site close to home.

Use a Download Accelerator

Download accelerators such as Star Downloader (www.stardownloader.com) and Download Express (www.metaproducts.com) request a file over several connections simultaneously. It's the equivalent of separating your groceries into a second shopping cart so that you and a friend can cruise through the express lane.

Sometimes it's faster, sometimes it's not, and sometimes the checker decides to take a lunch break, forcing you to get in line again.

That's right, many sites recently started cutting off downloads when a download accelerator is detected in action.

TechTV Labs recently tested several download accelerators. In general, the LabRats found that download accelerators got the best results for large files such as videos and high-resolution images.

The bottom line: Save the accelerators for your large downloads and search out mirror sites for smaller files.

Talkback

"Have We Fleshmet?"

Dave Roos

We at *The Screen Savers* love a good buzzword, especially when it sounds both ridiculous and mildly erotic.

As it turns out, the term *fleshmet* is older than the World Wide Web. It's a remnant of the early online days when virtual communities were sprouting on text-only networks. *Fleshmet* is the past tense of *fleshmeet*, which, of course, means to meet a person in the flesh rather than chatting with them exclusively online.

What's been your experience with online-only friendships? Are online and off-line friendships equally precious? Could you confide in an online friend?

Can you have a friend you haven't "fleshmet?"

Yes 43%

No 57%

43% Yes

57% No

Customize Your Browser in Windows XP Professional

Morgan Webb

If you have Windows XP Professional, did you know you can change your Internet Explorer title, logo, and toolbar right through the GUI. Just follow these steps:

1. You must be logged in as administrator for this tip to work.

2. Open the Group Policy Editor by going to Start, Run, and then typing **Gpedit.msc**. The Group Policy Editor is available only in Windows XP Professional.

3. Go to User Configuration\Windows Settings\Internet Explorer Maintenance\ Browser User Interface.

4. Click and modify Browser Title to change the title settings.

5. Choose Custom Logo to modify the "thinking" logo in the corner of your browser.

6. Choose and modify Browser Toolbar Customizations to change the bitmap background of your browser.

Customize and enjoy.

Download of the Day

GovernMail

Rich Migliozzi

GovernMail (www.governmail.com) is a nifty application that links you to government representatives in the United States and abroad. Once you download the program, you can view representatives' homepages and send them email. There's a special area for officials of the US Senate and House.

The best part of this program is that users can store their contact information in GovernMail and attach it to their messages, so the representatives can reply. Until now, it seemed like typing up a letter and dropping it in the mail was a waste of time. Did they get it? Did they read it? With GovernMail's easy-to-use browser, you can email one or 50 representatives at once. GovernMail also monitors the website for updates to listings and automatically downloads updates, so you'll always have the latest contact information.

Talkback

What's Your Online Addiction?

Dave Roos

Not everyone is as lucky as we are. In *The Screen Savers* cube farm, it's expected, even encouraged, that an employee spend a minimum of four to five hours a day online. It's our job. But for many folks, web access at work can be an irresistible, productivity-sucking black hole.

At-work web addictions have matured with the times. No longer are workers surreptitiously surfing for porn and gambling. Now it's legit destinations such as news and online-shopping sites that lure in bored cubicle slaves by the millions.

What's your Net addiction?

News   3%
Shopping   1%
Porn   92%
Research   4%

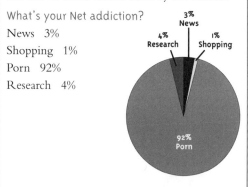

Three Things You Need to Know About Mozilla

Patrick Norton

Enter Mozilla.org (`http://mozilla.org`), and you'll find a geek's paradise—or at least an open-source programming geek's paradise. The rest of us can settle for downloading a great browser. Leo and I use Mozilla instead of Internet Explorer for nearly all of our browsing. I occasionally run into a site that doesn't work with Mozilla, but it's much more secure than IE. Here are my top three Mozilla tips.

Preferences

Want to change the homepage? Open Edit, Preferences, and the Preferences window launches. In Preferences you can set your homepage, tell Mozilla to show the last page you had open, change the look of the browser, and more.

Import

Just because you change your browser doesn't mean you have to lose all of your Internet Explorer Favorites. Here's how to transfer all those precious bookmarks:

1. Open Internet Explorer, go to File, and click on Import and Export.

2. The Import/Export Wizard starts. Click Next, highlight Export Favorites, and click Next. Choose the folder of Favorites you want to export (Favorites or one of its subfolders), and click Next. Check the Export to a File or Address option and use the Browse button to choose where you want to save the file. Click Next and then Finish. You now have a single HTML file with all your Favorites links.

3. Fire up Mozilla, open Bookmarks, and then open Manage Bookmarks.

4. In the Manage Bookmarks window, go to Tools and then Import. Dig up the file you just exported from IE.

5. Select Open. Your IE faves are now available in Mozilla!

Tabs

Leo really, really loves tabs. Tabs are like opening a new browser window, except in Mozilla it's a new tab in the same window. Tabs make it easy to open five or six pages on the same topic in the same window and quickly click your way among them. Just right-click a link and select Open Link in New Tab.

Web Tips

Save Mozilla Tabs

It's the pits when you make tabs in Mozilla and exit the browser. The tabs are gone. Here's how to save them:

1. Create a tab by going to the website you want to tab and pressing Ctrl+T on your keyboard.

2. Press Shift+Ctrl+D to save the tab grouping, and check Bookmark This Group of Tabs.

Laporte Support

Desktop Background Image

To change your desktop background to an image you've found on the web, right-click the image and select Set as Background.

You can change the name of the background image in Windows. Open your Windows folder and look for a file named Internet Explorer wallpaper.bmp. Rename the file.

Blog Tools Here

Megan Morrone and Michelle VonWald with Roman Loyola
Want to jump on the blogging bandwagon to share your thoughts with family, friends, and the rest of the online world? Then one of these popular weblog tools might be just for you.

Blogger (www.blogger.com) is pretty basic. Run by Google, the servers are pretty fast.

Blogger is a good solution if you want to host your blog on your domain name and server, and doesn't support CGI scripts or databases. Essentially, Blogger hosts the journal tool on its servers. Here's how Blogger works for your domain name:

1. Log on to Blogger and enter the FTP information to your website.

2. Use Blogger's journal entry tool to create content.

3. Blogger creates an HTML file of your journal. It then uses FTP to enter your server and transfer the blog HTML to your site.

4. When you visit your blog, it's updated with the new content.

Movable Type (www.movabletype.org) is more elegant and customizable than Blogger. Leo, Megan, and Morgan all use this one. You need your domain name and your server. It's not hard to set up, but it's not easy, either. It's totally free to use for noncommercial sites.

LiveJournal (www. livejournal.com) is a great weblog tool for beginners. If you want to easily communicate and have access to your friends' blogs, this is the way to go. Unlike Movable Type, you can't host your blog on your domain name or server.

Radio Userland
(http://radio.userland.com) is customizable like Movable Type, but you don't need a server. It's not free and it's definitely more on the geeky side. We used the trial version, and weren't thrilled, but that might be our personal preference.

Also take a look at **w.bloggar** (www.wbloggar.com) and **kung-foo.tv** (www.kung-foo.tv).

Watch Movie Trailers on Your Desktop

Cat Schwartz
I'm amazed that movie production houses constantly come out with cool flicks. I could spend all day at theaters, going from film to film, and never get bored. What's even better than the actual films? Movie trailers. Before you head out the door, sit back, relax, and watch the movie trailers on the Net. Here's the short list of some of the best sites that allow you to do this.

- **Paramount Motion Pictures** (www.paramount.com/motionpictures/)
- **Loews Cineplex Entertainment Corporation: enjoytheshow.com** (www.loewscineplex.com)
- **Movies.com** (http://movies.go.com)
- **QuickTime Movie Trailers** (www.apple.com/trailers/)

The QuickTime site is my favorite. If you're into the player, or if you just want a great selection of trailers, this part of the Apple site is the place to go. You'll see a number of current trailers from almost every movie house.

Take the time to preview films. Going to the movies is getting expensive, and this way you can get a taste of films and pay for only the ones that really look good in the previews.

Douglas Rushkoff's Open-Source Novel

Dave Roos

Douglas Rushkoff has one of those broadly critical minds that transcends typical academic and artistic boundaries. In short, he seems to know everything about everything, from the invasive marketing practices of Madison Avenue to the roots of modern Judaism, to the best way to design a webpage. His latest remarkable project is an open-source novel called *Exit Strategy* (www.rushkoff.com/bull.html).

Open-source novel? Here's how it works.

Rushkoff wrote a serial novel posted on the Yahoo! Internet Life website alternately called *Exit Strategy* and *Bull*. The novel is meant to be a "discovered" text from the year 2008 as seen through the eyes of its 23rd-century readers.

The novel includes explanatory footnotes from "anthro-technical" academic experts from the future.

The novel is open source, because you, the reader, can add footnotes. You can even add footnotes to the footnotes.

The result is a massively hyperlinked text (the first word, *I*, has five footnotes) filled with imaginative explanations for long-extinct conventions such as money and CEOs.

The published version of the novel includes the top 100 footnotes submitted by readers, as well as Rushkoff's original footnotes.

Brief Bio

Douglas Rushkoff is a media theorist, a cultural anthropologist, and the author of seven books on new media and popular culture. He is an adjunct assistant professor of communications at the Interactive Telecommunications Program (www.itp.nyu.edu/) at New York University.

Download of the Day

Big Ole Downloads

Megan Morrone

If you don't have a broadband connection, you might want to think twice about downloading these BODs (big ole downloads).

- **OpenOffice**—48.9MB (www.openoffice.org). If you were using the StarOffice 6.0 beta from Sun, you got a mean wakeup call when the beta expired. If you ever want to see your Star Office 6 documents again, you'll need to purchase StarOffice or download OpenOffice. OpenOffice is a full-featured office suite that's totally free and totally compatible with your existing MS Office documents. There's even a new developer's version of OpenOffice for OS X.

- **NASCAR Racing 2002 Season** demo— 66.62MB (http://download.com). Not only do you need a fast connection to download this game, but you also need accelerated hardware. The trial version includes only the Atlanta Motor Speedway and Richmond International Raceway (a far cry from the 23 tracks in the full version). Still, it gets my blood pumping.

Web Tips

Quick Maps

Type a business or home address into Google (without commas), and your first search result will be the map on Yahoo! Maps.

Twisted List: Weird World of Lego

Martin Sargent

I used to play with Legos when I was a kid. Sometimes I'd build little speakeasies or barber shops running illicit businesses out of the back room. But I gave all that up at around age 14 when I entered a pretty serious My Little Pony phase. Many people on the Internet, however, have taken the Lego habit into adulthood. Here are five of the most insane Lego sites on the Internet:

- **Block Death** (www.blockdeath.com). A museum of horrors dedicated to torture instruments, workplace tragedies, and other painful circumstances, all built out of Lego.

- **The Brick Testament** (www.thereverend.com/brick_testament). Not all Lego sites are instruments of evil. The Reverend Smith uses Legos to illustrate 38 long sequences from several books of the Bible, including Genesis, Exodus, the Gospels, Acts, and the Epistles of Paul.

- **The Lego Chef** (www.ifilm.com). If you're a fan of cult cooking show *Iron Chef*, take a look at the iFilm feature in which an episode is constructed almost entirely out of Legos (film by Steve Iervolino).

- **You as Lego** (www.reasonablyclever.com). If you've ever wanted to picture yourself in plastic, go to ReasonablyClever.com, where you can construct a Lego character with all of your facial and bodily features.

- **Monty Python LEGO** (www.ifilm.com). If you're not completely sick of the movie and of people quoting it in annoying voices, here's a complete scene-by-scene re-enactment of the Knights of the Round Table song from *Monty Python's Quest for the Holy Grail*, in Lego.

Download of the Day

Opera 7

Megan Morrone

Here are a few cool features in the latest version of this alternative browser (www.opera.com).

The Good

- I find it faster and less clunky than Internet Explorer.

- I know people who swear by Mozilla, but I've never found it quite stable enough on Windows.

- Preferences vs. Quick Preferences: Opera gives you direct access to the browser control features you use often, such as blocking ads, GIF animations, embedded audio, and other webmaster stupidities. Just choose File, Quick Preferences. If you want more control, go to Preferences.

- Opera easily blocks pop-up ads. Simply click on File, Quick Preferences, and select Refuse Pop-Up Windows.

- Mozilla lets you choose not to download images on webpages, but you have to reload the page for this feature to take effect. With Opera it's just an easy click on the image icon or a keyboard shortcut.

- New and cool skins can help you become the envy of friends and co-workers.

The Not-So-Good

- I tried using the new Fast Forward feature, but it never took me where I wanted to go.

- Opera is free, but if you don't register, you'll have to suffer through banner ads after the first few weeks.

- Opera 7 wasn't available for Mac at press time.

June

8

Wednesday
June 9
2004

Release/Renew Your IP Address

Roman Loyola

If you suddenly lose your broadband connection to the Internet, you might try using a utility in Windows 98 and Me called winipcfg (in Windows 2000, it's called ipconfig). Winipcfg allows you to see the IP information used by your network interface card. Note: This tip will work only on connections using DHCP. If you have DSL using PPPoE, this tip won't work.

To access winipcfg, follow these steps:

1. Click on the Start menu and select Run.

2. If you are using Windows 98 or Me, type **winipcfg** in the Open box. If you are using Windows 2000, type **ipconfig**.

3. A window should appear with IP information.

Winipcfg has two buttons. The Release button releases any IP addresses assigned to your NIC. The Renew button causes your NIC to get a new IP address. If you suddenly lose your broadband Ethernet connection, try releasing the IP address that your NIC is currently using and getting a new IP address.

There are two ways to release an IP address:

1. When you are in winipcfg (by following the previous steps), click the Release button.

2. At the Run command (Start menu, Run), type **winipcfg /release** for Windows 98 and Me. Type **ipconfig /release** for Windows 2000.

There are two ways to renew an IP address:

1. When you are in winipcfg (by following the previous steps), click the Renew button.

2. At the Run command (Start menu, Run), type **winipcfg /renew** for Windows 98 and Me. Type **ipconfig /renew** for Windows 2000.

If you try Release/Renew and your connection is still down, it might be time to give your ISP a call.

Download of the Day

Google Compute

Megan Morrone

We've got yet another reason to download the Google Toolbar (http://toolbar.google.com)! But first, let's review the fabulous features.

Google is testing a new feature that will help you kill pop-up ads. It won't kill all pop-up ads, but it will slay the ones that appear when you leave a site.

The toolbar also lets you search Google Images, Google Groups, and the Google Directory with only one extra click.

To get the Google Toolbar's new features, follow these steps:

- If you already have the Google Toolbar, you'll have to uninstall and reinstall it to get these extra features.
- After you've reinstalled, click the Google icon on your toolbar and choose Toolbar Options.
- Scroll down to the heading Experimental Features at the bottom of the page.
- Click the Experimental Features link.
- Select the features you'd like to add.
- Click OK.

Warning: Be careful not to click the Reset Layout button.

Google has teamed up with Folding@home (http://folding.stanford.edu) to participate in a distributed computing project. Download Google Computer (http://toolbar.google.com/dc/aboutdc.html). A small double helix icon appears on your toolbar. When you see that icon, you're contributing your extra CPU cycles.

To turn off Google Compute, click the icon and choose Stop Computing.

168

Cover Your Tracks on the Internet

Greg Melton

Using the Internet in public places like schools, libraries, or Internet cafes presents the perfect opportunity to check your email or bank account information when you're on the road. But, if you don't have the option of installing SurfSafe (www.surfsafe.info) wherever you go, you might leave critical data behind that could allow someone to access your accounts.

Windows has a few built-in features that are supposed to be productivity boosters, and by all accounts they are. How many times have you used AutoComplete to fill in a form or web address?

Well, if you're not paying attention while you're using a computer in a public place, AutoComplete, cookies, history, and the Windows temp file might come back to haunt you, unless you learn how to cover your tracks.

AutoComplete Forms and Passwords

Before logging on to check your email or bank account at a public computer is to turn off AutoComplete Forms and Passwords. This way, if you happen to use a popular, free web-based email account, your logon and password won't stick around after you've logged off the computer. Another thing to note is that Windows will prompt you to remember form passwords (only if it's configured correctly), and unless you're paying attention, you may click Yes instead of No.

To turn off AutoComplete in Internet Explorer, follow these directions:

1. Open Internet Explorer.
2. Choose Tools, then Internet Options.
3. Select the Content tab.
4. Click the AutoComplete button.
5. Make sure all the checkmarks are removed next to the text labeled Web Addresses, Forms, User names and passwords on forms.
6. Click both the Clear Forms and Clear Passwords buttons.
7. Click OK, and then click OK again to save your changes.

Cookies, Temp File, and History

The next step to covering your tracks on the Internet needs to occur directly after you've decided your Internet session is finished. This involves clearing the cookies, temp, and history folders. The temp folder or cache is where media files and webpages are stored after you've requested them.

Every webpage you request is sent directly to your temp folder or cache, where it sits until you need to access it again or it gets over written. Because the webpage is already on your computer, you won't have to wait for all the graphics associated with a particular webpage to download.

The history folder records every web address you've ever visited during a set period of time. Unless you clear the history before you leave your computer, all those web addresses you just visited will remain in the computer.

Clearing these settings isn't hard. In fact, they all appear on the same tab in the Internet Options dialog. To clear the setting follow these instructions:

1. Open Internet Explorer.
2. Choose Tools, then Internet Options.
3. You should now be on the General tab.
4. Under Temporary Internet files, click the Delete Cookies button and then click the Delete Files button to erase the entire temp folder.
5. Next, under History click Delete History.
6. Click OK.

Web Browsers for Linux

Chris DiBona
The state of the art in Linux web browsing includes Konqueror, Mozilla, Opera, and Netscape browsers. You might not know that you can use any one of about 50 browsers with Linux; however, many are experimental or immature. Older browsers such as Netscape are still available.

All of the major browsers support exciting features that make browsing pleasurable in ways that have escaped many non-Linux users. For example, both Mozilla and Konqueror let you disable pop-up ads, something missing in IE and Netscape. It's smart about how it does it, too; the browser detects when the user clicks on a link that will open in another window and allows that kind of action, while denying the ability of a webpage to open its own window without user interaction.

Linux browsers were the first to offer true page scaling, allowing for the viewing of a site on small-format PDAs and the scaling up so that a page can be comfortably read in a 1600×1200–pixel screen.

Mozilla

Mozilla (www.mozilla.org) is probably the most advanced Linux browser, considering the way that Red Hat has configured it in Red Hat 7.3. Everything works—and works well. You can bet that most sites will work with Mozilla.

Konqueror

Konqueror (www.konqueror.org) has many great features if you know how to look for them. For instance, if you browse an audio CD in your machine, Konqueror can automatically rip tracks from CDs while surfing them. Konqueror comes with a lot of plug-ins for odd image formats, too, but I think that it's a little frustrating to have to install Java and Flash all over again.

Plug-In Support

You'll have problems with some plug-ins being supported only via an emulator such as the CrossOver (www.codeweavers.com/products/crossover) plug-in.

I miss QuickTime (www.apple.com/quicktime) when surfing under Linux. That said, Quick-Time never worked right under Windows for me anyhow.

Other Browsers

The Linux browser landscape is rich and highly compatible, and is worth the time to examine. Here are some other Linux-compatible browsers:

- **Opera** (www.opera.com)
- **Netscape** (www.netscape.com)
- **Amaya** (www.w3.org/Amaya)
- **Cineast** (http://nestroy.wi-inf.uni-essen.de/ wafe/Cineast)
- **Emacs** (www.cs.indiana.edu/elisp/w3/docs.html)
- **Lynx** (http://lynx.browser.org)

Talkback

Selling Search Results

Dave Roos
Most search engines operate under a famously fishy moral code. With the exception of the editorially high-minded Google, all search engines employ some sort of advertising scheme in which outside sites bid for top billing. The result, of course, is an increasingly blurred line between "sponsored links" and legitimate matches.

Do you care how your search engine works?

Yes   66%

No   34%

Blog Report

Sarah Lane

As a fan of the web, of diaries, of people's innermost thoughts, and of voyeurism and raw emotion and links and whatnot, you'd think I'd be the perfect blog fan. And I am! From the funny to the informative, from the frightening to the creative, there's a blog out there for everyone. It just needs to be found.

Blog Breakdown

A blog is a weblog where folks post text and pics in a diary format organized by date. Within that format, the options are endless. The only no-no is neglecting it. I learned this the hard way when Megan, Morgan, Cat, and I slowly stopped blogging at Leoville. Boy, did I get reamed! I swear, that wasn't completely my fault. The other girls all got their own blogs, and I didn't want to be Leo's only angel!

Blogs cater to everybody. For example, I don't really like race cars, but I came across the blog of some dude who's absolutely crazy about 'em. I ended up reading a month's worth because I liked his style.

Blogs aren't just personal rants, either. Slashdot is a news-based blog that's enormously popular. Cnet's News.com is a bit of a blog, too, because it gets stacked by date. There are also blog collections where you can read a lot of blogs in one place. There are RSS feeds, too. They let you read blogs in a different way.

Sarah's Picks

Here are some blogs I like. You might not have discovered them. And if you have, give your sweet ass a pat for being as web-worldly as me!

- **Blogcritics.org** (www.blogcritics.org). A collection of blogs relating to music, books, movies, and other entertainment sources. These peeps are informed, have decent opinions, and write well.
- **Moby** (www.moby.com/index2.html). Moby not only rocks, but rants like the wind.
- **Gizmodo** (www.gizmodo.com). Gadgets blog. Fun!

- **Techdirt** (www.techdirt.com). News with a spin. I like its no-nonsense attitude.
- **Wil Wheaton Dot Net** (www.wilwheaton.net). Wil rules.

Download of the Day

Particle Jam

Following the success of Elf Bowling 3, TechTV and game developer NStorm have teamed up again to bring you another addictive online game, Particle Jam (www.nstorm.com).

Particle Jam is a fast-paced game of challenge and skill, with multiple scoring opportunities and a few hidden surprises. Similar to Atomica, you have to click three or more of the same particles before they fill the screen and explode in your face.

Sounds simple, right? Well, play once and you won't be able to stop. This game is the ultimate time waster.

Web Tips

Refresh Your Page

Nicole Guilfoyle

If you're reading yesterday's news on your favorite website, you're probably reading it from the cache. To refresh the page with new content, hold the Shift key on your keyboard and click the Refresh button in Internet Explorer.

New Blog on the Block

The Screen Savers Staff

Benjamin and Mena Trott co-created Movable Type (www.movabletype.org), a free, flexible content-management system programmed entirely in Perl (www.perl.com). Movable Type was written out of frustration with other blogging and online journal software. Movable Type isn't web-based like Blogger (www.blogger.com), so there are no server downtimes and lags.

Here are some other features that make Movable Type Leo's favorite blogware:

- **Powerful archiving.** Movable Type's powerful archiving allows you to archive your entries by month, week, and day by category, with each individual entry on its own page. This flexibility, along with the customizable archive URLs, allows usage of the system as a lightweight content-management system.

- **Importing.** If you want to switch to Movable Type from another content-management system, you won't lose all your existing data. You can import your old entries and comments into Movable Type and manage them as you would any other entry.

- **Entry categorization.** Organize your entries by creating a list of categories and then assigning each entry to a category. Movable Type 2.0 (probably out by the time you read this) will even allow you to assign an entry to multiple categories.

- **Linking templates to files.** Many users prefer editing their templates in a text editor rather than in a text box on an HTML form. Movable Type allows you to link a template to an external file. You can edit your templates in a text editor, and your changes will be automatically synchronized back into the Movable Type database.

- **Support.** It is safe to say that Benjamin and Mena live on Movable Type's support forums. They try to answer questions within a couple of hours. They are helped in this pursuit by a devoted group of Movable Type users.

You can see Movable Type in action. Read Mena's blog at www.dollarshort.org and Benjamin's blog at www.stupidfool.org/. Or, for a truly shining example of Movable Type, read none other than Leo's Blog (www.leoville.com/mt) on Leoville.

Mac Tips

Shadow Google

Megan Morrone

One of my favorite downloads for the PC is the Google Toolbar. This handy add-on lets you perform Google searches straight from your desktop. You can search the web, search for images or for newsgroups, and do oh so much more. But the toolbar only works in Windows and only with Internet Explorer.

Apple's browser Safari includes a Google toolbar within the interface, but if you prefer IE on OS X, try Shadow Google (http://homepage.mac.com/stupidfish23/downloads.html).

Shadow Google, written entirely in Cocoa, takes advantage of all that is good and pretty about OS X. It's basically a little window that floats on your desktop. Type your search term, press Enter, and it launches your favorite browser with your search results.

Check out the author's other free utilities while you're there.

Avant Browser

Megan Morrone

Avant Browser (www.avantbrowser.com) was formerly called IE Opera, not to be confused with the other popular free browsers IE (www.microsoft.com) and Opera (www.opera.com).

Avant Browser is stable and has many unique features. Here's what I like about Avant Browser:

- **Seamless integration.** Avant Browser automatically transfers your favorites, homepage, autocomplete entries, and history from IE.

- **No more pop-up ads.** You don't need another program to block pop-ups. Simply click on the Block icon on the toolbar, and you're pop-up free forever.

- **Default search engine.** Click the magnifying glass icon, and you get a search window similar to that in IE. The main difference is that Google is the default search engine. (You can make Google the default search engine in IE, but it's not easy.)

- **No clutter on the taskbar.** New browser windows appear at the bottom of the Avant Browser window, not in your taskbar. IE in XP lets you condense your browser windows into one small window, with access by right-click, but I hate this feature.

- **Mouse gestures:**
  - Hold down your right mouse button and click your left mouse button to go back a page.
  - Hold down your left mouse button and click your right mouse button to go forward a page.
  - Click a link with your middle mouse button, and the link opens in a new window.

- **Full screen button.** A handy button on the toolbar lets you increase your screen space. (IE lets you do this with the F11 button.)

- **Text size button.** The icon of the letter A lets you increase or decrease the size of the text on a webpage with a click of the mouse. (It's a hidden shortcut that you have to find on your own in IE.)

Change Internet Explorer's Default Search Engine

Nicole Guilfoyle

Here's how to change Internet Explorer's search settings so that you can automatically search using the engine of your choice:

1. Open IE and click the Search icon.
2. Click Customize, and choose One Service for All Searches.
3. Select the search engine of your choice from the list of engines, and click OK.

You may notice that Google is not included in the list of search engines.

To change Internet Explorer's Autosearch settings, follow these steps:

1. Open IE and click the Search icon.
2. Click Customize, and click Autosearch Settings.
3. Choose a search engine from the list. Google Sites is a choice for Autosearch. Click OK.

Address: Site of the Night

American Flags

David in Richmond (a.k.a. Flag Man)

Having spent 11 years in the Marine Corps, nothing brings me more pride and strength than the American flag. These websites outline the proper way to display the American flag:

- **The Flag of the United States of America.** http://usflag.org/
- **Flag Etiquette.** www.anyflag.com/etiquette.htm

Movies Online

Fawn Luu with Alison Strahan

The Internet is packed full of resources for movie buffs. It takes only seconds to find information about your favorite actors, read movie reviews, and find theaters and show times in your area. Some sites will even let you buy tickets online.

Entertainment News and Movie Reviews

The Internet Movie Database (http://imdb.com/) provides entertainment enthusiasts with everything from interviews with the stars to movie trailers. Use the database to find out what your favorite actor or actress will appear in next. You can even buy a copy of related flicks at Amazon.com.

Read a brief synopsis of movies currently playing in theaters at Yahoo! Movies (http://movies.yahoo.com). Browse the top ten movies at the box office to get ideas for your next date, or type your ZIP code in the search box to find show times in your area.

If you're not interested in any of the movies that are out now, look in the Coming Soon section to find upcoming new releases.

Find a Show Time

When you need to find more than just movie news and reviews, visit Moviefone.com (http://moviefone.com) or MovieTickets.com (http://movietickets.com). Both sites have a simple interface to help you find show times in your area.

Buy Tickets Online

You don't have to wait in line. Many theaters in major cities allow you to purchase tickets online at MovieTickets.com or Fandango (www.fandango.com). You can purchase tickets up to a week in advance. Many advance-purchase tickets are also available at Fandango.

1. Type in the name of a movie and your ZIP code, and click Go.

2. Select a location and show time.

3. Make the purchase by filling in the number of tickets you want and your credit card information.

To pick up your tickets, bring your credit card and confirmation. Collect your tickets from the will-call window, or swipe your credit card through a ticket kiosk installed in many of the larger theater complexes.

Print Movie Tickets at Home

Fandango also offers print-at-home ticketing for select theaters. Print your ticket-confirmation bar code on any home printer. A single bar code is used for all tickets purchased in the same transaction. At the cinema, the ticket-taker will scan your printout and give you ticket stubs.

Laporte Support

Disable Downloads

If your kids aren't very computer-savvy yet, disable downloading in Internet Explorer.

1. Click Tools and then Internet Options. Go to the Security tab.

2. Select Internet and click Custom Level.

3. Under Downloads, find File Downloads and select Disable.

4. Click OK and then click OK again.

You can also use the Windows System Policy Editor (www.microsoft.com) to alter the Windows Registry. Or, if you don't feel comfortable messing with the Registry, use third-party software such as CyberPatrol (www.cyberpatrol.com), Lockdown (www.securitysoft.com), WinU (www.bardon.com), or Fortres 101 (www.fortres.com).

Go to www.experts-exchange.com/ Operating_Systems/Win98/Q_20190267.html if you want some manual ways to disable downloads in Windows 98.

STG Cache Audit

Dan Mitchell

I'm not one for snooping around somebody else's computer, but stuff left in cache is fair game. I mean, if someone's doing naked yoga in front of an open window, you're going to look. It's human nature. Similarly, if someone's surfing pornography without clearing his or her browsing history, they're just asking for it.

STG Cache Audit makes it easier than ever to bust your kids, your spouse, your grandma, your co-workers, and various other porn addicts. It scans Internet Explorer's cache to tell you how often certain sites are visited and the date and time they're accessed. It also breaks down the information into several easy-to-digest results pages: Website, Links, Cookies, History, and Filtered.

Filter?

Sifting through your results can be overwhelming. The Filter option lets you add certain words to a master list. When you run the scan, you'll only see results containing those words ("Sex," "Warez," "Pee-Wee's Playhouse") in the Filtered View section.

Unless a user clears the cache, the program paints an accurate picture of that user's surfing habits.

Don't Deny It

Once you have the results, you'll want hard evidence. You can either print results from within the interface or export them to a text, HTML, or Excel file.

If you want to take a quick peek into someone's surfing habits, download STG Cache Audit (www.stgsys.com/cache.asp). If you don't want people to know what you're up to, close your curtains and clean out your cache once in a while.

Web Tips

If you forgot to bookmark a site but want to revisit it, follow these simple steps:

1. Launch Internet Explorer.
2. Click the History icon on your toolbar, or press Ctrl+H.
3. Search for the site by name or date.
4. Click the link.

Laporte Support

Build a Web Page Without Knowing HTML

If you use America Online, you can use AOL's tools. The tools use basic questions, and they're progressive, so you can do more with your site. The keyword is AOLPress.

If you use Tripod (www.tripod.lycos.com) or GeoCities (http://geocities.yahoo.com), you can use the tools they provide. They also host your webpage for free, but you can't use your domain name.

If you only want to keep a journal, you can use a weblog such as Blogger (www.blogger.com) or LiveJournal (www.livejournal.com).

HTML isn't hard to learn. Two great HTML resources are WebMonkey (www.webmonkey.com) and Dave's Site (www.davesite.com).

June

16

Address: Site of the Night

Deleted Domains

Thousands of cool domain names expire every day. Get the latest list and snatch 'em up. (http://deleteddomains.com)

Chimera Tweaks

Megan Morrone

Here are a few free tweaks for Chimera, the speedy web browser for OS X available at VersionTracker (www.versiontracker.com/macosx/).

ChimeraBooster

The biggest complaint Mac users have about OS X is slow web browsing. With a simple tweak to the terminal, Faq-Mac's ChimeraBooster (www.faq-mac.com/mt/archives/000337.html) promises even more velocity for this already speedy browser. The tool uses HTTP pipelining to accelerate the page-downloading process. It worked for me.

The developer's site is not in English, but the ReadMe file is.

Chimericon

One big drawback of Safari is the limits to customization. The same is true for Chimera. But with Reinhold Penner's Chimericon (www.versiontracker.com/macosx/), you now have nearly limitless choices for new icons and splash screens.

Chimericon includes an easy-to-use theme editor and premade themes. If you're really adventurous, you can even create your own themes.

Penner also offers free icons for Safari.

ChimeraKnight

Also by Reinhold Penner, ChimeraKnight allows you to automatically download the latest Chimera builds. Because Chimera is an open-source project with many different developers, the browser is constantly updated with the latest builds for stability, speed, and performance. If you're the type who forgets to update often, you'll want this tool to remind you.

You can find all of these tweaks at www.versiontracker.com. Just search for them by title.

Laporte Support

What's the Difference Between FTP and HTTP?

FTP stands for File Transfer Protocol. It's a series of protocols or rules that define how to transfer files across the Internet. It's a very popular way to send files across the Net.

To use FTP, you must have an FTP server and client. An FTP client is the software that you place on your machine that gives you access to an FTP server/site. You can find FTP software by searching for FTP at your favorite downloads site.

HTTP stands for Hypertext Transfer Protocol. It defines how messages are formatted and transmitted, and what actions web servers and browsers should take in response to various commands.

Talkback

They're Watching You

Dave Roos

According to your TiVo, you should really watch Six Feet Under. Meanwhile, Amazon.com knows what you want for Christmas before you've even made your list. What's going on here? By tracking your viewing and buying habits, more digital devices and websites are attempting to predict your interests with custom-made "smart" advertising.

Do "they" know too much about you?

Yes   81%

No   19%

19%
No

81%
Yes

Create Your Own Internet Radio Station

James Kim

Everybody's a DJ. They're coming out of the woodwork, thanks to the Internet and its broadcasting capabilities. It's easy to set up your "station" and play whatever you like, whenever you like (well, almost—there are some legal issues to be aware of).

SHOUTcast, a free-of-charge audio home-steading solution, can deliver live audio or archived broadcasts on demand. Along with the downloadable SHOUTcast tools, you'll need a server, an Internet connection (preferably higher than 56Kbps), and a collection of MP3s. Follow these steps:

1. Go to SHOUTcast (www.shoutcast.com) and download and install the latest version of Winamp.

2. Also download the latest version of the SHOUTcast DSP plug-in and Microsoft NetShow services. The DSP plug-in allows your Winamp player to communicate with a server (your audio needs to be "served" for people to listen to your station). The NetShow services installs a necessary audio codec if you don't already have it installed. Extract these files into your Winamp plug-ins folder.

3. Before you configure your SHOUTcast DSP plug-in, you need to set up a server. If you have a lot of bandwidth, you can create your server by downloading SHOUTcast server software. This can be a little tricky, so we recommend using a service. Go to Live365.com and become a member for free. Write down the IP address and port number Live365.com assigns you—you'll need them to configure the SHOUTcast DSP plug-in.

4. Configure the DSP plug-in. First, open the Winamp Preferences window and click the DSP/Effect subcategory under the Plug-Ins tree. Click on the SHOUTcast Source for Winamp; a configuration box pops up. Select Server by clicking the appropriate set box. In the new window, enter the Live365 IP address and port. Then enter your Live365 password. You should also enter the description and genre of your music.

5. Select your Format by clicking Set on the original SHOUTcast Source for Winamp window. Due to factors such as bandwidth and quality, it's best to set the format between 20Kbps and 32Kbps.

6. Fill your Winamp playlist with MP3s, and click Play. At the SHOUTcast Source for Winamp window, click Connect. If you see your Winamp player communicating with the Live365 server, you're broadcasting.

7. It's up to you to distribute your IP address to your friends, your family, and the world. They'll need to point a streaming-compatible player to the server (IP address plus port number) to listen to your broadcast. You can also go to Live365.com and search for your station.

Download of the Day

Desktop Weather

Roger Chang

Desktop Weather (http://registration.weather.com/services/ desktop.html?from=URS) is a small utility perfect for people who usually get weather updates by looking out the window. To get the download, you'll need to register with the Weather Channel. After it is installed, Desktop Weather displays current weather information, including temperature, humidity, and wind speed. Just choose a location, and results appear in a small desktop window.

When not sitting on your desktop, Desktop Weather resides on your taskbar, showing the current temperature in either Celsius or Fahrenheit. Desktop Weather is adware; a customized ad window displaying information about travel, health, driving, home and garden, or recreation appears next to the weather information. But this feature isn't very intrusive.

Add a Guest Book to Your Website

Megan Morrone

With the proliferation of message boards and the ability to comment on most weblogs, many web guest books have gone the way of the dodo. But guest books allow users to comment on your site and help you find out who's visiting your page.

Here are three great ways to add a guest book to your site.

Matt's Guest Book Script

Matt's Script Archive (www.scriptarchive.com) is the place for cool free scripts that add interactivity to your website. When I've talked about Matt's archive on *The Screen Savers*, I've received email from people who don't like Matt's scripts. Personally, I've never had a problem.

You can download files for your guest book. An email address is requested but not required. You'll get five files, including a help file that takes you through the process of uploading and customizing the guest book step by step. Adding the scripts to your site means you'll be serving the guest book yourself.

HTML Gear

Several sites will serve your guest book for you. I like HTML Gear (http://htmlgear.lycos.com) because it doesn't contain too many pop-up ads, and it lets users add images to their postings. But the service is no longer free. After you sign up, you can customize the guest book and then generate the HTML code to add to your website. Alxnet (www.alxnet.com) provides a similar service.

Bravenet's GuestMap

Bravenet has a new service that lets you get even more creative. GuestMap (www.bravenet.com) is a traditional guest book that also lets your users place a pin (or other icon) on a map so you can see where the guests are from. You simply sign up, customize the map, and add the generated code to your website.

Martin's Tips

Track Down Free Public Computers in Your 'Hood

Martin Sargent

I have four computers in my bedroom: one for work stuff, one for games, and two for recipes. Not everyone is so lucky. Some people don't even have one computer, and that's a real shame in a world where computer skills are increasingly necessary for gainful employment, schoolwork, and much more.

If you don't have a computer, chances are there are free computers in your community that you can use. The trick is finding them.

To find a free machine close to home, go to the library or a friend's house and visit ConnectNet.org (www.connectnet.org). Type in your ZIP code, and the site will list community centers and other public spaces where you can get your hands on free computers with Internet access. The site will even tell you whether the available machines are Macs or PCs.

Download of the Day

SiteGenWiz

Brett Larson

What could be better than a free, easy-to-use website creator? How about not having to know HTML to make a website? SiteGenWiz (www.enersoft.ch/_sgt/m2_1.htm), from Enersoft, is a freeware app from across the Atlantic that lets you quickly create simple websites. You can customize things such as the layout, background images, and text styles. Plus, you'll be able to update and even redesign your site at any time with just a few clicks.

Now you can build your Brett Larson fan site, and you don't have to learn HTML.

Alternative Browsers

Phil Allingham and Chris Kraus

Netscape Navigator and Internet Explorer are not the only Internet browsers. While the browser wars might not be headline news anymore, you still have some great choices.

Mozilla (www.mozilla.org). Mozilla is the base code that Netscape Navigator is built on. It's faster than Navigator and has better features than IE, including a download manager, an email client, a cookie manager, and tabbed browsing (the ability to have multiple pages open in one application window).

Opera (www.opera.com/download). This powerful browser is fast but extremely small. This is good news for those worried about RAM hogs or those who use an older PC. The newest versions, 5.0 and 6.0, are free.

NeoPlanet (www.neoplanet.com). This browser looks hip. It also includes many innovative enhancements to make surfing even easier.

You can install as many browsers as you want.

Clear Internet Explorer's Address Bar

Call for Help Staff

It's smart to clear your address bar's history if you don't want anyone to access information about your Internet viewing habits. It's also an easy way to eliminate incorrect URLs.

Internet Explorer

Click Tools, Internet Options, Clear History. You can also specify the number of days to keep sites in your history log.

Netscape Navigator

To avoid workarounds, upload the latest version of Netscape. Click Edit, select Preferences, click on Navigator on the left, on the right, click the Clear Location Bar button, and click OK.

AOL 8.0

This also clears keyword history. Go to settings on the toolbar, scroll to Preferences, click Toolbar and Sound, and click Clear History Now.

Clear AutoComplete Entries

Click Tools and select Internet Options. Go to the Content tab and click the AutoComplete button, and click the Clear Forms or Clear Passwords button. When IE finishes clearing your passwords and forms, click OK and then click OK again.

Address: Site of the Night

Ghostzilla

Martin Sargent

A large part of my work day is spent surfing the web looking for sites that might titillate *The Screen Savers* fans. If HR objects to some of my more "adventurous" surfing, I can say it's for research purposes, and they have to back off.

You probably don't have these luxuries. For many, even going to a site as innocuous as CNN.com at work might get you a reprimand. You should be working, after all. That's where Ghostzilla comes in.

Ghostzilla (www.ghostzilla.com) is a stealth web browser that lets you surf websites disguised as normal desktop documents, even Word files. Your boss would have to get very close to your computer to notice.

If he or she does get too close, just move the mouse pointer out of the Ghostzilla window, and it disappears. Move the pointer back, and up pops your window. It's brilliant.

Just remember, if you go to porn sites using Ghostzilla, your IT people can still see the addresses of those sites in their server log files. Don't be an idiot.

June 20

uJournal

Megan Morrone

More than a year ago, I introduced you to the blogging software LiveJournal (www.livejournal.com). As a follow-up, I also reviewed DeadJournal.com (www.deadjournal.com), a slightly twisted alternative. Here's another option to consider when choosing a weblog client.

LiveJournal Revisited

LiveJournal offers a program that you can download and use to update your journal. It's free, but you can help keep the community alive with a paid account (www.livejournal.com/paidaccounts).

Unfortunately, you need an access code to get a free account. You can browse and post comments on other LiveJournals, but you need to be invited to start your own.

A New Blogging Tool for U

Because LiveJournal is open source, anyone can use the code to create a blogging community. This is exactly how uJournal (www.uJournal.org) came to be. It's similar to LiveJournal, but it doesn't require a code to set up an account. If you run Windows or Linux, you can download the software (there is no Mac client) or update your journal straight from the web. Like LiveJournal, you can get a paid account for uJournal.

An Evilternative to LiveJournal

DeadJournal.com is the evil twin of Live-Journal. It's the same technology, but the user interface is much darker, literally and figuratively. The help files are pretty sarcastic, and many of the journals are riddled with angst.

Journals of Interest

- Megan's LiveJournal (www.livejournal.com/users/meganmorrone)
- Megan's uJournal (www.ujournal.org/users/meganmorrone)
- TechTV fan community (www.livejournal.com/users/techtv)

Download of the Day

Google Toolbar

Chris Kraus

It's no secret that Google search results are the best on the Net. Now you can get those same results right from your Internet Explorer toolbar. Google Toolbar (http://toolbar.google.com) attaches to Internet Explorer and comes bundled with some of Google's best search functions. Here's how to install it:

1. Surf to the Google Toolbar download page, choose your language, and choose Download.

2. Choose either the standard or the advanced toolbar, and run the install tool.

A Google search box appears on the left of your IE toolbar. Expect these features:

- **Site Search.** Search only the pages of the site you're visiting.
- **Word Find.** Find your search terms wherever they appear on the page.
- **Highlight.** Highlight your search terms as they appear on the page.
- **Page Rank.** Ranks the current page.
- **Page Info.** Access more information about a page, similar pages, pages that link back to that page, and a cached snapshot.

If you want to go straight to the Google home-page or its News, Images, Answers, or Groups pages, or if you want to uninstall the Google Toolbar, cascade out the menu under the Google icon and choose where you want to go. The toolbar works only on versions of Internet Explorer 5.0 or higher on a Windows machine.

Twisted List: Google Parasites

Martin Sargent

It's no secret that Google (www.google.com) is the best search engine on the Internet. When you're the best at what you do, entities that aren't as good at what they do try to compensate for ineffectiveness by feeding off your success.

I'm talking about Internet companies that drum up customers by banking exclusively on the fact that most Americans are either bad spellers or poor typists.

There are loads of Google parasites: the search engine Xoogle (www.xoogle.com), the ever-popular Qoogle (www.qoogle.com), and the very naughty Loogle (www.loogle.com). Moogle (www.moogle.com) leads you to RocketSearch (http://rocketsearch.com), and Koogle (www.koogle.com) is just plain pathetic.

Other Google knock-offs include these:

- **Voogle** (www.voogle.com) is an email company. For $12 a year, you can register an email address at a fun domain name, such as martinsargent@2damfunky.com, martinsargent@BabeCrew.com, and martinsargent@BradPittFanClub.com, plus hundreds more. You can also get a .us domain, such as martinsargent@AddictedToLove.us. In the end, I chose martinsargent@ebonyqueen.com and martinsargent@IhateDrugs.com.

- **Guugle** (www.guugle.com) takes you to Internet travel site Hotwire (www.hotwire.com). I hope Hotwire has good customer service reps, because if people can't spell Google, how are they going to spell Aruba or Puerto Vallarta?

- I love **Woogle** (www.woogle.com) because every time you go there, without fail you win Virtual Reality Casino. **Toogle** (www.toogle.com) takes you to the same place.

- A Google parasite that's actually a great site is **Boogle** (www.boogle.com). It is Google, but every time you use it to perform a Google search, there's a different graphic and wise phrase.

Download of the Day

GoogleSearchTool

Megan Morrone

The GoogleSearchTool (www.frysianfools.com/ggsearch) is a free utility from P.J. Kraaima. The program floats on your desktop, where you can type in search terms. When you press Enter, the program launches a window with your Google search results.

Some of you might wonder what makes this different from the Google Toolbar (http://toolbar.google.com/install). Unfortunately, the Google Toolbar works only on IE 5 or higher. If you use another browser, the GoogleSearchTool will work for you.

Megan's Tips

Print Your Favorites

If you want a printout of all your Favorites in Internet Explorer, you have to export them as an HTML file.

1. In Internet Explorer, click on File and select Import and Export.

2. A wizard starts. Follow along, remembering to export Favorites. After the wizard completes the task, file the HTML file. It's probably in My Documents.

3. Open the file in Internet Explorer.

4. Click on the File menu and select Print.

5. On the Options tab, check Print Table of Links.

How to Download

Greg Melton

Part of the initial lure of the Internet is the overabundant access to downloadable files. But when presented with the opportunity to click and save data files, new Internet users find that downloading isn't always as easy as it seems. With the help of a few pointers and a little software, you can manage to get high-quality downloads with the click of a mouse.

Sound files, programs, screen savers, images, and ZIP files are all downloadable. When you click to save them to your computer, don't just click OK when asked to continue. Ask yourself a few questions about the file you'd like to save. Is the file getting saved to a logical place? Will you be able to retrieve it easily? Is the file getting saved with a naming convention that makes sense? You should consider all these things before you download anything.

Create a Download Folder

Start by creating a folder on your desktop entitled Downloads. What you name this folder isn't as important as where you place the folder when you create it. The desktop is the ideal location to store a folder specifically for downloaded files.

Eventually, you'll find that you might want subdirectories within the main download folder for Music, Images, and Programs. This way, you can categorize the different types of files and avoid cluttering the main download folder. It will also make searching for files easier. You should also start a naming convention that when you need to find something.

Naming Conventions

Often when you save a file, it's already named. But the name that appears isn't always the best choice. Many times, the names are incomplete and don't describe the contents of a file. Or, it looks like a set of random numbers, with an occasional letter thrown in for good measure. So to help you find a file at a later date, get in the habit of clearly naming files.

Follow this naming structure to avoid any confusion when looking for a file:
Filename: Name_Short Description.

The underscore acts as a spacer between the two words, so use it often. Don't make the entire filename more than a maximum of 12–15 characters. The shorter the name, the better. Be creative, and be as descriptive as possible. If you find something that works well for you, keep using it.

Talkback

RIP URL

Dave Roos

Nothing is more permanent than death, and nothing is less permanent than a URL. Nevertheless, there is a growing trend of people who want to put website addresses on gravestones. Ananova.com reports that a man named James Kemp has created the first known cybergrave in Scotland for his father, Billy Kemp. The tombstone is engraved with the URL of his father's tribute site, BillyKemp.org.uk (the site may be down from heavy traffic).

Would you want a cybergravestone? Would you trust your loved ones or your ISP to re-register your URL for perpetuity? What if your tribute site got bought by a porn site? Oh, the embarrassment beyond the grave!

Do you want a cybergravestone?

Yes   33%

No   67%

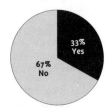

How to Download (continued)

Using a Browser to Download

One by-product of the browser war between Netscape and Microsoft is the way each browser performs the same tasks. Because Netscape was the first on the scene, it set the early standard of naming different browser functions. Microsoft followed soon afterward, with its naming structure for many of the same features.

Here's the method used to download different file types between IE and Netscape:

Browser	Image Files	Programs, Sound, and Other Files
IE	Save Picture As	Save Target As
Netscape	Save Image As	Save Link As

After you've selected a file to be downloaded, simply right-click the image or link. Depending on the browser you're using, use the table to make the appropriate selection. If you use IE, you'll see a pop-up window asking you whether to run from the current location or save to disk. In both instances the file is downloaded, but the Run from Current Location selection places the file in a temporary directory and then opens the file after the download is complete. If you choose Save to Disk, you will see the same thing a Netscape user sees: the Save As pop-up window.

In the Save As window, name the file, select where it should be stored, and double-check the file type to make sure it is the file you intend to download. If you want to download a program, check the extension and see if it's an .exe. Or, if it's an MP3, the file should end with an .mp3 extension. When everything checks out, click OK.

Download Manager

The Internet works in mysterious ways sometimes, so you might find that a download manager will help. These are nifty programs designed to aid in downloading all files known to man. If you get cut off in the middle of a huge download, never fear. They can pick up the pieces and start from the same place the cutoff occurred. Try installing the free Download Express (www.metaproducts.com) if you want to take the mystery out of successfully downloading something. Warning: Download managers have been known to track users' download habits. Download Express is one of the only free download managers that doesn't contain spyware.

Download of the Day

Browser Patches

Megan Morrone
Internet Explorer is full of security holes. Microsoft does a pretty good job of releasing patches, but sometimes it takes longer than we'd like. Thanks to Thor Larholm, we no longer have to wait for Microsoft to get its act together. His site at www.pivx.com/larholm/ includes all known vulnerabilities, links for further reference, and any Microsoft or third-party fixes currently available.

Laporte Support

IE Search options

You can change the search options in Internet Explorer 6. Open the side panel by clicking the Search button, and then select Customize. You can select which search engine you want to use.

Destroy Pop-Up Windows

Michelle VonWald, Greg Melton, and Phil Allingham

There's nothing worse than being hijacked by pop-up windows while surfing the web. You know what we mean. You click on a site, and suddenly a window with an ad pops up on your screen. You try to close it, and this action launches a blizzard of pop-up windows until your screen becomes filled with blinking banner ads, X-10 cameras, X-rated images, and monkeys looking to be punched.

Use a Better Browser

Mozilla 1.3 (www.mozilla.org) includes a built-in pop-up killer in its Tools menu. Here's what to do if you come across a site that bombards you with pop-ups:

1. Click Tools and choose Pop-Up Manager.
2. Select Suppress Pop-Ups from This Site.

You can also set up a list of sites to block:

1. Click Tools and choose Pop-Up Manager.
2. Select Manage Pop-Up Permissions.
3. Type the web addresses you want to add to the list.

Internet Explorer's Do-It-Yourself Solution

The quickest and easiest way to prevent pop-ups is to disable all scripting abilities inside your browser. In IE, just go to Tools, Internet Options; then click the Security tab and Custom Levels, and disable Active Scripting under Scripting.

But if you do this, you'll find that the Internet quickly becomes useless. Just about every site on the Internet uses some sort of scripting. No scripting means no image rollovers, style sheets, dynamic or cascading menus, or pop-up windows, of course. Before you decide to augment the way you view the web, here are two other viable solutions.

Smash, Punish, and Destroy

A couple good freeware applications called PopupVanish (www.kalavath.co.uk/popupvanish/) and Free Surfer mk II (www.kolumbus.fi) actively stop pop-ups. You have to okay which sites are allowed to let them through.

Another free program, Analog X Pow! (www.analogx.com/contents/download/network/pow.htm), works a little differently. It automatically detects pop-up windows and lets you decide what you want to do with them.

While most pop-up windows contain nothing more than advertising, some of them are integral to a site's navigation and style. Therefore, many pop-up–slaying programs let you blacklist pop-up windows as they appear. Once you blacklist a pop-up window, it will never appear again.

Because each webpage has a title, you manage your blacklist by tracking webpage titles. Pow! even lets you use wildcards to configure blacklisted pop-up windows.

Let's say that a certain pop-up window has a title of "Exclusive Deal of the Day for 04/30/2003." If the date changed every day, it wouldn't register as a pop-up window on your blacklist. Pow! lets you use an asterisk as a wildcard and configure your blacklist option of "Exclusive Deal of the Day ★" so everything that begins with "Exclusive Deal of the Day" remains blacklisted.

Pow! also lets you import blacklists from other people who use the program. This could become handy because it takes diligence to ban every pop-up window that appears on your screen.

Address: Site of the Night

The Secret Lives of Numbers

What's the most sought-after number on the web? Find out at The Secret Lives of Numbers (http://turbulence.org/Works/nums/index.html).

Deconstruct Your Favorite Web Pages

Craig Higdon

Are you the type of person who learns by example? Do you like to tear apart other people's work just for the heck of it? Maybe you're just looking for an easier way to find information on webpages. Here's a free file that lets you see how your favorite webpages are put together. It also pulls together lists of links or graphics on a page so that you won't need to scroll or trudge through source code to find the information you want.

IE Booster (www.paessler.com/iebooster/ index_eng.html) is an Internet Explorer extension that adds more options to your right-click contextual menu. Here's what you can do:

- Create a list of all hyperlinks on a page.
- Create a list of all graphics on a page and their locations.
- Resize the browser window to fit various screen formats.
- Copy page titles and link targets to the Clipboard as URLs.
- Copy selections as plain text.
- Reveal tables, forms, and borders.
- Show all forms or applets on a webpage.
- Show page source or source code for parts of a page.
- Show style sheets.
- Reveal server response.
- Make unsightly blemishes vanish.
- Increase your popularity with members of the opposite sex.
- Gain power and wealth.

Okay, I'm kidding about those last three. But seriously, folks, IE Booster is a sweet free file for novices and Internet experts alike. The program is especially useful for web designers or people who like to take things apart.

So put that scalpel away. IE Booster is all you need to get behind the scenes of your favorite webpages.

Download of the Day

Referrer Risk

Megan Morrone

Referrer Risk provides a tiny piece of HTML code that you can download and add to your website. Your visitors can then click on an image of the world. Each time they click, they'll conquer a $2° \times 2°$ parcel of land for your domain name.

You need your own website to conquer the world on your own. If you join someone else, you need only a Net connection and a lot of time.

You can get the code to dominate the world on your own (http://drunkmenworkhere.org/ 189.php?action=instructions).

Don't want to have any part in conquering the world? Hate referrer technology that tells webmasters where you came from? Try a program such as Proxomitron (www.proxomitron.org). It disables referral technology.

Megan's Tips

Finding Text in IE

To locate a word on a webpage, click Edit and then click Find on This Page. Type in the word you're looking for.

June
26

Sunday
June 27
2004

Blogs of *The Screen Savers*

Josh Lawrence

Blogmania has been sweeping the denizens of cyberspace, and your favorite crew members of *The Screen Savers* are no exception. Now you can find out what Leo, Megan, Morgan, Cat, Paul, and Sarah have to say in their online journals. You can respond to their entries as well. Just go to these sites to jump on the blogging bandwagon:

- **Leo's Blog:** www.leoville.com/mt/
- **Megan's Blog at Jumping Monkeys:** www.jumpingmonkeys.com/
- **MorganWebb.com:** www.morganwebb.com/
- **Cat's Blog:** www.catshwartz.com
- **Sarah's Blog:** www.sarahlane.com
- **TSS Executive Producer Paul Block's Blog:** www.leoville.com/paul/

Start your blog engines!

Laporte Support

Uninstall Internet Explorer

How do I uninstall Internet Explorer?

This is actually a bit tricky. Microsoft defines Internet Explorer not as a separate application, but as a Windows component.

1. Open the Add/Remove Programs control panel.
2. Click the Add/Remove Windows Components icon on the left to bring up a window that lets you uninstall Internet Explorer.

If you're removing Internet Explorer, you might want to try an alternative web browser:

- **Netscape** (www.netscape.com)
- **Mozilla** (www.mozilla.org)
- **Opera** (www.opera.com)

Download of the Day

Girafa

Dan Mitchell

The Internet is full of bogus links, 404 errors, and websites that haven't been updated in years. I know because every time I'm looking for something on the web, I end up clicking on links that waste my time. They go nowhere, they timeout, they take me to a porn site—you know what I mean. Well, fellow surfers, I'm going to help you take the guesswork out of navigating the Net.

Girafa (www.girafa.com/index.acr?c=1) gives you a visual representation of websites before you click.

1. Click the button to add Girafa to Internet Explorer's toolbar.
2. You'll be able to see thumbnail images of webpages on a side panel within the browser.
3. Selectively check links by highlighting the ones you're interested in and clicking the Visualize button.
4. Send links to friends as a graphical image of the site instead of a text link.

You can set up Girafa to show your favorite websites so you'll have easy access. More important, you can see if they've been updated.

You can search and get results in the Girafa interface. Pop in a search term using your favorite search engine and see thumbnails of the results. All the resulting pages are laid out for you!

So try Girafa and start visually navigating your way through cyberspace.

Twisted List: Martin's Equations

Martin Sargent

We all know that Dr. Michio Kaku is working on an equation (that would explain the universe. Well, coincidentally, I've been working on a few important equations of my own.

1. An equation to determine the minimum amount of work I have to do and still have my bosses view me as a valuable team member.

2. An equation to determine who I have the best chance of scoring with: Cat, Morgan, or Jessica.

3. An equation to determine how bored you would have to be to spend time at the Pringles website.

   Everyone go to the Pringles website (www.pringles.com) right now, so the webmaster gets really confused and the marketing department hires an outside agency to determine why there was such a huge spike in traffic. They'll probably be like, "It's because of our new flavor, cheese and onion!"

4. An equation to determine the circumference of Leo's head, taking into account that his hair is a universal constant.

5. An equation to explain why Carson Daly has a higher-paying TV job than I do.

Community Bulletin Boards

Alison Strahan

Are you a techie in need of a new job, apartment, or even a hang gliding partner? You can find everything you want at craigslist (www.craigslist.com).

This community bulletin board is brimming with just about every kind of help you can imagine. Listings range from employment opportunities (including tech jobs), to shared accommodations and computer goods.

Craigslist's goal is to offer an ad-free online forum and to engender real community. Visitors can view listings, sign up for the site's email newsletter, or participate in one of the many active message boards without any stress or obligation.

Although the site originally launched in the San Francisco Bay Area, craigslist has branched out. It now has links for most major US cities, including Seattle, New York, Washington, Boston, Atlanta, and more. There's even a site for Sydney, Australia.

Download of the Day

Webcam Watcher

Sarah Lane

If you want to simultaneously watch your fave webcams, Webcam Watcher (www.webcam-watcher.com/wcwdownloads.html) from Beau Software could be your dream program. I'm using version 3.0, which lets me watch up to 20 webcams at once. (Who does this?! But you can.) It has some nice features.

It'll save every single frame of a webcam when you have the software running. Or, you can set it to capture only frames that contain motion—a good one if you're stalking the love of your life and can't be bothered with the frames where he or she gets up to use the loo.

You can name the webcam whatever you want. It doesn't matter how it's been set up. All you need is the URL where the images show up online. Right-click the updating image to get that information.

Each camera you set up has its own folder in your Program Files/Beausoft/Webcamwatcher2 folder. As long as you have the cams running, they'll save captures in those folders. You won't miss a thing. Have a ball! And please don't forget to eat between viewings.

June
28

Free Money

Martin Sargent

There seem to be more "win free money" sites on the Internet than there are casinos in Las Vegas. So can you really log on penniless and log off a millionaire? Let's find out.

Money Portals

This is the first time I have publicly admitted this. A few months ago, I switched my home-page from CNN to iWon (www.iwon.com). Go ahead and call me a gullible simpleton. But if I'm going to log on to the Internet, why not give myself the outside chance of winning some money? The odds of iWon probably aren't any worse than the lottery, and I don't need to spend my grocery money every time I want to play.

iWon is an Internet portal much like Yahoo!. Because it debuted late in the portal game, it needed a hook to differentiate itself. So it gave everyone a chance to win money and fabulous prizes.

To start competing for prizes, you need to register and accumulate entry points. For every point you earn, you get one entry in a drawing, and you can earn up to 100 entry points per day. The points are used in a daily $10,000 drawing and also are banked for weekly, monthly, and yearly drawings. The more you use iWon, the better your odds of winning big money. Of course, even if you earn the maximum number of points every day, your odds are still crummy.

You earn points by simply using the iWon portal. For example, you get seven points for using the iWon search engine, four points for clicking on each news story, five points for looking at your customized stock or weather center, and so on. Inktomi powers the iWon search engine, which is the same company behind AOL, Yahoo!, Snap, and 90 other portals.

Have I won anything in two months? Nothing.

Play Games, Win Money

iWin.com is like the fun, waste-your-time brother of iWon. At iWin, it's all about the games. There's no news and information. You play Shockwave games to earn iCoins, and you spend your iCoins on sweepstakes entries for cash, vacations, cutlery sets, or whatever. You see how many other people have entered to win a particular prize, so you have some idea of your odds.

As with iWon, you need to give up a little information during registration. Also, every time you spend some iCoins on sweepstakes entries, you are forced to click on an ad banner to "confirm your entry." It's funny because most of the banner ads are for other "win free money" sites. What's worse than clicking on the ads, though, is the email that's sent to you for each prize giveaway you register for. I've never won anything at iWin.com either.

Download of the Day

Acronym Finder Registry Key

The Internet has brought all kinds of annoyances: privacy breaches, pop-up ads, and thousands of puzzling acronyms—created just to make a person feel inferior. Don't let that person be you.

Acronym Finder (www.acronymfinder.com) offers a simple download that adds Acronym Finder to your Internet Explorer right-click menu.

If you use IE, simply download the program and install. Acronym Finder makes a slight change to your Registry. Next time you're surfing the web, just select the acronym, right-click, and choose Acronym Finder Lookup. You'll see the results on Acronym Finder's page.

The only drawback is the Acronym Finder website itself. The content is still great, but it has greatly increased the number of pop-up ads. Acronym Finder has also tried to install Gator when I went to the site. As always, make sure you don't agree to or accept anything that randomly pops up when you're surfing the web.

Free Money (continued)

Money Grows on Trees

TreeLoot (www.treeloot.com) might have the most elegant business model on the Internet. The site displays a picture of a large tree divided into grid boxes.

You click on the grid boxes in hopes of finding money. After every click, a wise-cracking monkey encourages you to click again and to click on ad banners to increase your chance of winning. If you never click on any banners, a large gorilla threatens you.

I clicked on grid boxes in that tree for most of an afternoon. TechTV executives kept glancing my way as they walked by my cubicle.

I clicked on as many ad banners as I could stomach. I won nothing except some banana bucks, which are pretty useless as far as I can tell. You can't even buy bananas.

But TreeLoot is addictive. You think that the money will rain down if you click just one more time. Lots of other people are caught in TreeLoot's tentacles, too, because TreeLoot is easily one of the 100 most popular sites on the Internet.

The "Punch the Monkey and win $20" banner that TreeLoot uses to pull people into its site from other sites has one of the highest click rates of any banner ad on the Net—about 10%.

Win the Lottery?

At many Internet sites, you can pick six numbers in hopes of winning an online lottery. Your computer can also help you win the lottery sponsored by your home state.

You actually have a much better chance of winning your state's lottery than winning most online sweepstakes. For example, at Jackpot (www.jackpot.com), a venture run by IdeaLaB (the same people who gave us eToys.com, FreePC.com, Cooking.com, and scores of other websites), your odds of winning a $40,000 car are 1 in 259,000,000. Your odds of picking six correct numbers in a state-sponsored lottery with 50 numbers to choose from are 1 in15,890,700.

Lotto Buster (www.lottobuster.com) claims if you use its software to choose your state-sponsored lottery numbers, the odds are cut by as much as 70%. This is mathematically unsound. Lotto Buster analyzes number patterns and predicts what numbers are "hot" and "cold" during a particular lottery's history.

Warning: The chances of winning the lottery are the same every time. Services that track "trends" have no basis in real math or statistics. But, if you win the lottery, I think you owe me some money for letting you in on this. If you don't win, please send me $5 anyway. Now I'm heading over to the money tree to do battle with that monkey.

Download of the Day

Fire Instant Messenger

Megan Morrone

The days of incompatible instant-messenger systems are over. It's true that I still can't use ICQ (http://web.icq.com/) to IM someone who has only AIM (www.aim.com/index.adp). But I can download a multiplatform instant-message utility that lets me send and receive messages to several different IM clients using only one program.

There are a handful of these programs, but my favorite is Fire (www.epicware.com/fire.html), from Epicware because it's open source, and it works in Mac OS X (10.1 or higher).

The good: Right now Fire supports AIM, ICQ, Yahoo!, IRC, MSN, and Jabber IM messengers. Like all other OS X apps, Fire is beautifully designed. And unlike AIM, there are no ads.

The not-so-good: Fire's features aren't as intuitive as are other OS X application features. First, I had a little trouble figuring out how to send an IM to someone who wasn't on my buddy list. Also, if you're used to sending by pressing Return, you'll have to customize your preferences. Otherwise, just press Cmd+S.

Family Photography

Megan Morrone

Is it getting hot in here? Not in San Francisco, where we tape *The Screen Savers*. July is one of the coldest months, continuing the cycle of gloom that begins in June. Why do so many people want to live in San Francisco if it's so darn cold for most of the year? So they can come visit the set of *The Screen Savers* whenever they want, of course.

If this were a real almanac, I'd be giving you gardening tips that are appropriate for the month of July. But because I can't keep a begonia alive to save my life, you should be very happy that this is not a real almanac.

July is the month we celebrate our independence by watching loud, huge, exploding spectacles of red, white, and blue. What better month would there be then to dedicate capturing this spectacle and saving it on our hard drives? That's right, this month we focus on my favorite aspect of technology: digital photos and digital video. I've owned a digital camera for only a few years, but I will never, never go back to still pictures. I've only owned a digital video camera for a few months, and I need another hard drive. Man, video files are huge.

In the following pages, you'll find lots of tips from Leo and the rest of *The Screen Savers* gang, but we didn't stop there. We decided to bring in two photo experts from our extended *The Screen Savers* family: Bert Monroy and Mikkel Aaland. IMHO, Bert and Mikkel are the Bob Rosses of the digital age. I take digital photos, but they take digital photos and make them into art.

So give your poor sun-burned bum a break and spend some time inside learning everything you ever wanted to know about digital photography and videography, from buying the right camera to Photoshopping your head onto Britney Spears's body.

Shoot and Print Great Digital Pictures

Mikkel Aaland

To get perfect prints, set the print dimensions in your image editor. In Photoshop Elements, you can select dimensions in three ways:

1. Go to Image, Resize, Image Size.
2. Go to File and choose Print Preview.
3. Click Print Preview in the shortcuts bar.

Type the dimensions of your desired print in the Document Size fields in the Image Size dialog.

Use the pop-up menus to select different measurement systems, ranging from inches to centimeters. Don't make the image 8.5×11 if you want to print to 8.5×11 inch paper. Allow at least a quarter-inch border because most desktop printers aren't capable of printing or bleeding an image to the edge of the paper.

You set the resolution in the Image Size dialog. How much resolution is enough? Don't be misled by the specifications of the printer. For most desktop inkjet printers, 150–200dpi is enough, and anything over 200dpi is a waste. The print quality won't suffer.

If you reduce the size of the image in Print Preview, the resolution automatically increases proportionally. It doesn't change the overall number of pixels or affect the original image file.

Image Quality

You always get the best image quality from the RAW data format. This data comes directly from the sensor and requires special imaging software to view and process. (RAW is an option on many prosumer and professional digital cameras, but not on consumer cameras.)

If your camera supports it, the TIFF format is the next best option. TIFF files are even larger than RAW files, but there is no compression and, thus, no compression artifacts.

JPEG is the most commonly used file format. JPEG compresses data by throwing away information. Most digital cameras offer low to high JPEG compression. High compression means a smaller file size but less quality; low compression means less compression and less degradation. Generally, low-compressed JPEG is perfectly adequate.

You can change pixel resolution as well. For example, the Sony DSC-F 717 camera has a maximum resolution of 2560×1920 pixels. You can also set the resolution to 2048×1536 pixels, 1280×960 pixels, or 640×480 pixels. (You can change the aspect ratio as well.)

Most of these settings create smaller files, with a trade-off in quality. Think twice before choosing anything lower than the maximum resolution, especially if you shoot buildings or landscapes where detail is important.

Other Considerations

- **Focus.** Take time to frame and focus your shot carefully. Many autofocus systems require adjust and focus.

- **Lens sharpness.** You can't change the inherent quality of a lens. However, an optimal f/stop (the camera lens aperture setting) provides the best sharpness. For most lenses, the optimal f/stop is two to three stops narrower than the widest aperture. For example, if the widest aperture of your lens is f/2.8, then f/5.6 would be the optimal f/stop.

- **Camera movement.** Faster shutter speeds help minimize blur caused by camera movement. However, if you want a narrow f/stop to maximize the sharpness of a shot, or if you want increased depth of field, a faster shutter speed might not be possible.

Tripods are useful tools to help minimize movement caused by a shaky hand or the mechanics of the camera itself. Using shutter release cords or the camera's self-timer mode further reduces the camera movement.

Shoot and Print Great Digital Pictures (continued)

Adjust Sharpness

Unlike consumer-level digital cameras, many prosumer and professional digital cameras offer a variety of sharpness settings. You can access sharpness, contrast, and color saturation settings via the camera's menu display.

Sharpness values are expressed numerically or as Hard, Normal, or Soft. The sharpness settings have nothing to do with the optics of a camera or with the resolution—only with the data from the sensor.

When you increase sharpness, the image processor increases the contrast between adjacent pixels. However, it introduces noise and can make the image look coarse or rough. Many pros turn off sharpness or set it to the lowest value, so either use the lowest value or turn it off. If you are saving your data in the RAW format, sharpen settings are usually irrelevant.

Many image-editing programs offer more control over the sharpening process than the camera ever will.

White-Balance Your Digital Camera

Did you know that when you use film balanced for outdoor light in a room with fluorescent lights, the image comes out with a yucky green cast? With a digital camera, you don't have to worry about film matching a light source, but you do need to set the white balance to reproduce colors naturally. Most prosumer and professional digital cameras offer several white-balance options; consumer digital cameras are more limited.

- **Auto.** The camera automatically calculates the correct color balance. Auto generally works fine under outdoor light or when there are several different light sources.
- **Cloudy.** Use under a cloudy sky. Be sure to change the white balance when you move to a different setting. Cloudy will produce a blush in other light sources.

- **Fluorescent or Tungsten.** These options match your light source.
- **Color Temperature.** More advanced cameras express presets as color temperature values ranging from 3000K, the color temperature of incandescent light, to 7500K, the typical color temperature of a clear, sunny day.
- **Custom.** The custom white-balance setting is generally used when a single, dominant light source doesn't match the color temperature of any standard presets.
  1. Point the camera toward a white card or a large white area in a scene. (Some digital camera manufacturers, notably Nikon, say an 18% gray card also works.)
  2. Depress the White Balance Mode button.
  3. The camera makes a custom calculation. Depending on the specifications of the camera, the setting is saved with the camera's other preset settings.

- **Bracketing.** Some advanced cameras, such as the Nikon D100, offer white-balance bracketing, which instructs the camera to automatically shoot a series of images with slightly different white-balance settings, functioning much like exposure bracketing.

A lot of misconceptions surround white balance. Changing white-balance settings does nothing to the RAW data that comes off the sensor. White-balance settings are applied only in the image-processing stage of image capture. If you save your data in the RAW format, you can apply any white-balance setting with imaging software. If you use TIFF or JPEG formats, your camera white-balance settings are very important because these settings are applied directly to the image. You can alter color cast later in imaging software, but it takes work and the results are not always satisfactory.

Free Animation Education

Roman Loyola

I finally found time to go to the movie theater last night to see *The Matrix Reloaded*. Two hours and 18 minutes later, I cursed myself for not seeing the movie sooner. *The Matrix Reloaded* has changed my life.

It made me rethink my life as a web producer for *The Screen Savers*. No, I'm not going Michio Kaku on you and pondering whether we really live in the Matrix. It was the production of the movie, not its mystical pretensions, that had me in awe.

The Matrix Reloaded is a visual delight. Indeed, there are lots of movies now playing that present the audience with so much eye candy, you leave the theater on a virtual sugar high (at least that's how I felt after I left the theater). And who creates those cinematic confections? Computer animators.

That was my revelation: I want to be a computer animator.

No more dealing with Patrick's missed deadlines, writing lame instructions on how to use the Any key, or editing some guest's marketingspeak so it actually has value for you readers. I want to make Neo fight 100 Agent Smiths. I want to create realistic ocean reefs without ever going to the ocean. I want to make my own movie where my mutant power is the ability to maintain a washboard stomach by eating tons of fatty foods. (Shooting laser beams from my hands would be cool, too.)

No Tuition Necessary

Problem is, I have no skills. I need training, and that means I also need serious cash, because education ain't cheap.

However, thanks to 3D Buzz (`www.3dbuzz.com`), education is not only cheap, it's free.

3D Buzz offers free training for wannabe 3D animators and digital artists. The tutorials are available for download from the 3D Buzz website, or you can have CD-ROM tutorials mailed to you.

Like I said, the tutorials are free. All that's required is free registration. If you want CDs, you'll go on a weeks' long waiting list. You can better your position on the waiting list by making a donation of blank CD-Rs, CD mailers, or stamps (monetary donations are not accepted). You can also sign up for member sponsorship, which costs $35 a month.

Where to Start

Free training for skills that'll pay serious cash? What are you waiting for? Here are three courses you'll definitely want to investigate. There are tons more courses at 3D Buzz. Remember, you have to register at the site to access the tutorials.

- Maya has been used in popular films such as *Toy Story*, *Final Fantasy*, and the *Lord of the Rings* movies. Training can cost thousands of dollars, but 3D Buzz offers it for free.

- Photoshop 7 guru and frequent show guest Bert Monroy always dazzles the TSS crew and audience with his magical how-tos. Now you can be like Bert.

- UT2K3 Level Design. Want to be a game designer? 3D Buzz has a free tutorial on level design for Unreal Tournament 2003 using the UnrealEd level designer.

Address: **Site of the Night**

Zefrank.com

You can find an almost endless series of brilliantly hysterical Flash features at `www.zefrank.com`.

Seamlessly Join Multiple Scans with Photoshop

Bert Monroy

Have you ever had to scan an item that's larger than your scanner? The solution is to make separate scans of the overall image, or you can create a single file out of the multiple scans with Photoshop.

When you scan an item, make sure you scan a considerable amount of overlap from one scan to the next.

1. Start with the scan that will be the basis for the overall image.

Scan made in two parts with overlap of image

2. Increase the Canvas Size (Image, Canvas Size) to match the overall size of the original art. Make sure the element in that file is placed correctly within the file. For example, the lower-left part of the image should be in the lower-left part of the file.

3. Using the Move tool, drag the other scans into the new file. Place the other scans (now in layers) into the correct position, with the overlap over the image below it.

4. Place the layer in Difference mode (at the top of the Layer palette). Where the two layers overlap, difference is displayed in white. Where they're the same, it appears black.

5. Using the Move tool and the cursor keys, nudge the layer into position until the entire overlapping area is black. Black indicates that the layers are perfectly aligned.

6. Put the layer back in Normal mode and flatten it.

Roundup: Sub-$100 Scanners

James Kim

When most people go shopping for a computer, the scanner is a mere afterthought. But when you have images and documents that you want to digitize, you'll really want that scanner. We evaluated the scanners in our roundup based on speed and image quality. We also considered other features, including interface options, slide and negative trays, physical size, and software.

Buying Tips

- Unless you need a tiny scanner, get a CCD sensor.
- Don't be impressed with high-interpolated (software-aided) resolution. Pay attention to the optical resolution.
- A USB 2.0–compatible scanner offers faster scanning.

Scanner Speed Tests

We tested all scanners on a PC equipped with a 1.3GHz Pentium III processor, 256MB of RAM, an NVidia GeForce3 video card, and Windows XP. For the USB 2.0 scanners, we used a SIIG USB 2.0 PCI Adapter. For our time tests, we scanned images into Adobe Photoshop 7.0. We viewed images with a 17-inch Trinitron CRT monitor and printed images using a Canon i850 inkjet printer.

Download of the Day

Ten Second Films

Megan Morrone

Ten Second Films (www.tensecondfilms.com) isn't a production company. It's a competition put on by Candide Media Works (www.candidemedia.com) to find the best films that last only 10 seconds. Making a coherent 10-second film takes talent, especially in the editing department. Ten seconds is short. Very short. As a result, not all the entries are necessarily coherent— or, at least, not according to my definition of coherence. Watch the finalists' films. Since they're only seconds, you probably won't have trouble downloading them, even if you're on dialup. You'll need RealPlayer (www.real.com).

Benchmarks Are in Seconds. Lower Scores Are Better.					
Scanner	Colortest 150dpi, 24-bit	Grayscale 150dpi, 8-bit	4×6 color photo 150dpi, 24-bit	4×6 color photo 1200dpi, 24-bit	Magazine 300dpi, 24-bit
Canon CanoScan LiDE 30	26	6	16	161	56
HP Scanjet 3500c	7	6	8	159	42
Epson Perfection 1260 Photo	7	8	11	160	4
Visioneer OneTouch 9000 USB	6	4	5	48	18

Roundup: Sub-$100 Scanners (continued)

Epson Perfection 1260 Photo

Even without a USB 2.0 interface, the Perfection 1260 Photo is fast, nearly matching the HP 3500c in every time test. Image quality ranked behind the HP. The 1260 uses a utilitarian and task-based Twain driver that includes a scan-to-PDA feature.

Automated four-button scanning lets users quickly scan images to a scan-to-copy utility, Epson's photo-sharing website, and most email software programs. Prescan was a bit slow, at 15 seconds. The full-auto mode makes scanning almost too easy. The inclusion of a 35mm slide and negative adapter is a bonus for photographers. We recommend the Perfection 1260 for most users.

Pros: Slide adapter; fast scanner for USB 1.1
Cons: Slow prescan
Optical resolution: 1200×2400dpi
Bit depth: 48
Interface: USB 1.1

Canon CanoScan LiDE 30

The Canon CanoScan LiDE 30 is the smallest, at 1.3 inches thick and a scant 3.3 pounds. The scanner is powered through the USB bus, with front panel buttons for quickly scanning, copying, and emailing a scan.

The LiDE 30 consistently placed last in our image quality tests. It was also the slowest.

Nevertheless, the scan quality is good, and the entire experience, from setup to using the excellent software, was top-notch. If you prefer sleek and easy, and are okay dropping a half-notch in quality and speed, the LiDE is for you.

Pros: Tiny; sleek and simple; good software
Cons: Slow; image quality good but not the best
Optical resolution: 1200×2400 dpi
Bit depth: 48
Interface: USB 1.1

HP Scanjet 3500c

HP's Scanjet 3500c is a zippy performer, thanks to its USB 2.0 interface. It comes with a step-by-step installation and scanning guide, as well as a handy virtual toolbar that displays customizable one-step scan jobs. The Twain interface is modern and simple.

The largest scanner of the group, the 3500c, has one-step scan, email, and copy buttons. It also consistently produced the sharpest and most color-accurate scans. A longer-than-usual lamp warm-up time was its only blemish. Intuitive and useful software, great scans, and very good speed are a deal for the low price.

Pros: Simple software great for newbies; fast; best image quality
Cons: Lengthy lamp warm-up
Optical resolution: 1200×1200dpi
Bit depth: 48
Interface: USB 1.1, 2.0

Visioneer OneTouch 9000 USB

Visioneer consistently produces solid and affordable scanners, and the OneTouch 9000 USB continues the tradition. The 9000's speedy USB 2.0 interface beat the scan times of all its competitors. A 4×6 photo scan (150dpi) took only 5 seconds, but even more impressive was the 48-second scan of a 4×6 photo at 1200dpi.

Image quality is very good, but with slight oversaturation. The smallest of the three larger scanners, it has a unique wide design with the cover hinged along the long side of the scanner. There are also five quick scan buttons. The PaperPort Deluxe with integrated OCR software is functional, but could be more intuitive.

Pros: Very fast; very good image quality
Cons: PaperPort software isn't intuitive; Windows only; sharp but oversaturated images
Optical resolution: 1200×2400dpi
Bit depth: 48
Interface: USB 1.1, 2.0

197

Digital Day in the Life

Nicole Carrico

Nearly 100 of the world's top photojournalists set out to capture the content of Africa in 24 hours—on camera. The result of this ambitious undertaking are available in A Day in the Life of Africa (www.ditlafrica.com), the 14th release in the celebrated "Day in the Life" series.

This project differs from its predecessors in two significant ways. First and foremost, all publishing profits from A Day in the Life of Africa go to charity, supporting AIDS education programs in Africa. Second, the project was shot entirely using digital cameras.

Making a Day in the Life

1. Photographers used Olympus E20 and C4040 Zoom digital cameras. Images were recorded as high quality (SHQ) JPEGs (3.5MB files) and TIFFs (15MB files) to ensure publication-quality printing.

2. Images were stored on Lexar Media Professional Series 16X 256MB cards for the E20 and 128MB SmartMedia cards for the C4040.

3. When the CompactFlash and SmartMedia cards were full, images were downloaded to MindStor portable 5GB hard drives that could hold up to 1,400 high-quality JPEG-format images.

4. Images were viewed and organized in the field on laptops using Apple's iPhoto software. Back at project headquarters, the images were downloaded onto four Macintosh editing stations with Cinema Displays, where editors pared down the collection of 50,000 images to just over 300 using Camera Bits Photo Mechanic software.

5. After using noise-reduction and fractal-imaging software to achieve maximum-quality output, the images were reproduced in the Day in the Life of Africa book, website (www.ditlafrica.com), and photo exhibition.

Mac Tips

Jalbum

Megan Morrone

Apple's iPhoto makes it easy to create a photo slide show for your website, but Jalbum (www.datadosen.se/jalbum/install.htm) is even easier. After you download the program:

1. Put all the photos you want to use in a single folder.

2. Browse for the folder in the image directory window.

3. Create a style.

4. Specify the size of your thumbnails and your slides.

5. Click Create Album.

Jalbum creates the HTML you need. Just upload the index file, the images, the thumbs, the navigation GIFs, and the slides to your website and publish.

Now you can easily share your photos with friends. Jalbum works with OS X, Windows, Solaris, Linux, and UNIX.

July
7

Get the Most Out of Your Digital Camera

Nicole Guilfoyle with Chris Pirillo of Lockergnome
Point, shoot, upload, view, print. Boring. You can do so much more with your digital camera.

- **Traveler's best friend.** If you don't know the language, nobody's going to help you get back to your hotel—unless you put your digital camera to good use. Travel expert Rick Steves recommends taking a picture of your accommodations. If you get lost, show the pic to some natives and use gestures to ask them to point you in the right direction.

- **Poor man's scanner.** If you don't have a scanner, take a picture of your forms or receipts and load them into your PC.

- **Inventory.** You've photographed your receipts, now take pictures of the items you purchased, write down the serial and model numbers, and put it all together in a database. You'll love having this information (on a disk in a safe place) if anything is stolen or defective.

- **"Before and after" shots.** Somebody hit your car. You need to rebuild your staircase. Your walls need painting. You want to know which haircut or hair color looks best. Take "before and after" shots, and use your image editor to look at the pictures side by side. Print or email the comparison to friends for their opinion. Have "before and after" car-repair pictures handy for the insurance adjuster.

- **Make movies for your blog or website.** Most digital cameras let you record a few minutes of video. It's not the best quality, but it's perfect if you want to show off your dog's latest trick.

- **Shoot textures for video (or photo) art.** Your video and photo editor comes with some default textures (the sky, cement, stucco). Get a more realistic look by photographing real sidewalks, walls, or other textured objects that you think would look cool in your personal masterpiece.

Windows Tips

Resize Pics with a Right-Click

Morgan Webb
You want to change the size of a graphic, but you don't want to open it in an image editor, resize it, and then save with a different filename. You need Windows XP and its PowerToys.

1. Download the XP PowerToys Image Resizer from Microsoft (www.microsoft.com).

2. Run the downloaded file to install the Image Resizer.

3. Right-click a graphic and choose Resize.

Mac Tips

Still Life

Brett Larson
We've shown you how to turn your iMovie photos into exciting videos with an expensive production application. Here's how to do it for free using Still Life (www.apple.com/downloads/macosx/video/stilllife.html).

1. Open any photo.

2. Pick your photo start point and select either move, pan, scale, or zoom.

3. Pick any in-between points and an endpoint. You're ready to go.

Still Life exports directly to iMovie or to a QuickTime movie that you can put on the web.

July
8

Family Photos Online in a Flash

Megan Morrone

The only person I know who is more addicted to a digital camera than I am is my dad. Around any holiday, we furiously upload pictures to share with the family. So I decided to post as many pictures as possible in the least amount of time.

Each site provides a standard method for uploading photos, as well as a drag-and-drop tool to make the process easier. If you're using a newer version of Windows, the site prompts you to download and install the tool. If you're using an alternative operating system, you'll have to look for it. I rated the sites according to their upload accelerating tools:

- **Shutterfly** (www.shutterfly.com). The Best. The drag-and-drop tool automatically installed on my Windows XP machine. On my Mac, I simply clicked the Want the Fastest Way to Upload Photos? link. The tool was available in Mac OS X, Classic, and Linux. The browse function on the tool made it easy to select all my images at once.

- **Ofoto** (www.ofoto.com). The Average. The drag-and-drop tool doesn't automatically install. If you don't know it's there, you might suffer through the slow upload process, as I did the first few times. Also, the drag-and-drop tool doesn't have a browse function, so you have to arrange your Windows just right and select just the pics you want. Ofoto does have a tool for Mac, but it runs only in Classic mode. And Ofoto doesn't offer the tool for Linux.

- **Snapfish** (www.snapfish.com). The Worst. The drag-and-drop tool is fine for Windows users, although the other sites automatically start the upload when you add photos; the Snapfish tool makes you click Upload Photos. On the plus side, the Snapfish tool includes a browse function. The tool works only on Windows. Other operating systems are stuck with the slow upload method.

Speed of Upload

The following tests reflect only the upload speed. Remember, if you're not using the drag-and-drop tool, and if you can't browse easily for your photos, it adds significant time to the process.

The tests were performed using an XP laptop with my broadband wireless connection. The pictures were 1600×1200 and around 800KB each. I did two tests for each site and took the faster time of the two. I rounded up to the nearest second. These times are not Olympic-official, but I did the best I could.

- **Shutterfly**
  One picture: 36.09 seconds
  Five pictures: 1 minute, 49 seconds
- **Ofoto**
  One picture: 36.34 seconds
  Five pictures: 1 minute, 49 seconds
- **Snapfish**
  One picture: 44.97 seconds
  Five pictures: 2 minutes, 28 seconds

Snapfish also makes you watch ads while the photos are uploading. Maybe that's why it takes longer.

Other Features

All the sites offer free prints when you sign up, but don't forget the shipping charges. Of the three, only Shutterfly lets your friends and family view your pictures without signing up for an account.

I ordered photo cards from Ofoto because it had the best designs for the best prices, but that's a question of personal taste.

What Megapixels Mean

Patrick Norton

Megapixel has become more a marketing term than a technical measurement. Most folks assume that a megapixel is 1 million pixels. A 2-megapixel camera would have two million pixels. Sounds good. The problem is, there's no standardized measurement behind those megapixels. It could be a measurement of the total numbers of sensors inside your camera, even though the full-size image produced by those sensors has a few hundred thousand fewer pixels.

That said, the number of sensors inside the camera is only one element in the equation. The quality of the sensors (CCD or CMOS) and the quality of the lens that focuses light onto the sensors are two others. An expensive camera doesn't guarantee great optics.

After an image is picked up by the sensor, it's converted from analog to digital, interpolated into a particular resolution compression, and then saved to the camera's memory. All of this affects image quality.

When buying a digital camera, look for the following:

- A 1-megapixel camera is more than enough to feed a typical website. A 2-megapixel or 3-megapixel camera is better if you want 8×10 print images.

- No matter how many megapixels you're shopping for, look for quality optics, compact Flash storage, and a body and interface that feel comfortable in your hands and that are easy to use.

- Avoid digital zoom; it makes for awful images (a 3x or better optical zoom is a nice feature, however). While you're at it, keep an eye on battery life. You don't want to carry a bag full of batteries to keep your camera alive for the whole ballgame.

Helpful Links

- **The Luminous Landscape**
  (www.luminous-landscape.com) has a great article titled "Understanding Digital Camera Resolution."

- **Megapixel Myths**
  (http://megamyth.homestead.com) dispels the myth that more megapixels is always better.

- **How Digital Cameras Work**
  (www.howstuffworks.com/ digital-camera1.htm) is a good introduction to the technology.

Windows Tips

Select the Inverse

Morgan Webb

So you have a huge folder of pictures from your birthday party. They're all grand except for those three less-than-flattering shots of your friends. But you don't want to include the inferior pics when you burn the CD as an after-the-fact party favor.

You could carefully select everything but those pics, or simply select the pictures you don't want and tell your computer that you actually want the opposite.

1. Open a folder and select one or more items.
2. Select the Edit menu.
3. Select Invert Selection.
4. All your items except the ones you selected are now highlighted.

Address: Site of the Night

Flash Puppets

Dangle animated animals from virtual strings with this cool Flash Puppet Tool at www.lecielestbleu.com/html/puppettool.htm.

Sunday
July 11
2004

Compensate for Camera Distortion

Bert Monroy

Cameras, whether digital or analog, are subject to distortion caused by the lens. Professional cameras can compensate for this, but the average digital camera can't. If you take a panoramic shot of a cityscape, you'll notice that the buildings tend to lean inward toward the top center. To correct this, follow the simple steps outlined here:

1. Duplicate the background (image) into a layer.

2. Display the grid (View, Show, Grid). This makes alignment easier.

3. Zoom out of the image and increase the size of the window so you see a good amount of the gray nonworkspace.

4. Choose Distort (Edit, Transform, Distort).

5. Pull the tabs at the upper left and right of the image outward into the gray space. Distort it until the buildings line up with the grid.

6. When you have made enough of an adjustment to satisfy your needs, press Enter. The distortion takes place.

7. Flatten the file, and you're finished.

Ancient Scanning Secrets

Martin Sargent and Greg Melton

Mastering the ancient art of scanning documents and images isn't as challenging as you think.

The Right Resolution

Matching the resolution of your input and output devices is a fundamental digital-imaging skill. Think about it: Why scan an image at 600dpi if your inkjet printer can't produce images clearer than 200dpi? The print won't be true to the original image: It will be bigger and might not even fit on the printer paper.

Sometimes, though, you want to increase the size of an image through the scan and print process. For example, if you want to scan a small image (say a 3×5 photo) to have it exit the printer twice as big, you need to do some simple math to figure out the resolution to scan.

If you want the intended and original image sizes to stay the same, or if you want to increase the intended image size, here's the equation to keep in mind:

Resolution to Scan At = Printer dpi × (Intended Image Width ÷ Original Image Width)

Let's say that your printer dpi is 200 and you want to make a 6×10 image out of a 3×5 photograph. The math: $200 \times (6 \div 3) = 400$dpi

Thus, you want to scan the image at 400dpi to get the intended result.

Your computer monitor is also an output device. Generally, if your scanned images are for a webpage or an electronic photo album, you don't need to scan at more than 75dpi.

Keep the resolution lower to save hard-drive space. Plus, it takes far less time for the scanner to capture the image, anyone looking at the image on your website won't be able to tell whether you scanned it at 75dpi or 600dpi, and if you intend to email the image, it'll move across the Internet much faster at 75dpi.

File Format

Resolution isn't the only thing to consider. You must also consider the file format to save the image. If you have a monstrous hard drive and want pristine quality, save the image as a bitmap.

A bitmap is an uncompressed file format, meaning that it will consume a great deal of disk space. (An 8×10 photo scanned at 24-bit color at 600dpi will consume 84.4MB of disk space, nearly the size of a whole Zip disk.) Bitmaps are good, though, because there's no loss in image quality.

Generally, save your images as TIFF files. TIFF is a "lossless" compression format, meaning that you won't lose any detail, despite massive file size shrinkage. What's more, TIFF images can be exported into most graphics, layout, and word-processing programs.

For websites, save your images as 72dpi JPEGs. Though you'll give up image quality, JPEG files are drastically compressed. Small file size is a tremendous boon if your ISP offers 20MB of space for your website.

Windows Tips

If your mouse cursor is too small in XP, enlarge it!

1. Click Start, mouse over Settings, and click Control Panel.
2. Click the Mouse icon and go to Pointers.
3. In Scheme, select either Windows Standard (large) or Windows Standard (extra large).

Now you can actually see what you're clicking with.

Scanning Oversize Documents

Martin Sargent and Greg Melton

Most scanners let you scan documents or images only up to 8.5×11 inches. The standard scanner might not cover enough area to scan newspapers, maps, oversize magazines, or oversize books, so here are a few solutions to choose.

Automatic Stitch

Image stitching involves importing smaller scans into a graphics program to create a single document. Any program used to create a panoramic photo can be used to automatically reassemble scans.

- **LM Stitch** (free to try or $19.95 to buy, www.lostmarble.com/lmstitch.html)
- **Ulead Cool 360** (free to try for 15 days, or $39.95 to buy; www.ulead.com/cool360/runme.htm)
- **PanaVue Image Assembler** (free to try or $64 to buy, www.panavue.com/)

Manual Stitch

If a panoramic photo maker doesn't allow precise enough stitching control, use a standard image-editing program to manually stitch the scans together. Numerous programs can re-create an oversize document from smaller scans.

- **Photoshop Elements 2** ($99, www.adobe.com) Read Bert Monroy's stitching tips on July 4.
- **PhotoImpact** ($89.95, www.jasc.com/products/psp/)
- **Paint Shop Pro** ($99, www.jasc.com/products/psp)
- **GIMP** (free, www.gimp.org)

Both PowerPoint and Word offer crude image-manipulation features. If you're not trying to digitally re-create the Declaration of Independence, either one might do the job nicely.

Windows Tips

Say "No to All" in Windows XP

Morgan Webb

Here's the situation: You want to add a group of pictures to your My Pictures folder, but your My Pictures folder already contains some, but not all, of those pictures. Instead of sorting out which pictures are already in the folder and moving only the new ones, you can save time by moving the whole lot and letting Windows XP figure it out.

XP dutifully asks whether you want to replace any duplicate files. It gives you these choices for the duplicates: Yes to All (replace them all), Yes (replace this particular one), and No (do not replace this particular one).

Where's the No to All option? It'd be great to have if you wanted to save time or if you wanted to keep original versions of the files. To do this, you had to click No for each duplicate file, but not anymore. In Windows XP, you can hold down Shift while you click No, and that will act as if you had clicked a No to All option. It's a simple but cool little Windows XP secret. This does not work in Windows 98 or earlier.

Address: Site of the Night

FilmWise

Take some hilarious movie quizzes for inquisitive geeks at FilmWise, www.filmwise.com.

More Scanning Secrets: Be Clever

Martin Sargent and Greg Melton

There's no law saying that you can scan only flat things such as photographs and magazine articles. Be creative: You'd be surprised at what scans wonderfully and how many things you can do with the unorthodox images.

For example, 3D objects are fair game for flatbed scanners. Put the object—jewelry, food, cats, things you've found in the woods—on the glass plate and rest the scanner lid on it. When the scanned image appears in the image-editing software's viewing area, you'll be shocked at the quality.

No one has a copyright on things you've found in the woods. That means you can use those images on your website with no fear of infringing on anyone's copyright. In the case of food—and food scans beautifully—be sure not to leave greasy residue on the glass plate. A little spurt of window cleaner and a clean, lint-free cloth or a specialized lens-cleaning pad will do the trick.

Also think about scanning unorthodox objects to use as backgrounds for your webpages. For example, go outside and find some beautifully colored leaves. Lay them on the scanner so that you can't see the glass plate. Execute the scan. Use the resulting image as a webpage background. Holiday wrapping paper, wallpaper remnants, and fabric also make cool web backgrounds.

Scanning Printed Images

Magazines, newspapers, and books present the perfect material for scanning images. But to get the best results, you need to understand how images are manipulated so they print correctly using a printing press.

When you send an image to a printer, the printer must create what's called a halftone before it's printable. A halftone turns a regular image into a system of dots and checkers that are usually invisible to the eye. These dots and checkers simulate gradation of tone values and enable the image to be printed on a press.

When you scan printed images, be aware that these dots and checkers exist. Your scanning software should contain a setting that allows you to scan images from printed material. The scanning software will remove the dots and checkers so they don't appear on your final scan. Now you know why your scanned images always come out looking dotted and checkered.

Mac Tips

Where iPhoto Hides Your Photos

Megan Morrone

If you're an amateur photographer and use Mac OS X, chances are you already know about iPhoto. And unless your Mac has unlimited space, the hard drive is probably full of photos. At this point, you should back them up, which means you need to know where iPhoto stores them.

1. Click Go.
2. Choose Home.
3. Select Pictures.
4. Double-click the iPhoto Library folder.

The Mac uses a strange date-based numbering system to store photos. The folders are numbered by months of the year (for example, January=1, October=10). Within those numbered folders are more numbered folders that represent the days of the month. The easiest way to find your photos is through your albums.

If you want more control over your iPhoto library, try the iPhoto Library Manager (http://homepage.mac.com/bwebster/iphotolibrarymanager.html). It's a free download.

July
14

Make a Coffee-Table Book

Richard Statter

Do you remember the Hewlett-Packard commercial in which the guy makes a coffee-table book of his coffee table in various sceneries? If you have a Mac, you can easily use Apple's iPhoto (www.apple.com/iphoto) service to make a professionally printed, linen-bound book filled with prints of your digital photos or scans. Apple provides a great service if you own a Mac, but what do you do if you have a PC?

Make Your Coffee-Table Book

One surefire way to show off your most cherished memories to any household guest is to make a coffee-table book. I don't mean your standard photo album from K-mart filled with 4×6 photos. I'm talking about a professionally printed, linen-bound book that you design and lay out using photos you've scanned or digital pictures you've taken or collected.

Using a website called My Publisher (www.mypublisher.com), we turned a random collection of goofy staff pictures into a really cool book bound with blue linen cloth, complete with custom captions. The service was so easy that I'd bet almost anyone could do it—and I mean anyone.

My Publisher charges about $30 to create one book. If you want to create a custom layout, you must have at least ten pages of pictures. The custom layout allows you to mix and match the various templates and place the pictures that you want on each page in a predetermined area. It costs about $3 per page for each page over ten pages.

Preparation

To use My Publisher, just sign up on the site, and you're ready to upload your own photos. However, make sure you save the photos that you upload in the JPEG format. I recommend using a photo editor such as Paint Shop Pro (www.jasc.com/products/psp/), not only to save them as JPEGs, but to crop and adjust color levels. If you don't need to adjust color levels, IrfanView (free, www.irfanview.com) works fine to crop, resize, and save as JPEGs.

If you have standard photos you want to include, just scan them. If you want to brush up on your scanning skills or learn a few tricks, read "Ancient Scanning Secrets" on July 12.

Here's a quick tour of how My Publisher works:

1. Upload your photos to the My Publisher server via its web interface.

2. Design the type of layout you like (regular or custom).

3. Insert photos, along with captions, on each page. Enlarge or move the photos within each frame.

4. Choose a linen color (blue, red, or green).

5. Preview and order your book.

You'll receive $10 off each additional copy of the book, and you can purchase new copies after you receive your first copy. We received our book in just three days.

Windows Tips

Put Windows XP in Its Place

Morgan Webb

The nerve of Windows XP. It opens your My Pictures folder as a slide show without even asking. Luckily, you can change the behavior of any folder by changing what Windows thinks you're putting in it. Just right-click any folder (except My Documents), choose Properties, and click the Customize tab. Use the pull-down menu to choose how you want folders to behave. If you want your pictures to display as icons, just choose it to act as a regular folder. If you want thumbnails, choose one of the picture folder options.

Shopping for a Tiny Camera

Ray Weigel

The market for the world's smallest cameras keeps getting bigger. Miniature digital cameras are ideal for experienced photographers and casual users alike. They slip in and out of a shirt pocket easily and aren't nearly as obtrusive as their larger, higher-resolution cousins.

Before you buy, consider the same things you'd think about when you pick a regular-size digital camera:

- **Price.** You often have to make compromises among size, ease of use, and resolution. For example, the BenQ 300mini doesn't take the best pictures, but it's about $100. On the other hand, the Casio Exilim EX-S1 is slightly bigger and takes relatively decent pictures, but costs $200 more.

- **Resolution.** The more pixels a camera can capture, the sharper the picture. Minicams are currently topping out at around 1 megapixel. The Casio Exilim EX-S1 shoots pictures at a maximum resolution of 1.2 megapixels. It can store about 24 images. It has settings for lower-resolution pictures that take up less space, but the image quality suffers.

- **Ease of Use.** It's an important consideration, but it's also the most subjective, and it reveals itself only after you use the camera for a long time. Pay close attention to the camera's design. How close together are the buttons? How does the camera connect to your computer? How do you charge its batteries? Take a few pictures, shuffle through the menus, and try to get a demo of the software.

- **Zoom.** Digital or optical? Because of their size, minicams often use digital zoom, which isn't really zoom. Instead, it's an interpolation of pixels. Although this can work well in high-resolution cameras, the images can appear a little washed-out in mini-cameras.

- **Memory.** What type of memory does the camera use, and how many images can it store? Make sure the memory is compatible with your other computer hardware.

Windows Tips

Link Text Boxes in MS Word

Morgan Webb

Desktop publishing can be tricky. Sometimes simply adding another paragraph to an article can throw off the entire layout. Use Microsoft Word's linked text boxes to make layout easy.

1. Open a new Word document.

2. Go to View, Toolbars, Drawing, or right-click in an open space on the toolbar and check Drawing. The Drawing toolbar appears.

3. Click the Text Box icon. It looks like a little piece of paper with a big A in the corner.

4. Draw a text box any size you want.

5. Draw a second text box for your text to flow into when your first box is full. It can be on the same page or a different page.

6. Click the first box and Link (it looks like chain link) in the Text Box dialog. Or, right-click the border of the text box and choose Create Text Box Link.

7. Depending on your version of Word, your cursor either instantly turns into a measuring cup or becomes a measuring cup only when held over your second text box.

8. Using the measuring cup cursor, click the second text box to link the two boxes.

9. To format other text box options, double-click the highlighted border of the selected text box.

207

Make Your Own DVDs

Roger Chang and Nicole Guilfoyle

DVD players aren't the luxury items they were just a couple years ago. Most families prefer the quality and flexibility of the digital format to that of traditional VHS. So why are you still sending your family and friends home movies on videotape?

You need a computer with at least a 1GHz processor and a 20GB hard drive (we recommend 40GB); Windows 2000 or XP; a FireWire card; and a DVD burner, but you can get by with a CD-R if you only intend to make VCDs. You also need some way to get the video into the computer. We recommend the Dazzle Hollywood DV-Bridge (www.dazzle.com). It allows you to capture video from any analog source and convert it to DV on the fly. It works on a Mac or by itself, if you're really daring. Finally, you need video-editing software. If you invest in the Hollywood DV-Bridge, you can use MovieStar 5, its built-in editor.

Prep Your PC

Check your hard drive space before you start. Defrag your hard drive. If you have an external hard drive, use it as the primary storage area. Turn off any background applications.

Also check the source material. It's hard to work with clips in the gigabyte range. Keep the file size short. If you use a high-quality video, such as DV, try to keep the clips under 10 minutes. Anything longer makes for a long wait.

Import Video

The Hollywood DV-Bridge lets you quickly connect a video camera, VCR, or TV to your FireWire-enabled Mac or PC, and it converts analog signals to a digital format that you can manipulate with a computer.

1. Connect the Hollywood DV-Bridge to the open FireWire jack on your FireWire card.

2. Connect your RCA (composite) video cable or S-Video cable to the analog video camera, VCR, or TV; connect the other end to the Hollywood DV-Bridge. The

RCA cable is color-coded yellow. S-video cable is color-coded black.

3. Connect the audio cables color-coded in red and white to the corresponding jacks on the Hollywood DV-Bridge.

4. Play back your video from its source, and capture/record it using the Dazzle software or your video-editing software. We used Pinnacle Studio 8 (www.pinnaclesys.com).

Editing

MovieStar 5 takes you through most of the steps. Install the software update to make the software more stable.

1. Create a new project and give it a title, choose your video clips, and drag the content onto the edit line.

2. Break up and edit a single file using the Cut tool and the In and Out time adjustments to shorten the clips.

3. Select transitions or effects to go between clips and create the all-important title.

4. Tab over to the Effects, Transitions, or Title tab in the upper right.

5. Drag transitions between the clips, drag effects on top of clips, or drop titles at the beginning.

6. Export the video to a usable DVD format, such as MPEG 2.

Make Your DVD

To create a DVD, start DVD Complete, which also comes with Hollywood DV-Bridge. First-time users should use the wizard. Follow the onscreen instructions. You can tweak things such as chapters, title, and appearance. The program comes with about 20 menu templates.

Create chapters, choose an interface for your DVD, and finish the DVD project. You can create an image or burn a DVD. If you're not ready to burn to a DVD-R disc yet, select Image; otherwise, let it sizzle. Watch your finished product on a DVD drive or your set-top player. Voilá! You have a DVD.

Make New Photos Look Old

**Martin Sargent and
Greg Melton**

Ever see photos that appear to be from the late 1800s? They probably paid $50 to get that photo taken. You can do it on your scanner for free. Turning a vibrant color photo into a sepia-tone, old-looking image is easy.

First, scan the photo as normal. Then, using your image-editing software, crank up the Noise Filter to give the photo a dirty, grainy look. You can then convert the photo to grayscale or just monkey with the contrast a little. The next step is to colorize the image with a hue of about 30 and a saturation of 50.

Finally, blur or soften the image to give it an old, imprecise camera look. Mount it in an oval frame, and you've got a fake family heirloom. Some image-editing software packages, such as Photoshop Elements, have built-in tools for making new pictures look old.

You can also do the opposite. Let's say you find a photo of your great-grandmother taken in the 19th century. It's falling apart, and you want to preserve the image before it crumbles to dust. You can scan it and use editing software to erase all the scratches and holes and also correct color inconsistencies.

The best method is to clone an intact piece of the photo and then use its color value to paint over a ruined spot. Many image-editing programs can guide you through the process, or you can tinker with the image on your own. Make a copy of the original file so that if you mess up, you don't have to re-scan the image.

Stunning Flash Games

Cat Schwartz

Orisinal.com is a wonderful display of all you can do with Flash.

The Screen Savers staffer David Prager sent this link to everybody with a friendly warning: "Be careful…this will sap all of your time away." And that's exactly what it did.

Orisinal is a collection of simple, beautifully rendered animated games. The coloring of the site is pleasantly soft, a far cry from the average hectic game site.

The frog game, Hydrophobia, is a must-play. You're the green guy, and your froggy job is to eat the flies while jumping from pad to pad. This game, like all the games on the site, is way easy, and it made me feel as if I were actually a halfway decent player. The frog is pretty cute, too.

If you're into e-greetings, try Flowers, a digital garden in which you can pick and assemble a virtual bouquet and forward it to a friend. It is actually quite sweet, and I would love to get one from you if you feel like checking it out.

With 23 games and 6 miscellaneous thingama-jigs, this site really is a great time-wasting destination and a brilliant gallery of Flash delights.

Laporte Support

USB or FireWire

Your new hard drive has USB 2.0 and FireWire connectors. Which should you use? We say FireWire. It's faster than USB 2.0, and you can use it to connect digital cameras and other devices.

Don't buy a FireWire card, however. Patrick says buy a FireWire/USB 2.0 combo card. You'll pay a little more, but you'll get both.

July

18

Vallen JPegger

Dan Mitchell

There are plenty of good free image viewers, and everyone has a favorite—IrfanView (www.irfanview.com), SlowView (www.slowview.at), PixVue (www.pixvue.com). It looks like we're gonna have to add another one to the mix because this free file not only functions as a top-notch image viewer, but it includes several unique features that you won't find in other viewers.

Vallen JPegger (www.vallen.de/freeware/index.html) uses a Windows Explorer–style interface that makes it extremely easy to use. Select the folder you want to view, and you instantly see thumbnails of all your photos.

Tabs let you go from a thumbnail view to a larger photo view without opening new windows. You can also rotate, flip, and resize images.

Here are some other sweet features that make Vallen JPegger a force to be reckoned with:

- The program finds duplicate images. This is a great feature if you keep a lot of pictures in one folder.

- Sit back and relax with the built-in slide-show feature.

- You can use capture images of your desktop or any active window with a hot key of your choice.

- You'll have complete control over prints, including a nice preview before you waste ink. Choose between a single image, a contact sheet of all your thumbnails, or "postcards," where you can print multiple photos on one sheet of paper. This feature alone makes Vallen JPegger a force to be reckoned with.

- You can play MP3s directly within the interface and edit ID3 (MP3 information) tags.

- You can generate a list of all your MP3s. Select the folder holding your MP3 files. Tracks display with titles, artists, and album information. Push a button to export the list to Microsoft Excel.

Free image viewers might be a dime a dozen, but Vallen JPegger proves they're not all created equal.

Laporte Support

Photo Printers

Photo printers are a bit different than your regular office inkjet printer. They often use ink with a slightly different formula, and some use more than four colors (standard inkjets use four inks: red, green, blue, and black).

Photo printers excel in printing photo-quality images, but they often lack in text quality. If you have a laser printer or an inkjet for text, you might consider investing in a photo printer.

Keep in mind that inkjet prints aren't ideal for archiving. The prints fade over time, which means you might have to reprint the pictures in a few years.

If you are going to buy a photo printer, look at image quality. You want to see realistic tones, good contrast, and sharp detail.

Address: ## Site of the Night

Painful Desktop Wallpaper

Avert your eyes from these retina-melting, brain-frying, migraine-inducing samples of desktop wallpaper gone awry at http://members.cox.net/lxix/ithurts.

Extract Part of an Image

Bert Monroy

Photoshop's Extract command (Filter, Extract) is designed to pull portions of an image out of the overall image and eliminate the rest. This feature works best when there is a good contrast between the object to be extracted and its surroundings.

Extract an Image

Because the balance of the image is eliminated, work on a duplicate of the original.

1. All the command functions appear in a separate dialog. The image to be worked on appears in the dialog.

2. Using the Edge Highlighter Tool (top left), the area to be extracted is traced. The trick is to use a brush size large enough that the edge of the element and the colors of the background are equally seen within the stroke. You can switch brush sizes, if necessary.

3. When the entire element is traced, the part to be extracted is filled with the Fill Tool (bucket). This tells the Extract command which area you want to be left.

4. You can now preview the element or click OK. The element appears in a single layer with the rest of the image eliminated.

Windows Tips

Add Captions to Your Photos

Morgan Webb

You can add quirky text to your digital photos without expensive third-party software; everything you need is in Microsoft Paint. It's fun, and, best of all, it's free.

1. Open your photo in MS Paint (go to the Start menu, Run, and type **mspaint** in the box).

2. Click A on the floating toolbar to add text to your photographs. You can change the text color by selecting a color with the left mouse button. You can change the background color by choosing a color with the right mouse button.

3. You can make the text background transparent by selecting the Transparent option for the text tool on the floating toolbar.

4. You can make the illusion of a text shadow by typing the text twice, once in black and once in the color you want.

July
20

211

Resize Images for Email Transmission

Mikkel Aaland

One of the secrets of success in digital imaging is matching the size of the digital image to the requirements of the output. So, if your digital image is destined for print, you'll need more resolution than you would if it were destined for a monitor.

Most likely, the original image you're working with is larger or smaller than needed, and you'll have to resize it. Keep in mind that resizing, up or down, always involves some loss of image quality. It is also the last step you want to perform.

There is no optimal size for an email photo; it depends on the recipient's connection speeds. However, nothing is more irritating than getting an email attachment that takes a long time to download. I generally recommend that you get your digital photo down to between 40K and 60K before sending. Of course, you can settle for a larger byte size if your recipient has broadband.

Use Photoshop Elements to lower byte size:

1. With the digital photo open, select Save As from the File menu, and choose JPEG from the File Format options.

2. Select a JPEG value from the JPEG Options dialog. Start with Medium and observe the effect on the actual image. If the quality is acceptable, check the lower-left corner of the dialog for the file size. If it is too high, either choose a lower JPEG value or click Cancel and reduce the pixel values of the image using Photoshop Elements' resize capabilities.

3. To reduce the pixel values, choose Resize and then Image Size from the main Photoshop Elements menu. Under Pixel Dimensions, enter 800 pixels in the Width box and 72dpi in the Resolution box. When you are finished, click OK and go back to step 1. Save your image as a JPEG. This time, you should get a lower size.

Megan's Tips

Quick Google Tips

When searching for images in Google, click on Advanced Image Searching to search specifically for small, medium, or massive images. Make your Volume Control box smaller by pressing Ctrl+S. Press it again to make it bigger.

Download of the Day

Photocopier

Craig Higdon

Do you have a printer and a scanner? If not, I'll wait…. Go get one and hook them up {whistling}. Come on hurry up {more whistling}. Got it? Good.

Make Your Own Photocopier

OK, this free file links your printer, scanner, and computer together to make a photocopier. Know what a photocopier is? Good. Know how to use one? Good.

Start the program and get to photocopying.

What? Yeah, that thing down at the bottom is the contrast, if your copy is too dark, lighten it up. If it's too light, darken it. You're welcome.

If you're confused, you haven't downloaded it yet.

Note: If you, the free file shopper, think that my instructions are not thorough enough, you don't have the free file. Download it from www.nicocuppen.com/cphome.html.

Make sure your printer and scanner are connected. (You did get them right?) Run the program. Now as I've mentioned before, start photocopying.

Shoot Mini-Movies

Mikkel Aaland

For the most part, photographers know light and composition. They know how to use shutter speeds, f/stops, focal length, white balance, and flash to produce an image evoking an emotional response. When shooting a mini-movie, there are a few other things to keep in mind:

- A movie has to move. That means the subject must move, the camera must move, or, if the camera has the capability, the lens must zoom.

- Use lens zooms sparingly. Overuse is the biggest mistake beginner's make. Walk the camera toward the subject; if you use the lens to zoom in, remember that the longer the lens's focal length is, the more camera shake and motion is accentuated.

- Shoot tight because of the small viewing area.

- Get depth in the shot. Let the background go soft.

- If you move the camera, include something stable in the foreground to establish a relationship to the movement.

- Establish a scene by starting wide. Move in quickly to the meaningful action.

- Direct attention to where you want the viewer to look.

- A good mini-movie has a beginning, a middle, and an end.

- Watch TV commercials. They tell a complete story in about 15 to 30 seconds, the same amount of time many digital still cameras can produce.

Effective sound is audible, and that's not always easy with camera-mounted, limited microphones. Editing sound later in software is difficult, so I suggest using a scripted voice-over or turning on the stereo while you shoot to capture sound in real-time.

Watch the orientation of the camera when you shoot full motion. If you shoot with a vertical orientation, your mini-movie will display sideways on a monitor. Orientation can be changed later using software such as QuickTime Pro, but it's difficult to combine movies of different orientation.

Edit and Share Mini-Movies

It's easy to shoot a mini-movie and share your work on the camera LCD or plug your digital camera into a TV monitor. It's a bit more difficult if you want to edit the mini-movie or make a CD or a DVD, or reduce the file size to send via email or share on the web. Again, for all you budding movie makers, starting with mini-movies produced by digital still cameras is a good place to start.

The software I've suggested includes the following:

- **QuickTime Pro** (www.apple.com), which is bundled with many Mac computers and can be downloaded at no cost. With the free version, you can view most mini-movie files created by digital cameras. To edit mini-movies, you need to purchase a key for $29 that enables the editing and exporting functions of QuickTime.

- **iMovie and iDVD** (www.apple.com), two free applications for the Mac. Using these together and with QuickTime Pro, you can easily create a DVD for wide audiences.

- **TMPGEnc** (www.tmpgenc.net), a free file converter for Windows only.

- **Helix Producer Basic** (www.realnetworks.com), a cross-platform, free application to create highly compressible .rm files.

- **Microsoft Movie Maker** (www.microsoft.com), a free video-editing application for the PC that is bundled with Windows XP.

I haven't included the software packages that come bundled with some digital cameras. If they work for you, fine. Use them. I haven't had good luck with the ones I've tried.

Use Photoshop Elements to Grab Frames

Mikkel Aaland

Sometimes a single frame or a sequence of frames from your mini-movie is all you need. Photoshop Elements 2 makes it easy to import individual frames from your mini-movie through a Frame from Video import command. Earlier versions of Photoshop Elements don't have this command, nor does Photoshop 7.

With Photoshop Elements 2 open, here's the basic procedure for capturing a video frame:

1. Select File, Import, Frame from Video.

2. Browse to your .mov, .aif, or .mpeg file.

3. Play your movie using the controls at the bottom of the dialog. When you see the frame you want, select Grab Frame or press the spacebar.

You can select as many frames as you want. Each frame opens in its own window. You can do many things with the grabbed frames. Here are three suggestions.

Create an Animated GIF

To create an animated GIF, follow the steps for capturing a video frame, selecting at least three grabs from the beginning, middle, and end of your mini-movie. Then follow these directions:

1. Copy and paste each frame into a single file of three layers.

2. Select File, Save for Web.

3. In the Save for Web window, set your options to the following:

   • In the Optimized File Format box, select GIF.

   • In the Color Reduction Algorithm box, select Selective.

   • In the Dither Algorithm box, select Diffusion.

   • Under Colors and Dither, it's okay to use the default settings; however, later you might want to change the values to reduce the final file size of the animated GIF.

   • Most important, check the box next to Animation.

Animation options are found near the bottom of the window. You can choose to have the animation loop, and you can choose the frame delay rate. To test your animation, select Preview In at the bottom of the Save for Web window.

Create a Collage

It's easy to create a collage using a batch of frame grabs with Photoshop Elements' Create Photomerge command. Follow the steps for capturing a video frame, and select as many frames as you want using the Frame from Video import command. Then follow these directions:

1. Save and name each frame (choose File, Save). Save as .psd.

2. With the saved and named frames open in Photoshop Elements, select File, Create Photomerge. Your files should be listed in the dialog. Click OK.

3. Photomerge attempts to "merge" your grabs automatically but fails. Instead, you can drag and drop the thumbnails from Photomerge's lightbox and arrange them in the main work area.

Storyboard with Frame Grabs

To create storyboards with frame grabs, simply follow the steps for capturing a video frame and then create a new, blank Photoshop Elements file. The size you choose depends on what you want to do with the storyboard. Then follow these directions:

1. Select, copy, and paste each frame into the "master" document.

2. Use Photoshop Elements Move to arrange the frames in a desired order.

3. For precise layout, choose View, Grid.

The Alpha Channel

Bert Monroy

A Photoshop file can have 24 channels. Some of the channels are used by the color space. For example, RGB takes up 3 channels (red, green, and blue), leaving 21 channels that can be used as alpha channels.

Alpha channels are masks through which you can apply effects. The alpha channel is an 8-bit channel, which means it has 256 levels of gray, from 0 (black) to 255 (white). White acts as the selected area; black acts as the protected area. The level of gray in between determines the level of exposure. For example, 50% gray allows for 50% exposure. Alpha channels are basically specialized selection processes.

The selection tools let you segregate a portion of the image to be modified. The actual selection process does nothing to the image. It's the application of a filter, adjustment control, or any modification through that selection that affects the image. This is the concept behind the alpha channel. It is merely a selection to expose the image for an effect to be applied.

The beauty of alpha channels is that they can be saved, modified, or combined to create special effects. When you use the Lasso, you make a selection. When you deselect, the selection is gone. If you Save Selection (choose Select, Save Selection), it is sent to an alpha channel that can be recalled as many times as you need.

You can paint in the alpha channel with any of the tools. Filters also work in the alpha channels. The door is open to a multitude of possible effects, but keep in mind that you are making modifications to a mask, not the image. Through that mask, modifications are later made to the image. When you paint, you use shades of gray. No colors are available in the alpha channel because it is not an image or part of the image.

When you save a selection, you are given the choice to send it to a new document or to a separate file that can be accessed when you choose Load Selection (Select, Load Selection) to call up an alpha channel. Saving alpha channels to a new document lets you have thousands of alpha channels.

Create a Simple Frame in Photoshop Elements

Mikkel Aaland

Putting a simple frame around a photo in Photoshop is very easy. Here is how I suggest making a simple frame:

1. Open the image and select it (Select, Select All).

2. Select Edit, Stroke to create a thin black frame based on your selection.

3. Under Width, enter a pixel value. The exact value depends on the size of the image. Start with 4 pixels. If the line created is too thin, try a higher pixel value.

4. After creating a black frame, select the Effects palette from the palette dock and select Frames from the pop-up menu.

5. Select Drop Shadow Frame from the Frames options. Double-click. Elements does the rest.

6. If you want more canvas area, select Image, Resize, Canvas Size, and expand your canvas.

When you're finished, use the Photoshop Elements Type tool to add text, if you want.

July
24

Fixing Dog Eye in Photoshop Elements

Mikkel Aaland

Dog eyes occur when you use a flash to take a picture of a dog. It's similar to red eyes in people, but worse. For better night vision, dogs, like many animals, have far more rods in their eyes than people. Their eyes reflect light out and give a hellish glow when photographed with a flash. I'm sure you've seen animals' eyes glow if you drive on a dark road with your headlights on.

Normally, it's easy to remove red eye with Photoshop Elements' red-eye brush. However, when the highlights are completely blown away, the red-eye brush won't help.

As always with Photoshop Elements (and Photoshop), there are a couple of ways to proceed. Here are two methods using Photoshop Elements 2.

Method 1

1. Magnify and zoom in on the eyes.
2. Select Paint Bucket from the toolbar.
3. Make sure the foreground color in the color swatch at the bottom of the toolbar is set to black.
4. Position the Paint Bucket tool over the blown-out highlights of the eyes, and click. Repeat for both eyes.

This fills the white area with black. It's certainly not a perfect solution, but if you zoom out, it doesn't look too bad.

Method 2

1. Magnify and zoom in on the dog eyes.
2. With the Magic Wand or selection tool of your choice, select the white areas in the eye.
3. In the Layer palette, make a new layer.
4. With the new layer active, fill your two selections with black or any other color. (Choose Edit, Fill, or use the Paint Bucket.)
5. In the Layer Styles palette, in the Palette well, select Glass Buttons from the pop-up menu. Choose the "glass" color. You can change the color later.

Now the eye looks more realistic.

How do you change the color? Now you can actually use the red-eye brush:

1. Flatten your layers (Layer, Flatten Image).
2. Select the red-eye brush from the toolbar. Select a "replacement" color in the Options bar.
3. Click on the area that you want to change color, and then "paint" the replacement color over it.

Download of the Day

Auto-Illustrator

Megan Morrone
I've had enough of these fancy, expensive graphics programs. I'm a word person, not a visual person. Plus, I'm lazy. I want software that creates art for me.

Auto-Illustrator (www.auto-illustrator.com) is designed for Mac OS X, but it works in OS 8 and 9 as well. There's also a port for Windows 98, NT, 2000, and XP. I've tried it on my PC and my Mac, and found that it works much better on my Mac.

System requirements:

- G3/G4 Macintosh: 300MHz
- Windows: 600MHz
- 64MB RAM
- QuickTime 4 or higher

Shadows Over Rough Surfaces

Bert Monroy

Creating the illusion of shadows cast over the ground is a simple process. Just follow these steps:

1. Duplicate the layer of the object casting the shadow. Lock its transparency, fill it with black, and lower its opacity.

2. Distort the shadow (Edit, Transform, Distort) to simulate the shadow being cast across the ground.

3. If the ground has a rough-textured surface, you must displace the shadow to follow the texture.

4. Separate the file and make the ground surface the only layer showing. Save it.

5. In the file with the shadow, duplicate the layer of the shadow.

6. Select one of the layers with the shadow and choose the Displace filter (Filter, Distort, Displace). Click OK in the dialog that opens.

7. A second dialog opens, asking for a displacement map. This is the file you created with the ground texture.

8. Choose it and click OK. The shadow now distorts to follow the texture of the ground.

9. If part of the ground has no texture, the shadow should be smooth in that area. This is where you use the second shadow layer.

10. Select the smooth area of the ground and put it in its own layer.

11. Put the layer with the distorted shadow behind the layer of the smooth ground.

12. Place the layer with the smooth, undistorted shadow above the layer with the smooth ground, and convert the layers into a clipping group. Press Option+Alt and click between the two layers in the Layers palette.

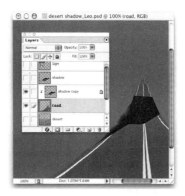

Digital-Camera Lighting Tricks

Mikkel Aaland

When you take a picture with a digital camera, you get a sharp contrast between light areas and dark areas. The contrast isn't always flattering in portraits. Not to get too technical, this happens because your digital camera has limited tonal range. You can use your image editor (Photoshop or Photoshop Elements, for example) to fix the image, to a point.

Start by changing your camera's flash setting to Fill Flash. Fill Flash tells the camera to mix ambient light with the light from the flash, for a pleasing effect. If you use direct flash without mixing it with the ambient light, the strobe light alone can create a very harsh image or an image full of contrast.

Fill Flash has its limitations. Your subject might find the flash distracting, and the strobe light, even when mixed, can still result in contrast. Soften the strobe light slightly by placing diffusion material over the strobe or your finger over, but not directly on, the middle of the strobe.

Use the Sun

One of my favorite methods for shooting a portrait is to use a reflector or white fill card to bounce light into shadow areas. Commercial products are available in most camera stores, but you can use a sheet of bright white cardboard or a sheet of standard white paper.

The secret is to move the reflective source until you catch the light and get the lighting effect you want. Then set the camera to aperture priority and select a wide aperture. The background appears soft and not distracting.

Sensitivity Training

Don't let low-light situations intimidate you. You won't be able to use the built-in pop-up strobe (common to most digital cameras) in all situations. For example, I couldn't use it to photograph my sleeping daughter unless I was willing to risk waking her up. I placed a lit candle at her bedside instead of using the strobe, which would've destroyed the ambience.

You can get a great shot in low light by increasing the sensitivity of your digital camera's sensor. Use the digital camera's menu to boost the ISO. Most digital cameras offer a range of ISO speeds, commonly from 80 to 800, but sometimes as high as 1,600. Adjust your ISO wisely. The faster the ISO is, the more chance there is of electronic noise. Check the manual for specific instructions.

Windows Tips

Use Thumbnail Icons to Preview Images

Roman Loyola

Windows 98, Me, 2000, and XP let you preview a photo by having its icon appear as a thumbnail. In Windows 98, follow these directions:

1. Launch Windows Explorer and find the folder that contains the images.

2. Right-click the folder and select Properties.

3. With the General tab open, check the Enable Thumbnail View box. Click OK to close the dialog.

4. Open the folder with the images.

5. Click the View menu and select Thumbnails.

In Windows Me, 2000, and XP:

1. Open the folder that contains the photos.

2. Click the View menu and select Thumbnails.

July 27

Manage Your Digital Photos

James Kim

Capture, browse, organize, edit, and share your digital images with these all-in-one photo applications.

Adobe Photoshop Album 1.0

Photoshop Album (www.adobe.com) integrates every feature you'll need to manage your images. Its excellent editing options include a basic set of red-eye–removal and cropping tools. You can fix levels, contrast, and color with a single-click. I really like the Before and After tab, where you can see how your changes will affect your image. Photoshop Album gives you three ways to find and sort photos:

- **Keywords.** Keep organized with this unique tag system. Create a new tag (keyword), or use a preset tab (Family, Friends, Places) and drag it onto a photo. When you click a tag, only the "tagged" photos appear.

- **As time goes by.** Use the timeline and calendar to view your photos chronologically, or look at photos taken within a specific time frame (the year 2002, for example). Each month on the timeline is represented by a color-coded bar. Click a month to access its library of images.

- **Similarity.** Search for images with similar colors. This feature works well when you want to find all pictures taken at night.

When you're ready to print, Album gives you options galore, including contact sheets, cropping tools, and excellent preview options. The user interface isn't the most intuitive (it's much better than ACDSee), but when you get over the learning curve, you'll wonder how you ever lived without this program.

Lifescape Solutions Picasa 1.5

Picasa (www.lifescapeinc.com/picasa) is a breath of fresh air. Its simple and elegant user interface looks great, makes sense, and centers on the creation, management, and viewing of albums. Album thumbnails (organized by date) are resizable and easy to browse.

The timeline view is exceptionally innovative. Thumbnails representing albums rotate through the interface. However, this graphical timeline is a much better way to browse and show slide shows than for image management.

Printing photos is a breeze. You have several layout options, a preview window, and cropping and optimization options. Sharing photos is easy, too. You can use Outlook or Picasa's web-based email client (it compresses files to 640×480), or you can export images to a folder in a specified resolution.

Picasa does it all, but it has some weaknesses. Unlike Photoshop Album, which opens a new and smaller window for each action, Picasa switches to a new page, so you can't work on two photos at once. Also, the editing options are basic, and although you can tag pictures with keywords, they aren't as easily accessible as in Photoshop Album. Watch for future updates.

ACDSee 5.0

ACDSee (www.acdsystems.com/English/Products/ACDSee/index) was my first image browser. It's come a long way since then, adding modern conveniences such as a calendar, drag-and-drop management, and a separate image-editing tool called FotoCanvas Lite.

One of ACDSee's biggest strengths is in how it acquires photos. It supports a host of digital cameras and has a built-in screen-capture feature. You can conveniently filter and sort images, batch process images, and create HTML albums.

ACDSee is a capable utility, but it lags behind the competition. I was often maddened by the confusing array of tabs on its interface, and the slide show features are weak. (You can't even save your slide shows.) Plus, ACDSee lacks user-friendly printing options. Yes, it offers contact sheets, but trying to print multiple pictures at specific sizes is next to impossible. We recommend that you install the free trial version before you shell out your hard-earned cash.

July
28

1394 and the Wild World of Video Capture

Patrick Norton

So you want to capture video, eh? Well put down that netcam and find a video camera. Chances are, it's got either S-Video, or a composite video jack. If you're lucky, you have the newer 1394 jack. We say "lucky" because 1394, also known as FireWire (or iLink, if you happen to be Sony Electronics), is a hot-swappable, plug-and-play connection. Think of it as USB on steroids, a pipeline big enough to pull NTSC video from a MiniDV camera in no time (although USB and 1394 work very differently).

How Does FireWire Work?

On a good day, FireWire is totally plug-and-play. Plug one end of a 1394 cable into a port in your computer; plug the other end into a 1394 camera, hard drive, or whatever; and load a driver if the OS asks for it. Mac and PC users will find the experience strikingly similar to using USB peripherals.

Both are open specs, but FireWire and USB don't have much more in common. First, 1394 offers a much bigger pipe into your computer, up to a theoretical maximum of 400Mbps. A 1394 port can connect up to 63 external devices to USB's 127. Also, unlike USB, 1394 supports isochronous data transfers. The data delivery is tied to time or has certain timing constraints, which makes it friendlier to multimedia content and huge files.

Compression Technologies

The 1394 boards can be used with 1394 video cameras. You can pull pure digital video straight from a camera and onto your computer. That means no degradation in quality due to bad cables, cheap cards, or a slow machine or hard drive.

While the digital video off of, say, a MiniDV camera is already compressed, it'll still take up some serious space. Full-size video at full quality sucks down 1GB for every five minutes of movie. To keep from taking all that space on your system, many software products import compressed video (12.5MB for five minutes, for comparison). To use that compressed video to create your masterpiece, click on a button and the software imports the necessary video in its full-quality glory and puts together your final creation.

The video quality is great. You can import audio and video over a single cable. As the iMac DV has shown, it can be incredibly easy to make a seriously good-looking home movie.

Download of the Day

TMPGEnc

Morgan Webb

VCDs are video CDs that you can burn using your computer and play on most DVD players. But, you need to know a few things before you can start burning video CDs.

You can't just burn an .avi file to a CD and expect it to play in your DVD player. The video format needs to be MPEG1, and you can turn many types of video files (and still images for, say, a video CD slide show) into the proper format with TMPGEnc, a free MPEG1 converter.

The interface is relatively intuitive, and it comes with a wizard to walk you through the process. The application supports MPEG2 encoding (if you want to make DVDs instead of VCDs) for 30 days, but the MPEG1 encoding is free forever. If you want to turn your movies into MPEGs to keep on CD, this application is for you.

VCDhelp.com (www.dawnload.net) has done an excellent job of decoding all the features for you.

Wedding Glasses

Bert Monroy

Make a wedding wine glass that features the happy couple. You need an image of the couple and an image of the wine glass. Here's how it's done.

1. Choose a Feather radius for the Lasso selection tool. The radius should be high enough to give you a soft edge.

2. Select the couple and copy the image to the image of a wine glass.

3. Place them in position.

4. With a very soft-edged Eraser, touch up any parts of the layer with the couple that might be overlapping the edge of the wine glass.

5. Double-click the layer of the couple to bring up the Layer Style dialog.

6. At the bottom of the Blending Options: Default section, you will find Blend If.

7. Move the highlight (white) sliders for the Underlying Layer over to expose any highlights that might be on the wine glass. Press Option (Alt on a PC) to separate the slider and to add a soft edge to the transition.

Laporte Support

Capture a Screen Shot

You can't use the Print Screen button to capture DVD screen shots. When you play a DVD in Windows, Windows doesn't really know that a DVD is playing. The video is playing in a video overlay, which plays on top of Windows.

You can't use a hardware DVD encoder to capture a DVD screen. You need a software DVD encoder.

I recommend PowerDVD (www.gocyberlink.com). It's $50, but you can use a trial version. PowerDVD has a feature that lets you capture individual screens from a DVD.

Patrick recommends searching for "DVD screen capture" on your favorite free download site. At Download.com, we found HyperSnap-DX ($35) and SnagIt ($39).

Address: Site of the Night

Make Your Own Movies

Martin Sargent

Is the muse speaking to you? Are you overcome with the urge to make your own movie, but you don't have the money for a digital video camera or the computing power to edit video? You can now begin to satisfy your creative longings at the make-your-own-movie site Dfilm (www.dfilm.com).

With the help of the web-based MovieMaker, making your directorial debut is as easy as pointing and clicking. A wizard walks you through the selection of sets, backgrounds, and characters. You can then add dialogue and music. When you've finished your juggernaut thrill-ride of a film, you can send it off to your friends.

Transfer Video to CD

Leo Laporte and Greg Melton
A VCD (video compact disc) is nothing more than a CD containing moving pictures and sound.

Digitizing is a way to convert analog video into data that you can store on your hard drive. To do this, you need a video capture card or, if you have a digital video camera, a 1394 or FireWire port.

The ATI All-in-Wonder Radeon 7500 (www.ati.com) is a good video card with capture capabilities. ATI also offers the less expensive TV-Wonder video capture card. Capture your video to hard drive using the best quality possible with a color depth of at least 24 bits per pixel. The chief limitation is the speed of your system and size of the hard drives.

Another alternative to capturing analog video is Dazzle's Hollywood DV-Bridge (www.dazzle.com). The Hollywood DV-Bridge is an external component that lets you convert analog video to digital video, or digital video to analog video. The device captures analog video without the need of a PC.

Hollywood DV-Bridge comes with MovieStar 5 (so you can edit all those old home movies) and Dazzle DVD Complete (so you can burn them to DVD). You need a FireWire card if you want to interface the Hollywood DV-Bridge with your PC.

When you have the movies on your drive, you need to convert the video to a format that's compatible with the VCD standard. The video files must be converted to MPEG-1 video with a specific resolution (352×240 for NTSC or 352×288 for PAL) at 29.97 frames per second.

Convert and Burn

If you don't want to take the easy route of using Nero to automatically encode and burn VCDs, use a separate conversion program.

If your video files are AVIs, you can use the free program avi2vcd (www.mnsi.net/~jschlic1). Another free conversion program is TMPGEnc (www.tmpgenc.net), which is capable of converting DivX, AVI, QuickTime, and Windows video to VCD-compatible MPEG-1 video.

After you've converted the video files, you need to create the VCDs' file structure and menus. To do this, use a free program called VCDEasy (www.vcdeasy.org). When the final VCD setup is complete, VCDEasy generates a CD-ROM image file that you can burn to CD.

All-in-One Solution

Nero Burning ROM (www.ahead.de) is one of the top CD-burning applications on the market and is capable of encoding and burning VCDs. Nero encodes the video files into a VCD-compatible format, arranges them onto CDs, and creates simple menus so you can navigate the video clips. It even lets you create slide-show presentations. If Nero didn't come with your CD burner, you can download a free full-featured demo version or purchase it for $69.

VCD Playback

If you want to watch the VCD on your PC, you need software that supports VCD playback. Although most PC DVD playback software can handle VCDs, some might require a VCD player to watch the VCD in Windows.

Most, but not all, DVD players support VCDs. If you're buying a new player, check the specs carefully if you want this functionality.

Additional Resources

If the general guidelines presented in this article don't cover your specific requirements, visit VCD Help (www.vcdhelp.com). This site features everything you will ever want to know about authoring, converting, and capturing VCDs, SVCDs, and DVDs.

Work at the Beach

Megan Morrone

I'm a new mom, and if I had to choose between my wireless router and my Diaper Genie, I'd choose the router. Rather than moving the sleeping baby to where the computer is, I can now move the computer to where the sleeping baby is, and I'm instantly connected to the Internet, no matter where that is.

This month we offer you tips and tricks for navigating this new, wild, and wonderful wireless world. Still, just because you can surf the web in bed, call your girlfriend from the car, or instant-message on your PDA during a meeting, that doesn't mean that you should.

If you'll allow me a Martha Stewart moment, I'd like to share with you a few tips on wireless etiquette, otherwise known as my own personal wireless annoyances:

- One of the major drawbacks of wireless is that it takes what people do in the privacy of their home or office, brings it out in the open, and makes me listen to it. And I'm not just talking about people who have loud cell phone conversations on the bus. If you're watching a DVD on an airplane, wear headphones, for goodness sake. (Check out Leo's article on noise-canceling headphones on August 21). If you're sitting next to me on a plane while I am quietly watching a DVD (with headphones), don't peek over my shoulder. It's annoying.

- If you're at a party at a house equipped with wireless Internet access, resist the urge to surf during said party. The only exception to this rule is if you need to settle an argument. In that case, do your Google search, gloat, and get off of there. Don't check your email.

- If you live next door to me and my open wireless network shows up on your PC, please feel free to use it, but don't spend the entire day downloading huge files from KaZaA. I keep my network open because I think it's nice to share, so please don't take advantage of my kindness to hack me. That's annoying.

- If you're a telemarketer, don't ever call my cell phone.

- If you're trying to sell wireless cards for laptops, don't try to pretend that this means that the card lets you surf the web anywhere. As far as I know, the world is not yet covered with free wireless networks. They exist many places, but not as many as those commercials would have you believe.

- It is perfectly acceptable to play games on your PDA during boring meetings; just make sure you turn off the sound. Also, refrain from yelling "Yes!" when you've just broken your Tetris personal best.

- Never gloat about how light, fast, long-lasting, or big-screened your laptop is. It doesn't become you.

- When in public, please limit the length of your cell phone conversations. If you have to talk, please keep it quiet. The only exception to this rule is if your conversation is very, very interesting. Then please speak up.

Noise-Canceling Headphones

Leo Laporte

Headphones are absolutely indispensable onboard an airplane. With all that jet noise and lip flapping from pilots doubling as tour guides, simple ear buds don't do the trick. If you want to listen to music or watch a movie on your laptop, you'll need to don noise-canceling headphones.

Noise-canceling headphones use electronics to phase out extraneous noise. Noise cancellation works best on continuous sound, such as jet engines. I tested two models of noise-canceling headphones and the high-end Etymotics in-ear headphones on my last three cross-country flights to see how they fare.

Bose QuietComfort

Bose heavily advertises these headphones to air travelers. Some airlines even offer them to first-class passengers. You'll pay around $250 for a pair of your own.

The QuietComfort (www.bose.com) headphones offer excellent noise cancellation. The battery-powered unit offers Hi, Lo, and Off settings. The Lo position offers about −10db of cancellation. On the Hi setting, you'll get even more attenuation, maybe as much as −20db.

The Bose headphones are a comfortable closed-ear design that wears well even on long flights. With maximum cancellation, the jet sound was reduced to a low hiss. I could still hear conversation at normal tones and pilot announcements, but they were much quieter. I could hear the music loud and clear and, I never had to struggle to hear even quiet movie dialogue.

I love Bose speakers. I use their multimedia system on my computer at home, and I used to love listening to my college roommate's 901s at extreme volume. But no one would accuse Bose of making hyperaccurate speakers. The QuietComfort headphones are definitely weighted toward the bass end. They sounded pretty tubby to me, especially after spending some time with the flatter Etymotics.

If you love the Bose sound, great, but you should audition these headphones before you buy. They're comfortable phones that definitely reduce cabin noise, but for the price I expected higher audio quality.

Panasonic RP-HC70

You don't expect much from a $40 pair of headphones, and that's what you'll get from the Panasonic RP-HC70 (www.prodcat.panasonic.com). They don't fit well, the sound is tinny, and the noise cancellation is weak.

They do a good enough job to let you watch a movie. If money's tight and high fidelity isn't a priority, the RP-HC70 is a good choice.

Etymotic Research ER-4P

The P models are of lower impedance, so you can use them on portable devices without a headphone amp. They worked great on my iPod and my portable CD player, and they were good for watching movies on my iBook.

The Etymotics don't do any noise canceling, but they do offer blissful quiet even on a noisy plane. Their in-ear design works like earplugs to offer −20db of noise reduction. When you listen to music at moderate levels, you can't hear engine noise, pilot announcements, or conversation.

For about $250.00, the Etymotics eliminate noise and offer an excellent audio experience. You do have to insert them fairly deeply into your ear canal, but once you get used to them, the Etymotics set a standard that is hard to beat.

For a better experience, try the Etymotics with a HeadRoom AirHead Amp (http://headroom.headphone.com). The amp remixes the sound to center it slightly, eliminating the extreme stereo effect you get from headphones. It really makes a difference.

HeadRoom doesn't just sell high-end headphones; the site is loaded with excellent advice and explanations. The folks at HeadRoom are the ultimate headphone geeks.

Synch Your Cell Phone with a PC

Greg Melton

If you have one set of contacts listed in your cell phone and another set stored on your PC, this is the perfect solution for merging the two sets. I can remember when all I needed was my trusted Rolodex. It wasn't easy to carry around, but at least it was easy to maintain. Now that my Rolodex has been replaced by a cell phone (which keeps track of all my contacts), I realize that I rely on both my cell phone and my PC to store contacts.

Because a cell phone is just an electronic device, I count on it dying one day. To provide some added reassurance, I'm going to synch my cell phone with my PC to create a backup of every contact stored in my phone. To do this, I need a data cable that will connect my phone to the serial port on the back of my PC.

First I checked with my wireless service provider. It should sell either a data cable or a kit that includes the data cable and synching software designed to work with my phone. I ended up using the Starfish (www.starfish.com) Data Connectivity Kit with TrueSync Software ($29.95) for Motorola phones.

The kit includes the data cable and synching software designed to work with a PC's personal information manager (PIM), such as Outlook or Lotus Notes on my PC. I don't use a PIM, so I installed the TrueSync software, which includes its own calendar and contact program.

After the cable is connected to the phone and the software is installed, I just press the Sync button to import all my contacts into the TrueSync software. After that, I can create new contacts and press the Sync button to export all the listings back to my phone.

Synching Solutions

There's no definitive solution for synching your phone to a PC. The typical method uses a data-transfer cable and specialized software, but that's not the only way. Some newer phones come with an infrared port that lets you synch with an infrared port on a laptop or desktop PC. If your phone comes with an infrared port, the only thing you'll need is the synching software.

For a Nokia phone, download its free synching software designed for your phone's model. Visit the Nokia (www.nokia.com) store to locate a data cable for your phone if it isn't infrared-capable. You should be able to find one by selecting the model of your phone under Data Products.

Amazon.com sells data cables for many different types of popular cell phones. Amco Cellular (www.amco-cellular.com) sells data cables for both Nokia and Ericsson cell phones.

Download of the Day

The Palm Desktop

Megan Morrone

Burn your File-O-Fax. Toss out your Rolodex.

Even if you don't have a PDA, you can digitally organize your life. Download a personal information manager (PIM) from the Palm website to use on your desktop PC (www.palm.com/support/downloads/win_desktop.html) or Mac (www.palm.com/software/desktop/mac.html).

If you own a Palm, you know how useful this software is. It comes with a calendar, address book, to-do list, and memo pad. All your information is easily portable if you decide to get a Palm-powered PDA. The latest version has a customizable user interface, expense tracking, and a variety of desktop alarms.

August
2

PDAs on the Cheap: Bargain-Basement PDAs for Less Than $200

Hahn Choi

I'm often asked "Which PDA should I Get?" My response is always "How much do you want to spend?" Most people want to use a PDA just to keep their contacts and schedules organized and the sweet spot is around $200.

Sony CLIE PEG-SJ22 Handheld

(www.sony.com) shares the familiar design of the SJ20 and its stubby design. This color version includes Sony's high-resolution (320×320) display. The screen is among the best in Palm OS–based PDAs. The SJ22 also boasts 16MB of memory, a plus for adding applications down the road. It comes with a memory stick slot for additional expansion.

Palm i705 (www.palm.com) offers wireless data capabilities for email, some slow web surfing, and instant messaging on the go. You'll need Palm.net service (starts at $20 a month) to use the wireless. If you want to try out the world of wireless data, the i705 is a more affordable place to start. If you decide you don't want the service, you can use the i705 without it just like other Palm OS–based PDA.

Dell Axim X5 (www.dell.com) is currently the most affordable Pocket PC–based PDA I could find. It's not the slickest-looking design I've ever seen, but you get a great feature set, including the latest processor, dual expansion (Secure Digital and Compact Flash), and a removable battery at an amazing price. Dell updates its pricing so frequently that it's tough to pin down, so check the website.

Talkback

Cell Phones for Tots?

Josh Lawrence

Contrary to what some believe, cell phones do have uses besides distracting already careless drivers and annoying strangers. For instance, they can be used to contact loved ones in case of emergencies, or parents can check on their unattended kids after school. At least, those are some of the justifications for second-graders to be sporting cell phones.

Are cell phones a legitimate tool of parenting? Parents' concerns about their children's well-being are certainly valid. Aren't cell phones the best modern tool for addressing this concern? And if that's the case, why not give seven-year-olds cell phones? Or are cell phone companies simply exploiting parents' fears and introducing yet another consumer urge to the childhood experience? Should cell phone use be limited to an older age?

How young is too young for a cell phone?

Birth 12%
Seven 40%
Sixteen 21%
Under 18 27%

Megan's Tips

Automating Net Connections

When you're on the road, you probably use a laptop with dialup Internet access. When you're at home, you probably use the same laptop, but on a broadband connection. There's an easy way to automate switching between these connections in Windows:

1. Go to the Control Panel and open Internet Options.

2. Click on the Connections tab and then turn on Dial Whenever a Network Connection Is Not Present.

What's Wi-Fi?

Nicole Guilfoyle

Wi-Fi is short for wireless fidelity. It's a term used by the Wireless Ethernet Compatibility Alliance (www.weca.net) to describe wireless networking technology. The term is used interchangeably with 802.11b.

How It Works

Instead of moving data through a network using an Ethernet cable, Wi-Fi uses radio waves in the 2.4GHz spectrum to move data across different frequencies. This is the same range used by your cordless phone. And like a cordless phone's signal, its signal can be distorted by large objects and walls.

Wireless Broadband

The best way for consumers to use this technology is to tap into a high-speed Internet connection. A wireless access point remains hooked up to your wired network (broadband connection). If you have the right PC card, your laptop, PC, or personal digital assistant (PDA) can get the signal. Certain cafes, airports, and universities let you tap into their wireless network so you can get Internet access on your Wi-Fi–equipped laptop.

The data transfer rate is usually between 4Mbps and 5Mbps, although TechTV Labs has seen rates reach 7Mbps to 8Mbps. Your typical broadband connection offers 1.5Mbps.

Patrick's Tips

Clear Dust from Your PDA and Cell Phone

A viewer wants to know how he can clean out those sneaky dust particles that get into his cell phone and PDA screens.

My method will likely void your warranty, so if you're not careful, you can damage your device. Follow my tip at your own risk.

Dust Off

Dust under the screen can be tricky to remove. If your cell phone or PDA has a plastic screen over its display, check the warranty. If the warranty has expired, open the case; grab a supply of canned air, swabs, and tissues; and clean that phone if you are mechanically inclined.

A PDA such as the Palm m105 is more troublesome. You can purchase a Torx T5 driver and open the case, but I'm almost positive you'd end up with plastic pieces of the case and a newly naked screen with a piece of dust under it.

You might have to completely replace that screen. Places such as Gethightech (www.gethightech.com) sell replacement screens on the cheap. This could save you money.

Did I mention that you'll void your warranty if you open the case on just about any electronic toy? Just checking.

Talkback

Shut Up or Pay Up

Is it time to make cell phone use a crime? Would fines discourage people from yammering wherever and whenever they please? Can you legislate good manners?

Should a ringing cell phone be a crime?

Yes 51%

No 49%

49% No

51% Yes

Must-Have PDA Downloads

Cat Schwartz

If you have a Palm PDA or Pocket PC, hopefully you're not just keeping phone numbers and a calendar on them. You can do so much more.

Handango

Handango (www.handango.com) houses hundreds of programs that you can easily download onto your PDA. It has programs for any PDA you have, including not just Palm and Pocket PC, but RIM, Symbian, and even SmartPhone.

Start at the homepage and pay attention to the links to featured downloads. They lead you to a full description of each program. When we reviewed the site, it had slow loading time, so be patient.

PalmGear.com

PalmGear.com (www.palmgear.com) gives you the goods right off the homepage the same way Handango does, but better. It splits up the programs into new releases and updated software.

All the downloads have easy-to-understand icons so you know quickly whether the program is free, a Zip file, and so on. You'll find games, utilities, and more for all PDAs. You can also find the latest PDA news located at bottom of the homepage.

A Few of Our Favorites

Just going to these sites will get you into the stuff you need for better PDA living. But in case you're overwhelmed, here are a few recommendations to get you started.

- **DateBk5** (www.handango.com) is a replacement to the standard functions on your PDA. They've not only made it cooler to look at, but it works better, too. Look on the left side and pick your OS to find hundreds more cool programs.

- **TomeRaider** (www.palmgear.com) lets you read whole encyclopedias, dictionaries, text docs, and just about anything made of words. It claims to be the most popular cross-platform text reader available and is pretty awesome.

- **PacMan** (www.palmgear.com) is a classic all ages can enjoy, even in tiny handheld form.

All right, so now you know where to find the coolest stuff for your PDA that you can't live without. Get out there and start tricking out that PDA, and stop using it for just a datebook. How boring is that?

Talkback

Remember When Phones Were Phones?

Dave Roos

Phone manufacturers are packing more features into smaller cell phones. Soon we'll be playing Unreal Tournament across a wireless network on a phone the size of a chicken's lower lip (hint: chickens don't have lips).

But what about sound quality? Consumers complain that fashionable, internal antennas catch weaker signals than their older, terribly uncool external cousins. And battery life? If you want to play MP3s, surf the web, and text-message your girlfriend at the same time, you'd better plug into the nearest outlet because that battery will be sapped in seconds.

Are cell phones getting better or worse?

Better   51%

Worse   49%

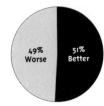

Cellular Text Messaging

Nicole Guilfoyle

Cellular services want you to believe that sending messages during concerts or meetings, or while sitting around your living room, is fun and easy, and you shouldn't worry if the process seems slow—you'll get faster as you send more messages.

Most cell phones have SMS (short message service) technology built in that allows you to send and receive short text messages. But typing a message using your cell phone's numeric keypad takes time and is often limited to 88 to 160 characters per message.

On the upside, SMS is great for delivering tidbits of information in a short period of time. Text messages are also easier to read than a numeric message (other than a phone number) on a pager.

To send a message, follow these steps:

1. Access Messaging on your phone's menu, choose Text Messaging, then choose New Message.

2. Search your phone book or type in the phone number of the message recipient. Separate multiple numbers with a comma.

3. Type a short message. Your phone will usually tell you how many characters you type.

4. Send your message.

When someone sends you a message, your phone will alert you and will usually display a mail envelope on your screen.

Use Your Keyboard

If you need to get in touch with someone, but you don't have your phone handy, send a message online. It's fast, simple, and free (for you, at least). Here are sites for a few major cellular providers:

- **AT&T Wireless Messaging Center** (www.mobile.att.net/messagecenter)
- **Cingular Wireless Messaging Center** (www.cingular.com/messaging)
- **SprintPCS Wireless Web Messaging** (www.textmefree.com)
- **Verizon Wireless Mobile Messenger** (www.vtext.com)

Several other online services let you send free text messages. Find a list at TextMeFree.com (www.textmefree.com). You can send within the United States, the United Kingdom, or the rest of Europe, or search for worldwide services.

Cost

Most companies charge 2 cents for every message received and 10 cents for every message sent, but the cost of a text-messaging service may already be included in your calling plan. Be sure to read the fine print.

Be careful to look for the price of text messaging and not wireless web services, such as AOL Instant Messenger or WAP (wireless application protocols) services that let you surf on your cell phone. For text-messaging tricks, see August 7.

Laporte Support

Wi-Fi and Wireless Phones

Both your phone and Wi-Fi use the 2.4GHz frequency range. Because the devices use the same frequency, interference is very likely. Wireless phones often have automatic switching, in which the phone switches channels in case it finds another device (such as 802.11b) using a channel. This helps prevent interference. What compounds the problem is that lots of devices use the 2.4GHz frequency range.

Move the base and the wireless access point to different locations. If they're close together, they'll interfere with each other. If moving doesn't work, consider using 802.11a Wi-Fi. It runs in the 5GHz frequency range.

Text-Messaging Tricks

Cat Schwartz

If you're not familiar with text-messaging shorthand, I'm going to get you up to speed. First, you don't have to spell out every word character by character when you text message. You can convey your feelings with emoticons or smileys (characters that tell the person you're messaging that you're happy, sad, or mad).

Learn basic SMS (short message service) messaging terms at the SMS Dictionary (www.mobtastic.com/sms/dictionary/sms_dictionary.asp). I recommend printing this page and keeping it handy until the shorthand becomes second nature.

SMS Glossary (www.smsglossary.com) is a great place to go to find out how to text a word or phrase quickly. To get an abbreviation, go to the A–Z Definitions (www.smsglossary.com/a-to-z.html) page and click its first letter or number. This site also has comprehensive lists of smileys.

Your Phone's Secret Txt Helper

All phones have some sort of language function that automatically completes a word for you. This function also helps you spell correctly. Here's how I send text messages from my Verizon phone.

1. Choose text message. Enter the phone number of the recipient. You'll be on the writing screen.

2. Enter your text. You'll have several write function choices:
    *   ABC = all caps.
    *   Abc = sentence case.
    *   123 = numbers.
    *   Symbols = faces and punctuation options.
    *   T9En Text Input = number keys representing letters.

3. Send.

T9En Text Input is my personal favorite. (The name of this function differs with each service.) Press a key once per letter. Your phone automatically guesses what word you're trying to type. For example, *cat* is 2, 2, 8. Words

change as you enter each letter. Press Select when the word you want appears. If a word is incorrect, press the zero key (0) to toggle through other words that match your pattern.

Here are a couple other useful shortcuts:

*   # inserts a space.
*   ★ shifts case.
*   1 punctuates your sentence.

For a complete guide to T9 Text Input, go to www.t9.com.

It's time to start sending those text messages. Good luck! I know you can do it! TTFN TTYL (Ta-ta for now. Talk to you later.)

VizualLogic Car DVD Players

Roman Loyola

The DVD craze is out of hand. It's not enough to have a DVD drive in your computer, a home entertainment center that rivals your local movie theater, or a portable DVD player for your favorite flick. You're not an official DVD nut until you have one in your car.

Dealer Works of Santa Clara, California (www.dealerworks.com) specializes in car mods and customized audio and video systems. It'll show you a Chevy Suburban outfitted with a ridiculous number of audio/video products by VizualLogic (www.vizualogic.com).

Here are prices from Dealer Works; pricing at other dealers may vary. The 7-inch TFT with DVD player, headphones, remotes, FM modulator, and installation costs $1,799 ($1,599 uninstalled). The 5.6-inch package with DVD player, FM modulator, remotes, wireless headphones, and installation costs $1,499 ($999 uninstalled).

Leo's Pick: Palm Zire 71

Leo Laporte

Whenever I buy a new piece of tech, you can bet that a newer, better, cheaper version will ship the next day. I call it the Laporte Effect. I guess it happens because I usually wait a while before buying. I have learned from bitter experience that it doesn't pay to buy the first version of anything.

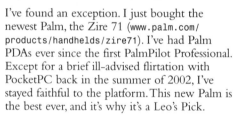

I've found an exception. I just bought the newest Palm, the Zire 71 (www.palm.com/products/handhelds/zire71). I've had Palm PDAs ever since the first PalmPilot Professional. Except for a brief ill-advised flirtation with PocketPC back in the summer of 2002, I've stayed faithful to the platform. This new Palm is the best ever, and it's why it's a Leo's Pick.

Features to Like

- The Zire 71 features a brilliant 320×320 16-bit transflective screen that compares favorably with the best PDAs.

- Its 14MHz ARM processor is the fastest to date.

- It runs PalmOS 5.21 and comes with 16MB of RAM and an SD expansion slot.

- There's a headphone jack (but you'll have to supply your own phones), and it can play MP3s using the supplied RealOne Mobile Player and QuickTime video using the Kinoma player.

What makes the Zire 71 unique is the built-in camera. It's only a single-megapixel 640×480 camera with fixed focal length, but it's handy. I used it to take pictures on the set. The color isn't perfect, but when you need a camera, it's nice to have one handy.

The Zire 71 is about $300 list. Sure, you could get a faster Dell Axim for that price, but if you need a Palm, this is the one to have.

Download of the Day

Baggle Bagger

Nicole Guilfoyle

Make a wish list, create a gift registry, and win prizes all at the same time. Gift shopping is never easy. Look at all the stuff you've had to return: sweaters two sizes too small, Elvis immortalized in wax, dog chew toys for your cat. It's time to take the guesswork out of shopping.

Baggle Bagger (www.baggle.com) is a wish list keeper. When you download and install it, a new Baggle icon should appear on your Internet Explorer toolbar. If it doesn't, click View, Toolbars, Customize. Click the Baggle icon, and click Add to move it to your toolbar.

The first time you use Baggle Bagger, it prompts you to create an account. You'll be able to view your wish list and share it with friends via the Baggle website.

Create a Wish List

Whenever you're browsing the online aisles and find something you want, add it to your wish list.

1. Click the Baggle icon on your IE toolbar.

2. Choose a bag or create a new list.

3. The wizard prompts you to highlight the product's name, price, and picture.

Using Your Wish List

Sign in using your username or email address. You'll see a list of your bags.

- Click the View button to get all the details for an item, or click the Buy button to buy online.

- Click Send to email your bag's link to friends and family.

- Click Manual Add to manually add items to your list.

Baggle Bagger is a great way to keep track of all the stuff you want to buy. Now you'll get the gifts you want.

Cell Phone Dilemma: GSM or CDMA?

Patrick Norton

GSM

If you think of yourself as a globe-trotting, world-traveling type, and you want your cell phone to work across oceans, go GSM. The Global System for Mobiles (www.gsmworld.com) is pretty much *the* standard outside of the United States. That isn't to say you can't use a GSM phone in the States; AT&T and lots of other providers support GSM.

CDMA

However, CDMA, or code division multiple access, is the more dominant spec in the United States. (There's also TDMA, time division multiple access, but it appears to be on the way out.) CDMA networks promise all the goodness of high-speed data transfer via 3G technology (or 2.5G, as some folks call the current version), although you'll need a phone that supports the faster speeds.

Ask Around

Specs are nice, but talk to friends, co-workers, and neighbors, and ask them how well their cellular services work in your area. Then do some more homework: Compare phones and pricing. Go with the best service you can find at the best price. GSM or CDMA—I doubt you'll care if it works well and it's not costing you an arm and a leg.

Related Links

- Wireless Advisor (www.wirelessadvisor.com) provides lists of your local cellular providers.
- To find a service provider, see http://wireless.fcc.gov, courtesy of the FCC.

Gentlemen, Charge Your Batteries

Dave Roos

Interested in electric car racing? Check these websites.

Electric Vehicle Links

- **The National Electric Drag Racing Association** (NEDRA, www.nedra.com) provides all the adrenaline-pumping action of short-track racing, with an environmental twist
- **Current Eliminator II**, the fastest electric vehicle in the world (www.wurts.net/electrifiedmotorsports/elecms2.htm)
- **KillaCycle**, the world's fastest electric motorcycle (www.killacycle.com)
- **Electric Vehicle Association of the Americas** (www.evaa.org/evaa/index.htm)
- **The Electric Auto Association** (www.eaaev.org)
- **History of Electric Vehicles** (http://sloan.stanford.edu/Evehicle)
- **Alternative-Fuel Vehicle Directory** (http://facultystaff.vwc.edu/~gnoe/avd.htm)

Patrick's Tips

Cell Phone Spare Parts

Looking for spare parts for your cell phone? Try Cell Phone Shop (www.cellphoneshop.net). It has a host of displays for the Nokia 5100, 6100, 8260/90, and 3360 phones. It also has microphones and even complete circuit boards for some Nokia cell phones, not to mention parts and tools for some Ericsson phones.

Here's the thing: If you don't have a popular phone, chances are you won't find parts. Fire up a Google search and see what you can find. Be patient. It might take a while.

Roundup: Cool Camera/Phone Combos

Hahn Choi

Want a new cell phone? Get one with an integrated digital camera. A camera/phone can snap a shot and send it over a next-generation wireless network. It's no wonder this fresh combination has more mass appeal than did earlier hybrid devices, which provided little more than mundane contact info and a bogged-down web experience.

But a camera/phone is primarily a phone. It won't replace your megapixel-plus camera. None of the phones we tested focused. Images were blurry on the outer edges, regardless of how far away the subject was. Nevertheless, these new camera/phones are undeniably cool. Find out which one rocks the most:

- **Nokia 3650**

- **Sony Ericsson P800** lab pick

- **Sanyo SCP-5300** lab pick

- **Siemens S56 with Mobile Camera accessory**

Why a Camera Phone?

- **For the memories.** Most people carry their cell phone all the time but leave their digital camera at home. With the two combined, you'll never miss an opportunity to immortalize the moment.

- **For photo caller ID.** You can associate images with entries in your phone book. When someone calls, you'll see their face, not just their name. In many cases, you can also transfer images to the phone.

- **To share shots.** Without a cellular data service, you'll quickly tire of taking pictures. A data service lets you email images to friends or, if your carrier offers it and your phone is capable, send images through Multimedia Messaging Service (MMS).

- **To print shots.** Well, maybe not. Resolution tops out at 640×480, which works fine for the web and email. Unless you're printing thumbnails, images are noticeably pixilated. (Sanyo's SCP-5300 phone showed the best color reproduction.)

Take Full Advantage with Data Service

A 640×480 JPEG image consumes about 70KB, which means you can send about 15 pictures per month on most plans. Carefully consider your usage pattern when you shop for your service plan. Most important, don't get sucked in by a fancy phone. In the long run, your service plan will cost more than the phone. We checked service pricing in the San Francisco Bay area. This is the minimum you'll pay. (Service plans may vary depending on your area.)

Provider	Sprint PCS	Cingular	T-Mobile	AT&T Wireless
Service	PCS Visio			
Wireless Internet Express	t-zones	mMode		
Cost per Month	$10	$6.99	$2.99	$2.99
Data	Unlimited	1MB	1MB	1MB
Price per KB	—	3 cents	1 cent	2 cents

233

What to Do If Your Mobile Device Takes a Swim

Patrick Norton

There's a particular sound that a mobile device makes when it hits a body of water, a sound unlike anything else. Your reaction to this sound will vary.

If a hated cell phone took the plunge, then that splashing sound means you finally have an excuse to call in that $5 a month "protection" or "insurance" plan the carrier sold you. You did buy the protection, right?

That sound isn't so joyful, though, if you've just soaked the PDA that contains the phone number of the cute guy you met on the train. Or drowned that pager with an adorable message from your son that's the only thing that'll keep you from strangling your idiot partner on a four-day business trip. Deep breaths, all is not lost.

Emergency Care

- First, get it out of the water as quickly as possible. Just splashed? Dry it off. Try to resist shaking it because vibrations can force water farther down into the case, which you want to avoid. Water on the outside isn't too bad, but water on the inside can cause instant short circuits or just linger for a while and cause corrosion.

- Don't turn it on. In fact, if you can, pull out the battery and leave it out until you're sure the device is dry.

- Know when to fire it up again. If there's moisture under the screen, you're probably not going to want to turn it on. If it's dripping, don't turn it on. If you're scared, don't turn it on. Let it dry for a day. (Do not put it in the oven or in the microwave—especially not the microwave. Trust me.)

- Mechanically inclined? Grab a hair dryer, open up the device, and start drying. Not mechanically inclined? Find somebody who is. Or take it to your local phone shop. Or call your provider and ask where to send it.

Wireless Tips

Is It Possible to Make a Dialup Connection Wireless?

Sure, you can make a dialup connection wireless. Back in the day, IBM made a big funky wireless modem, sort of a cordless phone for your notebook, called the IBM Cordless Computer Connection (http://domino.research.ibm.com). Good luck finding one of those on sale.

You might think about adding a phone jack to your wireless phone (www.halfbakery.com), if you're good with a soldering iron. It's funky, but from what I've heard, your connection won't get more than 12Kbps. That's about a quarter of what you could get plugging straight into the wall. Nix that.

Best solution? Put a Wi-Fi card in your computer and then connect to a desktop system in your house running Internet connection sharing. (You'll also need a Wi-Fi card in the desktop system.) Or, add a wireless access point and Internet connection sharing to the PC that uses the modem and dialup connection.

If you have the bucks, you can get a Wi-Fi base station with a built-in modem, such as the Apple AirPort (www.apple.com). It has a built-in modem right alongside the Ethernet port.

Should You Upgrade to Satellite Radio?

Hanh Choi

Satellite radio beams a pure digital signal to anywhere in the United States from miles above the Earth's surface. But unlike FM radio, it's not free.

Satellite Radio Rocks

Satellite radio sounds heaps better than FM, even through stock speakers in our car. Plus, the digital format lets stations transmit additional data, such as artist and track information, which is displayed on the controller.

Satellite radio has a national "footprint," meaning you can tune in to the same channels anywhere across the United States. Like any satellite technology, you need line of site to get a signal, which can be a problem in cities with tall buildings. Both Sirius and XM rely on repeaters to boost the signal in areas without a clear view of the sky.

Ultimately, it's the content that makes satellite radio so much better than plain old radio. Sirius and XM both offer 100 channels.

How to Get Satellite Radio

To add satellite radio to your car, you have to make a hardware investment starting around $250. The most affordable way is to add it to your existing stereo system through an FM modulator or tape adapter, if your car is so equipped.

A satellite radio system consists of an antenna, a tuner, and a controller. For XM, Sony's DRN-XM01 unit offers much more flexibility than do systems hardwired into the car. The DRN-XM01 combines the tuner and controller into a self-contained unit that you can take from vehicle to vehicle or into the house if you have the optional cradles.

XM or Sirius?

Selecting the best service is a tough call. Check the content each provides and select the one that best suits your tastes. We found something we liked in each service. However, XM is our choice because the service had fewer signal drops. Plus, with 25 times more subscribers than Sirius, XM seems to have more staying power to protect our hardware investment. Charges are approximately $10 a month for XM and $13 a month for Sirius.

XM Radio (1.800.852.9696)

- 70 music channels; 30 news, talk, and other formats

- Approximately 30 commercial-free music channels

- Around five to six minutes of commercials per hour on other channels

Sirius Radio (1.888.539.7474)

- 60 music channels; 40 news, talk, and other formats

- All 60 music channels are commercial-free

Patrick's Tips

Fix Your Cell Phone LCD

Long-suffering *The Screen Savers* producer David Prager cracked the screen on his Nokia 8260 (www.nokiausa.com). Time for a new phone? Nope. He found a supplier of Nokia parts online and bought a new LCD. David bought his LCD from the Cell Phone Shop (www.cellphoneshop.net) for under $20. The price may vary depending on your model cell phone.

Top Tips for Taking Apart Strange Stuff

- Work on a white sheet of paper to help you locate those tiny parts if you drop one.

- Lay screws and other parts out in the order you remove them. This makes it easier to remember where everything goes.

- If it doesn't work, don't force it. If it breaks, you'll end up replacing more than just your LCD screen.

Pat's Pocket PC Game Picks

Patrick Norton
In some moments I discover whole areas of weirdness in the world of computers, usually when I'm talking to some seriously sleep-deprived maniac at a hacker conference. This time I'm the sleep-deprived maniac. The area of weirdness? Pocket PC games. I had no idea there were so many games.

I went looking for a Tetris clone and finished the night with about 31 games either installed on my Jornada or in line to be tested. It's often been said that the Pocket PC is a Game Boy for adults. No kidding! Important note: Sometimes the game install did something a tad shady to my device, which required an OS reinstall. Arrgh. Back up before you test.

Pocket PC Gaming Tip

Go into Settings, click on the Personal tab, and open Sounds and Notifications, to disable the hardware buttons so you won't have to hear the insanely annoying clicking sounds when you play a game that uses the thumbwheel.

My Favorite Pocket PC Games

- **Snails** (http://ce.syntact.fi/snails) in combat. It's turn-based. It's odd. I launched rockets at other snails and then waited to see if they'd launch a nuke at me.

- **Fishing Fishing** (www.flux2game.com). The English is funky, the demo lasts about 45 seconds, and how the @#$%#$! do you catch a fish? It's an '80s-type arcade game. Slide the fishing bear side to side, and drag the hook up and down to catch the cartoon fish.

- **Tennis Addict** (www.hexacto.com). Most creative uses of the pen and the touch screen annoy me, but Tennis Addict pulls it off. I'm not a tennis fan, but I really enjoyed this one.

- **X-Ranger** (www.jimmysoftware.com). Pretty good visual effects, but will it get boring too quickly? Spin and shoot, spin and shoot.

- **Tetris.** My search on Tetris found 55 entries. How about the free Hetris (www.hnhsoft.com). Why did I lose so quickly? Is it because the game moves too fast? Am I out of practice? Is it the controls? I'll blame it on the controls and spend the rest of the night trying to beat my score.

- **Argentum** (www.ionside.com). This game feels a lot darker and packs more detailed graphics than Xen Games Strategiz Assault. Both are Command and Conquer clones.

- **Deep Down Race!** (www.geocities.com/barelyfish/ddr.html). Odd little digging game. Fun. I'm beginning to wonder if you can wear out the thumbpad on a Pocket PC.

A Few More Games

- **EA Sports Tiger Woods PGA Tour Golf** (www.ziosoft.com)
- **Black Jack** (www.flux2game.com)
- **Saffron** (www.jimmysoftware.com)
- **Leo's Flight Simulator** (http://web.jet.es/leobueno)
- **iGolf** (www.cecraft.com)
- **Lemonade Inc.** (www.hexacto.com)
- **Young Paladin Pinball** (www.cecraft.com)
- **V-Rally** (www.palmtop.nl/ce/poc_vrally.html)
- **The Mark** (www.flux2game.com)
- **Pocket Quake** (http://quake.pocketmatrix.com)
- **Blood & Ocean** (www.flux2game.com)
- **EA Sports FIFA 2000** (www.ziosoft.com)
- **Pocket Bass Pro** (www.ziosoft.com)
- **Argentum** (www.ionside.com)
- **Speedball 2** (www.portable-games.com)
- **SimCity 2000** (www.ziosoft.com)
- **Pocket Gambler** (www.ziosoft.com)
- **Turjah II** (www.turjah.com)
- **Kyle's Quest 2** (http://crimsonfire.com)
- **Shadowgate Classic** (www.shadowgate.com)
- **Diamond Mine** (www.astraware.com)
- **Rayman** (www.gameloft.com)

Quickly Transfer Data Without the Messy Cables

David Prager

There's a recent television commercial in which two PDA users, one on a train, the other on the platform, exchange a longing gaze. In the end, they're able to connect their PDAs via infrared and transfer the vital contact information they so desperately sought.

This kind of data transfer is often called beaming. It uses infrared beams. (It's also called IrDA.) Infrared is capable of transferring data between laptop computers (or any computer) with an infrared port.

With Windows XP, it's as easy as facing the computers' infrared ports at each other within a meter or less. The computers let you know they've sensed the other's presence by displaying a balloon tip. If there's no balloon tip, you may need to go into the Control Panel, double-click Wireless Link, and check the selected boxes to enable the port and accept file transfers.

When a computer is in proximity, select the infrared icon on your taskbar, and you're given the option to browse and send any files. The receiving computer is prompted if it wants to accept files. The process works both ways.

Here's how to configure the IrDA port for file sharing with Windows 2000 and XP:

1. Right-click My Network Places and select Properties.

2. Select Create a New Connection (WinXP) or Make New Connection (Win2K) to launch the New Connection Wizard.

3. Select Set Up an Advanced Connection.

4. Select Connect Directly to Another Computer.

5. Choose Host or Guest configuration (configure each computer for a role).

6. Complete the wizard, depending on whether you're setting up the Host or Guest computer. Make sure you select the IrDA port as the connection device.

The data transfer rates should be similar to those of a parallel port, or between 2,400bps and 115kbps with IrDA 1.0. The specification has been under continued development, so your throughput may even approach 4mbps and will continue to increase in the upcoming years. You can learn more about this technology and its networking uses at the Infrared Data Association (www.irda.org).

Mac Tips

Clean Your Laptop Screen

Megan Morrone

One problem with Mac laptops (and there is only one problem) is that when you close them, the keys touch the screen. This leads to little scratches and oil marks from your fingers.

I use Klear Screen (www.klearscreen.com) to get rid of the scratches. I also use a protective barrier to keep them from happening at all.

The ingeniously named ScreensavRz (www.devdepot.com) is a lint-free, optical-grade woven blend of polyester and nylon, designed specifically for the G4 PowerBook. They're also available for the G3 PowerBooks and the new iBooks. I just shake it clean, but you can also throw it in the washing machine.

ScreensavRz are around $15, and if that seems like too much, a cut up T-shirt works almost as well.

Web Tips

Foreign Money

How many pounds can you get for a dollar? How is the Peso doing against the Euro? Go to www.xe.com, which does currency conversion. The rates are updated constantly, so the values are always up to date.

Recharge Your Laptop in Your Car

Patrick Norton

You can recharge your notebook from inside your car if you have a 12-volt lighter socket. My truck has two: one for the lighter and one labeled 12V. You need an adapter to go between your notebook and the 12-volt lighter plug.

DC/DC

The classic solution is a DC/DC adapter that converts the car's 12-volt DC into the appropriate voltage and amperage for your notebook. These adapters often have lighter sockets and plugs that work on airplanes (if you can afford the airline seats that come with those plugs). Here are two examples:

- **Xtend PowerXtender** airplane and auto adapter ($100, www.xtendmicro.com) offers a cable that will fit your notebook. If you replace your notebook, you can buy a cable to fit your new notebook for around $30.

- **Targus** power adapters ($119, www.targus.com) are the Universal Auto/Air Notebook Adapter for Apple, Compaq, Dell, Gateway, Fujitsu, HP, IBM, Panasonic, Sharp, Sony, and Toshiba laptops.

DC/AC/DC

A less expensive option is a DC/AC power inverter. It turns the 12 volts in your car into 120-volt AC. Plug your notebook's regular power supply into the inverter. Inverters can power anything that plugs into a wall socket, as long as it doesn't pull more wattage than the inverter can supply.

APC (www.apc.com) makes the Travel Power 75 DC/AC Inverter for around $80 with both auto and airplane sockets. It has APC's usual host of thoughtful features, including LEDs that indicate whether there's enough power to feed its inverter. APC makes more heavy-duty inverters for car use only: the 140 Watt Mobile Power 140W DC/AC Inverter (about $50) and the 350 Watt Mobile Power 350W DC/AC Inverter 120V (about $80).

You might also see the PORT Mobile Power Inverter (www.targus.com). This 150-watt inverter costs about $70.

Except for the APC Travel Power 75, these are pretty much the same inverters you can buy at your local Wal-Mart.

Megan's Tips

Music for Your Palm

Hear Megan's beautiful (but annoying) music from the palm of her hand.

- **3 Alarm** (www.palmgear.com). You'll need an extensions manager such as HackMaster (www.daggerware.com)or X-Master to make this program work, but it's worth it. 3 Alarm lets you organize your Palm alarms and even add flashing backlights to really get your attention.

- **Elvis** (www.palmgear.com) is an interesting program that's very useful on long car rides, both for passing the time and for really annoying anyone else in the car. The creators call Elvis a "Jukebox for the PDA," but that's a bit of an exaggeration. The free version comes with two different song books with about a dozen Midi tunes.

- **Geek Sounds** (www.palmrat.com). Of all the MIDI music for the Palm, Geek Sounds is the best. It includes all your favorite geeky tunes, which you can use for your alarms or just for your listening pleasure. The collection, by Justin Cutler, includes themes from *Star Wars*, *Star Trek*, *Indiana Jones*, and more.

Get more music and sound downloads at PalmGear.com.

Wireless Internet Access on the Road

Patrick Norton

If you have the money, you have many wireless options on cross-country road trips. People have been using cables or cell phone modems with their laptops for years. It's not cheap, especially if you roam, and the speeds are slow.

Some Options

Sprint's PCS Vision (www.pcsvision.com) has gotten a lot of attention lately. In our testing, it delivered browsing speeds similar to a 56Kbps modem. A Type II PC card costs about $250, and Sprint's best consumer data plan will give you 120MB of data for about $120, with every extra kilobyte setting you back one-tenth of a cent (which means that every extra megabyte you download should cost around $10). A similar service is offered by Verizon (www.verizon.com).

Previously, I used the CDPD network for nation-wide wireless Internet access. It works if you're in a fairly big town. I used GoAmerica.com (www.goamerica.com). It's slow like a cell phone connection, but doesn't cost as much, when you get the "all you can eat" monthly plan.

New York City shouldn't be a problem, but I'll bet western Kansas will be. The only thing that won't fail you way out there is a satellite phone service such as Globalstar (www.globalstarusa.com). Sadly, satellite phones are just as slow as the others and are more expensive.

If you're feeling resourceful, go for an 802.11b card and find open networks as you travel. (Three cheers for poorly secured wireless access points!) Toaster.net (www.toaster.net) lists community Wi-Fi networks. Or try commercial 802.11b/Wi-Fi networks such as Boingo Wireless (www.boingo.com) and T-Mobile (www.tmobilebroadband.com). The notebook print stations at Kinko's often have free Internet access. And many Internet cafes will let you use an Ethernet connection pretty cheaply.

Paint Your Cell Phone

Yoshi DeHerrera

Why settle for a premade cover when you can paint your own design? Here are some tips for painting cell phone covers.

Completely disassemble the phone. Paint and the fumes can damage the sensitive electronics. Carefully mask off any areas you don't want painted.

Use a paint that's designed for models. It's intended for plastics and will be the easiest to work with. You can find it at most craft or hobby stores.

Preparation is the key to a good finish. Use plastic-model filler to fill in any nicks or areas you want smoothed out. Sand with a 400 grit sandpaper and wash thoroughly. Use dishwashing soap or a plastic cleaner that leaves no residue.

When painting, put the paint in a bowl of warm water (not boiling) for a few minutes. This will help the paint atomize better.

Let the paint dry at least 48 hours before using. The longer you can give it to dry, the better. Before the paint is fully cured, it's still soft and prone to being damaged.

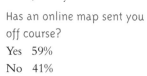

Talkback

You Can't Get There from Here

Dave Roos

How did anyone get anywhere before MapQuest.com? Did we use paper maps? Although online map services are useful, they have some serious kinks. If a mapping site has ever led you the wrong way down a one-way street, then you know what we're talking about.

Has an online map sent you off course?

Yes   59%

No   41%

Recharging Your Cell Phone Battery

Patrick Norton

The battery is the most important part of your cell phone; without it, your cell phone is just a useless lump. A little extra care with your cell phone battery can make it last a lot longer.

Lithium Batteries

Have a newer cell phone with a lithium battery? You don't have to wait for the battery to lose its charge completely before use a recharger. The rule of thumb is to recharge after it's down past halfway. Once in a while, let it fully die out before you charge it back up.

Older Phones

The batteries found in older analog phones (often nickel metal hydride or nickel cadmium) last longer if you wait for them to completely discharge before you fire 'em up on a charger.

Extra Power

Rely on your cell phone when you're away from home or the office? Not always in range of a car lighter socket or a place to plug in your cell phone? Pack an extra fully charged battery.

Tech Support Advice

Our intrepid associate producer Taylor called some of the big wireless providers to see what the folks at tech support had to say:

- **Cingular.** Charge the phone with the phone off. Never use a car charger. It only "shocks" the battery; it doesn't send enough wattage to charge a phone. Occasionally let your battery run out completely and charge for four hours.

- **AT&T Wireless.** When using batteries with nickel, use them until they are completely out of power and then recharge. Recharge lithium batteries at will.

- **Sprint PCS.** All phones are different. Check with your cell phone manual or the manufacturer's website.

Patrick's Tips

Pocket PC Connection Wizard

Want an easy way to connect a Pocket PC to a modem, network, virtual private network, cell phone, or who knows what? Download Microsoft Pocket PC Connection Wizard (www.microsoft.com/mobile/pocketpc/downloads/connwiz.asp). It runs on your desktop and offers a step-by-step walkthrough to set up your communications toys for your handheld.

We can't vouch for all of its options. Your Pocket PC must be connected to use the Connection Wizard. And like loading any software onto your Pocket PC, you'll need ActiveSync (www.microsoft.com/windowsmobile/default.mspx) installed and running.

Got it installed? Launch it and follow the steps. Keep an eye on email and other settings, because the wizard can automatically take email and instant messenger settings from your desktop. After you've made your choices, the wizard spits the settings onto your Pocket PC.

Unfortunately, the "Pocket PC Connection Wizard is intended for use with the Pocket PC 2002 software only." That means Microsoft doesn't claim that it works on older versions of Pocket PC. We haven't had a chance to test it with other versions of the Pocket PC OS, so we can't vouch for it, either.

Web Tips

Weather Updates

If you're looking for a site that will not only update you on the weather but also give you travel tips, diagnose your flu, and plan your vacation, go to Weather.com. You can even download an application that puts weather reports on your desktop.

Put a Planetarium on Your PDA

Call for Help Staff

Michael Portuesi, a member of the San Francisco Amateur Astronomers, says it's easy to turn your Palm-powered PDA into a portable planetarium.

Planetarium and Orrery offer different features. Both are made for the Palm operating system and work on color screens. Both are free, although the Orrery application is shareware and part of a larger sky-watching software bundle.

Planetarium (www.aho.ch/pilotplanets) is a general-purpose, star-charting tool for Palm devices. It has many of the essential features of star-charting software for desktop computers. Stargazers can use it to help them find the planets, constellations, and other objects in the night sky. It also has animation capabilities that help you learn how objects move in the night sky. You can even use your Palm as a compass with Planetarium.

The program also has some robust features that can be used by amateurs or professional astronomers. Through your Palm's serial port, try connecting your PDA to a computerized telescope to home in on various positions in the sky. With Planetarium, it's no longer necessary to use a PC to view star charts.

Orrery (www.astro-metrics.com) is one of a bundle of four astronomy-related programs at Astro-Metrics.com. The Orrery application is a solar system simulator, also for Palm devices. It plots and animates the motions of the nine planets. Orrery has a chart of planetary rise and set times. Users can get detailed information about each of the planets just by pointing the stylus at them. It's a tremendously useful learning tool, perfect for explaining astronomical concepts.

Get a Life

Cat Schwartz

I love to travel, but I have trouble finding my way around when I go someplace new, I spend way too much time searching for good salons, movie theaters, restaurants, and bars and clubs that play my kind of music. Citysearch (www.citysearch.com) is the best city-searching tool on the Net, so you can find the best places to wine, dine, party, and relax while you're away from home and it's easy to use. Here's how:

1. Type the name of the city you'll visit.

2. Select a category: attractions, bars, shopping, hotels, movies, or restaurants.

3. Continue clicking on links to narrow your search. You can also use the drop-down menus to tailor your search or just browse the categories.

4. When you select a category, look to the right of the page to find the essentials, including editor's picks and "best of" reviews.

Use the search tool to find more specific results. The tool brings up links to the contact info for your desired hot spot, plus basic info on the establishment's services. This is where you can find the establishment's phone number and address. The search tool comes in handy when you're making reservations.

The site also has a point rating based on user feedback. Pay attention to what other travelers and locals have to say.

August
18

241

Customize Your Ring Tones

Patrick Norton

Many cell phones come with canned rings, and that's all you get to choose from. Newer phones, however, let you customize your ring tones.

Don't know whether your cell phone can accept custom tones? Many ring tone websites list compatible phones. Some even let you test for compatibility.

Download Tones

Some phones require a download kit, in which you use a cable to connect your cell phone to your computer. You then create or download a ring tone (phones with a melody composer will let you type in a custom ring tone) and then upload it to the cell phone. Some cell phone carriers are set up to directly download ring tones to your phone through the same airwaves that carry your voice. Select a ring or pay for it, hit the magic button on your phone, and it's downloaded and installed.

Next thing you know, you can hear the theme song from *I Love Lucy* or *The Pink Panther*.

Get Custom Ring Tones

Some ring tone distributors work by having you call them. Then they transfer the ring tone to your cell phone. Watch for the fees these companies charge. Some charge $1.99 per minute per download, and a download can take up to three minutes. There are lots of websites where you can download ring tones. Be sure to also check the website of your carrier.

- **RingToneJukeBox.com** (www.ringtonejukebox.com). Supports ASCAP and BMI licenses, so you can get many commercial songs.
- **Ringtones.com** (http://us.ringtones.com).
- **Ringophone** (http://ringophone.com).
- **Zingy** (http://zingy.com).
- **How Stuff Works: Custom** Ringtones (www.howstuffworks.com).

The Future of Keyboard-Free Computing

Nicole Guilfoyle

Everyone wants an easy way to take notes on the go. It's a hassle to pull out your laptop if you're anywhere other than a coffee shop or stuck on a plane, train, or automobile. Using a stylus only gets you so far with a PDA, and you look like a weirdo if you start using your voice recognition software walking down the street. Dr. Carsten Mehring says he has the solution to all your computing conundrums.

Keyboard Independent Touch Typing (KITTY) is a wearable data input device. A sensor worn on the each finger and three sensors on each thumb let you turn your hands into a Qwerty-style keyboard. I know, I know, you've heard of these wearable devices before. The Senseboard Virtual Keyboard first hit our radar back in 2001, but there are a few important features that make KITTY different:

- As long as you know how to touch-type, you don't need to learn any new skills. Previous wearable input devices require a user to learn a new data entry method, usually only taught through the manufacturer. Even kids are learning how to touch-type in keyboarding class at school these days.
- KITTY is lightweight. You're not bogged down with heavy hardware and with the sensor-based version, you don't even need to worry about your hands getting sweaty in a glove.
- Signals are generated when you close a circuit. Other systems use continuous signal processing. Long story short, it's easier for a computer to interpret KITTY's discrete signals.

It's unclear how many words per minute a person will be able to type with KITTY, but it's a promising advancement in the world of wearable computers.

FutureDial Software

Patrick Norton

FutureDial (www.futuredial.com) thinks you're not getting enough out of your cell phone. Its suite of applications is supposed to remedy that.

SnapDialer

Broadband has spoiled me. I know this because I installed FutureDial SnapDialer this past weekend and was only modestly impressed. SnapDialer lets your laptop PC use an Internet-enabled mobile phone as a wireless modem for connecting to the Internet.

In minutes my cell phone had a 115-Kbps Internet connection (well, not quite 115, but we'll hit on that later). My mobile Internet dreams were fulfilled for $60, not including the wad of cash I dropped on my cell phone and my monthly payments to Sprint PCS.

It doesn't hurt that my monthly payment to Sprint includes unlimited access to PCS Vision (which I haven't been impressed with, www.pcsvision.com). However, it also includes slow access to weather info on a tiny screen and ridiculous charges to download a game. Still, by using SnapDialer ($30) and Future-Dial's Mobile Phone Data Cable ($30), I was able to do something I liked with PCS Vision for the very first time.

Bitrates

We're talking 56-Kbps modem performance, or somewhat better than 56-Kbps modem performance. You won't mistake this for your broadband at home. Then again, I can't use my home broadband in the middle of Golden Gate Park. I'd quote some of the online connection speed tests, but their results varied from 40 Kbps to 91 Kbps. I doubt SnapDialer had any effect on those speeds.

SnapSync

As always, the tightwad within wishes both the cable and the software were bundled with my recently purchased cell phone—especially since FutureDial's SnapSync (about $30, or $40 for SnapSync and SnapDialer bundled together) makes coordinating my phone numbers with

Microsoft Outlook painless. If you need support for other PIM programs, you'll have to look elsewhere.

SnapMedia

I'm not the "ringtone and photos on the phone" type, but here's a heads-up for those who are. FutureDial's SnapMedia promises to painlessly move media onto your phone.

Bottom line

All of FutureDial's applications run on Windows 98, Windows Me, Windows 2000, and Windows XP. The software and data cables are available most places that sell cell phones, not to mention online from FutureDial, which offers listings of the phones it supports. Snap-Dialer is supported only by Verizon and Sprint. SnapSync has support for a large array of phones from most major cell providers.

Windows Tips

Save Your Remote Desktop Connection Settings in XP

Morgan Webb

You probably remotely connect to only one or two computers—your home computer or your work computer. You can save the settings for those in a desktop icon for easy access. Note: These steps only work in Windows XP.

1. Choose Remote Desktop Connection from your Start menu.

2. Before you choose what computer you want to connect to, choose Options.

3. Fill out the computer information, including the IP address, user name, and password.

4. Choose Save As, and choose where you want your new icon to appear.

5. You can place the icon on your desktop for one-click access to the remote computers you use the most.

Take Your Favorite TV Shows With You

Cat Schwartz

Most of us just can't get enough TV. And most of us don't have a television in our cubicles at work, so tune in on the web or your PDA. Your favorite TV programs aren't streaming online—the big-daddy cable companies make sure that doesn't happen—but these sites come in a close second.

Mazingo (www.mazingo.net) is too cool. It lets you purchase TV programs for your PDA.

1. Sign up and pay your membership fee. A 24-hour trial is $6.95. If you like it, pay $14.95 a month or $94.95 for a whole year.

2. Download the player to your PDA.

3. Choose from more than 600 shows and download the one you want to watch!

4. Every time you synch your PDA, it updates with the new content.

The files aren't too big, but they're not small either. I suggest using a card reader. Also, don't put too many files on your PDA unless you have a newer model that can handle it.

wwiTV (wwitv.com/ns.htm) is a portal of streaming television that shows you what's airing in more than 100 countries around the globe. News and entertainment are hot topics:

1. From the wwiTV homepage, choose from TV or broadband stations.

2. Pick a country.

3. Browse through your choices and select a site.

4. You'll land on a page with the video.

If you know of a free stream not listed on the site, click the Add URL button at the top of the wwiTV homepage and suggest it.

LikeTelevision (http:// tesla.liketelevision.com) is the site for you if you crave the classics. For $12 a month you get access to the site's library of thousands of old-time movies, television shows, cartoons, and commercials. You'll also get access to a video download library and an image library with more than 12,000 pictures taken by the studios. Make sure you have a high-speed connection to get the most out of your subscriptions.

Mobile Tips

Five Tips to Extend Palm Battery Life

Nicole Guilfoyle

Palm handhelds rapidly consume battery power. It's not unusual for avid users to charge the device or insert a brand-new set of AAA's every day or two.

1. **Change power usage preferences.** Make your Palm automatically shut off when it's not in use for one or two minutes: Choose Prefs from the Application launcher, tap the drop-down menu in the upper-right corner and choose General, set Auto Off to one or two minutes.

2. **Adjust brightness.** Palm handhelds with a color screen use up batteries faster than Palms with a monochrome screen. Hold down the power button to turn down brightness and extend battery life.

3. **Use the right batteries.** If you power your handheld with standard batteries, use alkaline, not rechargeable ones. A Palm device may not properly gauge the drain on a rechargeable battery and may suddenly shut off without warning.

4. **Beam conservatively.** Beam only when it's necessary. The ability to share information quickly is a cool Palm feature, but you really don't need to beam all your information to the guy sitting next to you on the bus.

5. **Don't overclock.** Palm devices need more juice (battery power) to work at faster speeds. Overclocking might also void your warranty.

Make Your PC Wireless

Hahn Choi

Desktop computers have too many wires, and I'm on a quest to get rid of them. I've found some products that'll help clear up the clutter and give you more flexibility.

Wireless Keyboard and Mouse

- **Microsoft Wireless Optical Desktop for Bluetooth** (www.microsoft.com) is practical and well designed. It's Windows XP only, and communicates easily with a small USB Bluetooth base station. It can also communicate with other Bluetooth devices, such as cell phones, PDAs, and printers.

- **Logitech Cordless Elite Duo** (www.logitech.com) uses standard RF, so it's not as "advanced" as Microsoft's Bluetooth system. However, it supports both the Mac and Windows. Plus, it offers a stylish and comfortable design. The mouse is for righties only.

Network Without Wires

802.11b is currently the most affordable and widely used wireless networking technology. You can share your broadband connection with multiple computers without running network cables throughout the house. Notebook users can compute anywhere.

- **Netgear MR814 Cable/DSL Wireless Router** (www.netgear.com) is the core of a wireless network, acting as a hub among all the computers and enabling shared broadband use. I've used Netgear's MR814 for several months with two different service providers. It's rock-solid stable. It has an easy-to-use interface for initial configuration and management.

- **Linksys WET11 Wireless Ethernet Bridge** (www.linksys.com). You don't need to install drivers or applications; the computer thinks it's an Ethernet cable. You need a browser to configure the WET11, but the included CD makes configuration painless. The WET11 is more expensive than USB wireless ($105 street), but it offers the ability to connect to other devices, such as an Xbox or a PlayStation 2.

- **A wireless USB adapter** (around $60) is the most affordable way to get a wireless network. The signal can be obstructed with internal cards when the computer is placed close to a wall. With a wireless USB adapter, you can move the antenna to get the best signal. Buy from a reputable manufacturer such as D-Link, Linksys, or Netgear. They'll be around to offer support and driver updates.

You have a wireless network, but there's still one more cord to cut.

The Linksys EtherFast Wireless-Ready USB PrintServer (www.linksys.com; $85) alone doesn't have wireless capabilities. You'll have to buy a PC card (about $60). When it's wireless, you can put your printer anywhere within range. Linksys was the only manufacturer I could find to support USB, a requirement for newer printers. You configure the server through a web-based interface or a Windows-based application.

Talkback

Should All Electronic Distractions Be Banned from Cars?

Dave Roos

Automobile deaths and injuries are on the rise as more electronic gadgets make their way from the family room into the family car.

Should in-car electronic devices be banned?

Should all electronic devices be banned in the car?

Yes   19%

No   81%

Changing Cell Phone Service Providers

Patrick Norton

A viewer had cellular service accounts with Cricket (www.cricketcommunications.com) but now has two useless cell phone. Is it possible to have the Nokia phones reprogrammed for use with another phone company?

I wouldn't hold my breath if I were you, and I would be super careful about buying used cell phones on eBay (www.ebay.com). Even if the same cellular provider originally sold it, you may not be able to activate it, at least not without paying off any bills associated with that phone.

Two main issues arise with reactivating a phone with a new service provider:

1. Equipment compatibility. Which providers use a system compatible with your phone?

   Major providers use different protocols: Verizon and Sprint use CDMA, Cingular and AT&T use TDMA, and Voicestream and T-Mobile use GSM. Check the manufacturer's webpage or your manual to find out which protocol your phone uses. Then you can search for a compatible provider.

2. A subsidy lock on the phone may prevent activation with any but the original service. Most cell phone providers subsidize the cost of a phone. To recoup their cost or simply prevent subscribers from moving to other services, they secure the phone with a code available only to the service provider. If your phone is locked, you will not be able to program a new telephone number without this code.

   CDMA phones typically refer to this code as the master subsidy lock. TDMA phones use a SOC lock, while GSM phones use a SIM lock or SP lock to prevent the use of SIM cards from competing providers in their handsets. Whether or not your phone is locked, chances are, you'll need the code from the original service provider to move to a new provider.

The bottom line is, you can probably turn those paperweights back into phones, but it will take some time.

Download of the Day

SocialEYES

Megan Morrone

Have you heard of Speed Dating? For a nominal fee, you get to play a game of musical chairs with possible partners. From what I hear, you get a few minutes to talk to each person to find out if they're worth any more of your time.

If you own a Palm-powered handheld, you don't need to pay the nominal fee. In fact, you don't even need to talk to people at all, thanks to a program called SocialEYES (www.evolutionary.net/socialeyes/).

You can download this free program and fill out as many of the answer lists you like. The lists include your favorite movies, the U.S. president's performance, the best tennis players ever, and dozens of other lists of things you might discuss on a first date or chance meeting.

Getting Social

When you find a potential mate (who also owns a Palm-powered PDA), do the following:

1. Beam that person the program (tap the Beam Program button).

2. Have him fill out the lists.

3. When he's done, tap the SocialEYES! button.

4. Choose a list to beam.

5. Sit back and find out how compatible you are.

You can even draw a sketch of yourself and beam that to your possible future partner. Depending on how talented you are with the stylus, this isn't necessarily recommended. The program is free, to unlock the special features, you must purchase a code for $12.

Peak and Off-Peak Rates

Patrick Norton

If the call begins during peak time and continues through off-peak time, the caller is charged the peak rate for the whole call. The time in which a call originated is where it stays. Be aware of when peak hours end. If you're near the start of off-peak, end your call, call 'em back, and get charged at off-peak rates. Here's some info to help you keep track of peak hours.

Carrier	Days	Peak Hours
Verizon	M through F	6 a.m. to 8 p.m.
Sprint	M through F	7 a.m. to 9 p.m.
AT&T	M through F	7 a.m. to 9 p.m.
Cingular	M through F	7 a.m. to 9 p.m.
PacBell	M through F	7 a.m. to 9 p.m.

Weekends are off-peak for all these providers.

Generally, peak hours cover 14 hours a day, Monday through Friday. The times are applicable to the zone from which you're making the call. I can't call Mom back East on the cheap rates to until it's midnight on the East Coast.

Track to the Last Second

Another billing tip: Your bill gets rounded up—not in dollars and cents, but in seconds. If you are talking for 21 seconds, you get billed for a minute. If you talk for 61 seconds, you get billed for two minutes. You might as well talk until the end of your minute, if you're even keeping track that closely.

Web Tips

IM File Transfer

The best way to transfer large files between two computers on the Internet is through an instant messenger. In AOL Instant Messenger, just right-click the name of the recipient of the file and select Send File. Choose the file you want to sent, and then send it.

Talkback

Too Connected for Comfort?

Dave Roos

Carrying a cell phone is as important as wearing pants. Sometimes more so. The goal is to remain in constant contact with one's entire social circle. Plans are made, remade, moved, and removed according to the latest bit of news from the best-informed member of the cell-carrying swarm.

The Washington Post wrote a revealing (and more than a little disturbing) story about the culture and psychology of what it calls "digital swarms" or "smart mobs." *The Post* used Prince William of England as a startling example. Apparently, using cell phones and text messengers, William's admirers contact one another en masse, disclosing his whereabouts and thus remaining in constant pursuit, severely cramping the prince's style.

Would you participate in a smart mob? Have people become too connected? Can you survive without your cell phone? Have cell phones and text messengers changed social behavior forever?

Would you "smart mob"?

Yes   31%

No   69%

Boost the Apple AirPort

Brett Larson

Super-fast Wi-Fi has made its way to all the latest updates of Apple's hardware line, but what are you to do when you want to add it to your existing AirPort? Luckily, Apple decided to use a chipset that is used in Linksys's 802.11g cards, which means a simple trick in the terminal will have you up to g-speed in no time.

You need either the Linksys WMP54G Wireless-G PCI Adapter for desktops or the WPC54G Wireless-G Notebook Adapter. You'll also need the AirPort Extreme software, which comes with the base station or the extreme card.

1. Head over to OS X Hax to download the Perl script, which makes hacking your kernel extensions easy.

2. Install the AirPort Extreme software on your computer and shut down your machine.

3. Install the Wireless-G card.

4. Boot and then run the Perl script from the command line. You'll need to run the Perl script as root from the terminal by running the command su, and then entering your root password.

5. As root, change directories to where the Perl script is located (cd/User/username/Desktop, for example) and change the script to be executable. The easiest way is chmod a+x filename.perl. You can use the binary if you know how to do that.

6. Now you're set to run it; do that by typing ./filename.perl. The script will exit with a message if it worked correctly.

7. Reboot.

After rebooting, your machine should let you know that new AirPort hardware has been found, and you can configure it from the System Preferences application. Now you're surfing fast, without wires.

Wireless Tips

AirPort Alternatives

A viewer writes, "I recently bought an AirPort card for my Apple iBook (www.apple.com) and would like to know whether I have to buy Apple's expensive AirPort or whether I can use any other Wi-Fi router."

You don't have to buy the AirPort; the AirPort card in your iBook uses the same Wi-Fi specs used for Windows, Linux, and whatever.

When the AirPort came out, it not only featured the silver mushroom shape, but it also was the cheapest Wi-Fi–based wireless access point (WAP) ever introduced. It's a shame that the price (around $300) hasn't dropped as low as its competitors—probably the built-in 56K modem.

You'll probably have to work a bit harder to get WAP running on your iBook than a Windows user would. And you might have to enter your WAP code in hexadecimal code.

If you're looking for an alternative to the AirPort, try a WAP from Linksys (www.linksys.com).

Megan's Tips

Wireless Palm Resources

I've been resisting the wireless Palm for a while. I could download email, webpages, and games to my Handspring Visor and browse them offline just fine. Who needs wireless web browsing?

Then I borrowed a Palm i705 with an always-on wireless connection. Now I don't think I could ever go back. Here are two valuable tools that you can use with your wireless Palm:

- **Google .02** (www.palmgear.com). Submit a search to Google's low-bandwidth search engine.

- **MovieRaider** (www.palmgear.com). Use data from the Internet Movie Database.

You can find more resources like these at PalmGear.com.

Cell Phone Reception

Patrick Norton

Think of your cell phone as a radio—a very special radio. Your call goes from your cell phone/radio to an antenna owned by your cellular provider. Actually, it goes to the base station owned by your cell provider at the bottom of that antenna. The base station "talks" to your phone, keeping tabs on it so you can receive and send calls. Or, if you're out of your local dialing area, the base station relays the phone's SSID to the mother ship to see if it's valid. If it is, you're charged for access.

When you get the "out of range" notice on your phone, it means your phone can't make contact with a compatible base station.

Does your friend's cell phone work when yours doesn't? No surprise. Cell phones are rarely compatible with systems owned by other carriers. Other cellular providers use frequencies that might not be compatible with your phone. Other cellular providers use cellular access technologies that, again, might not be compatible with your phone.

Even if your friend has the same provider and is standing on the same street corner, if your friend has a different phone, its antenna might be more efficient than the one on your cell phone, so your friend's phone can get a signal while your phone can't.

Again, this is oversimplified. If you want to learn the nitty-gritty behind cell phones, read "How Cell Phones Work," from HowStuffWorks (www.howstuffworks.com).

Download of the Day

Pocket Exbert

Megan Morrone

If you've ever needed to generate the perfect buzzword to impress your boss and colleagues at an important business meeting, I'll show you a tool that will get you talking jargon in no time.

Pocket Exbert (www.palmgear.com) is a download for the Palm that allows you to tap your screen to view the perfect word or phrase for any situation. How does it know the perfect phrase, you ask? That's simple. Because most jargon means nothing, it can mean anything. Therefore, it's perfect for any situation. Here's an example:

> *Boss:* What are your long-term goals with the company?

> *Megan:* (tapping Handspring Visor) I'm thinking, horizontal holistic parallelism.

> *Boss:* Really? (excited) And then what?

> *Megan:* (tapping again) Probably polarized hybrid methodology.

> *Boss:* Interesting. Megan, what would you think if I offered you a raise?

> *Megan:* (again with the tapping) Preserving regional projection.

> Boss: What?

> *Megan:* (more tapping) Ameliorated maximized synergy?

> *Boss:* I said I wanted to give you a raise.

> *Megan:* (tapping, tapping) Versatile regional capabilities.

> *Boss:* Why do you keep tapping that?

> *Megan:* Uh… (runs away)

Remember, even the Pocket Exbert can overdo it.

Get RoadWired for the Road

Darci Wood

As the product princess, I took a look at some cool accessories from RoadWired (www.roadwired.com) to see how they stand up to my discriminating taste.

A Girl and Her Accessories

I filled the MegaMedia Computer Bag ($180) with a Gateway laptop, a CD-ROM drive, a floppy drive, an extra battery, a netcam, a Palm, a Palm cradle, a TI-86 calculator, a digital camera, and all the cables that go with these items. Not only did they all fit, tucked away in the little built-in compartments, but the MegaMedia left room for more. We threw in all the little geek toys and some girl stuff, to see if it could take it. And it did.

This is the first bag I have used that holds everything I carry around on a daily basis without overflowing into another bag. The numerous pockets built into the two main flaps and the ample padding offered great protection for all my stuff, and even with it overloaded, it was relatively lightweight. (RoadWired also offers this bag in leather for $300.) I took it to Los Angeles and back and wasn't anxious to ditch it as soon as I walked in the door. That's saying something.

Lighter Geek Days

The Digital Daypack ($169) is a perfect alternative when you don't need a huge bag. Padded like the MegaMedia, this backpack provides the ultimate protection for your laptop.

Another product that's worth taking a look at is the Laptop Sleeve ($40), complete with detachable strap. It holds your notebook inside either bag plus you can quickly lift out one bag, while you leave the bulk behind.

The fun item is definitely the RAPS! Advanced Protection System, which consists of a soft fleece square that can wrap your CD-ROM all snuggly with Velcro snaps. These come in large ($17), medium ($14), and small ($12).

The Bottom Line

The RoadWired gear held up to some pretty stringent traveling and is still going. Other RoadWired accessories submitted for review are made of the same ballistic nylon with neoprene trim and contain the ultra-padding. Expect MP3 players and cameras to work nicely in them as well. The bad thing about having a bag that fits all your stuff is that if you lose it, you're going to be one unhappy tech fan.

Patrick's Tips

PDA Browsers

Are there any do-it-all browsers that you can download for a PDA? The Springboard card comes with some software, but is there anything else?

Try Eudora's Internet Suite 2.1 (www.eudora.com). It's free and includes an HTTP-based browser.

It sounds like you really need a good site for downloading software. For Palm OS software I usually go to PalmGearHQ (www.palmgear.com), which has tons of stuff.

Looking for free stuff? The Gnome recommends FreewarePalm (www.freewarepalm.com), a site that specializes in free software for the Palm OS.

If you had a Pocket PC, you could use the built-in browser, or search Handango (www.handago.com), which is a download site for the Pocket PC.

How Many Wi-Fi Networks Are Too Many?

The Screen Savers **Staff**

The rule of thumb is to put five channels between wireless access points (WAPs) that are next to each other. Put two or more WAPs on the same channel (there are 11 channels of Wi-Fi, and the channels overlap) next to each other in an apartment building or a tightly packed neighborhood, and the bandwidth will definitely drop. Do some serious file transfers on those same WAPs, and you can effectively shut them down.

And that's just Wi-Fi. Tons of devices use the 2.4GHz frequency, from wireless phones to X10 home gadgets. Your microwave zaps your food with microwaves that transmit at 2.4GHz frequency. Wireless phones use it, too, but should automatically hop to a different frequency if they sense interference.

In theory, you shouldn't have too many problems if you pack your house with devices that use the open 2.4GHz frequency. Anecdotal evidence suggests that some products—most notably, phones—have created problems for other devices.

Don't sweat the microwave, but don't put your WAP next to it. It may slightly slow down your network while it's running. Try a different channel for your Wi-Fi, and try moving your WAP and antennas around.

If all else fails, you can move your network to 802.11a, which runs on a 5GHz frequency. That'll solve the 2.4-GHz problems—at least, until everybody in the neighborhood moves to 802.11a and crowds that spectrum, too.

Laporte Support

Hacked Wi-Fi

Open Wi-Fi networks can be havens for hackers. If you suspect that someone has hacked your wireless network, you need to take some precautions to protect yourself:

- Shut down your Wi-Fi network.
- Perform a virus scan on your computer to make sure no trojans or viruses are present.
- Install a software firewall on all of your computers. We recommend using ZoneAlarm (www.zonealarm.com).
- Install a firewall on your router. Check your manufacturer's website router for a firmware upgrade that will install a firewall.

Wireless Tips

Transferring from Palm to Pocket PC

To transfer files currently on your Palm desktop, you need another program that's compatible with the Pocket PC. One simple option is Microsoft Outlook (www.microsoft.com/outlook). Just install your Pocket PC, and all the data automatically updates.

Megan recommends using Chapura Pocket Mirror (www.chapura.com) to copy all of your files to Outlook.

Patrick recommends Yahoo (www.yahoo.com). Create a Yahoo! account, synchronize your address book and calendar with the Palm, and then synchronize with the Pocket PC. That's all there is to it!

A viewer suggests using the PocketMirror utility that comes with the Palm. The software transfers your data to Outlook.

August
28

Free Travel Tools for Your PDA

Megan Morrone

"Vacation, all I ever wanted. Vacation having a PDA." Okay, that's not how the song really goes, but I have it out for the Go-Go's. Where was I? Oh yeah, going on vacation with a PDA. Summer is here, so I thought you would like to see my favorite free PDA downloads for summer vacation.

- **FreeCurrency** (www.palmgear.com). This free currency converter offers a simple interface. The zip file also contains the full C++ code for the application.

- **Blocks** (www.palmblvd.com). As far as I'm concerned, it's impossible to survive an overseas flight without Tetris. I like Blocks, a Tetris clone for the PDA that's free.

- **TripPlanner 1.6** (www.palmgear.com). With the increasing popularity of e-tickets, do we still need all those paper itineraries? This simple free app allows you to enter all your necessary travel dates and flight information for easy access.

- **Converter 2.1** (www.palmgear.com). Who wants to do math on vacation? I don't. This handy download allows you to convert measurements, temperatures, and even foreign shoe sizes.

- **TipMe 1.23** (www.palmgear.com). If you're going on vacation, hopefully that means you're also going to go out to dinner. Use this tool to quickly calculate tips.

- **Travel Dictionary, English to Spanish, French, and Italian** (www.trueterm.com). Not surprisingly, this dictionary is huge (1510KB), but if you've got the space and you need to translate, this download is worth a try.

- **Avantgo** (https://avantgo.com). In my opinion, Avantgo is a pale comparison to Vindigo. Avantgo has more ads and a more confusing interface. However, if you're a wireless PDA user, you'll probably appreciate all the instant updates you can get while you're on the road. I've been trying to convince the folks around here that TechTV needs an Avantgo channel. No luck so far, but stay tuned.

Best Tech Travel Toys

Call for Help **staff**

There's nothing that says "summertime" more than filling the car with gas, suitcases, and the kids and heading out on a nice long road trip.

"Are we there yet?" Those famous backseat words can wear down even the most patient parent. That's why it's a good idea to give your kids something other than ice cream to think about while you're driving to the Grand Canyon.

The Interfact Reference Atlas from Two-Can Publishing (www.two-canpublishing.com) features cool maps, photos taken around the world, and 30 hours of games and quizzes that make learning and reading fun.

The Drive Across the Americas (www2.oregonscientific.com) interactive steering wheel from Oregon Scientific connects to your PC and links to interactive software. It gives lessons about geographic and historic landmarks, and even gives driving tips.

Web Tips

Stop Auto Complete

You can stop Internet Explorer from automatically completing forms and field for you.

- In Internet Explorer, click on the Tools menu and select Internet Options.
- Click on the Content tab.
- Click on the AutoComplete button.
- Uncheck Forms.

Read e-Books on Your PDA

Patrick Norton

To read e-books on a PDA, all you need is a reader and some e-books (www.ebooks.com).

The Palm Reader from Peanut Press (www.peanutpress.com) is free for the Palm and Pocket PC, and allows you to read just about any eBook on your PDA.

Now you need something to read. Peanut Press has, 'em, as does Amazon.com (www.amazon.com) and Barnes and Noble (http://ebooks.barnesandnoble.com). It feels a little Microsoft Reader–centric, if you don't dig, but Amazon.com has an excellent selection of e-books. Take a look at the new Raymond Chandler e-books.

Not everything available in print is out on e-book. I'll never know how Amazon.com's search engine came up with *SpongeBob Squarepants* when I searched for Tom Clancy.

Love the classics? Visit the Gutenberg Project (www.gutenberg.org). You'll have to convert them to e-books, but they are way cool. Books from the Modern Library collection (www.peanutpress.com) are also available.

Here are more readers for Palm. (Got a Pocket PC? It should have Microsoft Reader [www.microsoft.com/reader/default.asp] built in, but you don't have to use it):

- **Mobipocket** (www.mobipocket.com)
- **TomeReader** (www.tomeraider.com)
- **Adobe Reader** (www.adobe.com/products/acrobat/readstep2.html)
- **Readers for Palm** (www.the-gadgeteer.com/docreaders-review.html)
- **Memoware** (www.memoware.com)

Before you fire out an email to tell me that paper books aren't dead, don't bother. However, I have yet to own a book that can stash all the works of Shakespeare, Walt Whitman's *Leaves of Grass*, and a few detective novels (just for fun). That's the power of e-books.

Patrick's Tips

Pat's Favorite Palm PDA Games

Want to load up your Palm PDA with some games? Try some of my favorites:

- **Real World BlackJack** (www.freewarepalm.com/games/realworldblackjack.shtml)
- **Kyle's Quest 2** (http://crimsonfire.com)
- **Caverns of Kalisto** (www.freewarepalm.com/games/cavernsofkalisto.shtml)
- **Game of Life** (www.freewarepalm.com/games/aragonpdagameoflife.shtml)
- **Artillery Duel** (www.freewarepalm.com/games/artilleryduel.shtml)
- **IQ3D** (www.freewarepalm.com/games/iq3d.shtml)
- **Lemmings** (www.freewarepalm.com/games/lemmings.shtml)
- **Blocks 1.2** (www.palmblvd.com/software/pc/Blocks-2000-08-31-palm-pc.html)
- **Expresso Run** (www.ziointeractive.com)
- **Donky Kung** (www.ardiri.com)
- **Tiger Woods PGA Tour** Golf (www.ziointeractive.com)

August
30

Web Tips

Have you ever been on a site where the text is too small? Well, you can change that. One way is to use the browser menu to select View, Text Size, and then the size you want. But, if you have a mousewheel, there's an easier way. You can hold down the Ctrl key and scroll down to make the text bigger, hold down Ctrl and scroll up to make the text smaller. Handy, yes?

Laptop Travel Tips

Michelle VonWald

People use laptops to increase mobility—and not just to travel between office and home. Don't be afraid to take your laptop on the road.

Back Up Data

Extreme heat, jostling, vibration, and moisture can damage your notebook, and you could lose data. That's why it's crucial to back up before you travel. Also be sure to leave a copy of your important data at home.

Laptop Transportation Tips

Travel bag: A laptop bag is essential. Although it might be easier to throw your laptop into a purse, it needs protection from jostling. Invest in a bag designed to protect your machine. We like the Pelican Laptop Computer Case 1490CC1 (www.manofrubber.com/pelicomputer.html).

X-ray machines: Despite popular belief, x-ray machines do not damage laptops or data. To be safe, turn off your laptop and make sure the case is properly closed before setting it on the conveyer belt.

Cable locks: The problem with having a lightweight laptop is that it's easy to steal. You can purchase locks and alarms to thwart a potential thief. To use a cable lock, simply wrap the cable around something that can't move (desk, pole, bench) and attach it to your laptop via the security slot. We like the Notebook MicroSaver Security Cable (www.kensington.com/html/1098.html).

Identify your bag: You can also use neon tape or stripes on your laptop's bag for quick identification. If you use an easily identifiable bag, thieves will be discouraged. A lime-green stripe makes your bag easier to identify than all those black bags used by business travelers.

Record the serial number: Before you leave on any trip, record your laptop's serial number in two places. Keep one separated from your laptop, and keep the other at home. If your laptop is stolen, you can give the serial number to the authorities to aid in the search.

Laptop Power Tips

Battery life: When you depend on your notebook, a dead battery turns it into an expensive paperweight. Bring extra batteries, and learn how to increase battery life. TechTV Labs recommends the PowerPad 120 from Electrovaya (www.electrofuel.com). Another alternative is to pick up the iSun (www.isunpower.com), a portable, solar battery charger.

Power strips, adapters, and cords: Bring a power strip in case the hotel room doesn't have one. You still need surge protection on the road. Bring an extra power cord if you'll be traveling in a remote location, in case one is damaged. Vacationing in Europe? Don't forget to purchase an electrical outlet adapter for your laptop, to adjust for the difference in voltage. The Targus Travel Pack (www.targus.com) has easily identifiable adapters to keep you connected all over the world.

Laptop Connection on the Road

Configure settings: If you're traveling abroad, change your dial settings to the country you're visiting. This will stop your modem from searching for a U.S. dial tone and eliminate jet-lag frustration for you.

ISP: Find an ISP that offers free national or international dialup. AOL and EarthLink offer free local access numbers for most of North America and for many countries abroad.

Email: The easiest way to access email while on the road is with a web-based email account such as Yahoo! or Hotmail. Just go online and read your mail on any computer. Otherwise, your POP email configurations on your laptop will still work as long as you connect to the Net. If you require a wireless Internet connection on the road, read "Wireless Internet Access on the Road," on August 16.

Back to School

Megan Morrone

The most popular email question I get is "Is Leo's hair real?" The second most popular email question I get is "What was your major in college and what kind of computer certification classes did you have to take to get your job?" The answer to both questions might surprise you. Let's tackle the second one first. Across the board, we are all largely self-taught. Leo studied Chinese history, Patrick and Martin both have degrees in literature, Morgan majored in rhetoric, and my diploma comes from the creative writing department. We all had early experiences with computers, but our real interests in technology didn't surface until after college. As for the answer to the other question, you'll have to come visit the set and give Leo's steely mane a yank on your own to find out.

I'm embarrassed to say that even though I graduated from college in 1995 (at least ten years after the invention of the Internet), I never surfed the web while I was school. In fact, my only experience with the online world was as a resident advisor (a.k.a. dorm mother). While I was busy trying to make sure the most boisterous and outgoing students on my hall weren't bringing booze back to their dorm rooms, one of the smartest, shyest, and (I had thought) sweetest young freshman boys had Internet access in his room and was secretly charging other students by the hour to come in and surf porn on his dial-up connection. He lived right next door to me, and I had no idea. I don't even remember how he got caught. I didn't even know that you could surf porn on the Internet.

This was the first experience I had with how the lack of knowledge leads to the lack of authority when one person knows more about technology than you do. Now more than ever, the people in the know are children, and the people out of it are their parents and teachers. Kids always think they know more than their parents and their teachers, but when it comes to technology, they often do.

I know that even though there are quite a few older folks out there who know their way around the inside of a PC, the truth is that it's harder to learn and feel comfortable with technology if you didn't grow up with it. Harder, but not impossible. Remember that horrible 1980's Rodney Dangerfield vehicle *Back to School*, in which the over-40 Dangerfield heads back to college and becomes an instant success? Consider this almanac your own version of the movie, only without Robert Downey Jr. and the keg parties.

So whether you're a student or a teacher, a parent or a child, I hope you'll enjoy this month of hints and tips and interesting technology stuff that we've compiled to help even the score between those who know tech and those who don't.

Best Homework Helper Sites

Martin Sargent

When I was in junior high school, I really loved pizza, but man, I hated homework. Maybe if I'd had the Internet to help me with my book learning, homework wouldn't have been such a bummer. If you use any of these sites to plagiarize stuff, I'll hunt you down and give you a fat lip.

- **BigChalk** (www.bigchalk.com). Big Chalk is a massive resource covering every imaginable subject—even if you attend one of those fancy, forward-looking private schools. With more than 100,000 links, it provides resources for students at every grade level, elementary through high school.

- **BJ Pinchbeck's Homework Helper** (www.discoveryschool.com). BJ Pinchbeck (his friends call him "Beege") is 14 years old. In 1996, with the help of his dad, this homework wizard started a collection of homework links at www.bjpinchbeck.com. Today it resides at DiscoverySchool.com (a great site in its own right) and includes more than 700 links for everything from math to gym class.

- **Multnomah County Library** (www.multnomah.lib.or.us/lib/homework/index.html). The librarians in Multnomah County, Oregon, do an amazing job of bringing together homework resources. Tap into this no-frills topical guide for sites on everything from animals to social issues. The library also provides helpful advice on evaluating websites and using search engines.

- **Jiskha Homework Help** (www.jiskha.com). Don't ask me what a jiskha is, but go ahead and ask your homework questions at Jiskha Homework Help. The homework help forums are a wonderful resource with interesting articles covering an extensive range of subjects.

- **Help from the Big Guys** (http://school.aol.com/main_sub/explore_subject.adp). You don't need an AOL account to use this stellar homework resource. Choose your grade and subject, and you'll receive a list of helpful resources.

- **Yahoo's Yahooligans** division (www.yahooligans.com/School_Bell/) also offers an extensive directory of sites you can use to research your projects.

- **Cool and Useful Student Resources** (www.teleport.com/~burrell/). Jenna Burrell designed this site for high school students. It's easy to navigate and covers a broad spectrum of topics. Burrell gives a brief description of each site and ranks them according to their quantity and quality of information.

The Bookmobile: Digital Library on Wheels

Josh Lawrence

The Internet Archive's Bookmobile (www.archive.org) is a traveling book factory. The Ford Aerostar van is stocked with four laptops, two HP printers, a Fastback Model 8 binder (www.fastback.com), a manual cutter, and a MotoSat (www.motosat.com) satellite dish on the roof.

The Bookmobile travels to schools, libraries, and retirement homes to let people print copies of public-domain books. The texts are downloaded from the Internet via the satellite dish and printed on the spot for free. The Internet Archive's aim is to create a vast online library with free access to one and all, and the Bookmobile is a real-world traveling extension of this goal. Be sure to browse the Internet Archive site (www.archive.org/index.php).

Free e-Books by Great Women Writers

Megan Morrone

I've heard all the complaints from people who don't like reading lengthy texts online or on a PDA. Frankly, I agree. I've spent years arguing that nothing beats the weight of a book in your hand, the smell of the paper, and the sensation of turning the pages. Nothing? How about if that "nothing" happens to be free?

Selected texts by women:

- The Works of Louisa May Alcott (includes *Little Women*) (http://readroom.ipl.org)
- *Frankenstein* and *Valperga*, by Mary Shelly (www.bibliomania.com/0/0/43/frameset.html)
- *Uncle Tom's Cabin*, by Harriet Beecher Stowe (www.bibliomania.com/0/0/48/91)
- *The Age of Innocence* and *The Moving Finger*, by Edith Wharton (www.bibliomania.com/0/0/56/frameset.html)
- Early short stories by Virginia Woolf (www.bartleby.com/85/)

Collections:

- Electronic Text Center's e-Books by Women Writers (http://etext.lib.virginia.edu/ebooks/subjects/subjects-women.html)
- A Celebration of Women Writers (http://digital.library.upenn.edu/women/)
- Project Gutenberg (search by author) (www.gutenberg.net/)

Excerpts from popular fiction by women:

- From *The Girl's Guide to Hunting and Fishing*, by Melissa Bank (www.bookbrowse.com/index.cfm?page=title&titleID=13&view=excerpt)
- From *Prodigal Summer*, by Barbara Kingsolver (www.ivillage.com/books/excerpt/fict/articles/0,11872,240801_192349,00.html)
- From *In America*, by Susan Sontag (www.ivillage.com/books/excerpt/fict/articles/0,11872,240801_99108,00.html)
- From *Back When We Were Grownups*, by Anne Tyler (www.ivillage.com/books/excerpt/fict/articles/0,11872,240801_250782,00.html)

Jurassic Park, the Institute

Nicole Carrico

You read the book. You saw the movies. Now, thanks in no small part to the contributions of Bob Bakker, you can visit the Institute. Established in October 2001 by Universal Studios and Amblin Entertainment, Jurassic Park Institute (JPI) aims to combine all forms of media to create the most exciting, dynamic forum for dinosaur entertainment, study, and research the world has ever known.

With the launch of Jurassic Park Institute Online (www.jpinstitute.com), JPI has taken the first step toward its stated goal "to provide kids, families, educators, and scientists with the ultimate resource for dinosaur learning and fun."

Dino Master

Bakker is uniquely qualified to assist the Institute. This world-renowned dinosaur expert is credited with bringing to prominence the idea that dinosaurs were warm-blooded. One of his recent projects attempted to re-create the booming bleat of a brontosaurus.

In addition to his scientific work, Bakker wrote *Raptor Red*, a fictional account of the life of a Utahraptor. Another recent project is the Institute's new online resource for educators known as Dino Lab (www.jpinstitute.com/dinolab/).

Address: Site of the Night

Girls Go Tech

The Girl Scouts of America are on a campaign to bridge the "techno-gender" divide. See www.girlscouts.org/girlsgotech/.

Digital Encyclopedias

Ray Weigel

When I was growing up, my family had a set of 1973 World Book Encyclopedias on the bookshelf in the living room. I would dig through the pages to look up everything from "ant colony" to "zebras." The books had transparent pages with cut-away images showing how different systems of the body are laid out.

Today's encyclopedias come on DVD or CD instead of hefty books. They offer the following:

- Multimedia components such as images, video, sound clips, and maps are everywhere.

- High-end versions include an entire reference suite with dictionaries, atlases, and research tools.

- They're often less expensive than hard-cover encyclopedia sets.

Software

Microsoft's Encarta Reference Library is generally considered to be the premier disc-based encyclopedia. This suite includes a wide breadth of information, has a pretty interface, and is well designed. But it should be considered a starting place for discovering information about a subject.

Encarta contains simplistic articles with loads of basic information. However, material is lacking for anything more than a high school report. Use it in conjunction with periodicals, newspaper articles, and other online sources, and you'll have a total research solution.

Free Online Encyclopedias

Most free Internet encyclopedias revolve around specific topics, such as Stanford's Encyclopedia of Philosophy (`http://plato.stanford.edu`), sniggle.net: The Culture Jammer's Encyclopedia (`www.sniggle.net`), and Encyclopedia Mythica (`www.pantheon.org`). But a few free resources might be of more help to high school and college students.

- **Bartleby.com** (`www.bartleby.com`) is a place to find great books online. Get free quotes and poetry.

- **Encyclopedia.com**
  (`http://encyclopedia.com`) is eLibrary's free cousin and the hip version of the *Columbia Encyclopedia*, sixth edition, online. It's written for high school and college students. You don't get as much as you would from eLibrary, but it has informative encyclopedia articles on a wide variety of subjects.

- **Abyz Web Links**
  (`www.abyznewslinks.com`) provides links to more than 18,200 news sources from around the world.

- **Infoplease** (`www.infoplease.com`) has a collection of fun and crazy facts.

Pay Online Encyclopedias

Pay-to-play online encyclopedias are often Internet versions of printed books. Subscription-based online encyclopedias cost more than CD or DVD encyclopedias, but you won't have to install any software.

- **World Book Online**
  (`www.worldbookonline.com`) includes every article from its 22-volume print encyclopedia and 9,500 pictures. A thousand documents are added every month. A subscription is $49.95 a year.

- **eLibrary** (`http://ask.elibrary.com`) helps you keep up on what's happening in the world. At $79.95 a year, eLibrary is pricey, but you get access to a database full of magazine and newspaper articles, as well as transcripts of radio and television news shows.

With a combination of disc-based encyclopedias and Internet encyclopedias, you'll have a reference combination suitable for a master's student at Harvard.

Unlock Mysteries of the Deep

Nicole Guilfoyle

The depths of the world's oceans are shrouded in mystery—mysteries the scientists and engineers at the Monterey Bay Aquarium Research Institute (MBARI) are working to reveal. Paul R. McGill, electrical engineer at MBARI, discussed the institute, its projects, and the new technology improving underwater exploration.

Monterey Bay is one of the most biologically diverse bodies of water in the world. It's bisected by the Monterey Canyon, with depths up to 3,600 meters. Researchers need a sharp mind and sturdy technology to brave the ocean's hazards, including underwater tremors, volcanic activity, and water pressure. MBARI's research vessels and data-collection methods use technology (and engineers) to keep scientists relatively safe from these dangers.

MBARI has more than 50 projects on its list of current projects (www.mbari.org/rd/projects/2003/2003_current_projects.html), encompassing ocean science, marine biology, ecology, chemistry, and geology. Items on the list range from a submarine volcanism project tracking how oceanic volcanoes form and change, to developing new ways to interpret data gathered from remotely operated vehicles (ROVs).

For example, hundreds of earthquakes occur just off the California coastline every day. Pressurized underwater seismometers lodged in the seafloor record each one. Other devices measure ocean currents and log data. But most interesting of all (for the average person) is the launch of an ROV.

ROVs

MBARI operates two ROVs, Tiburon and Ventana. These unmanned vessels are connected to a support ship that controls them. The ROVs can perform experiments, collect data, maintain underwater instruments, and even record what they see.

"The ROV has a camera and the camera is taking video footage in the deep ocean," said Debbie Nail Meyer, MBARI communications coordinator, in an interview with "Tech Live's" David Stevenson. "It's then transmitted up the fiber-optic line that's within the tether that connects the ROV to the ship. Once on the ship the video is then transmitted over an invisible microwave link to a high point here on the [Monterey] peninsula. There are microwave transmitters [there] that send it back to MBARI."

If you're interested in finding out what the ships are doing right now, visit MBARI's "Where Are the Ships?" page (www.mbari.org/cruises/both.asp).

Twisted List

School Supplies

Megan Morrone

Don't go back to school without these websites:

- **ReadPlease** (www.readplease.com). Why read when you can listen? You can download this text-to-speech software for free.

- **Student's Guide to MLA Style** (www.docstyles.com). A must for every high school or college student.

- **Chicago Manual of Style** (www.press.uchicago.edu). Another must for every high school or college student.

- **LiveJournal** (www.livejournal.com). Start a weblog so your friends and family can keep up with you. LiveJournal is great for teens and college students.

- **Digital Blasphemy Wallpaper** (www.digitalblasphemy.com). Impress your school chums with cool new wallpaper for your PC or Mac.

September
4

John Conway's Game of Life

Dave Roos

Now that mathematician John Nash has opened the Oscar door for eccentric Princeton number crunchers, someone should make a movie about John H. Conway, theoretical math whiz and inventor of the game of Life.

Rules of the Game

No, Conway didn't invent Life, the board game. Blame that one on Hasbro. Conway's game is a simple mathematical exercise with potentially broad applications in the fields of science and technology.

Life (www.bitstorm.org/gameoflife) is a lot like Mine Sweeper, the addictive Windows time waster. The Life game is played on a grid separated into individual cells, like graph paper.

The game is based around three simple rules that dictate the behavior of the cells in the grid. A player begins by filling in certain cells and leaving others empty. An empty cell is called "dead," and a filled-in cell is called "live."

When a cell is established as dead or live, it must play by Conway's three rules:

1. **Birth.** A dead cell with exactly three live neighbors becomes a live cell. This means that if an empty cell on the grid is touching three filled-in cells (diagonals included), it must be filled in as well.

2. **Survival.** A live cell with two or three live neighbors stays alive.

3. **Overcrowding and loneliness.** In all other cases, a cell dies or remains dead. This means that if a dead cell is touching fewer than three live cells, or a live cell is touching fewer than two other live cells, they must die.

Just Play It

This all sounds very confusing on paper, but computer programmers have put Conway's rules in code, creating software that automatically generates the game's self-replicating patterns.

Either draw your own patterns or select from the drop-down menu of predrawn grids. Life enthusiasts have discovered hundreds of starting patterns that spawn beautiful and chaotic results.

What's the Big Deal?

Life is more than a game. Conway's discovery single-handedly launched the field of cellular automata, the study of systems in which simple rules are applied to create complex results. Scientists hope that such theories of "emergent complexity" can one day help us understand the ultra-complex rules that dictate evolution.

By starting with the simplest system, such as Conway's game of Life, scientists and mathematicians can begin to build a framework for isolating and modeling the seemingly random patterns of nature.

Download of the Day

WinGlobe

Megan Morrone

According to a recent National Geographic magazine study, 65% of Americans between the ages of 18 and 24 can't locate France on a world map; 29% can't locate the Pacific Ocean; and a sad, sad 11% can't even locate the United States.

Don't be part of the geographically illiterate. Check out WinGlobe (www.djuga.net/winglobe.html), an interactive globe for your Windows desktop. Click anywhere on the globe to see the name of the country or city, the local time, the population, and the weather.

WinGlobe is free to try and $15 to buy.

September
5

Our Expanding Universe

Nicole Carrico

Picture yourself standing on the surface of a balloon. Now imagine that the balloon is slowly inflating beneath you. As the surface area increases, the balloon expands in all directions away from you at once, giving you the impression of being at the center. Now imagine taking five steps in any direction. The perception remains the same. Regardless of your position on the balloon, that position appears to be the central point of this expansion.

Dr. Donald Goldsmith is co-writer of PBS's series *The Astronomers* and NOVA's *Is Anybody Out There?*, and is the author of numerous books. He uses this analogy to describe our position in an expanding universe. Astronomers, including Edwin Hubble, have observed the relative distances of faraway galaxies and noted that the farther away galaxies are, the more rapidly they appear to be expanding. Does this mean Earth is the center of the universe? As much as we may like to believe this, cosmology takes the view that the perception on any other planet would be identical. Like the balloon, every point in the universe is moving away from every other point simultaneously, ever increasing the boundaries of space.

Dark Energy

Astronomers used to believe that the universe would eventually stop expanding and begin to contract due to gravity's attractive force. New theories, however, indicate a counterforce to gravity called dark energy.

According to Dr. Goldsmith, dark energy exists in very small quantities throughout the universe, but those amounts are increasing as the universe expands. The fight between gravity and dark energy is relatively even while our universe is young, but as expansion increases and more dark energy is created, it is believed that gravity will begin to lose the battle.

Intriguing Space Websites

- **Astronomy Picture of the Day** (http://antwrp.gsfc.nasa.gov/apod/astropix.html)
- **Bad Astronomy in Movies** (www.badastronomy.com)
- **Search for Extraterrestrial Intelligence** (www.seti.org)
- **Sun, Moon, Stars** (www.infoplease.com/spot/sunmoonjul02.html)
- **Planets Around Other Stars** (www.exoplanets.org)

Download of the Day

WeatherPop and Meteorologist

Megan Morrone

The weather outside is frightful, but the fire is so delightful. And how do I know this? Because I use a Mac. Here are two programs that will display the current weather conditions on your OS X desktop. One is free, and one is free to try but $8 to buy.

By all accounts, Meteorologist (the free program) by Humongous Elephants and Tigers is a rip-off of WeatherPop from Glucose. They both show the current weather. I think WeatherPop (www.glu.com/products/weatherpop) has a better-looking interface, but Meteorologist (www.apple.com/downloads) does have a few extra features that I like. Both WeatherPop and Meteorologist display the weather on your menu bar; only WeatherPop displays weather in your Dock.

September

6

Top Five Myths About Women and Technology

Morgan Webb

Myth no. 1: Women tend to be right-brained, but technology is a logical, left-brain field.

A variation of this myth: Women aren't good at math or science because of biological differences. A speaker repeating this myth might not believe it to be true in all cases. But this same speaker will likely think, as a general rule, that women aren't as good at or interested in science because their brains are different from men's.

These beliefs are perpetuated in many forms, from books that spout the inevitability of gender difference to glossy documentaries using scientific statistics to prove that it's neurologically more difficult for men to do housework. Sound ridiculous? Read the documentary *Why Men Don't Iron*, at www.frif.com/new99/whymen.html.

I agree that women's brains are different from men's, and I appreciate people's efforts to explore and explain prevailing social trends in new ways. However, you can find a wide range of conclusions from the same comparative studies of male and female cognition.

This is an emotional issue for everyone involved, and a single set of data can solicit widely different conclusions that reflect the prejudice of the interpreter.

In any case, when we're talking about the women in our own lives—our sisters, mothers, and daughters—scientific explanations and limitations become meaningless and even offensive. The belief that women are biologically less logical than men serves to perpetuate rather than explain unfortunate social trends. If we accept the under-representation of women in scientific fields as an unavoidable result of biology, we're less likely to support programs and movements that could encourage a significant female presence in these industries.

When it comes down to it, I don't believe that there's a significant enough difference between the brains of men and women to biologically hinder women from success in any field in which men excel.

Myth no. 2: There aren't many women in the technology field because women have lives.

The field of technology is a complicated one, and it takes a lot of dedication to program for eight hours, add blue LEDs to your case fan, and then squeeze in a four-hour session of EverQuest before dozing off to *Star Trek: Voyager* in late-night syndication.

Yes, in general, women do have lives, with work, kids, the supermarket, good friends, and dinner parties. It's true, women have lives—but so do men. Many male fans of *The Screen Savers* are in the technology field, and I'm willing to bet that most of them get up in the morning and shower, take coffee breaks with their co-workers, and then go home and see friends and girlfriends and wives. They pick up their kids from school and watch T-ball games on Saturday afternoons. They go out on Saturday nights, and when they speak of their latest exploits, most of the time they're not talking about computers.

Address: Site of the Night

Viewing the World from Space

To see the world from a new perspective, take a look at http://terraserver.microsoft.com.

Top Five Myths About Women and Technology (continued)

Myth no. 3: Women aren't into hardware and gadgets.

We all know plenty of men who don't know what SCSI stands for, can't tell an AGP from an ISSA, and aren't aware of the horrifying limitations of integrated video. There are a lot of men and women alike who are interested in computers only as far as computers are implements for simple business utilities, email, and entertainment.

As for gadgets, sometimes women (and men, too, for that matter) realize that an electric light-up thing-a-ma-bob is gimmicky for the sake of being gimmicky and is not particularly useful. If it's useful, males should take a minute to show us why it's cool and let us explore it ourselves. It's hard to be interested in gadgets when our husbands/brothers/boyfriends are ripping them out of our hands and jumping up and down with excitement. Sometimes it takes a little while to get used to a gadget and integrate it into our lives. Some women aren't interested in the intricacies of Crusoe processors. Women are just as apt as men to eschew technology for other interests. Some women don't like makeup, and some men don't like baseball.

Myth no. 4: Women are just starting to break into the tech industry.

Women helped build the tech industry, although they often don't get the credit they deserve. You can read about some prominent women in the history of technology and mathematics at www.cs.yale.edu/homes/tap/past-women.html.

The ENIAC was the first electronic, general-purpose computer. It was built to calculate ballistics trajectories during World War II. These complex calculations had previously been made by a group of 80 female mathematicians. When the ENIAC was built, it needed to be programmed, and who came to the call? Six women: Ruth Teitelbaum, Kay Mauchley

Antonelli, Betty Holberton, Jean Bartik, Frances Spence, and Marlyn Meltzer. These women were the first computer programmers in the world (they were called "computers"), and although they were forgotten for some time, they've been recently recognized for their contributions to computing.

Myth no. 5: There aren't many women in the technology industry.

This is true. There aren't many women in technology. Women account for only 9% of engineers and 26% of computer scientists (U.S. Department of Commerce). Women received 37% of the degrees for undergraduate computer science in 1984. Today they receive, on average, 20% (National Council for Research on Women, Wow Facts). Where there are women in technology fields, they earn less than men across the board (sometimes up to $10,000 less). Perhaps it's a lack of role models, unfavorable perceptions of the IT field (nerdy, unattractive, and antisocial), or any number of other factors. No matter what we think is the cause, women are undeniably under-represented in the field of science and technology.

References and Further Reading

- **Women in Technology International** (www.witi.com)
- **National Council for Research on Women** (www.ncrw.org)
- **Tech Divas** (www.techdivas.com)
- **Expanding Women's Role in Science and Technology**, U.S. Department of Commerce (www.ta.doc.gov/speeches/techwomn.htm)
- **Wow Facts, Women in Technology** (www.ewowfacts.com)
- **More on the female ENIAC programmers** (www.witi.org)

September
8

Home Workshop Tips: Beginning Experiments

Yoshi DeHerrera

If you're not familiar with the inner workings of your beloved high-tech devices, fixing them may seem impossible. I'll let you in on a little secret: Anyone can learn how to fix electronic devices. Electronics, like anything else, is something you have to learn, so start with the basics. With the Internet as your library, you have access to all the information you'll need. Here are some links to information and kits that will start you on your way:

- **Basic Electronics** (`http://ourworld.compuserve.com`). This is a very good source for learning basic electronics. The page was made by Graham Knott, an electronics teacher at Cambridge Regional College in England. He describes in clear language electronic components and theory, and he provides skill exercises and projects. I recommend reading all the pages here and trying some of the experiments.

- **Electronics Hobbyist** (`www.amasci.com`). Here's a good collection of links. The newsgroups are particularly useful. A great deal of the time, you can find what you're looking for by browsing the existing posts. If that doesn't work, post a question; it has a good chance of being answered. Do searches for other newsgroups that deal with electronics. There are tons of them.

- **Educational kits/projects and science links** (`http://kitsrus.com`). I sampled four of these kits. They explain the electronic theory behind each kit, keeping the language simple and easy to understand. These kits are well suited for those with little electronic knowledge or for first-timers.

- **JCM Inventures** (`www.jcminventures.com`). They have "Cybug Robot Kits" for making robotic ecosystems.

- Also visit the **Robot Room** (`www.robotroom.com`).

Windows Tips

Windows' Hidden Scientific Calculator

Morgan Webb

Use your calculator for more than just a little addition and subtraction.

Unearth the Scientific Calculator

1. Open your calculator in the Accessories menu, or you can go to Start, Run and type **calc**. Pretty basic, right?

2. Go to the View menu and choose Scientific.

Bam! You get exponents, sine and cosine, a statistical calculator, a hex editor, a binary calculator (you can kiss the days of Xoring by hand goodbye), and much more.

Windows' standard calculator is great for everyday calculations, but when you want to get down and dirty with the numbers, open the scientific view for some high-quality calculations.

Address: Site of the Night

Space Store

Space Store (`www.spacestore.com`) is your no. 1 store for NASA action figures and funky Apollo patches.

High-Resolution Camera for Mars

Josh Lawrence

We're going back to Mars. Well, not us personally, but thanks to Dr. Virginia Gulick, a research scientist at NASA's Ames Research Center at Moffett Field, we're going to get a taste of the red planet. Gulick talked about her work on the next Mars Reconnaissance Orbiter mission (www.jpl.nasa.gov/missions/future/mars2005andbeyond.html) and the Marsoweb website (http://marsoweb.nas.nasa.gov).

Photographing Mars

Gulick is part of the instrument team for the HiRISE high-resolution camera that will go on board the 2005 Orbiter mission. This camera will allow high-resolution color pictures of the planet's surface to be taken for the first time. Also, the high resolution will be able to see more topography up close and in far greater detail than before, scout out future landing sites, and see previous Mars landers that failed (for example, the Mars polar lander that went missing in 1998).

You can get technical facts and specs for the HiRISE camera at http://hirise.lpl.arizona.edu/.

Virtual Mars Online

The HiRISE camera will spawn its own website when it goes online in 2005, but for now, you can get a look at Mars online via the Marsoweb website (http://marsoweb.nas.nasa.gov). You can get VRML 3D perspective views of Mars and navigate interactive maps (http://marsoweb.nas.nasa.gov/dataViz) of possible landing sites.

Also be sure to visit the Mars clickworker experiment (http://clickworkers.arc.nasa.gov/top), where your mouse clicks can help the study of Mars.

Explore Other Countries: Get Ready for a Multicultural Adventure

Cat Schwartz

Before you try to help the world, travel, or look up info about countries for school, get to know what a country is all about. I found a great site for our overseas viewers, as well as U.S. viewers interested in exploring other cultures.

Surprise, surprise, the Central Intelligence Agency (yes, the CIA) keeps tabs on everything going on in countries around the world. Luckily, the all-encompassing *World Fact Book* (www.cia.gov/cia/publications/factbook) isn't on a secret list of confidential documents.

Use the drop-down menu at the top of the page to search for information about more than 100 countries. Here's what you'll find if you click past the basic information and go deeper into the site:

- History of the country
- Frequently updated maps of each country and its cities
- Population numbers
- Type of government
- Media and methods of communication
- Transportation systems
- Military status
- Political issues
- Economic background and status

Keep the entire publication handy offline by downloading the .zip file available at www.cia.gov/cia/download.html.

Quake Hunters

Nicole Carrico

According to old wives' tales, the best way to predict an earthquake is to pay attention to your pets. Animals are said to behave strangely in the hours before a seismic disturbance; birds call out in the dead of night, horses become restless, and the ever-practical ferrets focus on protecting their valuables.

For those of us not lucky enough to cohabitate with clairvoyant critters, there is the Berkeley Seismological Laboratory (BSL). This Organized Research Unit of UC Berkeley has a history of quake tracking that dates back to 1887. Now focused primarily on geophysical monitoring, earthquake information dissemination, and education and outreach, the lab wields a dazzling array of high-tech instruments to predict the arrival of seismic waves. In addition, it employs broadband and the Internet to keep the public informed.

Tools for Earthquake Tracking

- **The Berkeley Seismological Laboratory** website (www.seismo.berkeley.edu/seismo) includes comprehensive information on goals and initiatives of the BSL, as well as an exhaustive collection of links.

- **The U.S. Geological Survey** (www.usgs.gov) offers up-to-the-minute maps of recent earthquake activity in the United States.

- To investigate any quake on Earth, try the **Advanced National Seismic System's Global Earthquake Catalog** (http://quake.geo.berkeley.edu).

- Get updates on seismic disturbances sent directly to your inbox by subscribing to the **Earthquake Notification Mailing Lists** (http://quake.usgs.gov).

- Geek out entirely and **Make Your Own Seismogram** (http://quake.geo.berkeley.edu/bdsn/make_seismogram.html).

Windows Tips

Make Fractions in MS Word

Morgan Webb

Microsoft Word deals with fractions in a strange way. If you type "1/2," it changes to ½, but if you type "2/3," it remains 2/3. Not only is that not consistent form (which, by definition, is bad form), but the poor, neglected fractions look unprofessional. The solution isn't straightforward, but there is a simple way to get around this problem.

First, go to Tools and then AutoCorrect. Select the AutoFormat tab. Now uncheck Fractions 1/2 with Fraction Character ½. This stops Word from changing the format of some fractions and not others. Next, decide how you want to make fractions. You can use a complicated system of subscript and superscript letters, or you can use the fraction maker:

1. While in a Word document, hit Ctrl+F9. You should get some bold braces highlighted in gray.

2. While inside these braces, type **eq\f(x,y)** where **x** is the numerator and **y** is the denominator.

3. Press Shift+F9 while inside the braces. This changes the equation into a nice fraction. If you don't type the formula correctly, you'll get an error message. Try it again.

How do you like your new fraction? I admit that the system is a little clunky, but now that you have your nice fraction, you can use Word AutoCorrect to autocorrect it every time:

1. Highlight your new fraction.

2. Go to Tools and then AutoCorrect.

3. Your new fraction should be in the Replace With field. Add your fraction (x/y) into the field to be replaced.

Now every time you type 1/7, for example, it'll turn into a fraction with the numerator over the denominator.

Build Famous Robots

Roman Loyola and David Roos

Robot building has evolved from the side project of devoted modelers to a popular hobby of enthusiastic science-fiction fans. Because of the availability and affordability of parts and tools, everyone can have their own R2-D2 or Robby the Robot. Interested in making your own famous robot? Visit the following sites for information, parts, designs, instructions, and more.

- **B9** (www.banzai.net/jeffbot). Also known as the Will Robinson robot from *Lost in Space.*
- **B9 Club** (www.b9robotbuildersclub.com). Community of B9 creators.
- **Robby the Robot** (www.the-robotman.com/ nv_fs.html). The robot from the movie *Forbidden Planet.*
- **R2-D2** (www.robotbuilders.net/r2). The spunky droid from *Star Wars.*
- **Drones from *Silent Running*** (www.robotbuilders.net/droneroom). Huey, Duey, and Luie from the 1971 movie.
- **Starship Modeler** (www.starshipmodeler.com). Website for science-fiction and space scale.

Address: ## Site of the Day

Making Helicopters Do Crazy Things

Josh Lawrence

MIT's Information Control Engineering Group likes to make helicopters do things they normally shouldn't, such as repeated acrobatic flips, loops, and rolls in midflight.

Get videos, photos, and information on the hardware inside the helicopter at the Information Control Engineering Group website (http://gewurtz.mit.edu/research/heli.htm).

Download of the Day

Workman Paper Airplanes

Megan Morrone

I hear a lot of praise for the paperless office these days. Sure, it's good for the trees. But if you think about it, a paperless office leads to a paper airplane–less office. And what does that lead to? No fun.

My husband teaches at a high school where the kids all have laptops. They often take tests and write papers on their iBooks and then email them to my husband. After he grades them, he emails them back. So, if he gives them a grade they don't like, they can't turn it into a paper airplane and throw it at him when his back is turned. That's simply wrong.

Thankfully, the fun of paper airplanes hasn't disappeared entirely. To promote its books on paper-airplane design, Workman Publishing (www.workman.com) has an online paper-airplane simulator. All you need is a simple Flash plug-in, and you can hone your paper-airplane design skills by adjusting the angle, thrust, and elevation of the plane. Click on the Launch button, and the distance, altitude, revolutions, and time aloft are all measured for you.

Visit the Workman Flight Simulator

The Macromedia Flash plug-in should install automatically. If it doesn't, grab it at www.macromedia.com.

When you've been cleared for flight, Workman also lets you download a few paper-airplane designs. If you can find a piece of paper, you can even print them and fly them yourself. Just make sure your teacher (or boss) has his or her back turned. You can download paper airplanes at www.workman.com/fliersclub/download.html.

All Aboard the Blimp

Morgan Webb and Cat Schwartz

Don't call it a dirigible. This baby is a Lightship. The Sanyo Lightship (www.sanyo.com/aboutsanyo/ blimp.cfm) is the first blimp of its size capable of glowing in the night sky, thanks to its two 1,000-watt metal halide bulbs and a semitransparent envelope. In its five-year existence, the Lightship has traveled more than 70,000 miles to 31 cities and carried more than 10,000 passengers. Have you ever been in a blimp? It's strange. The ride was smooth as silk, but our captain said that on warmer days, currents of rising air make the blimp drift up and down as if it's riding ocean waves.

Lightship Specs

Length: 165 feet

Height: 55 feet

Width: 46 feet

Volume: 148,300 cubic feet

Gas: Nonflammable helium

Cabin length: 15.7 feet

Passenger seats: Nine

Restrooms: None (and no quick landings, either)

Engines: Two Lycoming IO-360 direct-drive, four-cylinder, fuel-injected, horizontally opposed, air-cooled engines. Propellers are 65-inches in diameter.

Max speed: 65 mph

Max altitude: 10,000 feet

For more specs from Sanyo, go to www.sanyo.com/aboutsanyo/blimp_about.cfm.

September

13

Learn how blimps work at HowStuffWorks (www.howstuffworks.com/blimp.htmwork).

The Blimpcam

Each Lightship has a designated onboard camera operator. The fully digital video camera sends signals to a microwave dish on the ground that provides live feeds to all sorts of sporting events, from drag races to football games.

Sanyo brags that the blimpcam can zoom down to focus on a single blade of grass and is often the first to find lost golf balls. Of course, the blimpcam is most famous for its panoramic aerial shots.

Fun Facts

- The Lightship's 17-member crew—pilot, camera operator, and ground crew—travel with the blimp year-round.

- Fewer people are trained and qualified to fly a Lightship than to fly the Space Shuttle. The Lightship's pilot, Stephen Tomlin, has been flying blimps for the past 14 years.

- The Sanyo Lightship was the first blimp to host a wedding, in November 1999.

Check the Sanyo site for more fun facts (www.sanyo.com/aboutsanyo/ blimp_funfacts.cfm).

Download of the Day

Talkany

Nicole Carrico

Let's face it. Sitting alone all day in front of a computer terminal takes a toll on your social skills. After spending a month chained to his hard drive and deprived of human interaction, even the irrepressible Leo Laporte has lost some of his pronunciation and enunciation skills.

Luckily, Megan Morrone tracked down Talkany (www.confound.com/programs), a free download available at Confound.com. Not only can you put words in your PC's mouth, but you also can select from such variables as personality, pitch, speed, and even vocal effort. Want to hear a woman sing out your name in breathy tones? Then Talkany is the tool for you.

Organize Your Send To Folder

Morgan Webb

Nothing streamlines the computing process like a well-oiled Send To menu. When you right-click a file, one of your options is called Send To, and in the expanding menu that originates from it, you have the option to send your file to a number of applications or locations on your computer.

Find That Folder

The contents of that menu correlate to the contents of a folder on your system, not surprisingly named Send To. This folder can be found in different places according to your version of Windows, but you can do a search for the folder and you should see it immediately.

In Windows 98, you can find the file in the C:\Windows directory. In Windows XP, you'll find it in C:\Documents and Settings\User. The Send To folder is hidden by default in Windows XP, so you might have to go to Tools, Folder Options, Show Hidden Files and Folders. If you don't find it immediately, keep looking. You definitely have one.

Get It Organized

Once you have located your Send To folder, examine its contents. You will see that it reflects the contents of your right-click Send To menu.

The first thing you need to do is clear out all that junk in there from the 15 applications that added icons of their own volition (I hate that). Go ahead and delete what you don't use, because these are just shortcuts, not the applications themselves. Now that you have found your Send To folder and cleaned out the dead wood, you can customize it. You can add additional folders within the Send To folder to hold groups of applications, such as a multimedia folder, or audio.

If you do a lot of image manipulation, your multimedia folder could contain shortcuts to Adobe Photoshop and Microsoft Paint, so you could right-click an image file and choose which editing application suits your needs.

The audio folder could contain shortcuts to some of your favorite audio player or audio-manipulation software.

You could make a word-processing folder to send your text files to Notepad, Word, or some other text editor, depending on your specific needs.

Only you know how you use your computer and what you need in your Send To menu, but with some folders and a little organization, you can tailor your Send To menu to suit your needs.

Download of the Day

Jefferson 1.1b5

Megan Morrone

You may have already heard of Thomas (http://thomas.loc.gov/home/thomas2.html), the legislative database on the Internet. Thanks to Fritz Anderson for creating an easier and more user-friendly way to track Congressional bills straight from your OS X desktop.

Jefferson lets you search by bill, subject, or sponsor and brings up detailed information. Is this the perfect download for everyone? No. But if you're a law student, it's a godsend. And after all, the government is keeping tabs on you. Shouldn't you be keeping tabs on it?

Jefferson is for Mac OS X only. If you use Windows, you can still search the Thomas site. Also try GovernMail (www.governmail.com), a free utility that lets you connect with government representatives.

September
14

Address: Site of the Night

The Museum of Hoaxes

Debunk popular myths and urban legends from the past and present at The Museum of Hoaxes (www.museumofhoaxes.com).

Getting Schooled in Videogames

David Stevenson

Imagine turning your passion for Pac-Man into a college degree. More schools nationwide offer video-gaming studies.But these programs aren't all fun and games. At The Art Institutes—which recently launched one of the nation's only accredited Bachelor of Science degrees in video game art and design at its Phoenix, Los Angeles, and San Francisco locations—students take a heady mix of art courses, computer programming, physics, college algebra, and cultural studies.

"We're looking for students who have a passion for games, because that part of the passion then will leap back into their art and get them through college," says Mary Clarke-Miller, an academic department director at The Art Institutes. "This is a very serious program."

The DigiPen Institute of Technology in Washington also offers a bachelor's degree in game programming.The goal of that program, as well as The Art Institutes', is to produce top-notch game designers. And insiders say this fast-growing industry can use the fresh talent.

In 2001, gaming companies sold $9.4 billion worth of consoles and games, according to the NPD Group.That's $1 billion more than Hollywood took in at the box office last year. That means these gaming classes can prove both creative and lucrative for graduates. On average, game developers make about $61,000 a year, according to the International Game Developers Association. But does a degree or certification in gaming design guarantee a job? Not necessarily, says Konami producer Michael McHale, but it certainly can't hurt. "Anyone with an education is [going to] have a leg up on anyone else, but that education should be augmented by things you're doing outside of school," McHale says. "You should be looking at a lot of games; you should be trying to create your own models and textures and artwork."

LucasArts Entertainment designer Joseph "Jerril" Yoo, who teaches character animation for The Art Institutes in San Francisco, says this kind of course will eventually breed a better gaming experience.

"We'll get talent who are stronger, [and] we'll produce hopefully better content and also better design because of the training,"Yoo says.

Download of the Day

Wake Up to Your PC

Megan Morrone

College. It was the best of times. It was the worst of times. The best of times? You didn't have class until noon. The worst of times? Days you had class at 8:30 a.m. Seriously, could you be expected to remember to reset your alarm clock accordingly? I didn't think so.

Thanks to a kid named Vinod, you don't have to. He's created the College Alarm Clock (www.geocities.com/vinodtandon/cac).This PC clock lets you set different wake-up times for each day of the week. And instead of annoying beeping sounds, you can wake to music from your very own CDs or MP3s.The College Alarm Clock doesn't just launch music. If you need programs to launch at certain times on certain days, this free utility can do that, too.

Address: Site of the Day

Wired College Kids

The Pew Internet and American Life Project reports that 86% of college students have used the Internet, compared to 59% of the overall U.S. population. The study, titled "The Internet Goes to College" (www.pewinternet.org/reports/toc.asp?Report=71), surveys more than 2,000 students. Forty-two percent say their primary use is keeping in touch with friends and family by email or instant messenger. Only 38% say they use the Net primarily for academic reasons.

Storm Chaser Tech

Dave Roos

Tim Samaras is insane. Why else would a grown man who has seen the movie *Twister* willfully drive into the path of killer storms and tornadoes? It's all in the name of science, Samaras would say. And for those sexy storm chaser groupies. On May 7, 2002, Samaras and partner Brad Carter made storm-chasing history by deploying weather probes directly in the path of a roaring twister. Samaras' groundbreaking tornado research was recently the subject of an episode of *Out There* (www.nationalgeographic.com/outthere), on the National Geographic Channel. Here's a list of the gear mounted inside Samaras' white minivan, most of it accessible from the driver's seat.

The Hardware

The PC at the heart of the operation is a Pentium III 1GHz with 512MB of RAM, a 60GB hard drive, a KDS 17-inch LCD, and a wireless keyboard. Included with the hardware is the following:

* Boltek lightning-detection card (www.boltek.com)
* FireWire card
* National Instruments 12-bit analog-to-digital convertor card (www.ni.com)
* ATI Radeon All-in-Wonder video card (64MB, www.ati.com)
* Four-port RS-232 expansion card
* PCMCIA expansion slot with an Ositech (www.ositech.com) Cellflex Cellular modem card

The Software

* Boltek Lightning Detection System for azimuth and distance of lightning strikes (www.boltek.com/stracker.htm)
* Pinnacle Studio video-editing software for cutting footage on the fly (www.pinnaclesys.com)
* National Instruments LabView graphical programming software for internal instrument measurements (http://amp.ni.com)
* ATI television tuner and video recorder
* DeLorme GPS mapping software (www.delorme.com)
* SwiftWX software for gathering weather data on the road (www.swiftwx.com)

* Icom PCR-100 VHF scanning software (www.icomamerica.com)
* Davis Instruments data-logging software for weather measurements (www.davisnet.com/home_flash.asp)

Other Gadgets and Gear

* Two VHF/UHF amateur transceivers
* Motorola Startac cellular phone with hands-free adapter and a custom-built interface for cellular data
* Davis weather station (www.davisnet.com/home_flash.asp)
* Sony TRV-900 camcorder (www.sonystyle.com)
* Sony DSS receiver (www.sonystyle.co)
* KVH TracVision LM (www.kvh.com/LandMobile/index.asp) satellite tracking system to obtain weather data from the Weather Channel (www.weather.com)

Custom Contraptions

* Tim designed an auxiliary battery system using a 250AH lead acid battery system with a custom-designed charging system that powers a 1,500-watt DC-to-AC inverter.
* The latest redesign will include a two-way satellite link for 400Kbps to 1Mbps Internet access.
* Everything in the van is custom-built and installed, including the camera mount, desktop computer housing, camera tripod holder, LCD screen holder, and so on. It's all designed for one thing: storm chasing!

September
16

The Tech of Ctrl+Alt+Delete

Patrick Norton

Back in the day, when you press Ctrl+Alt+Delete on your keyboard at the same time, your system would reboot. It was easier than crawling around to find the cold reboot stud. You can thank IBM engineer David Bradley for that. (Bradley's also known for his world-class on-stage Bill Gates zing about Ctrl+Alt+Delete: "I may have invented it, but Microsoft made it popular.")

With Windows XP, Microsoft made Ctrl, Alt, and Delete more useful. Hit the magic three-finger salute, and you get the Windows Task Manager. The Task Manager has a host of uses.

Across the bottom of the Task Manager, you'll find stats on processes (the number of processes running), CPU Usage (as a percent), and the Commit Charge (reveals your virtual memory usage).

Across the top, you'll see four tabs. The Applications tab lists all the applications running on your system. You can use it to end a locked-up task or to bring a task to the front of the machine. The Performance and Networking tabs let you look at system and network (duh) performance graphs and stats. The Processes tab is where things get really interesting. Processes are all the individual tasks running on your OS. Most of them look pretty inexplicable: WZQKPICK.EXE, SPOOLSV.EXE, and the ever-popular SVCHOST.EXE.

All of these processes use power that your system could channel to others areas, but if you kill the wrong process, you'll stop your system or your applications from functioning.

Sysinternals.com's Process Explorer (www.sysinternals.com) offers help in figuring out what's going on. It tells you what process belongs to the OS or to various applications, along with a ton of information on what's going on with each process.

Use it with Black Viper's Windows XP Home and Professional Service Configurations (www.blackviper.com), and you can figure out which processes you can kill. Better yet, turn them off and not have them running on your system in the first place.

Download of the Day

NASA Maps

Patrick Norton

I love maps. Road maps. Charts of my sailing adventures. I have this big ol' map that tracked my cousin as he bounced around Europe. Maps convey so much information. And, ooh, the bright, shiny colors!

The only thing better than a map is a free map. NASA is giving away some seriously nifty free maps generated by the Shuttle Radar Topography Mission (SRTM). Topography maps mean no state boundary lines, interstate divisions, or channel markers. They're just the most richly detailed reliefs of North America I've ever seen.

The full TIFF version of the maps weighs in at a whopping 208MB. A smaller 11MB JPEG version still looks great. As a special bonus, NASA has a map that highlights the Mexican crater from the meteor that many think killed off the dinosaurs. Download the NASA maps at http://photojournal.jpl.nasa.gov/zcatalog/PIA03377.

Site of the Night

Address:

Powers of Ten

Experience your world from 100 light years away to animated swirling visions of subatomic particles at http://micro.magnet.fsu.edu.

Reading Lies on Your Face

Gary Nurenberg

Do you blush when you lie? Does blood rush to your face and give you away? Those questions form the premise for an award-winning high school science fair project that could lead to a new kind of lie detector. Scott Newman, 16, developed a device based on infrared photography as a science project at his Yorktown High School in Arlington, Virginia. The idea came from a shared family trait.

"Actually, my mom blushes a lot and I turn pretty red myself," Newman says. "The idea was, when you lie, you get that same sort of feeling of heat, that feeling of anxiety in your face, just like you're blushing. It's not really visible to the human eye, so the idea was maybe we could use an infrared camera to detect that change in facial heat."

Newman went to NASA, which allowed him to use a sophisticated infrared camera to test some of its employees. He consulted a psychology teacher about what questions would work best, and then quizzed 15 workers at the Goddard Space Flight Center just outside Washington, DC. Each test subject was told to lie at a specific point in the conversation.

"I caught 13 out of the 15, which is 86%, which is very reliable," Newman says. The student added that conventional polygraphs are accurate 83 percent of the time.

Newman's science project includes the infrared photographs that document his findings. The pictures show test subjects before and after they fib. In most cases, the infrared photographs show splotches of red on the subject's face when the subject is telling a lie. The red represents increased blood flow to the face or neck. Some good liars had an opposite reaction. They did not register more facial heat.

"Some people fall into that 'stone cold liar' category," says Deborah Waldron, Newman's school science advisor. "They would lie and then the question would be over and then their facial temperature would drop significantly, so instead of rising when they were lying and the pressure was on, they sort of thought, 'Hey, I got away with it and I can relax,' and their temperature dropped. So there are two ways that

Scott could use the process to catch people: One is if their facial temperature rose. [The other is] after the fact if their facial temperature dropped significantly."

Newman says he can see his approach being used at airline ticket counters. If passengers lie when answering questions posed before one can fly commercially, an infrared camera could unobtrusively capture the increasingly red face or the temperature drop after the lie is told.

Passengers could be tested without their knowledge, which Newman knows raises privacy issues. The Army has expressed an interest in developing the technology, and Newman has applied for a patent. Honest.

Download of the Day

IESpeaker

Brett Larson

Here's how to get Internet Explorer to read to you so that you can do other things while you surf.

IESpeaker (www.iespeaker.com), from AcquisNet, is easy to use:

1. Highlight a block of text on any website.
2. Right-click and select Speak from the contextual menu.
3. Your computer says aloud whatever you have highlighted.

This is also a great tool for kids who aren't quite up to par on reading. IESpeaker offers a little help here and there, just like reading toys on the market. All you need to do is teach your kids to highlight the word they don't understand, right-click, and choose Speak.

September
18

Hot Health and Fitness Gadgets

James Kim

Want to see raw data on how your heart is pumping? How about how far you walk in a day?

Timex Digital Heart Rate Fitness System (100-Lap Model)

The $140 Timex Digital Heart Rate Fitness System—a water-resistant, 100-lap Ironman Triathlon watch with chronometer, timer, and alarm—is a winner (www.timex.com). It's got an indestructible yet lightweight body design, a simple five-button interface (with an Indiglo backlight), and a stretchy Velcro wrist strap. The watch can store up to 100 lap/split times, which can easily be reviewed in recall mode.

It's the built-in heart-rate monitor that makes this watch truly interesting. Strap the heart-rate monitor around your chest, and it sends your heart rate through an FM signal to the watch. What's more, heart-rate data is stored with each lap time, and you can set the watch to monitor your heart rate within the bounds of five fitness zones: light exercise, weight management, aerobic, optimal conditioning, and, for guys like me, elite athlete. Yeah, right.

Braun PrecisionSensor BP 2550

Keep tabs on your blood pressure and heart rate quickly and easily with this wrist-mounted monitor. The $80 BP 2550 looks like a gigantic watch with a large LCD display, two big blue and red buttons, and a European-looking modern design (www.braun.com/uk/precisionsensor).

It's simple to use, and measurements are accurate if used correctly. When the BP 2550 is strapped to your wrist (the Velcro strap can accommodate large wrists), you need to hold your wrist at heart level for reliable measurements. The instrument guides you to the optimal position with graphical arrows. Then,

wait for the strap to tighten and slowly loosen; voilà, you've got a measurement for systolic and diastolic blood pressure, plus your heart rate. It's like visiting the doctor for a checkup anytime you want.

Measurements (and date and time) can be saved for two users. This is a nice tool if you need to keep track of your blood pressure.

Sharper Image Talking Pedometer

Smaller than a pager, this $25 device measures the distance you've walked or run in steps or miles using a very low-tech method: Each time a loose mechanism inside the pedometer rocks back and forth, a step is recorded. This step is then used to calculate how many miles you've racked up. Of course, the user must set the length of an average step beforehand—mine is 14 inches (www.sharperimage.com).

The device has a three-part LCD, which displays the number of steps taken, miles (down to 100th of a mile), and time. Designed to clip to a shirt or waistband, it's actually a lot more accurate when clipped onto your shoelace. (I was pretty shocked to learn that I had walked a mile and a half one day at work.)

As its name implies, the Sharper Image Talking Pedometer also talks: "You have walked 2,500 steps. The distance is 0.63 miles." Seven cheesy music tracks play in synch with your exercise tempo. Definitely turn off this option.

Address: **Site of the Night**

High IQ Society

Can you beat the smartest man in the world? Neither could we. Visit the High IQ Society at www.highiqsociety.org.

September

19

Get the Most Bang for Your Buck

Roger Chang

When the Sunday paper arrives on my doorstep, I don't turn to world events, the sports page, or even the comics. No, I grab the inserts from Circuit City, Best Buy, Target, and The Good Guys to look at all the gadgets, TVs, and computers on sale. Every once in a while, I'm planning to buy something and it's hard to sort through the big yellow banners. "CHEAP!" "Buy me now!" "Get 0% financing for a gazillion months!" What a headache.

Don't Give in to the Pressure

Wow, a $350 PC? Sounds like a good deal to me, but it may be too good to be true. You need to know what you're getting to make an informed decision. Here are a few general rules:

- When buying a PC, get as much as you can afford. There's always another faster computer coming out with more standard features. Buy something that'll last you at least a couple years.

- If you're not satisfied with your options, it's not the right time to buy, no matter how attractive the price is. What's hot today will be on sale in another three to six months when the latest and greatest models are released. Wait to get a bargain or the options you desperately want.

- When looking for deals, always read the fine print. If you see a PC advertised for $300, it probably doesn't include a lot of software, a monitor, a keyboard, or a mouse. Be prepared to visit the store's website or visit the retailer to get all the details.

Comparing Ads

The product you're interested in is advertised next to a similar product of the same price. Don't pull your hair out. Here's what to do:

1. Make sure you're getting an operating system.

2. Look at the options. Gamers should get as much memory as they can afford, an AMD chipset, and a high-quality video card. Everyday folks will probably do better with a Pentium processor. When you see "1800 AMD" on one side of the page and "1.8 Pentium 4" on the other, know that it's the same speed.

3. Look at more expensive options. That inexpensive camera may not be digital. You might have to spend only a few more bucks to get a nice flat-panel display instead of a CRT. Are you getting a CD writer or a DVD drive? Often more expensive PCs will come with bundled software such as Microsoft Office, a photo editor, or financial software. Figure out how much you'd have to pay to buy the software separately. You may be getting a deal.

4. Does the price of your item include free tech support and a warranty? A bargain-basement item isn't worth it if you need to pay $30 every time there's a problem. If face-to-face service is more important than dealing with service over the phone, buy locally from a smaller PC retailer instead of shopping online.

5. Look out for proprietary parts. Look for a PC that contains brand-name hardware so you can upgrade at a later date, if need be.

6. Finally, find out what other people have to say about products before you step foot into the store. We recommend looking at Epinions and ResellerRatings.com. Know what you want and what you're willing to settle for.

Don't give in to the pressure. Yes, again. A salesperson may try to convince you to buy a model that's in stock. Now that you know what you're looking for, don't get pressured into making a purchase you'll regret. If a salesman gets too pushy, just walk away.

September 21

Roundup: Multifunction Printers

Andrew Hawn

According to Bureau of Labor Statistics, in 2002 well over 20 million people were working from home or telecommuting. If you count yourself in the ranks of the rapidly growing "self-employed," you know how important it is to make your tiny home office seem big and important to the outside world. Thankfully, today's crop of multifunctional office printer/fax/scanner/copier combos can help. But like anything that claims to do everything, all-in-ones have their share of blind spots when it comes to serving every need. TechTV Labs reviewed three multifunction devices ranging in price from around $200 to $400 from Canon, HP, and Lexmark.

Speed and Additional Costs

Multifunction printers are primarily used to print and fax. Scanning and copying are no less important, but they're less often needed. You shouldn't expect any multifunction printer to compare to the monstrous printer/copiers or superfast fax machines commonly found in an office. Although every multifunction box boasts breakneck speeds, testing consistently shows them to be about half that speed in practical usage.

Although some of the multifunction devices we tested are better at conserving resources than others, you will pay early and often for consumables such as ink and paper. In testing the HP psc 2210 all-in-one, for example, we ran out of color ink in just under 60 color prints and copies (30 in draft mode and 30 in high-quality mode). Depending on how often you use your device, you should be aware of device consumable costs before purchasing.

Quality and Ease of Use

Thankfully, multifunction printers have taken advantage of better-quality print engines and easier-to-use interfaces. All the devices we tested offer good color prints and very speedy draft text printing and copying. When it came to imaging, the HP psc 2210 stood well above the other printers in this roundup, with noticeably better color saturation and crisp detail quality.

At higher-end price points, the Canon multifunction printers offer very easy-to-use "PC-less" integrated fax features and Flash memory readers for direct "camera-to-printer" image printing. By contrast, the cheaper Lexmark X85 provides neither "PC-less" faxing functionality nor an integrated Flash memory card reader for photo printing. The X85's dependence on a PC with a modem for its faxing features is a drawback that we found unacceptable for an all-in-one.

Product	Canon MultiPass F80	HP PSC 2210 LAB PICK	Lexmark X85
Print 10-page B&W draft; best quality (in minutes)	1:03; 5:01	1:18; 14:20	1:40; 2:19
Print high-res color image at best quality (in minutes)	2:36	4:59	34:02
Copy 10 pages B&W draft; best quality (in minutes)	1:17; 1:45	1:34; 17:19	2:15; 3:15
Copy 10 high-res color images at best quality (in minutes)	16:34	30:01	58
Scan 300dpi image (in minutes)	0:15	0:27	0:21

602Pro PC Suite

Megan Morrone

You don't have to pay for Microsoft Office. I mean, you can if you want to, but you don't have to. Thanks to Lance for recommending 602Pro PC Suite (www.software602.com). It's a free alternative to Microsoft Office, and I like it. You may have already heard of Sun's free 48.9MB office suite, OpenOffice (www.openoffice.org), but at 16.2MB, 602Pro is quite a bit smaller.

What 602Pro PC Suite Has

- Word processor (includes a good spell checker)
- Spreadsheet program
- Photo-editing program
- Photo album
- Extensive help documents included in download

602Pro is an MS Office clone, and a pretty good one, at that. It even features a few additional amenities, such as the ability to preview items as you explore. You no longer have to guess a word-processing document's contents by its name; 602Pro lets you preview the first few sentences of a document. Each program is compatible with its MS Office counterpart, so don't worry about not being able to open documents.

What 602Pro PC Suite Doesn't Have

- A presentation program (such as Power-Point—OpenOffice includes a decent one)
- A text editor (such as Notepad—OpenOffice also includes this)
- A thesaurus for the word processor
- Text-to-speech capabilities
- Free tech support

If you want any of the missing features, you can get them by upgrading to the Plus version.

If you're a small business (with fewer than five employees) or a family with its own domain name, you might want to try 602Pro's LAN Suite (www.software602.com). The LAN Suite lets you communicate over a network, share Internet access, start your own web and mail servers, and protect it all with a free firewall. The paid version of 602Pro LAN Suite supports more users and provides greater security.

Although there's no presentation program, Premysl Pech, president of Software602, says, "You can run a pretty sophisticated slide show in our 602Album with text, pictures, sounds, voice, and web links or bubble comments. So we do not have [a] presentation program, but we have presentation ability within the product. (We can also create HTML presentations easily or upload your album to the web.)"

Laporte Support

Web Libraries

I recommend the following sites to look up information:

- **Project Guttenberg** (http://promo.net/pg). Free online access to books available in the public domain. Has books available in plain text for speech-recognition software.
- **The Library of Congress** (www.loc.gov). The largest library in the world. Serves as the research arm of Congress.
- **Safari Bookshelf** (http://safari.oreilly.com). Pay service that lets you access O'Reilly and New Riders technical books.
- **Google** (www.google.com). Think of the web as a library. Google is the way to search it.
- **Google Groups** (www.google.com/grphp?hl=en&ie=UTF-8&oe=UTF-8&q=++&tab=wg). Lets you search newsgroups, where there's a wealth of information.

September
22

Notesbrowser Free

Craig Higdon

I don't have much time. I'm late for a meeting. I need to get my dog to the vet, my clothes to the bank, and my money to the cleaners. Wait, no, that's not what I meant. I'm late to the vet, need to get my dog to the bank, and—aaaarrrghhh. If your life is as hectic as mine, take a minute to find out more about Notesbrowser Free (www.notesbrowser.com). It'll help you keep all this stuff straight. I can't believe I ever lived without it.

Notesbrowser Free is a desktop organizer built with flexibility in mind. It has all the basics:

- To-do list
- Calendar
- Address book
- Note pad

Every page has built-in tabs with tons of space to plan your hectic schedule. Customize the font ("important" equals red), add bullets, change the font, indent, or strike to make things easier to see. But that's just the beginning.

Easy Computing

Notesbrowser Free can work as a hub for all your common computer activity. It will help you manage your MP3 collection, provide shortcuts to important programs, and bookmark web pages. Here's how to create a shortcut or bookmark:

1. Drag the file, URL, or shortcut into Notesbrowser Free.
2. Double-click the new icon to launch the file.

It also has a search function similar to the Find Next command in most Windows applications so that you can find what you need fast.

Fun Extras

Delivery boys will need to watch out when you turn on the Pizza Timer. This countdown clock plays an MP3 when the timer hits zero.

You can also skin the interface. It comes with a couple skins, but you can download more or make one yourself.

Screen Space

My only beef with the program is that it doesn't come with a restore/maximize function. It's either full-screen or minimized, with nothing in between. This might sound like a small beef, but when you want to just pull your notes to the top of your desktop without obscuring everything else, it gets to be a hassle.

We recommend downloading Notesbrowser Free. You get a free personal information manager, Fido gets to the vet, George Washington gets to the bank, and you get home in time to watch *Matlock*.

Download of the Day

CleverKeys

Roger Chang

Learn about a utility that lets you get instant definitions and synonyms. CleverKeys (www.cleverkeys.com/ck.html?p=home&os=) is a small text-search utility for Windows and Mac OS.

1. Install and enable CleverKeys.
2. Highlight the text you want to know more about and hit the magic key combo (Ctrl+L).
3. The utility searches Dictionary.com (as well as a web search through the site), Thesaurus.com, and Amazon.com for information.

I wish the program included a user-defined site search feature. But CleverKeys does a good job finding a word definition or synonym in a pinch.

America 1900 Family Tree Builder

Fawn Luu

Use America 1900 Family Tree Builder to track ancestors. Although the bare-bones program goes back only four generations, it will give you a lot more insight into your relatives than other programs.

Create your tree by entering your name and the name of your parents, grandparents, and great-grandparents. If you need help finding an ancestor online, click the Genealogy Reference button for a list of useful websites.

Now here's the fun part. If you want to learn more about what was going on in the world when your relative grew up, select his or her name and choose a region. You'll get an event timeline and pictures from the period. As the name of the program suggests, this works only for people alive during the 1900s.

The only downside is that there aren't any spaces for siblings. Still, this is a great tool for whipping up a basic family tree in no time.

Download America 1900 Family Tree Builder at www.pbs.org/wgbh/amex/1900/sfeature.

Download of the Day

iFind

Megan Morrone

Google is good, but if you want to research a topic thoroughly, you're going to need a stronger tool.

iFind (www.kbsim.com/download.html) is a free download that lets you search six sites and gives you more context for each result. That way you won't have to click on every link to find out if it's useful. Simply type your search term or terms into the long window below the iFind banner, and press Enter. After your results are listed, you can view them in the Document View. To get more information, click on a term in the left window and then click Context View.

Address: Site of the Night

Are You Accomplished?

Martin Sargent

When I was an optimistic young boy, before having my high hopes pulverized by the dark forces of a cruel world, I looked forward to an auspicious future. By the time I was 26, my current age, I was certain to have met the girl of my dreams, purchased a beautiful home, written the great American novel, and starred in several Academy Award–winning films.

As it turns out, my lot in life at 26 consists of sharing an apartment with three roommates and creating "Top Five" lists for a computer help show. Presidency, here I come.

The Museum of Conceptual Art has a site (www.museumofconceptualart.com/accomplished), appropriately titled "Things Other People Accomplished When They Were Your Age," that has provided no comfort whatsoever. This malevolent little site prompts you for your age and responds with a list of achievements attained by other, more productive members of society when they were your age.

Here's a sample of the accomplishments credited to 26-year-olds:

- Albert Einstein published five major research papers in a German physics journal, fundamentally changing man's view of the universe and leading to such inventions as television and the atomic bomb.
- Benjamin Franklin published the first edition of *Poor Richard's Almanac*, which was to play a large role in molding the diverse American character.
- College dropout Steve Wozniak co-founded Apple Computer.
- Ken Kesey published his first novel, *One Flew over the Cuckoo's Nest*.
- Napoleon Bonaparte conquered Italy.

I'm filing a lawsuit against my guidance counselor.

September
24

Ten-Minute Website

Michelle VonWald

Building a basic website doesn't need to cost anything in terms of time or money. Learn how to create a simple website using free resources.

Find a Host

Many free hosts are available, such as Angelfire (http://angelfire.lycos.com) or GeoCities (http://geocities.yahoo.com). Be warned that a free service does come with a price: advertising on your site. If that doesn't bother you, you're ready to get started.

Get Started

We chose GeoCities. To start, visit GeoCities and click on the Sign Up for a Free Website link. Next, you're prompted to choose the type of advertising you want on your site. After you select a few, click Submit This Form to get your Yahoo ID and URL. At the bottom of the page, click the blue button that reads Build Your Website Now!

Choose a Tool

To build your site, choose one of the tools Yahoo offers Yahoo PageWizards (http://geocities.yahoo.com/v/w/) or Yahoo Page-Builders (http://geocities.yahoo.com/v/pb.html). PageWizards is billed as "easy," so it's the tool we chose to build our website with.

When you're at the PageWizard page, just pick a background theme and select Begin:

1. Enter your title and introductory text.
2. Either upload a picture or use the default image associated with your background theme. Then click Next.
3. Enter your favorite links and click Next.
4. Enter your personal information and click Next.
5. Name your page and click Next.
6. Click Done.

You can check the simple page we created in less than 10 minutes at www.geocities.com/techchickus/CallforHelpFan.html.

Add-Ons and Cool Tools

You can add some cool features from the Advanced toolbox in the upper-right corner of your GeoCities homepage. You can download the tools to add photos to your free web page, edit HTML code, or track the traffic on your website.

What Are You Waiting For?

If you need a way to share photos and information with friends or family, this is one of the easiest solutions. You'll have a bare-bones website in less time than it takes to make a pot of coffee.

Web Tips

Master the Web

Nicole Guilfoyle

You're ready to build your own website. Not one of those "what you see is what you get" cookie-cutter sites, but something that lets you highlight your creativity and artistic flare.

Webmonkey: The Web Developer's Resource (http://hotwired.lycos.com/webmonkey) guides you through novice, intermediate, and advanced web design (dubbed Beginners, Builders, and Masters on the site).

You'll also find tools, tips, resource links, and articles under the How-To Library and Quick Reference areas. Learn HTML, find out how to animate images, get JavaScript code, use Flash, and much more.

The HTML Cheatsheet, Special Characters, Browser Chart, and Color Codes pages are must-have items worthy of their own folder in your Favorites or Bookmarks lists. Print them and tack them up next to your computer.

Now that you have the tools and skills, you may think you have what it takes to break into the web industry. Go to http://hotwired.lycos.com/webmonkey/jobs/tips for tips on beginning your job search. Good luck!

Build Your Own Macaquarium

Billy Parkinson

Is that old Rev-A iMac no more than an over-size bookend? Is it propping open the front door? Blocking a wheel while you change a tire? Brett has one more thing you can do with your old iMac: Turn it into an aquarium.

No kidding. Just head to MacAquarium (where we got ours, www.macaquarium.com) or RedLightRunner (www.redlightrunner.com/macaquariums.html). Either vendor can outfit you with all you'll need to turn that old iMac into a marine-life marvel.

You have to supply the fish, but the kits come with everything else, including a pump, rocks, and a filtering system. If you can't seem to part with your trusty old friend, the sites can even furnish you with a gutted iMac case (for an extra cost, of course).

There may be more sites out there that can supply you with similar kits, so get on the Internet and search.

Assembly is simple, if you follow the instructions. No tools or special skills are required. You can even get the kids involved.

Both sites offer kits to convert older Mac Classics into aquariums. If you want that old-school cred, give one of those a try. (They're a bit cheaper, too.)

If you want some more Mac aquatics, take a look at these sites:

- **Aquaria by Jim**
  (www.techquarium.com/oldsite)
- **Macquarium.seltzer.org**
  (http://macquarium.seltzer.org)
- **Applefritter's How to Build a MacQuarium**
  (www.applefritter.com/hacks/macquarium/construct/index.html)

Download of the Day

Distributed Computing Projects for Your Home PC

Megan Morrone

Use your idle PC for a greater good. You probably already know that you can download the Seti@Home (www.setiathome.ssl.berkeley.edu) screen saver to your home PC or Mac to help in the search for extraterrestrial intelligence.

Here are a few more distributed computing programs that you might like to try:

1. **United Devices Cure for Cancer** (http://members.ud.com/download/gold). Help find a cure for cancer.

2. **Parabon Computing** (www.ComputeAgainstCancer.org). An alternative way to help find a cure for cancer that lets you choose which organization you'd like to donate cycles to.

3. **Evolution@Home** (www.evolutionary-research.org). Aid in the creation of an evolutionary ecology model to help uncover the causes of extinction of endangered animals.

4. **Distributed.net** (www.distributed.net). Help with extensive cryptography projects.

5. **Genome@Home** (http://genomeathome.stanford.edu). Assist in unraveling our genetic information.

6. **Drug Design Optimization Lab** (www.d2ol.com). Search for a drug to fight anthrax, smallpox, and Ebola.

About Distributed Computing Projects

It is best to download these programs on your home PC or to ask permission before you download them on your work PC. Some companies and schools don't let their idle cycles go easily.

September
26

Twisted List: Five Hot Word Tricks

Martin Sargent

When I learned these five Microsoft Word tricks, I was so excited that I immediately telephoned all my friends and extended family in hopes of enhancing their lives with my new-found wisdom. All of them except for my cousin Earl (who's pretty lonely and generally not invited to family reunions) quickly found excuses to end the conversation. But maybe you'll appreciate them.

Save Energy with a New Way to Paste

If you sit at a keyboard as much as I do, you get powerfully tired with all the clicking and keystroking. Anytime I can save a keystroke, I figure that's one more second I can do some more computing. So I became ecstatic when I learned this energy-saving trick.

Instead of choosing Edit, Paste, or stroking Ctrl+V to paste, all you need to do is press the Insert key (that's right, just *one button*). But you need to tell Word that's how you want to play the game. Choose Tools, Options, and click on the Edit tab. Select the Use INS Key for Paste check box, and click OK. From now on, by simply pressing Insert, you'll perform a paste.

There's a really great side benefit to this trick. From now on, Insert mode—that really annoying feature that always comes on by mistake where your typing overwrites existing typing—is automatically disabled. Hallelujah.

How to Select Columns of Text

One of the angriest moments of my life was when I was trying to select just one column of text in Word. When you try to do this with the mouse and you have more than one column of text, all the columns get selected, not just the one you want. Let me show you what I mean by a bunch of columns of text, using the sports that Leo, Patrick, and I are good at as an example:

Martin	Leo	Patrick
Football	Tiddlywinks	Parcheesi
Baseball	Lawn darts	Pin the Tail on
Rugby		the Donkey
Hockey		Dungeons &
Soccer		Dragons
Skiing		
Boxing		
Kung Fu		
Steeplechase		
Many more		

To select the sports that Leo is good at, I'd end up highlighting listings from mine and Patrick's columns if I just tried to drag the mouse. But if I hold down Alt while selecting Leo's sports repertoire, I can select just the column that I want.

Begin Where You Ended

If you're like me and completed six Ph.D. degrees, you've written a lot of long essays—or theses, as we academics call them. You edit and rewrite a lot. If your essay is really lengthy and you want to find out exactly where you ended up during your last editing session, all you need to do is press Shift+F5 after you open the Word document. You're immediately whisked directly to where you last worked in the document.

Address: Site of the Night

All Too Flat

Enjoy the pseudo-scientific silliness of debunking the fish myth at www.alltooflat.com.

Twisted List:
Five Hot Word Tricks
(continued)

The Microsoft Word Cloning Debate

I have argued with many people over the years about the best way to copy and paste text or images in Microsoft Word. Sometimes it gets ugly. One time the neighbors had to call the police. But regardless of what stupid dummy-heads might say, here is the best way to copy something from one point in the document to another (if the source and location are close in the document, that is).

Select the thing you want to copy with the mouse, just like a normal person would. Now press and hold the Ctrl key and drag the thing to be cloned to wherever you want to put it in the document. When I taught this trick to UN Secretary General Kofi Annan at last year's World Tribunal on Microsoft Office Tricks, he shed a tear of joy and approval.

Take Total Control of Graphics in Word

Normally, when you try to move a graphic around a Word 2000 or later document by dragging and dropping, you can never really get it to go precisely where you want, because it snaps against the closest grid line. Grid lines are invisible in Word, but they look like a sheet of graph paper cast across your document. To see the grid lines, or even to change the size of the grids, choose View, Toolbars, and open the Drawing toolbar. On the Drawing toolbar, choose Draw, Grid. Click on the Display Grid Lines Onscreen check box, and set some parameters for the grid. Click OK, and you'll see the grid.

To escape the power of the grid and move an object to wherever you want, hold down Alt when you're moving the object. When you want to let it drop, release the mouse button, not the Alt key, or the object will succumb to the awful grid, not your artistic whim.

Morgan's Tips

Global IME

My brother has studied Japanese in school for many years, and for as long as I can remember, he dual-booted Japanese Windows and English Windows. Not only was this an annoying inconvenience for him, but it was a serious strain on his tiny hard drive.

The discovery of Microsoft's Global IMEs (input method editors) was a lifesaver, and we immediately dumped the Japanese OS and freed up more space for those precious MP3s. The IMEs let you switch between typing English and typing your chosen Asian language in any MS Office application.

You alternate between languages with a simple click of an icon in your system tray (or your language bar, depending on your version of Windows). These IMEs are available for any version of Office. Just make sure you're downloading the correct version.

Download your chosen IME. Read the instructions carefully. Depending on your versions of Office and Windows, you may need to download an extra add-in or language pack so your computer can recognize the text.

- **Simplified Chinese for Office 2000 and XP** (http://office.microsoft.com/downloads/2002/imechs.aspx)
- **Traditional Chinese for Office 2000 and XP** (http://office.microsoft.com/downloads/2002/imecht.aspx)
- **Japanese for Office 2000 and XP** (http://office.microsoft.com/downloads/2002/imejpn.aspx)
- **Korean for Office 2000 and XP** (http://office.microsoft.com/downloads/2002/imekor.aspx)
- **Global IMEs for previous versions of Office** (www.microsoft.com/msdownload/iebuild/ime5_win32/en/ime5_win32.htm)

SnapStream

Patrick Norton

Leo and I are often asked about software alternatives to TiVo and ReplayTV. We found one called SnapStream Personal Video Station 3 (www.snapstream.com/Products/Products_PVS3.asp). It's cheap: about $50 without a monthly subscription fee. The idea: Run the software on your PC and get all the TV pausing, rewinding, and recording goodness of a dedicated PVR, without having to hack the machine to add more hard drive storage, move your shows to a DVD, or whatever.

Want to run PVS 3? Here's what you need:

- Windows 98, Me, XP, or 2000
- 733MHz Pentium III or faster processor

One advantage that dedicated TiVo or ReplayTV boxes have over software running on your PC is chips dedicated to encoding video. On your computer, your processor has to do the work, as well as any other task you throw at it. A faster processor helps. SnapStream recommends that you use at least a 1.4GHz Pentium 4 or equivalent AMD Athon chip.

- 128MB of RAM; SnapStream recommends 256MB.
- Lots of hard drive space. TV eats up hard drive space quickly, especially if you're encoding at the highest quality, which can take more than a gig per half-hour show.
- TV tuner card or USB tuner.

This is the most crucial component: You need to bring the TV signal into your system. See the list of compatible tuners at www.snapstream.com/Products/Products_PVS3_SysReq.asp. If you don't plan on using PVS 3 on your desktop or via a wireless mouse across the living room, you also need a compatible remote control.

Up and Running

PVS 3 installed in less than ten minutes, including loading a Hauppauge TV Tuner into the box. If you know your ZIP code and the source of your TV (antenna/broadcast, cable, satellite) you can set up the software in minutes. Just make sure you have the correct time and time zone. The wrong time zone on my PC fouled up my ability to record shows. I used a remote control to navigate PVS 3's interface much like a TiVo's, and, of course, recorded shows to watch later.

Only one thing annoyed me in PVS 3: There's no way to type in the name of a show or actor to search the listing in the UI (remote control) mode. You must enter the Web mode (and grab a keyboard) to do so. SnapStream hopes to add a keyboard function, after version 3 gets released.

Low on Memory? Upgrade Your Brain

Dave Roos

Attention, all you graying baby boomers. Turn up your hearing aid and put down that jumbo jar of ginko biloba. An amazing new technology in development called a personal awareness assistant is being developed by Accenture (www.accenture.com). It will collect snippets of conversation and geographical data to help you recall the names of people you met five minutes ago. ("Was that Susan or Donna?")

Could you use a personal awareness assistant? Leo has already signed up for six, just in case he forgets where he left the other five.

Do you need a personal awareness assistant?

Yes 9%

No 71%

What was the question again? 20%

9% Yes
71% No
20% What was the question again?

News on Your Desktop

Nicole Guilfoyle

This week's hottest celebrity couple breaks up. The stock market plummets. New laws pass. Your favorite team has a day game. The world doesn't wait for you to get off work, so here are a few ways for you to keep yourself informed at the office.

WorldFlash

WorldFlash (www.worldflash.com) delivers the latest headlines, weather, sports, and stock information. You can even search for a stock symbol to get real-time stock quotes. Choose from more than 150 reliable news sources from around the world, including BBC News, Wired News, *Business Week*, and *The New York Times*. Unlike most other desktop news tickers, WorldFlash lets you select local news as well as world news sources. Here's how to customize your ticker:

1. Pick a category and move it to the Active or Inactive News Sources list.

2. Scroll along each tab to further narrow down the news you want about weather in a certain area, sports teams, and other news.

3. Click OK.

4. If you want to email a headline, right-click the WorldFlash icon and choose Email This Headline.

WorldFlash has a 90-day free trial. Pay $39.95 if you decide to keep it.

News

This free download delivers news headlines from some of the most trusted news authorities including, ABC News, Bloomberg News, CBS News, Cnet, CNN, and ESPN, to name a few (www.desktopnews.com/Download).

Click the Desktop News icon and choose Options to decide where you want to dock the ticker on your desktop. Then start setting your news preferences by clicking the Desktop News icon again and choosing Preferences. Here's what you'll find on each tab.

- **Channels.** Decide which type of information you want from each news source. Leave the options you don't want unchecked.

- **Components.** Select buttons for your Desktop News toolbar. You can select anything from a shortcut to the Yahoo! homepage to a Google button for quick searches.

- **Quotes.** Add stock symbols for your favorite investments.

- **General.** Specify if you want Desktop News to launch at startup and how fast you want the ticker to move.

AOL Instant Messenger

Here's how to launch the ticker built into AIM (www.aim.com):

1. Sign onto the AIM service.

2. Click My AIM and choose News Ticker.

The news will scroll across the top of your desktop as long as you stay logged on. Here's how to customize the news ticker:

1. Press F3 or click My AIM, Edit Options, and choose Edit Preferences.

2. Click News Ticker.

3. Check all the headline types you want: News, Entertainment, Business, and Sports.

4. Say whether you want the ticker to appear when you sign on.

5. Decide how often you want information to update and how fast you want the ticker to scroll.

6. Click OK.

AIM also has a separate stock ticker. Follow the same steps to set it up, choosing Stock Ticker instead of News Ticker.

September

30

Control Your Email, Battle Spam

Megan Morrone
This month is dedicated to our love/hate relationship with email. We love it because it saves us time, we hate it because it wastes our time. We love it because it lets us easily contact people we never could contact before. We hate it because it lets people we want to avoid contact us.

The tips on the following pages are devoted to stopping spam at your ISP, filtering spam from your inbox, sending safe attachments, and keeping yourself safe from email viruses. All of these tips, however, won't keep you safe from the hoaxes and urban legends sent to you by your friends and family. Whether you're an email veteran or a novice, here is a list of things that you should know before you click the send button:

- Bill Gates (Walt Disney, or any other rich person) will not send you money for forwarding an email.
- The Gap won't send you a pair of cargo pants for every email you forward. The world is not big enough for that many pairs of cargo pants.
- The Nigerians do not need you to help them set up a bank account.
- There is no "Good Times" virus
- There is no "Bad Times" virus.
- There is no "Yellow Teletubby" virus.
- There is no sulfnbk.exe virus. There is no jdbgmgr.exe virus. These are both legitimate files that your computer may contain and neither of them is dangerous.
- Public restrooms are not infested with killer butt-biting spiders.
- Dallas movie theaters are not littered with dirty needles.
- A serial killer is not luring women from their home with tapes of a crying baby.
- Your car will not ignite if you use your cell phone at the gas pump.
- Penny Brown is not missing.
- You can't save NPR and PBS by signing and forwarding an email petition to everyone you know.
- The phrase "I usually never forward these, but…" is usually a lie.
- The phrase, "this is not a hoax," means "this is a hoax."
- The phrase "forward this to everyone you know" means "delete immediately."

Kill Spam Dead

Leo Laporte

I use a two-step approach to fighting junk email. My first line of defense is my ISP, Sonic.net. Like many ISPs, Sonic filters for spam on its mail server with a program called SpamAssassin (www.spamassassin.org). As the end user, I set the score threshold. Email messages that score too high are held on the server and never reach my inbox.

I've found that a score of 6.5 stops 90% of the mail I don't want. SpamAssassin kills an average of 120 spam messages a day on my main account. That's megabytes of hair-restoration ads I don't download. I review the spam mailbox every few days to make sure it hasn't trapped anything I want. I've used it for a while, and it's quite reliable.

But what about the 10% that sneak by SpamAssassin? For that, I use client-side filtering. I do all my email on Mac OS X and use the streamlined and powerful PowerMail (www.ctmdev.com). I also use an add-on spam filter called SpamSieve (www.c-command.com/spamsieve/) by Michael Tsai. SpamSieve also works with MailSmith, Apple Mail, and Entourage. SpamSieve uses Bayesian filtering. Paul Graham was probably the first person to recommend Bayesian filtering for fighting junk email.

As Graham describes, most spam filters work like pesticides: They breed smarter spammers. Because a Bayesian-based filter learns and evolves, it can keep up with spammers. It doesn't always work, but it does a very good job. SpamSieve processed 8,018 spam messages and 48,195 good messages with a 98.7% accuracy rate. It missed only 572 penis-enlarger ads and incorrectly marked 186 messages from my mom as spam. (This might be the first time "penis enlarger" and "my mom" have ever appeared together in a sentence.) That's still 186 false positives too many, but it's the best I've found. SpamSieve is particularly accurate with mailing lists. Many spam filters incorrectly tag newsletters as spam. Thanks to SpamAssassin and SpamSieve, I haven't missed any newsletters.

SpamAssassin uses a combination of Bayesian techniques, rule-based filters, and white-and-black lists. Its developers are constantly fiddling with the rules, so it seems to keep up with the spammers.

Why do spammers try so hard to get past mail filters? If I'm filtering on the word *Viagra*, I don't want messages about it. Why spell it "V i a g r a?" Maybe because many spammers aren't trying to sell anything at all. According to a recent study by Wired News (www.wired.com; February 12, 2003 "Spam Offers: Some Legit, Most Not"), most spam is designed to harvest your email address. Never reply to spam, even to complain.

I don't have much experience with Windows-based spam filters, Bayesian or otherwise. I've been trying a Bayesian-based program called Ella (www.openfieldsoftware.com). It's an Outlook plug-in that does a good job. Open Field plans to release it as an automatic mail categorizer, much like John Graham-Cumming's POPFile (http://popfile.sourceforge.net).

I also subscribe to SpamCop (http://spamcop.net), but I don't use it to filter my mail. For $30 a year, you can run your incoming mail through SpamCop before it hits your inbox. If your ISP doesn't offer SpamAssassin, this is a good alternative, but SpamCop stopped too much legitimate mail, especially from mailing lists. However, I use my SpamCop email address whenever I give an address to a website. The @spamcop.net address seems to deter them from selling my name.

AOL Kids

Nicole Guilfoyle

All America Online screen names are not created equal. When creating a screen name, it's important to give your kids an account for their age group. This is especially important for children age 12 and younger.

First, always monitor your child's Internet use. Online predators might attempt to contact your children no matter what. But AOL makes it a little easier to keep your kids safe.

By choosing the Kids Only screen name settings for children 12 and younger, you have a little more control over what your child does while he or she is online. AOL sets limits on email, chat, and the sites your child is allowed to visit. The holder of the master screen name can customize these settings at any time by going to AOL keyword Parental Controls.

What Makes Kids Only Different?

- You don't get the full version of AOL when you sign on to the Kids Only (KO) interface. It's bright and colorful, and it contains limited links to email, games, homework help, and other age-appropriate sites.

- AOL moderators pay special attention to KO chat and message boards.

- Use Parental Controls to place limits on who can send your child instant messages and email.

- AOL will not collect or share information about your child (except the screen name to participate in activities) without your permission.

- You're notified if your child decides to enter a Kids Only contest or sweepstakes. You are given the opportunity to prevent your child from participating.

- If your child signs up for a KO newsletter, you can unsubscribe.

Finally, limit the time your kids spend online, so that they don't spend too much time visiting gaming sites or in chat rooms. Even tech-savvy kids need to go outside and play.

Download of the Day

Eudora

Megan Morrone

Long, long ago on a computer far, far away, I used an email program called Eudora (www.eudora.com/download). It was fast, free, and easy. Why, oh why, did I give it up in favor of Outlook Express? Who knows? Why do I do anything? It wasn't until recently, during yet another OE crash, that it dawned on me: I could go back to Eudora! So I did.

What I like about Eudora 5.1.1:

- Better virus protection (no scripting capabilities)

- Usage stats that let you track how much time you spend with email and how many email messages you receive and respond to

- A better spell checker (www.eudora.com/email/features/wp.html)

- Capability to work in Windows and in Mac OS X, 9, and 8

There are two free versions of Eudora, the ad-supported version and the lite version. The paid version is $29.95 or $39.95, depending on whether you've purchased Eudora in the past.

Megan's Tips

Set Default Fonts for Email

In Outlook Express, go to Tools, Options, Compose to set the default fonts and sizes for your email messages.

Duplicate Outlook Express Messages

Michelle VonWald with Richard Statter

Outlook Express allows you to check multiple email accounts, one of which is Hotmail. We're not really sure why this happens, but according to our viewers, duplicate Hotmail messages are often downloaded in the Outlook Express inbox.

The best way to solve this problem is to delete your Hotmail account in Outlook Express and set it up again. Follow these instructions to remove your Hotmail account:

1. Open Tools, Accounts.
2. Select the Mail tab.
3. Highlight the Hotmail account and click the Remove button.

To add your Hotmail account back, follow these steps:

1. Open Tools, Accounts.
2. Create an entry for an account as usual, using the Add button.
3. When you specify an address ending in @hotmail.com, OE recognizes it as a web-based account and gives you a number of web-specific options, including downloading your Hotmail folder structure.

Web Tips

Retrieve Deleted Email on AOL

Nicole Guilfoyle

I usually get a little carried away cleaning my email inbox. I sometimes delete messages from friends and family by mistake. Luckily, America Online lets me retrieve email deleted within the past 24 hours.

1. Click Mail and select Recently Deleted Mail.
2. Highlight the message you want to retrieve.
3. Click Keep As New to move it back to your inbox.

You can use the Permanently Delete button to erase other messages, but it isn't necessary. AOL automatically dumps these email messages after 24 hours.

Download of the Day

iHateSpam

Megan Morrone

I've tried a handful of free email spam filters, and I have yet to be completely satisfied with one. I got to thinking that maybe the only way to effectively and easily get rid of spam is to part with a little bit of cash, so I downloaded the demo versions of iHateSpam for Outlook and Outlook Express.

Sunbelt Software's iHateSpam (www.sunbelt-software.com) was one of the easier programs to set up. iHateSpam quarantines spam email to a specified folder. It has a set of rules to determine what is spam. It mines your contact list to determine who your friends are and lets you train it never to quarantine email from certain people (friends) and to always quarantine email from other people (enemies). The Outlook version will even mine all your individual folders. All the training happens from a handy toolbar in your email program.

iHateSpam got rid of about 90% of all my spam. When I looked through the quarantine folder, I found about 1% of the quarantined email was not actually spam. You can also block all email that appears in foreign characters. If you never expect to get email in foreign character sets, turn on this feature. iHateSpam also works behind corporate firewalls, so you can use it at work. The only major drawback is that the program works only with Outlook or Outlook Express but works in Windows 95/98/Me/NT/2000 and XP.

Linux Evolution Graphical Mail Client

Chris DiBona

I've received a number of email messages asking me for a good—no, scratch that, great—email program for Linux. I suggest Evolution. It's written (mostly) by the folks at Ximian (`http://Ximian.com`) and has been called "Outlook for the Gnome desktop." However, I think that gives Evolution short shrift.

Evolution shares Outlook's functionality, and for a small fee, you can buy a connector that lets you connect with a corporate exchange database. Evolution includes all the necessary functions: contacts, task management, calendar, and inbox.

So what's the big deal? Evolution also has an innovative mail-handling scheme. There are standard folders for sorting, but Evolution also supports something called virtual folders, or vFolders.

vFolders are rule-based folders for messages in the system. Suppose you have an email from tom@rupertcorp.com. You can have that email appear in your New Messages vFolder, your Tom vFolder, and your rupertcorp vFolder. There's only one message, but it can be accessed via multiple folders.

The Summary function contains weather, news from different websites, and a summary of your tasks, appointments, and waiting email. It's a digital dashboard that's extensible to include in any site, plus it's useful for organizing your day.

I'd like to see more import options for the program, although it does synch with my Palm PDA.

You can download the open-source application for free. You can also buy both Ximian and the Ximianized Gnome desktop as a bundle with the StarOffice office suite at the Ximian site. While you're at it, you might want to buy a stuffed monkey.

Talkback

No Stop to Spam

Dave Roos

According to Brightmail Inc. (`www.brightmail.com`), a major vendor of anti-spam software, 40% of all email traffic is spam, double what it was six months ago. By the end of the year, over half of the mail crowding the nation's inboxes will be ads for weight-loss pills and bargain-basement mortgage rates.

We're losing the spam battle big time. As the study illustrates, ISPs and system administrators can't keep up with an increasingly cunning crowd of con artists and "marketing" groups. It's costing businesses millions to protect their employees and clients from an unknown enemy that hides behind autogenerated email addresses with no traceable source.

What percentage of your email is spam?

Zero   1%

15   23%

40   47%

100   19%

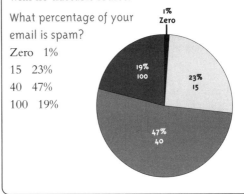

Request a Read Receipt in Outlook

Nicole Guilfoyle

Nothing is more frustrating than sending an email and waiting minutes, hours, days, or even weeks for a reply. Before you begin to think that your friends and co-workers are ignoring you, find out whether they read your message.

Outlook Express

To get a read receipt for an individual email, follow these steps:

1. Compose a message.
2. Before you click Send, go to Tools and check Request Read Receipt.

You can also tell Outlook Express that you want a Read Receipt for every message you send:

1. Choose Options from the OE Tools menu.
2. Go to the Receipts tab and put a check next to Request a Read Receipt for All Sent Messages.
3. Click OK.

Outlook 2000

Outlook 2000 is included in the fabulous Microsoft Office 2000 Suite of applications. To get a read receipt for an individual email, follow these steps:

1. Compose a message.
2. Before you click Send, go to View and choose Options.
3. Under Tracking, check Request a Read Receipt for This Message.

To get a read receipt for every message you send, follow these steps:

1. Click Tools and choose Options.
2. Go to the Preferences tab and click the Email Options button.
3. Click the Tracking Options button.
4. Check Request a Read Receipt for All Messages I send, and click OK.

Avoiding Attachment Trouble

Billy Parkinson

Cyberspace is a dangerous, virus–filled place, and you're probably wondering, "How should I handle all the attachments I get in my email?"

First, know who's sending the email that contains an attachment. The identity of the sender can speak volumes. Be sure to tell your friends and family if you're sending them an attachment. If you're really nice, you'll scan the attachment for viruses before you send it. Don't worry, a virus won't attach itself to the message after you click Send.

If you don't know the person who sent the email, or if the email address looks suspicious, you probably shouldn't open the file. Malicious viruses and worms infecting the Internet can send themselves from the address books of even your best friends. If you're not expecting an attachment from someone, it's probably best to scan the file with a virus scanner.

Where do you get a virus scanner? Here's a free (and safe!) download of AVG's antivirus tool: www.grisoft.com/us/us_dwnl_trial.php.

Address: Site of the Night

You Are My Friend Generator

Plug any name into http:// name.youaremyfriend.com, and it will spit out a personalized message that will surely warm your heart.

October
5

Send Email from Word, Excel, PowerPoint

Nicole Guilfoyle

A shortcut in Microsoft Office lets you send email from Word, Excel, and PowerPoint without opening Outlook or Outlook Express. There are two really simple ways to send email from your MS Office applications.

Use the Email Icon

1. Click the Email icon between the Save and Print icons. It looks like an envelope.
2. Choose to send the document, spreadsheet, or presentation as an attachment or in the body of your email.
3. Choose an email identity.
4. Fill out email information as usual.

Use the Send To Option

1. Go to File and choose Send To.
2. Choose Mail Recipient if you want to send the document, spreadsheet, or presentation in the body of the email. Choose Mail Recipient (as Attachment) if you want to send it as an attachment.
3. Choose an email identity and fill out email information as usual.

Download of the Day

Popcorn

Roger Chang

Popcorn (www.ultrafunk.com/products/popcorn) is like its movie-snack namesake: light and easy-to-use.

Popcorn lets you check multiple email accounts by reading mail off POP3 servers. People accustomed to more calorie-laden email clients such as Outlook may find it lacking.

True, it doesn't have complicated mail filters, an HTML viewer, or support for gee-whiz multimedia attachments. This also means it's less susceptible to macro viruses and funky email messages that make OE take forever to load. Browsing and sorting email are much, much quicker.

Windows Tips

Turn Off Zip Support

Morgan Webb

XP's built-in Zip support is dandy for the beginning user, but it can limit advanced users who want to control Zip files with WinZip (or some other decompression utility).

Windows XP treats zipped archives just like regular folders, but puts a zipper on the folder icon to notify you that it's a zipped archive. You can compress and decompress files, but the built-in support lacks the functionality of a full-fledged application.

Right-click a compressed folder and choose the General tab. Then, where it says Opens With, click the change button and change the file association to WinZip (www.winzip.com). Your icons should change to archive icons.

You can also totally clear the built-in Zip support by running a .dll. Go to the article at www.annoyances.org/exec/show/article03-202 for a string you enter in the Run box. This string clears your built-in Zip support and allows you to use the robust applications that you're used to.

Jessica's Tips

IM File Transfer

The best way to transfer large files between two computers on the Internet is through an instant messenger. In AOL Instant Messenger, just right-click the name of the recipient of the file and select Send file. Choose the file you want to sent, and then send it.

October

6

Leo's Email: Stop Spyware

Leo Laporte

Steve Gibson first raised the issue of spyware, or adware as some call it, on his website (http://grc.com/optout.htm). He defines spyware as "any software which employs a user's Internet connection in the background without their knowledge or explicit permission."

Shareware programs that are supported through banner ads generally install spyware. Spyware has a legitimate use: to update the ads and measure click-through so the software author can get paid. To do this, the spyware program must communicate periodically with the home office using your Internet connection. Almost all ad-supported shareware programs do this.

The problems that arise are twofold. No one can tell exactly what information the spyware is sending back to the home office. It could be specific personal information about your surfing habits or even data from your files. The traffic is encrypted so you can't be sure what's being sent back. Also, spyware programs usually remain on your hard drive even after the shareware program that installed it has been removed, consuming space, RAM, and CPU cycles.

From OptOut to Ad-aware

Steve created OptOut, a program that detects known spyware on your hard drive, but the explosive growth of spyware companies outpaced Steve's considerable energies. He stopped updating OptOut and began recommending a free program from Lavasoft (www.lavasoftusa.com) called Ad-aware.

Spybot—Search & Destroy

Now there are excellent spyware killers other than Ad-aware. The best, in our opinion, is the free Spybot—Search & Destroy by Patrick Kolla (http://security.kolla.de). It's effective and up-to-date. Run it regularly to detect spyware on your system. Understand that removing spyware may violate your license agreement with some programs and may also cause banner ad–supported programs on your system to stop functioning.

In most cases, shareware authors contract with a company that specializes in providing back-end support the ad banners. If you do install a program with banner ads, it's very important that you learn which spyware server the program uses, and read the privacy policies of both the shareware you're installing and the spyware server it uses. You can learn more about the various spyware programs at the SpyChecker database (www.spychecker.com).

Laporte Support

Filter Outlook Express Email

Automatically put your TSS newsletters in a special folder in Microsoft Outlook Express.

You need to create a message rule. It's not hard, and once you learn how, you'll want to create other rules for your email. Here's what you do:

- Open the newsletter (or other email you want to filter). Find an item that consistently shows up in the email header. For instance, in the TSS newsletter, you might select the To email address because it's the same from email to email.

- Launch Outlook Express and click on the Tools menu.

- Select Message Rules.

- In the first box, select Where the To Line Contains Certain People.

- Add the newsletter email address to the rule.

- In the bottom box, define the action that needs to be performed. Select Move It to a Specific Folder.

- Create the folder.

Jaguar's Spam Filters

Leo Laporte and Roman Loyola

Apple's email program that comes with Mac OS X, called Mail, is often eschewed for mail programs that have more features. Fortunately, the updated Mail program available with Jaguar has many new features, including a spam-filtering service that can help ease the load in your inbox.

Train the Spam Sieve

Mail's spam filtering is based on what Apple calls "adaptive latent semantic analysis." In plain English, Mail determines what is and isn't spam based on the content of the email you receive. Mail takes the email you've designated as spam, identifies patterns of content within that email, and uses this analysis to identify spam in future email. If you're interested in learning more about adaptive latent semantic analysis, check out a paper by the University of Colorado at http://lsa.colorado.edu/papers/dp1.LSAintro.pdf.

The key to Mail's filtering success is proper "training." When you first launch the new version of Mail, the spam feature is essentially blank. It has no definition of spam. You need to train the application to be able to correctly identify spam.

How to Train Mail's Spam Filter

The beauty of Mail's complex spam filter is that it's very easy to train and use. By default, the filter is set to its Training option. Here's how you access the spam-filter option:

1. Launch Mail. Click the Mail menu and point to Junk Mail.
2. A pop-up menu should appear. If you haven't modified it, it will be set to Training.

In Training mode, Mail is learning to define spam. When you get spam in your inbox, you tell Mail about the email by selecting it and then clicking the Junk button. Mail then uses that offending email as part of its definition of spam and identifies it as spam by using a color code. As you select more email as spam, the definition grows and Mail gets better at identifying spam.

If you get an email that's incorrectly identified as spam, all you have to do is select the email and then click the Not Junk button. Mail will then create a definition in its filter to designate future email like this one as not spam.

Mail's Spam Filter Goes Automatic

When you've decided that Mail has been a good student and is done training, you can set the spam filter to Automatic. Here's how you switch to Automatic mode:

1. Click the Mail menu and point to Junk Mail.
2. A pop-up menu should appear. Select Automatic.

In Automatic mode, Mail automatically moves email that fits the spam criteria into the Junk box.

Make sure you keep it in Training mode for a while to build a robust definition of spam. That way, when you switch to Automatic, you won't lose "real" email to your Junk folder.

You can inspect your Junk folder to see if an important email was erroneously marked as spam. Select the message and then click the Not Junk button.

Download of the Day

Proteus 2.0

Megan Morrone

Proteus (www.indigofield.com) is a chat client for Mac OS X that lets you talk to people using AIM, ICQ, IRC, Yahoo!, and MSN. It's a beautifully Aquafied program that looks as if it were created by Apple programs.

Proteus 2.0 is free to try and $10 to buy. Make sure to choose v.202 if you're not using Jaguar.

If you use Windows, try Trillian (www.trillian.cc).

October
8

Save Attachments to Disk

Nicole Guilfoyle

Your email attachments aren't stuck in Outlook Express forever. No, you don't have to copy and paste whatever's in them into a different program to save them. Follow these steps to save the attachments to a disk or your hard drive:

1. Select the email containing the attachment you want to save, and either choose Save Attachments from the File menu or right-click the Attachment icon (it looks like a paper clip) and choose Save Attachments.

2. Select the attachment you want to save.

3. Under Save To, click the Browse button and select where you want to save the attachment. You'll be able to choose your hard drive, floppy drive, or any external drive. Click OK.

4. Make sure you have a disk in your drive, and click Save.

Save Multiple Email Attachments at Once

I love using my email account to share files with friends, family, and co-workers. We trade just about everything—MP3s, video files, digital photos, documents, and more. I usually don't want to keep these files in my email program, so I save them to my hard drive. Microsoft Outlook and Outlook Express speed up this process by letting me save multiple attachments at once.

Are Your Attachments Safe?

First, you need to make sure you're not saving something that'll harm your system. Attachments can contain malicious computer viruses. Here are a couple ways to keep your system safe:

- Use your antivirus program to scan attachments.

- Don't just open attachments from people you know. Many viruses go through the Outlook Express Address Book and mail themselves out. Open and save only files you're expecting.

Save Multiple Attachments at Once

Now you're ready to save your attachments. Instead of opening each file individually, follow these steps:

1. Go to File and choose Save Attachments.

2. Browse to where you want to save the files on your hard drive. You might want to make a special Attachments folder in My Documents. Click Save.

Navigate to the files on your hard drive to view them anytime you want.

Download of the Day

ePrompter

Megan Morrone

Every good geek has more than one email account. Sure, we know how to download them all into one account, but that's messy, like letting your dessert touch your main course.

You can easily configure ePrompter (www.eprompter.com) to check all your web-based and POP accounts. ePrompter works with Yahoo! Mail, AOL, Hotmail, EarthLink, and more.

ePrompter sits in your system tray and flashes the number of messages you have in each account. If that bothers you, set up ePrompter as your screen saver so you'll know how many messages you have when you return to your desk.

With one click, you can view all your new messages separated by account, and you can reply to them from that very window, without the chance of your ketchup touching your pudding.

Back Up Your Address Book

Morgan Webb

We all know it's a really bad idea to have only one copy of your data on one hard drive. You need to create another copy, and you need to save it in a format that you can easily access. You can even print your data and keep a hard copy in your files. If you use the Windows XP address book, the whole process is a snap.

1. Open your address book in the accessories menu.
2. Go to File, Export, Other Address Book.
3. Choose the file type you want to export to, such as a text file. A text file is a good option because it's easily printed and universally compatible.
4. Follow the instructions for the fields you want to export.

You can also export your address book from Outlook XP.

1. Open Microsoft Outlook.
2. Enter your contacts page.
3. Choose File, Import and Export.
4. Choose to Export to a file.
5. You can choose from a good number of file formats. You can export to one or more to keep your addresses and contact information safe.

Web Tips

Know Your IP

There are two ways to get your basic TCP/IP configurations, including your IP address:

- For Windows 2000 and XP, Open the Run box, type **cmd**, and click OK. Then type **ipconfig/all**.
- For Windows 98 and Me, follow the above steps, but type **winipcfg** at the Run box.

Talkback

Mixed Messages

Dave Roos

Email address books and instant message "buddy lists" are a tech necessity, but the one-click convenience comes at a price. With one careless flick of the wrist, you can check the wrong address box and accidentally send "Mom" a private missive meant for "Mandi." Yuck!

According to mobile service provider Boltblue International, one in three people has accidentally text-messaged the wrong person.

The misdirected messages have brought disastrous (or at least embarrassing) results, including several love notes sent to confused relatives and insulted co-workers. The most common explanation for the mistaken messages is the proximity of names in a cell phone address book. One slip of the scroll button and—boom!—you've got some 'splaining to do.

Have you ever sent a digital message to the wrong person?

Yes 55%

No 45%

45% No

55% Yes

Check Your Email from Anywhere in the World

Martin Sargent and Roger Chang

You email addicts shouldn't be reading this. You sad little junkies who ache for the chirp or song that announces a new email message, like so many Pavlov's dogs aching for the ring of the meat bell.

We hate to be pushers, but we need to tell you about a few simple products and services that let you receive and reply to email when there's no computer in sight. Just promise that you won't use them when you're riding a ski lift or sitting in the third pew of church or something.

Listen to Your Email

Email-by-phone from j2 Global Communications (www.j2.com) is good medicine for sans-computer tremors. You can access email from any phone in the world. Call a toll-free number, input your j2 account and PINs, and a computerized, Stephen Hawking–like voice reads your email.

You can respond to email by leaving j2 a voice message that'll appear in your recipient's email inbox in the form of an audio attachment. The recipient can click on the file attachment and your voice will flow, with remarkable clarity, from their computer speakers.

Even if you never leave your computer, you can use j2 to receive voice mail and faxes in your email inbox. It's the epitome of unified messaging. Voice mail messages appear as audio sound files. You can save, annotate, and forward these audio messages just as you can with regular email.

Listen to the Fax

A one-minute voice mail message is about 100K, so you don't have to worry about massive files clogging the network. When friends and business associates send faxes to your j2 number, the documents appear in your email inbox just like the voice mails. Click on the fax file attachment, and the document appears on your computer screen, ready to print or annotate. A typical graphical fax consumes less than 50K of space.

The Bottom Line

After a $15 activation fee, you pay $12.50 per month for 30 minutes of use, plus 10 cents for each additional minute. As addictive drugs go, that's pretty cheap.

j2 is impressive, but not perfect. To use most of j2's services, your email system needs to use POP-3 or Post Office Protocol. Many popular email services, such as America Online and Hotmail, don't use POP-3. What's more, if your email server resides behind a corporate firewall, email by phone won't work.

Another Option

If you already have a Yahoo! Mail account (http://mail.yahoo.com), you can have your email read to you over the phone for $4.95 a month.

Talkback

Is It Spam If You Opt In?

Dave Roos

"Registration required" is the new online reality. Without thought, we trade our personal information for free access to online newspapers, software downloads, and useful Internet services. But hidden stealthily within most website registration forms lies a tiny check box that effectively sells your soul (and your email address) to spammers.

By not unchecking the box that says Send Me Offers, you have officially "opted in" for thousands of junk email messages.

Is it spam if you say okay?

Yes   50%

No   50%

50% Yes   50% No

Check Your Email from Anywhere in the World (continued)

Is That Email in Your Pocket?

What happens when scientists retire from NASA? They go to work for PocketScience and invent PocketMail, another way to receive and respond to email without a computer.

The PocketMail service works with two devices: PocketMail Composer (`https://shop.pocket.com/?a=composer`) and BackFlip for the Palm (`https://shop.pocket.com/?a=bf-palm`). Both devices weigh less than 9 ounces.

Both devices are slightly longer and thicker than a checkbook. The PocketMail Composer sports a full Qwerty keyboard and flip-out monochrome LCDs that display eight lines of 40 characters. The LCDs are sort of dim, but the keypads are big enough to type short messages without too much grief.

How It Works

On the back of each device is a snap-out acoustic coupler. You receive and send email by holding the coupler to the receiver of any phone on which you've dialed the toll-free PocketMail number. You press a button, and the device begins chirping and squawking like a flock of mechanical birds.

We tested both devices on the pay phone outside our office, one of the noisiest places in San Francisco. The message transfers went off without a hitch.

To receive messages, messages must be sent to your dedicated PocketMail email address (such as `sasquatch@pocketmail.com`). Your computer-based email accounts must be set to forward messages to your PocketMail address.

The Drawbacks

These addictive little gizmos can't send and receive messages of more than 4,000 characters. You also can't use PocketMail with digital wireless phones that can't switch to analog.

We've heard excellent reports on the Pocket-Mail service, but it's difficult to compose lengthy emails on one of these devices. It has a tiny keyboard that leads to errors if you have big fingers. Practice makes it less typo-prone.

If you already use email on a Palm, BackFlip might be the perfect solution. Just clip it on, install the software, and go.

Get a Phone Card

You need a phone card before you travel internationally with any of these devices. Inside the United States and Canada, you can dial a 1-800 number to catch your mail. Outside the United States, it's a regular toll number in the 408 area code.

What Email Can You Get?

Like many HTML-based mail systems, you can configure a PocketMail device to copy email from existing accounts, whether they use POP-3, IMAP4, or even AOL.

PocketMail's online user support pages offer assistance. If you get a ton of mail, you should use the message title preview feature, which downloads only the sender and subject fields for each email. You can then decide which email to download in its entirety.

Don't Tire Out Your Arm

You should also consider getting a Velcro strap for any of the PocketMail devices if you regularly send or receive more than five or six messages at a time. It takes around 30 seconds for three messages to upload or download. When you've got a lot of messages (or a few very long ones), holding the box to a handset can get tiring.

Remember to pack extra batteries. The models we tested were fairly thrifty, but hey, you don't want to run out. The PocketMail composer uses 2 AA batteries, and the BackFlip uses 2 AAA batteries.

October
12

Iris Packet Sniffing

Kevin Rose

Some of you might find this a bit scary. It's scary because it shows how insecure your information is on the Net. Give me a laptop, a network card, and software called Iris, and I can show you almost every email, instant message, and webpage requested across a network. Scary, huh? I don't know what's scarier, that your private information is floating around out there or that it's extremely easy to find.

Hop Around the Block

When you do anything on the Internet, your computer sends out little digital packets of information. These packets travel from your network card though many wires, eventually reaching your gateway. From there they're relayed through hops to reach their destination server.

Packet sniffing captures those packets of information on their way to your local machine. Many software packages capture packets, but only a few decode the packets into useful information.

Capture and Decode

Iris isn't just a packet-capturing program. It's also a decoder, turning what appears to be useless garbage (raw packet info) into viewable websites, email messages, and instant-messenger conversations.

Iris makes it easy to capture and decode packets on a network, but it does more. Iris has features for statistics, reports, filtering options, and scheduling. It's geared toward the corporate network administrator. At $995, it's no bargain, but you can download it at www.eeye.com/html/Products/Iris and use it free for 15 days. You can learn a grip (a lot) in 15 days.

Secure Yourself

Still a little freaked out that someone could intercept your information and read your most private thoughts? Here are a few tips to secure your information:

- Use encrypted instant messaging. Trillian Pro ($25, www.trillian.cc) offers encryption, and it's compatible with AIM, MSN, ICQ, Yahoo!, and IRC.

- Encrypt your email. Leo recommends Pretty Good Privacy (PGP, www.pgp.com). It's free, but the email recipient needs to use your public key to decrypt the email. Hushmail (www.hushmail.com) is a free web-based, encrypted email service.

- Encrypt your email attachments. PGP offers file encryption.

Windows Tips

Color Your Outlook Messages

Morgan Webb

Make messages from your boyfriend pink, email from your mom red, and messages from your boss a nice, nonthreatening light gray. Outlook 2002 has great tools to color-code your incoming mail.

- Click Tools and then Organize.
- Choose the Using Colors tab.
- Select a message from a sender you want to highlight.
- Choose a color from the palette, and click Apply Color.

That's it! Now every message from that sender will turn the color you choose.

Surf and Email Anonymously

Russ Pitts with Nicole Guilfoyle

Every time you browse the web, you leave a digital trail. You can protect your identity on the Net in two ways: encryption and IP redirection. Encryption, such as PGP, secures email but still lets a snooper track you on the Net. IP redirection drowns your real IP address in a sea of others, although the address still exists in a log that could find its way into court.

All anonymity services use at least one of these methods. The best use versions of both. We looked at three anonymity services, each offering slightly different services at wildly different prices.

Megaproxy

Megaproxy (www.megaproxy.com) couldn't be easier to use. Simply go to the website, enter the URL for the website you want to visit, and click Surf. You'll need to agree to the terms of service. When you're at your first website, you'll see a Megaproxy toolbar at the top of your browser window. Type any new web address in the address bar to surf in secret.

Anonymizer

Anonymizer (www.anonymizer.com) not only offers a complete anonymity package for a monthly fee, but also lets you surf through its servers (thereby hiding the original IP address) for no charge.

You get faster service if you pay. Anonymizer charges monthly on a sliding scale, but the company requires you to sign up for the pay service account. The more anonymity you want, the more you pay. The company even offers anonymous email.

Subdimension

Subdimension (www.subdimension.com) offers free, anonymous email and web surfing.

Its website says, "We ask NO QUESTIONS! We don't want to know who you are or why you need free email." Supposedly, it can't rat on you to the fuzz if it doesn't know who you are. Sounds good to me.

Freedom from Zero-Knowledge

Our favorite anonymity service is Freedom from Zero-Knowledge Systems (www.freedom.net). Version 3.2 provides anonymous web browsing, email, Telnet access, SSL, SSH, news groups, and IRC chatting.

Freedom protects your identity with a combination of encryption and redirection through Zero-Knowledge's collection of servers, called The Freedom Network.

It uses an unusual approach to isolating your actual identity. It calls the false identity Nym. When you buy Freedom, you get a serial number. You redeem that serial number for a token that you can then redeem for a Nym identity.

Freedom claims your real identity is completely isolated. It has to ask for your credit card number by law, but it drops that info after six months.

Web Tips

Easy Email Attachments

Nicole Guilfoyle

Here's an easier way to send email attachments using Outlook, Outlook Express, and Netscape Messenger. If you already know where the file is on your hard drive, why spend time browsing to find and attach it? Instead, follow these steps:

1. Open Windows Explorer or My Computer and find the file you want to attach.

2. Open your email client.

3. Right-click the file on your hard drive, click Send To, and choose Mail Recipient.

Or just drag and drop the file into a new email message.

October
14

Highlight Email Containing Attachments in Outlook Express

Nicole Guilfoyle

Viruses love Outlook Express. Many times the virus from an email attachment is designed to go into your address book and mail itself to everyone on your email list. Here are a few easy ways to protect yourself:

Increase Outlook Express Security

1. Go to Tools, Options, and the Security tab.
2. Place a check next to Warn Me When Other Applications Try and Send Mail as Me and Do Not Allow Attachments to Be Opened or Saved That Could Potentially Be a Virus.
3. Go to View, Layout, and make sure the Preview pane is disabled.

Don't Open Attachments

If we've said it once, we've said it a thousand times: "Don't open attachments!" Before you even dare open an email attachment, verify that it's a legitimate file from someone you know. When you're pretty sure it's safe to open, scan the file with your antivirus software to make sure it's really OK.

Spot Attachments Faster

You can use the Mail Rules feature to spot messages with attachments:

1. Click Tools, Message Rules, Mail.
2. Make a new rule.
   - Under Select the Conditions for Your Rule, check Where the Message Has an Attachment.
   - Under Select the Actions for Your Rule, check Highlight It with Color.
   - Choose a color, name your rule, and click OK.

Potentially hazardous attachments will now stick out like sore thumbs.

Windows Tips

Group Outlook Messages

Morgan Webb

You can group your Outlook email by one of dozens of fields:

1. Go to your open Outlook 2002 email inbox.
2. Right-click the column header and choose Group by Box.
3. A new row appears above your inbox with Drag a Column Header Here to Group by That Column in faded gray.
4. You can drag a column header (such as From) into this box to sort by sender's name, or you can select from an extensive list.
5. To access all your choices, right-click the column header again and choose Field Chooser. You can drag and drop any of these choices into your new row to sort all messages by the field you choose.
6. To undo this operation, just drag your new field back into the Field Chooser.

This is a convenient tool to quickly sort and unsort by many different fields.

Address: Site of the Night

Torture a Spammer

Exact revenge for all those annoying emails at Torture a Spammer, http://torturegame.emailsherpa.com/.

Save Your Hotmail to Your Hard Drive

Greg Melton

Most web-based email providers supply only 2MB to 5MB of storage space before they delete messages to free up space in your account. It takes only a single email with a large attachment to have your stored messages deleted.

How can you avoid losing your messages? You can delete old messages, you can buy additional space, or you can archive your email.

Tools of the Trade

To archive a web-based email account, we're going to use Outlook Express. Outlook Express synchs directly with Hotmail (which uses the HTTP protocol), as well as other web-based email providers that support the POP3/SMTP standard.

If you don't have Outlook Express 6.0, you should consider upgrading. Version 6.0 is bundled with Internet Explorer 6.0. You don't have to upgrade, but you might need to follow slightly different steps with other versions of Outlook Express. For Explorer 6.0, go to http://windowsupdate.microsoft.com.

Import Hotmail

To archive web-based email, follow these directions to import your mail account into Outlook Express:

1. Go to Start, Programs, Outlook Express.
2. From Outlook's Tools menu, choose Accounts.
3. Click the Mail tab. (You set up wizards to import your web-based email account in the Mail tab.)
4. Click the Add button, choose Mail.
5. Give the account a name; click Next.
6. Fill in your Hotmail email address; click Next.
7. In the Email Servers Name section, the incoming mail server should already be set to HTTP and the mail service provider should be set to Hotmail. Leave this page alone, and click Next.
8. In the Internet Mail Logon screen, use your entire Hotmail email address as your logon name. Type your password in the Password box, and click Next.

9. Click Finish, and close the Internet Account window.
10. A pop-up window will ask if you'd like to download all the folders in your account. Click OK.
11. Click the Send/Receive button to download the contents of those folders onto your system. The messages remain on the Hotmail server even after they're downloaded.

Archive Messages

Now that you've downloaded all the messages to your Hotmail account, it's time to archive. Create a new folder on your Desktop, and name it something like "Email Archive."

Drag the email messages you want to archive to the folder you just created.

1. Click the inbox under your Hotmail account, and click any message in your Hotmail account.
2. While the message you selected is active, press Ctrl+A to select all the messages in your account.
3. Click Restore in the upper-right corner of Outlook Express, between the Minimize and Close buttons.
4. Reposition Outlook Express so you can see the messages you selected and the Email Archive folder on your desktop.
5. Click, hold, and drag the highlighted messages onto the Email Archive folder. When you see a little plus sign, release your mouse button to copy the messages to the Email Archive folder.
6. Double-click the Email Archive folder to see if everything transferred correctly.

303

Sunday
October 17
2004

When Is It Safe to Open Email Attachments?

***Call for Help* Staff**
We all love sharing photos, video clips, and documents via email, but opening attachments can be dangerous. Clicking on some files can launch malicious code, infecting your PC with a virus, worm, or Trojan horse. Antivirus software can help protect your system, but it's not always foolproof, as we show when we answer this question from a viewer:

> "I have McAfee Anti-Virus, and it scans for viruses automatically. Can I open an email with an attachment and be safe?"

It is relatively safe to save the attachment to a disk and then scan it with an antivirus program, but any attachment introduces the risk of a virus. There is a lag of a day or two between the time a virus begins to spread and when the antivirus program is updated. You are vulnerable for those few days.

There's also a category of programs called Trojan horses that are not strictly viruses and are not necessarily known to antivirus companies. A nasty program is placed inside a beautiful package that's sent as an attachment. Open the attachment, and you can infect your system. A safe rule of thumb is to never open email attachments. This is the only way to ensure that your computer remains free of viruses.

Windows Tips

Windows Updates
Going to Windows Update (http://v4.window-supdate.microsoft.com) is a pain. Let Windows do the dirty work.

- Right-click My Computer, choose Properties.
- Select the Automatic Updates tab.
- Check Keep My Computer up to Date.

Download of the Day

Spell Checker for OE
Phil Allingham
Microsoft, in all its wisdom, loves to tie its products together. Apparently, it's easier for Microsoft to use Word's dictionary than to build another one for OE. That makes sense, but there are two issues: People who don't have Microsoft Word are out of luck, and combining various versions of Word and OE seems to render the spell check useless.

If you're smart, you'll download Spell Checker for OE (www.geocities.com/vampirefo), and kiss those spelling errors goodbye. Install it to activate the spell-check feature in Outlook Express.

Laporte Support

Overactive Spam Filter

Kevin Rose's mom was receiving 70 spam messages a day on her Hotmail account, so her helpful son moved her email account to Outlook Express and installed Cloudmark's SpamNet, a trusted spam filter. The only problem is, now she gets none of her email at all—only a "bad password" message.

Kevin used Remote Desktop to fix her account. In Outlook, he went to Tools, Email Accounts, View/Change Existing Account and selected her account. Then he gave her a new password in the Change Password fields. This is a common problem when a computer expert sets up something for a beginner and then leaves before the beginner knows what's been changed and why it doesn't work. "Beware geeks bearing gifts!"

Forward AOL Email

Nicole Guilfoyle
Email forwarded from America Online accounts is often stuffed with extra information, such as greater than (>) and less than (<) symbols, the email addresses of former recipients, and delivery information. How do you forward email (in AOL) without sending all the other email addresses in the message?

AOL Forwarding Solution

The easiest way to forward email from your AOL account without getting all the extra stuff is to highlight the information you want to send and click the Forward button. However, this might not strip the delivery information from all messages. A better way is to copy the text you want to forward and paste it into a new message. You'll need to reattach any files or pictures you're trying to forward.

Strip Out > and < Symbols

You may notice that every time an email is forwarded, more greater than and less than symbols are added at each line break. Strip them out before you resend your message.

If you don't want to backspace over every symbol, there are free tools such as ClipCache (www.rosecitysoftware.com) and StripMail (www.dsoft.com) that will do it for you.

Web Tips

Send Email Faster

Nicole Guilfoyle
Everyone writes personal email at work. But it's hard to send your messages when the boss is looking over your shoulder.

1. Sign on to your email server when you open Outlook or Outlook Express.

2. Write your message.

3. Press Alt+S to send your email right away without having to click the Send button.

You can even use this hotkey combination while Outlook or Outlook Express is minimized. This way, you can send your email fast without anyone knowing.

Laporte Support

Default Web Browser

Change a setting so Mozilla launches instead of Internet Explorer when you click an email link using Microsoft Outlook. Check two settings in Mozilla.

Default Browser

1. Launch Mozilla.

2. Go to Edit, choose Preferences.

3. Expand the Navigator category.

4. Under the Default Browser heading, click the Set Default Browser button.

Mozilla System Properties

1. Launch Mozilla.

2. Go to Edit, choose Preferences.

3. Expand the Advanced category by clicking the triangle next to it. Choose System.

4. In the top window labeled Windows Should Use Mozilla to Open These File Types, check the box for HTML. If you want to use Mozilla to open the other file types in the box, check those, too.

5. In the bottom window labeled Windows Should Use Mozilla to Handle These Protocols, check the boxes for http: and https:. Check the box for Alert Me If Other Applications Change These Settings.

October
18

305

Email Header Secrets

Megan Morrone

Every email message contains two types of headers. You're probably familiar with the partial headers (sender, recipient, and subject). If you want to know more, you'll have to view the extended headers.

Find the Header Information

To read an email header, first you must find it. Different email clients hide headers in different ways.

View headers in Outlook and Outlook Express:

1. Click File.
2. Choose Properties.
3. Select the Details tab.

View headers in Outlook 98:

1. Click the View menu.
2. Select Options.
3. Extended headers are under Internet Headers.

View headers in Netscape Mail:

1. Click View.
2. Choose Headers.
3. Select All.

View headers in Eudora:

1. Click Tools.
2. Choose Options.
3. Select Fonts & Display.
4. Make sure the Show All Headers box is checked.

In newer versions of Eudora, just click the BLAH button on your toolbar.

What Email Headers Mean

From top to bottom, here's what your email header means:

```
Return-Path: <megan@techtv.com>
```

This is the sender's address:

```
Received: from
```

This header contain the sender's name and the reverse-DNS lookup of the sender's IP address. A new received: from is added at each place the message passes along the way.

If I send a message to you, it will contain information from my machine, my mail server's machine, your mail server's machine, your machine, and any machine it visited in between. The newest received line is always placed on top. Follow this path to learn more about where your message has been.

Spammers can forge some of these headers, but it's pretty tough to forge all of them. If you think you're the victim of a forgery, check for discrepancies. The bottom line is usually the real origination:

```
with SMTP id KAA10292
```

This means that the system uses Simple Mail Transfer Protocol to send messages. Most email systems use SMTP. The machine uses the ID number to track messages. Network administrators use this ID number to find messages in the log files:

```
Fri, 20 Oct 2004 10:36:53 -0700 (PDT)
```

This is the time when the servers communicated with one another:

```
X-Sender or X-Mailer
```

These headers represent more layers of authentication. Because these features are optional and are added by the user, spammers and hackers can tamper with them:

```
Mime-Version: 1.0
```

Mime stands for Multipurpose Internet Mail Extensions. It lets you exchange audio, video, images, and other attachments via email:

```
Content-type: text/plain; charset=us-
ascii
```

This part of the header tells you what kind of attachments the message contains. The previous example means I've sent an ASCII attachment. Everything I listed here can be forged, but not as easily as simply forging your email's return address. Good luck with your detective work.

October

19

Stop XP's Messenger from Loading

Morgan Webb

If you don't use Windows Messenger, you might find Windows XP slightly annoying. Windows XP really wants you to use Messenger, not in an evil plot to decrease productivity, but to get you used to one of the major players in the .NET platform. Consequently, even if you have purposely exited the Messenger, when you open Outlook or Outlook Express, a glance into your system tray will show the little program back again. There is a solution, and it doesn't include any drastic, deleterious steps.

Make Messenger Scram

1. Go to your Programs folder.
2. Rename the Messenger folder to MessengerNo or MessengerIHateYou or MyNameIsMrHappy. Messenger will no longer load when you open Outlook.
3. To get your Messenger back, just rename GodzillaAteMyPants back to Messenger, and all will be restored—especially your dignity.

Address: Site of the Night

PhoneSpell

Martin Sargent

Ever wish you had a really cool phone number in which the corresponding letters to the seven digits actually spelled something cool, such as 555-NERD or THE-PIMP? Well, maybe you do.

If you want to find out if the digits in your phone number compose a word or phrase, go to PhoneSpell (www.phonespell.org). Just type your phone number into the box, and it'll tell you what the number spells.

Windows Tips

Choose How Much .NET You Want

Morgan Webb

You need to know what .NET means before you decide how much .NET you want. Here's what you need to know:

- .NET signs you in with one password (often linked to free services, such as MSN Messenger and Hotmail).
- .NET allows you to be registered with many sites and services around the Internet.
- Microsoft wants you to use your .NET Passport, so it likes to sign you in and keep you signed in.

In Windows XP, you can check your privacy settings and see what information .NET has about you:

1. Choose User Accounts from your Control Panel.
2. Double-click the user account whose .NET information you want to see.
3. Choose Change My .NET Passport, and select Change Passport Attributes.
4. If you're not already signed into your Passport account, sign in now.
5. You can see and change the information it has about you, including your name, birth date, and state of residence.
6. Scroll down to the bottom of the page. Three check boxes give permission for .NET to share your name and email address with third-party websites. Make sure these check boxes are unchecked.

You can delete your passport account altogether:

1. Open User Accounts from the Control Panel, and select the user account you want to modify.
2. Under Related Tasks, choose Manage My Network Passwords.
3. Highlight the passport account you want to delete, and click Remove.

October
20

Email Pictures

Greg Melton

Use this guide to email pictures located on a CD-ROM:

1. Open Windows Explorer by going to Start, Programs, Windows Explorer. Or use Windows+E on your keyboard for a shortcut.

2. Locate the pictures on the CD-ROM.

3. Hold down the Ctrl key and click all the pictures you'd like to email.

4. Right-click any of the highlighted pictures, mouse over Send To, and select Mail Recipient.

5. You should now see all the pictures attached to a new message in your default email program.

If the disc you have is a special Kodak Picture CD, it should come with a built-in application that allows you to email or print pictures. You need to configure the Kodak Picture CD mail settings before you can send mail using its built-in application. Because there are many different volumes and versions of the Kodak Picture CD, the easiest way to figure out how to configure your email settings go to the Support Center at www.kodak.com.

Download of the Day

SpamPal

Megan Morrone

SpamPal (www.spampal.org.uk) is a cool little utility that sets up a proxy server to trap spam and send it to a folder before it clutters your inbox. I've tried several spam killers in the past, and so far, SpamPal is the most effective.

Configure SpamPal with your email account. Don't forget to set up your spam filters to send the junk to a separate folder. SpamPal comes with several built-in filters, but if it's not catching all the spam, you can configure it further from the icon in your system tray.

Windows Tips

Get Organized with Virtual Desktop Manager

Sarah Lane

Are you someone who likes to work on a ton of programs but hates having a million little tabs open in your taskbar? Then you should grab Virtual Desktop Manager (www.microsoft.com/windowsxp/pro/downloads/powertoys.asp) for Windows XP. This nifty download lets you see your desktop four different ways at once.

Four Fabulous Views

It's important to realize that Desktop Manager isn't running four different instances of your desktop. Instead, it runs in your taskbar and groups, say, graphics programs together, Word docs together, and Internet/email programs together. You can toggle through lots of programs using only four buttons.

Of course, you can also use the four-box view to keep things in order. It's all about organization. You can also set four different desktop backgrounds, and even use keyboard shortcuts to toggle between desktops if you want to abandon the toolbar completely. I also recommend turning off Use Animations by right-clicking on the Manager in your taskbar. Speeds things up a little.

You're a perfect candidate for this program if you frequently have so many minimized programs on your taskbar that you can't keep 'em straight. Try it out: Download, play with some options, and see if you like it!

Email Without a PC

Andrew Hawn

Not everyone wants, or needs, all the power, expense, and inconvenience (and frustration, for that matter) that a full notebook or desktop computer provides. Email is another story. Even if you don't want to browse the web or frag your friends in Unreal, most people, even my grandmother, still need email access. So when Grandma asked me for "the email" in her quasi-Southern drawl, I suggested one of the email-only devices.

Email-Only Devices

Earthlink's MailStation 350 provides the basics of email without the hassle. It's one of the easiest email-only devices to set up. The hardware costs about $100, and dialup service is $13 a month. You'll get an email address and limited news updates (www.earthlink.net).

PDAs Pack a Punch

Today's PDAs and PDA/cell phone hybrids are much more capable than the basic contact and calendar handhelds of two and three years ago. Many offer integrated keyboards (portable keyboards such as the Targus Universal IR Keyboard [www.targus.com] are also available), built-in Wi-Fi 802.11b wireless access, and 3G wireless wide-area network service.

Most 3G service plans allow PDA/cell phone hybrids such as the TMobile HipTop (with support for direct wireless AOL email and AIM, www.danger.com) and Sony Ericsson P800 (www.sonyericsson.com) to access email pretty much anywhere there's wireless service. All you need is a POP email account, and you're good to go. Heck, you don't even need that. Hotmail and Yahoo! Mail services are free. All you need is the connection.

Using a PDA or hybrid for email is a good option if you're not tech-savvy.

Download of the Day

AlbumDIY

Dan Mitchell

Sending photos in an email is pretty impersonal. Most of the time, those precious images end up in the Recycle Bin or "saved" at the bottom of someone's inbox. Here's how to create a multi-media photo album that looks like you really put some effort into it.

AlbumDIY (www.visimon.com/index_en.htm) is a wizard-based program that lets you design every aspect of your photo album and then email it as an executable. The recipient on the other end doesn't need the program to open the album. The album is completely your creation. You can see the changes as you make them. Here's how you use it:

1. Click Create a New Album to get started.
2. Follow the wizard to customize the look of the album. You can use stock designs and graphics or browse for your own.
3. When your album looks good, the wizard walks you through adding photos.
4. Click a picture and resize it on the page to adjust the layout of the pages.
5. Add more pictures to the page and adjust until you have the desired layout.
6. Add optional text and graphics to the pages.

Now it's time to add music, so that when recipients open the album, they're greeted with some mood-setting tunes:

1. Click Insert and select New Multimedia.
2. Choose an audio file. As far as I can tell, any audio format works. (I used MP3.)
3. When you're ready to send your creation, click File and choose Build/Distribute Album. You can password-protect the album, save it to your hard drive, and email it out.

AlbumDIY also includes a slide-show mode, a full-screen mode, and a picture-only option. It's a fun, easy-to-use way to send photos. The results look amazing. Best of all, it's free.

October

22

Stop Spam in Its Tracks

Morgan Webb

There's no perfect way to stop spam, but just as spammers will never stop sending it, we will never stop trying to block it. There are a number of sophisticated spam-filtration techniques, but Outlook 2002 has a rudimentary filter already built in. You can flag certain junk mail senders as automatically trash-bound with the flick of a couple of key strokes, so you'll never again wonder if now is a good time to refinance your home.

Mac OS X 10.2 users are laughing because their new content-based spam filters are much more sophisticated than those included with Outlook. Read how the OS X 10.2 filters work on October 8, and try not to get too jealous. Here's how to use the ones you have, if you're using Outlook (not Outlook Express) 2002.

Block That Spam

1. While looking at your inbox, go to Tools, Organize. A new panel should appear above your inbox.

2. Click the Junk Email tab. You need to have downloaded mail for the tab to appear.

3. You can choose to automatically gray out spam messages or automatically move the messages to a certain folder. Turn on the feature.

4. Highlight a junk mail message. Go to Actions, Junk Email, Add to Junk Senders List.

5. You can also use the shortcut Alt+A, J, J, again to add the message to junkmail.

6. Delete the spam message. Future messages from the sender will be treated as you specified in the third step.

Download of the Day

MyIM

Megan Morrone

Get rid of the ads in AIM with MyIM (http://home.rochester.rr.com/artcfox/MyIM/Download.html). The program is easy to use and has other cool features. Simply download and run it, and your ads are gone.

Other cool things MyIM does:

- Logs into more than one AIM screen name and chats with both simultaneously.
- Makes AIM transparent (works only with Windows 2000/XP).
- Customizes your AIM toolbar.

Unfortunately, MyIM doesn't work with the newest version of AIM, which is now the only version available on AOL's site. You can download an older version of AIM at MyIM or at OldVersion.com (www.oldversion.com/aol.shtml). You need version 4.8 or earlier.

Laporte Support

Shut Off Outlook's Preview Pane

Viruses are precisely why we recommend turning off the Preview feature in Outlook Express. Open Outlook Express and select View, Layout. Under Preview Pane, uncheck Show Preview Pane and save your changes. This prevents you from previewing your messages without opening them and protects your computer from viruses carried in HTML messages.

Default Email in IE

Greg Melton

Have you ever noticed that when you click on an email link on a webpage, your browser automatically opens an email program window? This is a great feature, but only if the email program that appears is the one you regularly use. When I try to send email from a website, I get a pop-up saying there's no program to send email. Why? You need to change a setting in Internet Explorer so that it correctly displays the email client of your choice:

1. Click the Start menu, Settings, and select Control Panel.
2. Double-click Internet Options, and select Programs tab.
3. Use the Email pull-down menu and change it to the email client of your choice.
4. When finished selecting, click Apply.
5. Test your new change on the next email link you see.

Laporte Support

Outlook Express Attachments

Sometimes OE won't open attachments for security reasons. Viruses are often sent through email as an attachment. If you open such an attachment, you launch the virus. We always tell people to never open attachments in email, even if the email is from a friend. Friends often inadvertently spread viruses.

You can override OE's restriction, but it's dangerous. Do so at your own risk.

1. In Outlook Express, click Tools and select Options.
2. Click the Security tab.
3. Look in the Virus Protection area. Uncheck the box for Don't Allow Attachments to Be Saved Because of Potential Viruses.

Web Tips

Unsend Email

Nicole Guilfoyle

Oops! You didn't intend to send out that email. Don't worry. It's not too late to get it back if both you and the recipients are on America Online.

1. Click Mail and choose Read Mail.
2. Go to the Sent Mail tab and select the email you want to unsend.
3. Click Unsend.

Why Isn't It Working?

You can unsend an email only if it hasn't been opened. You don't need to draw suspicion by asking around. Just check to see if anyone's read the email using your AOL Mail tools.

1. Click Mail and choose Read Mail.
2. Go to the Sent Mail tab and select the email you want to unsend.
3. Click the Status button. If your email is Not Yet Read, you can retrieve it.

Also, you can unsend only email that hasn't left the AOL server domain. You won't be able to retrieve email sent to a non-AOL account, such as Hotmail or Yahoo!

Make Macros in MS Office

Morgan Webb

You write the same documents every day, make the same file changes, and add the same text. Microsoft Word and Excel can be customized to make the program work for you.

You can record and use macros to automatically add your official letterhead, add the formal introduction you use over and over, cut, paste, indent, italicize, format, move, insert, and do anything you can do. Follow these steps:

- Open Word. Go to Tools, Macro, Record New Macro.

- Type a useful name for your impending macro.

- Choose Keyboard if you want to assign a shortcut key to your macro, or choose Toolbars if you want a toolbar button.

- If you chose Keyboard, assign a shortcut key, click Assign, and Close to start recording. If you chose Toolbars, drag the new button in the Commands column up to your toolbar.

- When you close these windows, you will have a new little toolbar with commands like a tape deck. Perform the action you want to record, and click the Stop button when you are finished.

- You're finished. I know, that was easy. Hit your keyboard shortcut or toolbar button to use your new macro over and over and over again.

Web Tips

Save Yahoo! Email

First, try a free file called YahooPops (`http://yahoopops.sourceforge.net/downloads.html`). It communicates with your Yahoo! account and lets you save the messages into programs such as Outlook, Outlook Express, and Eudora.

Another option is to forward each email message you want to save to another email account (from your ISP, Hotmail, etc.) and erase it off the Yahoo! server to free up space.

Address: Site of the Night

Email Admin Game

Martin Sargent

Some people have the perfect job: a job that combines intellectual rigor with high adventure, a job that confers on them the admiration of their fellow human beings. Examples: the archaeologist who finds the lost temple, the doctor who saves the innocent child's life, the entertainer who electrifies and inspires the audience with a performance.

And the email administrator who keeps his company's electronic mail system running smoothly. Now, thanks to the game Spool from BVRP USA Software and UserFriendly.org (`www.bvrpusa.com/uf/game1.asp`), you can virtually live the exciting and rewarding life of an email administrator, experiencing, if only for a fleeting few minutes, what it's like to hold one of the most cherished of occupations.

The goal of the game is to keep spam and viruses from entering employees' computers while allowing good mail to flow freely, like fallen leaves in an unpolluted mountain stream, to the workers' inboxes.

The viruses are represented by the scary-fanged faces; the spam is represented by the envelopes with the red X. If you fail to uphold your solemn oath as email administrator and allow too many viruses or spam into inboxes, or if you delete too much good mail, the employees revolt and go home for the day. The life of the email administrator, though glamorous, is also fraught with danger.

Secret of Using Outlook Express with Dialup

Nicole Guilfoyle

You dial up to the Net and launch Outlook Express to check your email. Everything seems to be going fine until you finish sending and receiving your messages.

When Outlook Express 6 is finished receiving mail, it shuts down your Internet connection. What is happening? Don't worry. Outlook Express isn't working against you. It's trying to be helpful in its own no-nonsense way. You have an option selected that tells Outlook Express to disconnect your dialup connection when it finishes sending and receiving email.

This option is designed for people who just want to download messages from email servers and get offline fast. It's perfect for dialup users who don't have unlimited Internet access so they never forget to sign off after checking their email.

Here's how to disable the option:

1. Choose Options from the Tools menu.
2. Go to the Connection tab and uncheck Hang Up After Sending and Receiving.
3. Click Apply and OK.

Now you'll be able to check your email and surf without being disconnected by Outlook Express. If you later decide that you want to quickly pop online, get your messages, and log off, put that check back next to Hang Up After Sending and Receiving.

Megan's Tips

XP's Keyboard

Windows XP has a software keyboard you can use in place of your keyboard.

1. Go to Start, Accessories, Accessibility.
2. Click on the on-screen keyboard.

Download of the Day

Hivelogic Email Address Encoder

Megan Morrone

If you have a website, you probably want to give visitors your email address. But when you post it on your page, you're leaving yourself wide open to spambots that troll the web looking for defenseless email addresses to scoop up and attack with spam or sell to spammers.

You're also leaving yourself vulnerable to viruses. Some email viruses actually go into the cache of the person affected by the virus and find email addresses in webpages the person has visited. If someone has visited your site lately, you're in trouble.

Thanks to Dan P. Benjamin at Hivelogic for creating a simple antispam tool that you can use on the web or download to your Mac or PC. Enter your email address and link text, and click on Encode it. Dan's tool translates your address to special characters and wraps it in JavaScript. The result is simple code that you can cut and paste onto your website that spambots are too stupid to decipher.

You can download the Hivelogic Email Address Encoder for PC at www.hivelogic.com. You can download the Hivelogic Email Address Encoder for Mac OS X, Linux, and UNIX Variants at www.hiveware.com. Or use the Hivelogic web form, http://hivelogic.com/encoder.

October
26

313

Breaking the Chain of Spam

Cat Schwartz

Just over half of my 300 emails a day are spam. You've seen these annoying emails, everything from "Click Here for a New Car" to "Free Money Is Here for You" and worse. I'm bringing you some relief.

First, sign up for a free email account and use it to sign up for services so that your private account isn't bombarded with spam. After that's taken care of, get your friends to stop sending chain letters.

To get rid of those pesky chain letters that promise all sorts of bad luck, good health, and love, love, love, visit BreakTheChain.org (www.breakthechain.org). The folks running the site take time to look into the validity of each and every chain letter submitted to the site. There are thousands of reviews to look at. You can search for a keyword within the title of the email, and you're likely to find a write-up about it.

Report the Spammers

Reporting spam to your Internet service provider is easier than ever. Most ISPs, including AOL, now include a Report Spam button on the email interface. Nice touch. Useful change. Most free email services also provide spam filtering and reporting. Yahoo! Mail (http:// mail.yahoo.com) recently improved its SpamGuard feature.

Wash Your Mail

MailWasher (www.mailwasher.net/ download.php)works independently, so it doesn't matter which email client you use. It does not work with web-based email.

Once it's set up, MailWasher will ask whether the mail you are looking at needs to be deleted or bounced. If you want to keep the mail, don't check either of the boxes. If the mail is spam, just click the Bounce button, and it sends an email to the sender saying that your address is no longer valid, which should cause the spam to stop. After some time, the spam will dwindle down to the mail you love.

Download of the Day

HideOE

Megan Morrone

HideOE (www.r2.com.au/downloads/ index.html?id=hideoe) is a simple download that sends Outlook Express to your system tray (instead of your taskbar) when you minimize the program. Click the icon to read your mail.

Talkback

Save a Tree, Send Spam

Dave Roos

The U.S. Postal Service has its fair share of flaws, to put it mildly. On an average day, I get ten pieces of mail. Four are bills for previous occupants; three are preapproved credit card applications, two are grocery circulars, and one is the crumpled, creased, and presumably chewed remains of an envelope stamped "Photos: Do not bend."

My paper recycling bin fills up faster than the complaint box at the DMV, and what's worse, there's absolutely nothing I can do about it. There's no such thing as a "junk mail filter," and complaining to my mailman only ensures further misdirection of my precious holiday cards and phone bills.

Would you rather delete ten spam emails or throw away ten Pottery Barn catalogs?

Which is worse?

Paper junk mail   45%

Email spam   55%

55%
Email spam

45%
Junk mail

Email Huge Files in Outlook Express

Nicole Guilfoyle and Phil Allingham

We're constantly asked for ways to make it easier to email large files.

You don't need to pick and choose which files you want to split. Outlook Express will do it for you.

1. Click Tools and choose Accounts.
2. Select the account you want to use, and click Properties.
3. Go to the Advanced tab. Under Posting, put a check next to Break Apart Messages Larger Than.
4. Set the message size to 500KB; most ISPs will accept only 1MB. Click OK.

Whenever you email a huge file, Outlook Express will send it in manageable pieces.

Now you need to tell your friends how to reassemble those pieces on their end.

1. Click your inbox, click Messages, and choose Combine and Decode.
2. Select the messages you need to combine, and make sure they're in order.
3. Combine 'em!

NetMeeting in Windows XP

Roman Loyola

NetMeeting hasn't disappeared. It's just hiding. Microsoft wants Windows XP users to rely on Windows Messenger for communicating on the Internet. If you used NetMeeting (Windows built-in netcam program) in the past, you're supposed to switch to Windows Messenger.

If you want to use NetMeeting, here's how you can find it:

1. Click on the Start menu.
2. Select Run.
3. Type **conf** in the Open field and click OK.

NetMeeting launches. You'll have to go through the setup wizard the first time you launch it.

Web Tips

AOL and Outlook Express

Michelle VonWald

AOL is an ISP; it lets you receive email and surf the Net. Outlook Express is an email client, but it needs a Net connection or ISP to receive and send email.

AOL doesn't make it easy to use Outlook Express. You can download a third-party software called eNetBot (www.enetbot.com). It can be difficult to configure, but if you want to keep AOL as your gateway to the Net, it can be a viable solution. If you need a better email client, you might want to try Netscape Mail (www.netscape.com) or Eudora (www.eudora.com). Both are free and compatible with AOL.

Address: Site of the Night

Google Watch

Is Google merely a useful search engine or a vicious, calculating monopoly? Visit www.google-watch.org and decide for yourself.

October
28

Get the Best Dialup Speed

Tom Merritt

If your dialup modem is set for 56 Kbps, you've probably noticed that it never runs at more than 45 Kbps. That's because you never get the full speed out of your dialup modem. A speed of 45 Kbps on a 56-Kbps modem is reasonable and no cause for concern.

Six factors contribute to the speed of your connection:

- Your modem speed
- Your phone-cord quality
- Your phone-line quality
- Your ISP
- Your modem
- The Internet's speed

Your computer may report a 56-Kbps connection, but that might not be accurate. Why? FCC regulations state that line speeds can't exceed 53 Kbps. So even though modems are advertised as being 56 Kbps, you'll never be able to reach a modem's full potential using your telephone line. More likely it's a quirk in the way your modem reports the speed. To find out your true speed, go to DSL Reports (www.dslreports.com) and follow the links, or download AnalogX's NetStat Live (www.analogx.com).

When to Worry

If your connection speed is more than 15 Kbps below your modem rating, you might want to worry. I wouldn't worry about 42-Kbps on a 56-Kbps modem, but I would worry about 28 Kbps.

What to Do

NetStat Live or another diagnostic tool will help you determine if your modem operates properly. If you're sure about your modem, move on.

Phone cord: Is it old, frayed, or broken? Make sure it's a good, clean cord. You can plug a phone into it and listen to see if it works well. Still have doubts? Replace it with a new one.

Phone line: You can diagnose your own line or get the phone company to do it for a fee. Your phone company may clean the line for free if you claim that you can't clearly hear callers or that elderly callers can't hear you. Phone companies will not clean your line for free if you just want to increase your data rate.

Your ISP: Sometimes your ISP doesn't have the bandwidth to handle all its users. Speak up. Enough people complaining about service may get your ISP to add more capacity. You could alert it to a problem that it didn't know existed. You may also consider trying a different access number.

Your modem: Even though your modem is brand new, it may need upgrading. By upgrading we mean its firmware or drivers. Firmware is the modem's internal programming that you can update at a later date. Check the manufacturer's website to see if it has a "modem update" section for downloading the latest firmware version. Some manufacturers may also refer to this as a "driver update." Firmware upgrades are easy to install. Just follow the directions.

The Internet: Sometimes the Net gets slow. This usually doesn't affect your connection to your ISP, but it can. If your connection speed is only slow every so often, and everything else listed above works well, you can blame the Net.

October
10

Decipher Modem Speeds

Roger Chang

What is the difference between 32 Kbps, 115000, and 480000 when I look at my modem speed? Is one faster than the others?

Modem speed is a confusing subject for many people. The previous numbers, while related to a computer's modem, do not refer to the same thing. For example, the RPM speed of a car's engine does not indicate the speed of the car while in motion. That's indicated by the speedometer.

Let's take a look at the numbers 32 Kbps, 115000, and 480000. Modems come in several speeds. The most common speeds are 28.8 Kbps, 33.6 Kbps, and 56 Kbps. Kbps stands for *kilobits per second*. It's a measurement of how much data can be transferred in a given time. In this case, how many thousands of bits per second. All these numbers refer to the highest dialup connection speed possible. The connection speed will influence the speed at which you can receive and send data using a modem.

FCC regulations state that a 56-Kbps modem can download at a maximum speed of 53 Kbps and upload at a maximum speed of 33.6 Kbps. However, the modems can attain these speeds only if everything is perfect. Read "Get the Best Dialup Speed" (October 29) to learn why a 56-Kbps modem usually never connects at 56 Kbps.

The last two numbers, 115000 and 480000, are the speeds at which the modem communicates with the COM (communication) port. Back when consumer-level dialup modems were new, PC users connected a modem via the serial COM port on the back of their PCs.

Modems have moved inside PCs, but the old way of connecting to the COM port hasn't changed. The modern modem still communicates with the PC via a COM port. The connection speed between the modem and COM port is measured in bits (expressed as a lowercase "b"), and are the numbers 115000 and 480000.

Download of the Day

3D Traceroute

Megan Morrone

3D Traceroute (www.hlembke.de/prod/ 3dtraceroute/#do) is a free tool that lets you diagnose a slow Internet connection, find out who's behind a website, analyze your email headers, and more. 3D Traceroute is a unique traceroute and PING program with a few dozen extra features built in.

A sampling of 3D Traceroute's features:

- Use Traceroute to trace packets from your PC to an Internet host to find out why your pages might be slow to load. (View with OpenGL for more eye candy.)
- Use PING to diagnose your Internet connection.
- Use a Whois search to find out who is behind any website.
- Use Email Header analyzer (under the Tools section) for help in tracking down spammers.

3D Traceroute even contains a basic web browser.

How to use 3D Traceroute:

1. Download the program.
2. Double-click the dt3r icon.
3. Enter a URL to trace, or click the red arrow in the green circle to get a list of URLs you've recently visited.
4. Click Trace.
5. To view with OpenGL, click the box in the upper-right corner of the window.

You'll find the other tools under their respective tabs. They're fairly self-explanatory.

October

30

Sunday
October 31
2004

Halloween

Halloween

Megan Morrone

Today is the official day for scaring your friends and neighbors, and there's no better way to scare them than by downloading creepy sounds, screams, and your favorite lines from horror movies and adding them to your PC.

Here are links to my favorite sound WAVs:

- **Insane Clownz Circus Music** (http://pages.prodigy.net/area512/circus1.html)
- **Partners in Rhyme** (www.partnersinrhyme.com/pir/PIRsfx.html)
- **Daily .WAV** (www.dailywav.com). Search for your favorite movie sounds.

If you want to go all out and show your spooky spirit, you need a Halloween desktop theme.

- **Daniel Morante's Halloween Theme 1.0** (www.unibia.com/themes/halloween.zip)
- **ThemeWorld's Tux Halloween Theme** (www.themeworld.com/cgi-bin/preview.pl/themes/4phalwn1.zip)
- **Schroedscape Themes** (http://schroedscape.com/dowlow.html#theme)

If you're running Windows 98 or Windows 95 and you have the Plus! Pack installed, make sure you unzip the files to C:/Program Files/Plus!/Themes. If you don't have the Plus! Pack, you'll need a Theme Manager, such as Desktop Architect.

You can find tons of monster icons at a site called Icons Plus (www.iconsplus.com).

Here are sites that offer Halloween-themed wallpapers:

- **Billy Bear's Desktop Wallpaper** (www.billybear4kids.com/desktop/halloween/paper.htm)
- **A1 Emporium's House of Halloween** (http://a1emporium.com/index557.html)
- **BlackDog's Halloween Wallpaper** (www.blackdog.net/holiday/halloween/wallpaper.html)

- **Google's Directory of Halloween Wallpaper** (http://directory.google.com/Top/Computers/Software/Desktop_Customization/Wallpaper/Holidays/Halloween/)

Halloween Screen Savers

If you want to show your Halloween spirit only when you're not using your PC, you need a screen saver:

- **Dream Scenes Coolscreams Halloween Screen Saver** (www.dreamscenes.net/coolhalscree.html). I love this screen saver, but only the trial version is free.
- **The Pumpkin Puzzle Screen Saver** (www.webicurean.com/halloween/screensavers.shtml). Make sure you unzip the files into your C:/Windows/System directory, or cut and paste the file there.
- **Acez Halloween Haunting Screen Saver** (www.acez.com/download.htm#halloween). Be sure to uncheck the box that asks you to change your start page.
- **Halloween Screen Savers for Mac from MacScreenSavers.com** (www.macscreen-savers.com/halloween.html).

Ghoulish Games

- **Hallow Meenies** (www.zapspot.com/games/hallowmeenies/).
- **Spider Clock** (www.timebydesign.com/threeItems.html). This download isn't technically a game, but it will impress your friends.
- **Virtual Pumpkin Carving for Macs** (www.stimpsoft.com/products/halloween.html). StimpSoft is no longer developing or supporting its software, but this download still works in OS X and 10.2.

November 2004

Troubleshooting

Megan Morrone

November is the month of Thanksgiving. The cool weather outside makes it a perfect time to gather family and friends around the old network router. That's right, Thanksgiving isn't just for turkey and yams anymore—now it's for networking and troubleshooting.

In November, we offer a mélange of tips as varied as the food on the Thanksgiving table. You'll learn to upgrade your motherboard, speed up your downloads, add more RAM to your computer, and much more.

We also dedicate much of this month to troubleshooting your PC. We know that whenever groups of family and friends gather for a holiday, the topic inevitable turns to computers. If you're the geek of the group, you probably spend most of this time enmeshed in OPPC (other people's personal computers). This kind of troubleshooting can be either rewarding or frustrating. It can be rewarding if you can diagnose your family's problem quickly and help them solve it. It's amazing how simply jiggling a connection can make you look like Superman. But more often than not, we long-suffering geeks end up spending many hours of our much-needed holiday break locked in the computer room running antivirus software, defragging, and generally wondering why a license isn't required to operate a PC.

Of course, this depends on your relationship with your family. Some might prefer the solitary computer room to the living room full of relatives. If this is true of you, then commit the following pages to memory and I can almost guarantee that your expertise will keep the family from bugging you about how you don't have a job/wife/husband/house/kids/clean pair of underwear. If you'd rather pass the troubleshooting torch, then may I suggest you buy several copies of this book and pass them around to every member of your family this holiday season?

Manage Windows Startup Items

Leo Laporte

Your Windows PC does a lot of work, so every resource the computer uses is valuable. Every application that launches at startup takes up processing power that you can use for something more worthy.

Here are the key areas where startup applications reside: autoexec.bat, config.sys, win.ini, system.ini, Windows Registry, Startup folder, and Windows NT/2000/XP services.

To clean out these areas, use the utilities listed.

Microsoft System Configuration Utility

Windows 95, 98, Me, and XP have a utility called the Microsoft System Configuration Utility, or MSCONFIG, that lets you turn on or off applications at startup.

To use MSCONFIG, follow these steps:

1. Go to Start, Run.

2. Type **msconfig**, and click OK.

3. In MSCONFIG, select the Startup tab.

4. Uncheck any programs you're familiar with. If you're not sure, leave it checked! Otherwise, you might inadvertently turn off something that you need to compute normally.

5. When you are finished selecting programs, click OK, and restart your computer.

Windows NT and 2000

You don't have MSCONFIG in Windows NT or 2000; try Mike Lin's Startup Control Panel (www.mlin.net/StartupCPL.shtml). It works a little like MSCONFIG. It's also compatible with Windows 95, 98, and Me.

Close Programs to Install

Greg Melton

Installing a program isn't as easy as it seems. Windows prompts you to close all open programs during an installation because of the DLL file.

A DLL (dynamic link library) file contains certain code or instructions that can be shared by any program or process on your computer. When you install a new program, it might attempt to overwrite an existing DLL file that's used by one or more programs on your computer.

If one of these programs is open when you install new software, your computer could crash during installation. This was a huge problem in older versions of Windows, but XP is better at managing DLL and system files.

How to Close Open Programs

To close any open application, right-click the program in your taskbar and select Close. Do this for each open program.

If you don't see any open programs or documents listed in your taskbar, you don't have to close anything. Only the installation application for the program you're trying to install should be listed.

You should also disable any antivirus program you might have running. Some antivirus programs, such as Norton AntiVirus, think the installation of a new program is actually a virus trying to infect your PC.

If your antivirus program is on, it should appear in your system tray next to the clock. Just right-click your antivirus icon and disable it. If it doesn't have a disable option, launch the antivirus program and run through the steps to disable it. After you've installed the program, re-enable your antivirus software.

OpenSecrets.org

Megan Morrone

If you live in the US and you're over 18, today you will be electing our president. What are you doing reading this? Get out and vote.

In honor of this day that comes but once every four years, I want to tell you about my favorite political website of all time—OpenSecrets.org. For years The Center for Responsive Politics has provided an extensive guide to where money comes from and where it goes to in the political world. This information has always been publicly available, but with the help of the Internet and the good folks at Open Secrets, now it's easier than ever to find.

No matter what political party you belong to, Open Secrets is a treasure chest of information that will help you make informed decisions before you vote. If you're ever curious about why your elected official is proposing or supporting a particular piece of legislation, simply go to Open Secrets and easily search for who's been donating to that politician. The database at Open Secrets includes general contributions, as well as the more nefarious soft money donations.

Here's a sampling of what else you'll find at Open Secrets.org:

- A running tally of how much money each presidential candidate has raised and how much they've spent (www.opensecrets.org/presidential/).

- Who's been sleeping over in the White House and how much money they paid to get there (www.opensecrets.org/bush/sleepovers.asp).

- The percentage of money certain companies gave to particular political parties. In 2002 Philip Morris gave $4,054,565 total, 23% to the Democrats, and 77% to the Republicans (www.opensecrets.org/orgs/).

- How much certain industries give to each party (www.opensecrets.org/industries/). In 2002 the computer/Internet industry as a whole gave $12,611,843 to the Democrats and $13,017,965 to the Republicans.

OpenSecrets.org gives you a good idea of how much cash a vote is worth, so make sure you don't squander your vote today.

Windows Tips

The Fastest Way to Shut Down Windows XP

Morgan Webb

You can actually shut down Windows XP without a click, but first you have to get set up.

1. Go to the Control Panel and choose Power Options.

2. Select the Advanced tab.

3. Under Power Buttons, you can choose what happens when you press the power button on your computer. It's probably set to shut down, but it's a good idea to make sure before you start wantonly shutting down your machine.

   Note: Some motherboards don't support this feature. If you don't have Power Buttons in your Advanced tab and you feel comfortable poking around your BIOS, you can see if you can enable this feature in BIOS. But you might just be out of luck due to your motherboard—sorry!

4. If it's not set to shut down, choose it from the drop-down list.

5. Now you're ready to shut off the computer. Just hit the power button. Don't touch the keyboard, and keep your hands off that mouse. It's perfectly safe to shut down your computer with the touch of a button. Enjoy!

November

2

Patrick's Top Tips for Upgrading Your Motherboard

Patrick Norton

Changing a motherboard is a lot like swapping the engine in a car. Just having the new engine doesn't quite cut it. The engine has to fit in the bay and connect to the transmission, plus you need all the bits and pieces that make it work. A motherboard swap is a lot less complicated, but you should still prepare. Here are my top suggestions for upgrading your motherboard.

Before You Buy

Make sure your processor will fit the new motherboard. And make sure the motherboard will fit in your PC. Yeah, I know, these first two tips are obvious, but you'd be surprised at the number of people who overlook these two simple, basic requirements.

If you upgrade the chip to a Pentium 4 along with a new motherboard, make sure you have a power supply that works with the motherboard. Some P4 setups require an additional four-pin connector along with the standard ATX power connector.

Prepare Your Hardware

Label your connections. Masking tape works just fine. You can usually learn the name of something (IDE 1, IDE 2, and so on) by looking at the motherboard or by digging into the manual. (What? You didn't save the manual? Try the company's website.)

Renew the thermal grease. You'll be pulling your processor off the old mobo, along with the heat sink. Freshen up the goop that keeps your processor cool.

Prepare Your Software

Before you tear your system apart, download any new drivers available on the motherboard maker's website. Either download 'em onto your hard drive or burn them to a CD-R. And make sure you've got the driver disk that came with your motherboard.

Check the BIOS. It's shocking how many motherboards don't have the latest BIOS loaded. Of course, the BIOS often changes long after you've installed the motherboard. I usually make sure the motherboard boots okay at least once before I start working on the BIOS.

Windows 98 will happily take a new motherboard if you load the new drivers. When you install a new motherboard, it's a good time to back up, wipe the hard drive clean, and do a fresh install of the OS and software.

With Windows XP, often the PC won't boot after the parts are installed on the new motherboard; just install Windows XP again from scratch. As far as we know, that's not an activation problem. Windows NT had similar problems.

Unplug the power before you start, and touch the case to ground any static electricity. And whatever you do, don't drink anything over the open case.

Download of the Day

Useless Creations 3D Screen Savers

Morgan Webb

Everyone loves a good screen saver. In my quest for the latest and greatest, I've found a site offering a plethora of excellent options.

Useless Creations (www.uselesscreations.com) has a series of cool 3D screen savers, and they don't cost a thing. I opted for *Star Wars* Space Battle, in which a full-scale space war takes place between Rebel and Imperial ships, and it features the Millennium Falcon. My favorite part is when they blow up with laser fire. Kapow! Download it today. Your friends will be extremely jealous.

Dual Boot Linux and Windows

Chris DiBona

Life using Linux is good. It's so good that sometimes we need to load Windows and realize how wonderful and stable Linux is. Seriously, sometimes things can only be done under Windows— games, for instance. I'm often asked how to load both Linux and Windows on the same machine.

I'm not talking about running Windows apps under Linux, or running Windows and Linux at the same time. I'm talking about using the machine to host two operating systems. When you boot the machine, you can choose which operating system you want: Windows or Linux.

It's really quite simple:

1. Load Windows XP onto the machine, leaving a partition for Linux.
2. Load Linux onto the partition that you created.
3. Make the Linux root partition the active one.

Seem simple? That's because at its heart it is.

Dual Boot Instructions

Start with a fresh machine with no regard for current data on it. If you want to preserve an installation, I recommend Partition Magic (www.powerquest.com/partitionmagic) or a similar utility to reduce the size of your Windows installation to make a partition for Linux.

How much should you leave for Linux? I think 4GB or so will keep you pretty happy, but, honestly hard drives are so big, you shouldn't feel bad about giving it more.

Instructions for installing Windows:

1. Format using the FAT file system. Why? Linux speaks FAT really well. While NTFS is nice, the Linux driver is sort of beta right now. Since it will be handy for you to access the Windows side of things from Linux (maybe you store MP3s on your Windows partition) I'd say stick with good old FAT.

2. When you reach the part where you set up your Windows partition, simply create an initial partition for Windows that is 5GB less than the size of the drive. Then continue to install Windows as you normally would.

3. After you've installed Windows, pop in your Linux distribution CD (as usual, I recommend Red Hat for its nice install). When it asks about partitioning, choose the partition utility you prefer. I usually use fdisk, but many prefer the easy-to-use Disk Druid. What size should the swap be? Depends on how much memory you have. Twice the physical memory is one rule of thumb, but you really don't need more than 256MB on a desktop machine.

4. The last bit of magic is to make the Linux root partition active and make sure the Windows partition is not active. If you forget this step, you will either jump directly into Windows, or you will get an OS not found error as your computer's BIOS will be unable to decide which partition is the active one.

That's pretty much all there is to it. During configuration, Red Hat will recognize your Windows partition and (mostly) automatically add it to the boot loader so you will see an option to load Windows.

Once in Linux, you can mount the Windows partition by using a command like **mount/ dev/hda1/mnt/dosc** and have full access to the Windows side of things from Linux.

House Call: Upgrading the Roots and Shoots Computer

Leo Laporte with Josh Lawrence

Saddled with a sluggish computer system that was running out of hard drive space, the West Coast Roots and Shoots office (www.janegoodall.org/rs/rs_history.html) of the Jane Goodall Institute needed some help, and *The Screen Savers* were there.

The Upgrade

Roots and Shoots is a school research program specializing in humanitarian and environmental education. We visited its Berkeley, California, branch to see if we could solve the organization's computer woes.

The system was running Windows 98 and had a 2GB hard drive with only 20MB of space left. That could certainly be the cause for slowdown. I decided to install a 60GB hard drive.

Our plan was to copy all the data from the old drive to the new drive and then boot the system from the new drive.

I installed the new drive by setting its jumper to slave and connecting it to the open connector on the IDE cable. The new drive we installed is a new model, an ultra-DMA model with an 80-pin connector. It can safely be used with the 40-pin IDE connector that this older motherboard has.

We booted the machine. Yes, it saw the new drive, but when we opened My Computer, it didn't appear. That's because the new drive hadn't been partitioned and formatted yet.

I downloaded the Data Lifeguard Tools at the Western Digital site (www.wdc.com). The tools allowed us to partition, format, and copy the data from the old drive in one fell swoop. The Data Lifeguard Tools (http://support.wdc.com/download/index.asp) install on a formatted floppy. We formatted the floppy, installed the program, and rebooted the machine.

We ran the tools to prepare the disk and installed EZ Bios so the older motherboard BIOS could see all 60GB of the new drive.

We shut down and opened the machine again to swap the jumpers. Now the old drive is the slave and the new drive is the master. We turned it on, the new drive booted, and we opened My Computer. We could see the new drive as C: with 60GB and the old drive as D:. We deleted most of the contents on the old drive, except My Documents.

We planned use the old drive as a backup unit, so we installed Second Copy (http://secondcopy.com) to automatically back up My Documents from C: to D:.

All finished. We spritzed the case to clean out the dust, closed up, and headed for home.

Extra Steps

I also found a couple of small things that were slowing the system:

- The organization had inherited the system from an architectural firm, so it had a bunch of unnecessary drivers for AutoCAD and other similar programs. We deleted these.

- An old version of McAfee VirusScan had been uninstalled from the computer, but the 98 Registry thought it was still there; the computer gave an error message about a missing .dll every time it booted. I followed the steps at www.isu.edu:8000/kb/disppage.php?doc_id=588&sec_id= to get rid of the Registry entry.

Be sure to visit the Jane Goodall Institute site, www.janegoodall.org.

Host a LAN Party

Patrick Norton

A LAN party isn't just an opportunity to show off your prowess in Quake. It's also a chance for you and your friends and family to get together via networked computers and have a smashing good time.

Want to throw your own LAN party? We're not going to beat the LAN Party guides available from The LANParty Hosting Guide (www.lanparty.com/theguide/) or Tweak3D.Net (www.tweak3d.net/articles/howtolanparty/). But here are our top LAN party tips:

- Stick to well under 20 players for your first LAN party. The networking will be a lot easier to execute—trust us.
- Be prepared. Everyone you invite should know what games to have loaded, should have a list of patches and updates, should have an NIC installed in their system (or an 802.11 card, if you're wireless), and should have anything else they need to bring.
- Set up the server early. You don't want to be figuring out how to host a server while ten friends are waiting. You also don't want to learn how to set up the network on the fly in front of that live (and probably impatient) audience.
- Snacks are crucial, as are drinks. Have lots of both.
- Garages are great for LAN parties. Chances are, you're less likely to get yelled at by your housemates, mom, or significant other. Think about where you're going to put 20 folks and their computers before they all show up.
- Is anybody sleeping over? Lots of LAN parties run from Friday night to the wee hours of Saturday morning. Make sure there's a spare bedroom, a couch, or floor space so people can crash.
- Make sure everyone writes down their home network connections before you blow 'em out to set up the LAN. I prefer a DHCP server to set up a TCP/IP network; a home router (such as a Linksys Etherfast Cable/DSL Router) can speed up the setup. Don't want to write down those network settings? Windows XP can manage multiple network setups. Users of older operating systems can pick up a copy of NetSwitcher (www.netswitcher.com) for $15.

Laporte Support

Gigabit Ethernet Hubs

Regular Ethernet is 10Mbps. Gigabit Ethernet is 100Mbps. It's a bigger pipe, which means faster downloads. If you're handling large files, gigabit Ethernet can be handy.

The problem is that gigabit Ethernet hubs are more expensive than standard Ethernet hubs because the demand isn't as high. Gigabit Ethernet is becoming more popular, so the prices will eventually drop, but $150 to $300 for a gigabit Ethernet hub is normal. Patrick recommends Linksys (www.linksys.com) or D-Link hubs (www.dlink.com).

Web Tips

Linuxiso.org offers FTP download sites for the most popular distros of Linux from all over the world. Options include:

- **Red Hat** (www.redhat.com)
- **Mandrake Linux** (www.mandrakelinux.com/en/)
- **SuSE** (www.suse.com/index_us.html)

Yellow Dog Linux (www.yellowdoglinux.com) for all you Mac-heads.

Shop for Your Thanksgiving Feast Online

Alison Strahan

Thanksgiving is serious business, so take a little time to do some research, to prepare a feast that fits your sense of the occasion. The first step to planning Thanksgiving dinner is to choose what you're going to cook. Here's how to find your turkey or vegetarian alternative.

Vegetarian Turkey

If you're a vegetarian who enjoys the turkey tradition but not the meat, there's a new curd—I mean, bird—on the block. Tofurkey (www.tofurkey.com/mainF.htm) is a 100% vegan roast with soy drumettes, stuffing, gravy, and wishbones. The Tofurky meal serves four. Be sure to check shipping costs if you buy online; they can be steep. I suggest using the site's list of retail stores to find a shop in your neighborhood that carries Tofurky so that you can pick one up for yourself.

Organic Turkey

People who prefer poultry should read the down-to-earth tips on choosing a fresh, frozen, organic, or kosher turkey at The Reluctant Gourmet (www.reluctantgourmet.com/turkey_tips.htm). The USDA (www.fsis.usda.gov/OA/pubs/farmfreeze.htm) supplies guidelines for organic turkey. Finding an organic turkey can sometimes be difficult. If you're having trouble, visit your local health food store or farmer's market. You'll also have access to organic or free-range turkeys if you join a co-op or community agriculture program (www.prairienet.org/co-op/directory/).

Go Local

Your local grocer and specialty shops will be selling turkey, ham, full meals, and all the fixings for the holiday. But you may not need to go to the store to shop. Many stores now have an online companion. A couple good examples are Haverhill Beef—Butcher Shop and Meat Market (www.haverhillbeef.com) in Haverhill, Massachusetts, and Andronicos (www.andronicos.com), in the San Francisco Bay Area.

Order Meals Online

Carnivores around the United States can have turkeys, ham, or entire Thanksgiving meals delivered from Omaha Steaks (www.omahasteaks.com) or Hickory Farms (www.hickoryfarms.com/welcome.asp). Just order online. Shipping is determined on a sliding scale at both sites. But remember, shipping costs increase with the size of your order. Before you place an order online or by phone, check the size of your ham or turkey so that you'll be able to feed all your guests and make enough room for it in the refrigerator.

Cooking Safety

The National Turkey Federation (www.turkeyfed.org/consumer/thanks.html) supplies tips on everything from thawing and roasting to the best way to determine when the bird is cooked, which is a source of frustration even for accomplished chefs.

Laporte Support

Troubleshoot Startup Options

To troubleshoot your startup options, right-click on My Computer and select Properties. Click the Advanced tab and click the Startup and Recovery Options button to set the default operating system. Note: There will be only one choice if Windows XP is the only OS on your computer.

If you're troubleshooting your PC, you might need to delay times for the operating system and recovery options menus. You might also want to edit the BOOT.INI file. You can edit it from the dialog by clicking the Edit button. To get to the delayed operating system choice menu, click the Edit button and duplicate the first line in the BOOT.INI file. This will trick XP into thinking there are two operating systems on the hard drive, forcing the menu to show up each time you boot.

How to Add RAM

Leo Laporte with Phil Allingham

Don't let your computer slow you down. Follow these easy steps to add more memory to your computer. It's easy, and it's about the cheapest way you can soup up the performance of your PC. Almost everyone can use more memory.

What Type of Memory Do You Need?

Start by checking your computer manual for the kind of memory you need. The number of memory types is expanding, so you really need to be careful when buying RAM.

The main kinds of memory right now are SDRAM, DDR SDRAM, Rambus (or RIMM), and SODIMM, which is used in laptops. Given the possible confusion, buy memory from a vendor that will exchange it if there's a problem. Crucial Technology (www.crucial.com), Kingston Technology (www.kingston.com), and PNY Technologies (www.pny.com) are all good bets.

Ground Yourself

Now open your computer. Your manual once again comes in handy because every computer case is different. When you've got the computer open, ground yourself to drain off any static charge. Static electricity is harmless to you, but it can fry the computer chips.

It's best to use a grounding strip. You can find one at almost any electronics store. If you can't find one, touch a metal part of the computer's case to discharge any static.

Add Memory

Almost all memory is now inserted upright. Just release the tabs and gently push the memory stick into place. The tabs should snap up, lock, and hold the memory.

Older PCs might use SIMMs. SIMM slots are white and are held in place by clips at each end.

Insert the SIMM at a 45° angle and gently tilt it up until it's upright. The clips should snap into place, and the SIMM should be held firmly in its slot. If it's wobbly or uneven, release the clips and try again.

You're Finished

After you've added the memory, turn on the PC. The computer should recognize the new memory automatically. Again, check your manual for any exceptions. That's it! You've added more memory to your computer, and you should realize a real performance increase.

Talkback

Where Is Your "Computer Room"?

Dave Roos

A decade ago, every home had this weird little place called the "computer room." It was hot, it was small, and it smelled like grandma's closet. Who knows? Maybe it was Grandma's closet. The point is that we felt the computer needed to be hidden away in some darkened den, separate from the rest of the "living" quarters.

But that has changed. With the popularity of portable PCs and the widespread embrace of computer culture, the PC has made a leap into living rooms, kitchens, dining rooms, and, yes, even the bathrooms of the world.

Where does the computer belong?

Living room 10%

Bedroom   13%

Office   16%

Bathroom   1%

Every room   61%

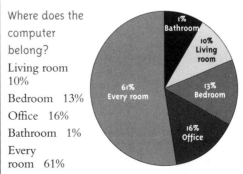

Home Networking Gets Easy

Patrick Norton and Greg Melton

A network is a group of two or more computers linked together. Networks make it easy to move information from one computer to another (especially large files that don't fit on a floppy or Zip disk). Networks also let you share hardware, such as printers, and connect to servers or the Internet.

A home network makes it easy to share Internet access, whether over a phone line, cable modem, or DSL modem. Usually, one machine is attached to the modem while the other machines talk to it. Support for this kind of network is built into Windows 98 SE, Me, and XP. You'll need some extra software to make this work on older systems. Whatever software you use, the computer you connect to the modem must be left on 24×7, or the other computers won't be able to access the Internet.

A better option is to use an external box for your network. The box connects to your cable/DSL modem and uses something called DHCP to connect all your computers (it's also easier to set up the network); it allows any of the machines to connect to the web at any time. It also acts as a firewall to protect your home network from Internet hackers. Linksys (www.linksys.com) makes our current favorite, the Linksys Instant Broadband EtherFast Cable/DSL Router (approximately $80).

Today putting a network in your home doesn't have to be difficult. It can take less than an hour to set up, and it doesn't have to involve wires. If you can plug in a phone line, you can network the computers in your house. Consider these questions:

- Can you run wires through your home?
- Are there phone jacks in every room that you want to network?
- How much do you want to spend?

Now you need to figure out what kind of networking hardware you're going to use. The least expensive option is a traditional Ethernet network, which entails running wire and either plugging a USB/Ethernet adapter into the computer or installing a card inside your computer. If you shop carefully, you can create an Ethernet network of three computers for less than $100.

If you have a phone jack in every room, you can create an HPNA 2.0 network. HPNA (Home Phone Network Alliance) uses phone lines to connect your PCs. Like Ethernet, it uses either a USB adapter or an internal card. You can create an HPNA network of two computers for less than $100 (see www.pcbay.net/pcbay1) if you install internal PCI cards. A USB setup (see www.dlink.com), which doesn't require opening your PC, is another option.

The option we recommend is also the most expensive: a wireless network. 802.11b (also known as Apple's AirPort or Wi-Fi) is a wireless networking system that runs as fast as either Ethernet or HPNA 2.0.

Because 802.11b uses 2.4GHz radio signals, you don't need to run cables. If you own a notebook computer, a wireless network lets you connect to the Net from anywhere in your home. That means you can work from the couch as easily as from your desk.

Home Networking Gets Easy (continued)

If You Have a Phone, You Have a Network

A home phone line network (HPN) is an easy way to connect computers. After you've attached the HPNA adapter to a computer, plug the adapter into a phone jack.

Don't worry about losing the phone line; the adapter has a pass-through for the phone. NetGear's (www.netgear.com) PA301 HPNA Home Phoneline PCI Adapters cost about $30 each, while NetGear's PA101 HPNA Home Phoneline USB Adapters cost $50 each. The USB adapter doesn't require installing a card. On the other hand, we've seen HPN built into modems.

In theory, any HPN device should connect to any other, no matter who manufactured it, and many manufacturers offer HPNA kits. Generally, bundled software in the kit sets up the network for you.

Dump the Wires, Baby!

Of all the home networking systems, wireless networks are the most convenient. Apple's AirPort system has received the most attention. At a theoretical maximum of 11Mbps, it should run as fast as hardwired Ethernet. Better yet, the design is slick and the system works rather well.

The AirPort works on an open wireless networking standard called 802.11 or Wi-Fi that, oddly enough, has been out on the PC for a while. Although you can use the AirPort base station with PCs, you need special software to configure it. After you get the base-station or wireless router in place, all you need is a wireless PCMCIA card for a notebook or a PCI wireless adapter for a desktop PC.

Alternatives to the AirPort include the Linksys WAP11 Wireless Access Point ($170, www.linksys.com) and D-Link's D-LinkAir ($169, www.dlink.com). As with an Ethernet network, you could leave one system running 24×7 to connect the rest of the network to the Internet. We prefer to use a base station to

connect to the Internet. The AirPort includes not only an Ethernet port to attach to a cable/DSL modem, but also a built-in 56Kbps modem.

One thing to keep in mind: If you're thinking about installing an 802.11 wireless network, make sure all the components are manufactured by the same company. It's possible to mix and match components, but the setup won't be as smooth.

Here's an example of products you'll need to wirelessly network a laptop and desktop PC using 802.11b:

- Linksys BEFW11S4 Wireless 4-Port Cable/DSL Router
- Linksys WPC11 Wireless Network PC Card
- Linksys WMP11 Instant Wireless PCI Adapter (wirelessly enables a standard desktop computer)

Sarah's Tips

IE Security

If you really want to know when you're moving from a secure to an insecure site in Internet Explorer, do this:

1. In IE, click the Tools menu and select Internet Options.
2. Click the Advanced tab.
3. Scroll to the bottom.
4. Check the option for Warn If Changing Between Secure to Not Secure Mode.

Top Five Reasons That Safari Is Better Than Internet Explorer

Megan Morrone

It's a fact. Nobody likes change. That's why so many Mac users have yet to switch from Internet Explorer to Safari, Apple's new web browser. Microsoft announced that they'll no longer be updating Internet Explorer for Mac, so you better get used to Safari or you'll be left back at base camp.

Here are the top five reasons Safari is better than Internet Explorer:

1. **Google integration.** There's no need to waste time going to Google's front page or to waste space by downloading special Google search programs. Safari includes a built-in search box right next to your address bar. Simply type in your search terms and press Enter. Safari takes you directly to your search results page.

2. **The SnapBack button.** After you've delved deep into a webpage on your search results, and you still haven't found what you're looking for, simply click the orange arrow on Safari's Google search box and you'll go back to the search results page, without wasting time with the back button.

3. **Tabbed browsing.** The second version of Safari incorporated tabbed browsing for those of us used to Mozilla. To turn on tabs, go to the browser, click Safari (on the top of your screen), choose Preferences, and click the Tabs icon. Then click the box that says "Enable Tabbed Browsing."

4. **Built-in pop-up blocking.** No one likes pop-up ads. To turn them off in Safari, click the word Safari (on the top of your screen) and choose Block Pop-up Windows.

5. **Speed, stability, and security.** Safari renders webpages faster than Internet Explorer. Trust me. It does. The technology is based on open-source software, which means it's also bound to be more stable and more secure than Internet Explorer. To manage your cookies in Safari, click Safari, choose Preferences, and select the lock icon.

Mac Tips

Pick Me!

Brett Larson

This free download jumped right out, screaming, "Pick me! Pick me!" Strangely, it sounded like Eddie Murphy. No, I'm not hallucinating. This fun app at www.noware.iscrappy.com puts Donkey, the character Murphy voiced in *Shrek*, right in your Dock. As you'll see, Donkey helps you maintain your sanity by forcing you to take an occasional break.

The catch? You can't tell when or where Donkey will appear, nor can you set the preferences for anything other than, "Jump up and down and say 'Pick me!' over and over."

It's not an extremely useful file, but it's a fun application, especially if you install it on a friend's computer without telling him. Sure, you can uninstall it, but all you have to do to shut up Donkey is bring him to the front.

Possessed PC

Martin Sargent

Computers do strange things. Sometimes a computer stops working properly for no good reason. You'd swear it's possessed. When a possessed PC starts troubling you, don't panic. First, clear your head. There are few things as frustrating as a PC that acts kooky for no reason. To troubleshoot effectively, you must be calm. Deep breaths, good thoughts.

- **Use deductive reasoning.** Look for evidence and start a process of elimination. For example, if your monitor suddenly stops displaying properly, you can probably rule out the hard drive and the processor. Your target is the monitor and its cabling, and the video card and its software drivers.

- **Check the simple stuff.** Make sure all the cables are attached firmly and correctly. Look for signs of damage to cables or connectors, such as bent pins.

- **Scan for viruses.** Viruses are evil little devil spawn. If your system starts acting screwy, scan for viruses using antivirus software. We suggest Norton AntiVirus.

- **See what's changed recently.** What have you done to your system lately? Any time you install new hardware or software, you change the state of your system. It's like taking a new medication: It can fix a problem but also cause side effects and conflict with other medications you've been taking for a while. Try uninstalling programs you've recently added, one at a time, and see if the problem goes away. If your system is loaded with software and peripherals you rarely use, get rid of them. A spartan system always runs best.

- **Check the company's website.** If a certain piece of software or hardware starts acting funny or doesn't work at all when you first start using it, check the manufacturer's website. There might be software patches or driver updates available for download.

  Also check the FAQ section for problems with the product when used with certain system configurations or other products. You can also consult newsgroups to see if other users have figured out ways to fix your problem.

- **Try a troubleshooting application.** Although I've never had great success with them, try using one to identify the culprit. Symantec's Norton Utilities (www.symantec.com) are well-regarded diagnostic tools.

- **Read the manuals.** Manuals typically contain troubleshooting tips for common problems. Help files are even easier to use than manuals because you can search specific problems by keyword. Use them.

- **Start fresh.** When all else fails, including calling tech support, you might consider reinstalling Windows.

Laporte Support

Data Transfer Via Serial

You need special cables to transfer data from one PC to another using the serial or parallel ports.

- For a serial connection, you need a serial null modem cable. CableMax (www.cablemax.com) has a bunch of these cables available.

- For a parallel connection, you can get a special parallel cable at Direct Parallel (www.lpt.com).

- I suggest buying the cables from LapLink (www.laplink.com), because they also have software packages that you can use to perform the data transfers.

Check www.weno.net if you want to learn how to connect a pair of PCs in Windows using a serial connection.

Set System Restore's Clock

Dan Huard

Windows' System Restore got its start with the infamous Windows Millennium Edition. Why exactly did a lifesaver utility such as System Restore make its debut in such a bad product? Microsoft knew all along that Me is crash-prone. Hence the birth of System Restore.

What Does System Restore Do?

System Restore takes snapshots of your system status and archives them for retrieval, so if your PC crashes, you can restore your system files. Your system files are critical to the smooth operation of your OS.

What Doesn't System Restore Do?

It won't restore Word documents, pictures, data folders, email, and so on. It is not a backup utility.

How Can It Be Modified?

System Restore creates a restore point every 24 hours and saves each restore point for up to 90 days. Both of these can be adjusted, but not very easily. Here's how:

1. Open Regedit. Go to Start, Run, and type **"regedit"**.

2. Navigate to HKLM\SOFTWARE\ Microsoft\WindowsNT\CurrentVersion\ System Restore.

3. To modify how many restore points are created, double-click the RPGlobalInterval key.

4. Change the Value Data from 86,400 (in seconds), which is 24 hours, to anything you'd like. For example, 43,200 is 12 hours, so a restore point will be created every 12 hours. If the default Value Data field number is different (it should be 86,400), then it's probably in hexadecimal format. Click the button titled Decimal to display the correct default setting.

5. To modify how many restore points are saved, double-click the RPLifeInterval key.

6. Change the Value Data field from 7,776,000 (in seconds), which is 90 days, to anything you'd like. For example, opt for 30 days instead. That should equate to a value of 2,592,000 seconds.

Helpful Tips for a Successful System Restore

- If your PC gets infected with a virus, you may be able to restore your system to a previous time. But if the virus has infected an email or your documents, you're out of luck. System Restore can restore only system files.

- To manually delete your most recent System Restore, click Start, Accessories, System Tools, Disk Cleanup. Choose the More Options tab and click the Clean Up button from the System Restore Section.

- Your restore points are hidden (only in NTFS). Accidental deletion of these is very unlikely.

 ## Laporte Support

Wireless Keyboard

Can using a wireless keyboard interfere with the neighbors' computers, or can the neighbors see what you're typing?

Most wireless input devices use a weak signal that doesn't travel very far. To intercept the signal, the intercepting device needs to be very close to your keyboard and mouse. We use Logitech wireless input devices, and sometimes we have trouble with the signals when the transmitter is under the desk. Logitech keyboards have a feature that allows you to create an encryption code for your transmission, making it more secure. There are no encryption schemes for wireless devices. Chances are, the neighbors won't be able to get your signal. Stick with a company that specializes in input devices, such as Logitech (www.logitech.com).

Speed Up Your Mac

Leo Laporte

Credit goes to Andrew Welch, the legendary Mac programmer from Ambrosia Software (www.ambrosiasw.com), for this discovery. He has documented it fully on Mac OS X Hints (http://www.macosxhints.com/article.php?story=20011008024501793), but to summarize: You can save RAM and maybe even speed up your Mac by compressing the window images it stores in memory.

Hack Your Mac

In the first versions of OS X, window buffer compression was disabled. It's turned on in OS X 10.2 (Jaguar), but if you're using an older version, try this hack:

1. Open Terminal and enter this command:

   ```
   sudo pico /library/preferences/
   com.apple.windowserver.plist
   ```

   The code sudo runs the command as root (you need to enter your administrator password before continuing), and pico is a small text editor that comes with OS X. You're editing a preference list or "plist" file. Many obscure system settings are hidden in these XML files. Edit them with care, because you can really hose your system. Indeed, it's a good idea to make a backup copy of any plist file before you change it.

2. In this case, you're going to add the following text immediately below the first tag:

   ```
   <key>BackingCompression</key>
   <dict>
    <key>compressionScanTime</key>
    <real>5.000000000000000e+00</real>
    <key>minCompressableSize</key>
    <integer>8193</integer>
    <key>minCompressionRatio</key>
    <real>1.100000023841858e+00</real>
   </dict>
   ```

Check your typing carefully. Any mistake could have disastrous consequences. Press Ctrl+X to exit pico. Press Y to save your changes on the way out.

Visit the Mac OS X Hints site for more detailed caveats and a fuller explanation of what's happening. Again, this hack is unnecessary in Jaguar, where compression is turned on by default.

Download of the Day

ASCII Generator

Megan Morrone

Create ASCII art of your very own. ASCII Generator (http://go.to/ascgen), a free download, turns your photographs into ASCII art with a click of the mouse.

1. Open ASCII Generator and click on the icon of the face.

2. Browse for a picture you have saved on your desktop.

3. Select an area of the picture or click OK to select the entire image.

4. Save the image by hitting Ctrl+S, or click the disk icon.

November

14

Build a 500GB Server

Patrick Norton

Call me the king of the obvious, but in my world, a file server is a place to stash your files. But have you ever wanted to access a file on your daughter's computer while you're working on your own? A file server gives you a central point for file access. It can also be a place where you keep backup copies of files. A file server should be a safe place to stash your files. It should be accessible to the network but not the neighbors, so you should put it behind a firewall.

Share and Share Alike

Almost anyone with a computer can provide file-server services. Just make sure the system is on your network, and turn on file sharing. Ta-da, storage anybody on your network can use. (Tip: Make a special drive or partition for the file sharing to keep folks out of the rest of that system.)

Don't want to share your desktop system? Do what I did: Recycle an old PC and use it as a file server. If you use Windows 98 or XP, just turn on file sharing. To make the system more stable, try ClarkConnect Home Edition (www.clarkconnect.org). Similar to Smooth-Wall (www.smoothwall.org), ClarkConnect offers a Linux (Red Hat, to be exact) firewall, but it can also be a file, email, or web server.

Big Drives, Big Trouble

Enough about the virtues of a file server. You want to hear all about the 500GB of storage I planned to stuff into this server. What was I thinking? Five hundred gigabytes of storage, online, on the home network.

That Pentium 266 system I've been recycling won't see more than the first 8.4GB of the 250GB hard drives Western Digital was kind enough to loan me. And there's no BIOS upgrade I can find that will fix this.

Heck, without some help, Windows 98, NT, Me, 2000, and XP won't see more than 137GB of any hard drive. Fortunately, Western Digital includes a PCI ATA adapter and the Data Lifeguard Tools to take care of that.

Big Honkin' Drives

Drives are getting ridiculously huge. You can hit a terabyte (that's 1000GB) with just four drives. The Western Digital Caviar (www.westerndigital.com) is available in 250GB capacities. You can build a half-terabyte server with two drives for about $350 per drive. (Maxtor has some 250GB 5400rpm drives that sell for around $270 online.)

You can find smaller drives, 180GB or 120GB, for as little as $170 or $93. If you're building your file server on an older motherboard, you'll probably need a PCI ATA/EIDE adapter to see the full capacity of those drives.

Wireless Tips

Router DMZ

If you have a router and find yourself stuck behind a firewall and unable to access the Internet, you might need to put in the demilitarized zone (DMZ). Here's how to do it for a Linksys router. (If you have a different router, check the manual or the manufacturer's website.)

1. On the router's setup page, click the Advanced link.

2. Click the DMZ Host link.

3. In the settings, enter the last octet of the internal IP address.

The Uses of Ping

Morgan Webb

When you ping a computer, you send it a packet of generic information that the computer then bounces back to you, the sender.

"Are you there?" your computer says. The other computer either can be silent—meaning that it is unavailable or nonexistent—or can respond with a generic "Yes, I am here."

Troubleshooting with Ping

Ping is a quick and useful tool for troubleshooting network problems. Say you're having trouble establishing a remote desktop connection with your work computer. You have its IP address, so you ping the computer. If the ping comes back normally, the problem might be on your end. If there's no word from the remote computer, perhaps its firewall is enabled, or it might be turned off. In either case, you've narrowed the possibilities.

Keeping Track of Traffic

Ping is also used to monitor network traffic. Say your favorite site is slow one day. You can ping the site to see how many packets are lost between you and your site, thus learning how slow those loads are. The ping utility counts the number of packets sent, compares it with the packets received, and tells you a percentage of packets lost. When you lose a packet in a webpage, the computer has to identify the packet as missing and then request the replacement from the server, which can be a time-consuming process.

Using Ping

1. Go to Start, Run, and type **command**.
2. At the prompt, type **ping techtv.com** (**ping** is constant but **techtv.com** can be replaced with any website or IP address).
3. Your computer will send four packets and return the trip time, in milliseconds, for each packet.

4. You can set your computer to ping a computer indefinitely by typing **ping –t techtv.com**. This gives you the number of packets lost over a longer period of time. Hit Ctrl+C to stop the ping.
5. Type **ping** by itself to learn what other options are available and to learn more about the syntax of the utility.

Laporte Support

USB Wi-Fi Adapters

A viewer asked, "I have five computers, and I want to share a cable modem. Is using USB for the five computers a bad thing, or would it be better to use PCI Wi-Fi cards?"

You can attach the access points to your Mac or PC in many ways. The classic way is to open the computer case and install a PCI Wi-Fi expansion card.

Don't want to open the case? Try a USB Wi-Fi adapter. It plugs into an open USB port outside the case.

Whether you use five USB adapters or five PCI adapters, either setup should work fine. I have yet to see benchmarking results that showed much (if any) decline between PCI and USB implementations of Wi-Fi.

Looking for USB Wi-Fi adapters? I like Practically Networked (www.practicallynetworked.com).

November
16

Create a Dummy User Account for OS Troubleshooting

Leo Laporte

Create an extra administrator account on your Windows XP or Mac OS X machine, and don't use it. This dummy account will come in handy if you ever have trouble with your main account.

If you can log on to your dummy account but not your main account, the problem is the user-specific settings of your main account. Pay particular attention to the Startup or logon items. On the Mac, check items in the ~/Library folder.

To create a dummy user in Mac OS X, open the Accounts System Preferences pane and click New User. Give the user the same password as your day-to-day account. And be sure to enable Administrator privileges for the new account.

To create a dummy user in XP, go to Start, Control Panel, User Accounts and select Create a New Account. Then follow the steps that the wizard takes you through, being sure to select the Computer Administrator option and to give it your normal password.

Download of the Day

NeoTrace

Sarah Lane

If you're a frequent reader of my blog (www.sarahlane.com/blog/), you know I've had my share of nasty-comment posters. Ah, such is life when you're a woman on TV. Deleting posts is OK, but sometimes it's hard to keep up.

I use Movable Type, which lets me view the IP addresses of everyone who posts and allows me to ban IPs if I like. The problem is most people have dynamic (changing) IP addresses, so you can keep banning the same person over and over and they'll keep getting through.

But what if you're really bothered by someone and need to figure out who they are and where they are? Allow me to introduce you to NeoTrace (www.mcafee.com/myapps/neoworx/default.asp). This program is helpful in tracking down otherwise anonymous blog posters.

Sneaky Little Poster

For example, there's a person (let's call him Timmy) who lives just outside Little Rock, Arkansas. Timmy posts with multiple names, email addys, IPs, and so on. If I didn't know how to trace him, I'd think a whole brigade of hurtful jesters was invading my blog. But no! NeoTrace showed me that it's actually just one person posting over and over from the same computer with a dynamic IP address. Ah, well that changes things somewhat, doesn't it? Tsk-tsk, Timmy.

NeoTrace lists the ISP people are connected to and how to reach it. If I so desired, I could contact the ISP (in this case, SBC), report the harassing behavior, and submit evidence.

Bottom Line

You don't ever have to be harassed online, and NeoTrace is a great program to kick your online detective skills into high gear. NeoTrace is a product of NeoWorx, which was bought by McAfee a couple years ago. It's free to try, $30 to buy.

Linux Alternatip: Kill Processes

Kevin Rose

You're right in the middle of your favorite Linux application, and your computer locks. Rather than reboot your system, you can use a simple command to kill the locked application.

The first step is to identify the process name. This is done from the terminal command prompt using the `ps` command.

Once you execute the command you'll see something that looks roughly like this:

```
PID TTY TIME COMMAND
10550 pts/3 0:01 /bin/csh
10574 pts/4 0:02 /bin/csh
10590 pts/4 0:09 APP
```

Each line represents one process, with a process being loosely defined as a running instance of a program. The column headed PID (process ID) shows the assigned process numbers of the processes. The heading COMMAND shows the location of the executed process.

The APP application is the locked one, so we will issue a kill command for that PID:

```
kill 10590
```

This basic form of kill asks the processes to exit politely, giving them a chance to save any open files before they terminate.

If this doesn't work you can always try a more forceful exit:

```
kill -KILL 9 10590
```

`kill -KILL` terminates the process without any warning.

These commands can also be executed via Telnet for remote process termination. For a complete man page on the kill command, check out `http://man.he.net/?topic=kill&section=all`.

Download of the Day

TClock2

Morgan Webb

Who doesn't love to mod Windows? Well this is one of my favorite tools for personalizing your desktop. I've used TClock2 (`www.deskmod.com`) for several months, and I love it more every day. It adds an extra configuration menu accessible through your clock. Here are just a few things it can do:

- In Windows 98, make your icon text background transparent.
- Shrink your desktop icons and put the text to the side rather than below your icons.
- Change the appearance of your clock to show the date and time in a variety of formats.
- Turn on a screen saver, event, or application with one to four clicks on the clock.
- Set an alarm.
- Change the look of your taskbar and Start button.
- Skin your Programs menu sidebar.
- Much, much more!

Best of all, it's free! So what are you waiting for?

Get some TClock2 skins at these sites, and make your Start button and Programs menu the envy of all:

- **Yuki's Skins**, `www1.odn.ne.jp`
- **Customize.org**, `www.customize.org`
- **DeviantArt**, `www.deviantart.com`

Build a Power Meter for $5

Patrick Norton

Ever wonder how much energy your PC uses? I do every time I think about buying a UPS to protect my system from power outages and other ills. And, hey, 'cause I'm a geek, I'm curious about how much energy that extra fridge in the basement uses, too.

Enter the power meter, an electronic device that measures AC power consumption in watts, and, if you're lucky, in kilowatt hours. Then you just multiply your kilowatt hours against your local electric utility's rates and find out how much the PC (or the fridge) really costs to run.

Solar energy maven Tom Elliot knows the fine art of solar energy. Elliot has serious energy consumption concerns: No sunlight means no new electricity, which means draining the house's batteries. How long can his home run on battery power? He measures the electricity consumed by each appliance (or computer) with Brand Electronics Digital Power Meter Model 4-1850 (www.silentpcreview.com). It tracks watts (power) and energy (kilowatt hours) used by any 117 vac appliance you plug into it.

The Digital Power Meter's ability to calculate cost per month based on what you pay per kilowatt hour is pretty slick. I found it rock solid and easy to use. At about $150, the price is steep, even if all you have to do is plug in your gadget and navigate through a menu to enter your local price for electricity.

Enter the fine folks at SilentPCReview.com and an article by Mike Chin called "A $5 DIY Power Meter" (www.silentpcreview.com). Five bucks? That's more my price range.

Reduce your monthly power bill with the Kill-A-Watt (www.ccrane.com/kill_a_watt.asp). This little gadget tracks down the power hogs in your home so you can decide whether they really need to remain plugged in.

Laporte Support

Memory Loss

A viewer has PC100 RAM in his PC. He installed PC133 RAM, and now his computer recognizes only half the memory value of the RAM (that is, a 512MB RAM stick is being recognized as 256MB). How can he fix this?

The problem has nothing to do with PC100 and PC133. The problem lies in your motherboard and how it handles certain RAM constructions. Your motherboard seems to have trouble with dual-bank memory. Dual-bank memory is a RAM stick with chips on both sides of the stick. The motherboard sees only the memory on one side of the stick.

You need to exchange your memory for single-bank sticks. These sticks have memory on one side.

Sarah's Tips

Boot from Windows CD

To do a fresh install of Windows, you need to boot from the CD. To do that, set the boot priority so that your system knows to go to the CD-ROM drive to boot.

1. Enter your computer's BIOS by pressing a certain key during boot. Your computer should say something like "Press F4 to enter setup" during boot.

2. When you're in the BIOS, look for a setting for your boot priority.

3. When you find the boot priority, set it to CD-ROM.

Top Five Reasons to Go Broadband

Morgan Webb

1. **Answer your phone.** One of the best things about broadband is that it doesn't tie up your precious phone, so you can use your phone line for talking while it's also transmitting digital signals.

   If you have an extra phone line for $20 a month and a dialup account for $20 a month, you're already paying the same price as broadband and getting a miserably slow connection.

2. **Experience high design.** Broadband shows you the flashy high design of the Internet, such as the site www.foulds2000.freeserve.co.uk/index_v2.html, which advertises designer Andy Fould's work in Flash. I could play for hours with all the fun interactive menus he's designed, but if I had dialup, I'd spend most of my time waiting for them to load.

3. **Be part of the streaming video revolution.** Visit BMW Films (www.bmwfilms.com) for some great streaming independent films. You can also experience online concerts, music videos, streaming NFL (www.nflfilms.com) and NBA (www.nba.com) replays, and even instructional tutorials, all of which are nearly impossible without broadband.

4. **Play online games.** Stop blaming your connection for your bad aim, and stop slowing everyone down with your pitiful dialup ping times. If you have a good connection, you can frag your enemy mercilessly.

5. **Download! Download! Download!** You can download music—legally, of course—from sites such as MP3.com. You can also download personal mixes from friends' sites. Then you can burn them to CDs and play them on your CD player.

   You can also go to Download.com to grab huge open-source Microsoft Office alternatives, freeware, trial versions of Flash and Dreamweaver, and even demo versions of games such as Tony Hawk Pro Skater 3 and Unreal Tournament 2003.

   Applications, movies, and music usually come in immense files. Broadband helps you get them while you're still young.

There are tons of other things I love about broadband, such as crystal-clear videoconferencing and superfast online shopping. Beware! Once you go broadband, you'll never go back!

Laporte Support

Web Server Setup

A viewer has a cable broadband connection and three static IP addresses. Should he set up his web server behind or outside of his router?

Your web server is going to attract a lot of attention to your connection. The best thing to do is dedicate one of your IP addresses to the web server so you're not exposing the other connections to the web traffic.

You can put the web server behind the router, but people won't see your server. To allow people through, you need to create a demilitarized zone (DMZ) in the router. This opens the router to allow traffic.

November

20

OBD-II in a Nutshell

Patrick Norton

Have you ever seen the Check Engine symbol light up on your dashboard? It means something's gone wrong (perhaps a little wrong, maybe a lot wrong) with your vehicle. Nearly every American-made car since 1996 can self-diagnose problems and report tons of information in real time, thanks to the On-Board Diagnostics-II (OBD-II) system.

According to B&B Electronics, OBD-II (www.davisnet.com) "is an expanded set of standards and practices developed by SAE and adopted by the EPA and CARB (California Air Resources Board) for implementation by January 1, 1996."

Among other things, it specifies that an OBD-II port will be somewhere within reach of your steering wheel. If you plug an OBD-II reader into it, you can tap directly into your engine control unit (ECU) and get valuable car data, including the following:

- Vehicle speed
- Engine speed
- Coolant temperature
- Engine load
- Intake manifold pressure
- Airflow rate
- Intake air temperature
- Timing advance
- Fuel pressure
- Fuel system status
- O2 sensor voltage
- Battery voltage

You can also use diagnostic trouble codes that tell you when your ECU has to report a specific ailment.

At around $180, the CarChip costs about the same as other OBD-II software/cable packages that use a Palm OS device or PC for displaying data. Unlike most OBD-II readers, the DriveRight CarChip E/X doesn't show data in real time. It plugs into your OBD-II port and gathers up to 300 hours of data. Then you remove the device from your vehicle and connect it to a PC via a serial cable.

The CarChip software downloads the information from the device to the computer and lets you view your harvest in various formats: charted, plotted, or tabular. The DriveRight CarChip E/X can gather information from only 4 of the 23 possible parameters. A full, comprehensive set of data requires multiple test runs with the DriveRight CarChip E/X.

Why Use OBD-II

Wondering why I'm so curious? If I had the OBD-II tools to monitor my engine's temperature, I'd have found the problem with my engine's thermostat a few months ago and saved nearly $300 at my local dealer.

If you have a car built in 1996 or later, learn more about OBD-II and what it can teach you about how your car is running. You'll learn lots. And you may save tons of money.

Download of the Day

WinDriversBackup

Megan Morrone

WinDriversBackup (www.jermar.com/wdrvbck.htm), from JerMar Software, can scan your system for drivers and easily back them all up in one place.

Why do you need to back up your drivers?

When programs are buggy, sometimes all you need to do is uninstall and reinstall the drivers. If your system is prone to crashes, back up your drivers on another machine, and they're saved for emergencies. WinDriversBackup is network compatible, so you can easily back up your drivers on a remote computer. WinDriversBackup is free, but you can pay for the professional version for more features.

Antec Performance Hard Drive Cooling System

Patrick Norton

A cooler system runs better. Cooling is crucial for overclocking. But can a hard drive cooler—specifically, the Antec Performance Hard Drive Cooling System (www.antec-inc.com)—really trim the heat inside your case? In our tests, we found the built-in temperature sensors on the $25 device more impressive than its cooling abilities.

Comes with Fins

The Cooling System is a piece of extruded aluminum case just large enough to seat a standard 3.5-inch desktop hard drive inside it. It has lots of fins, presumably to radiate heat, and packs a pair of thermally controlled fans behind the plastic faceplate, next to the digital readout. The whole package fits into a single 5.25-inch drive bay, with the plastic display and digital readout facing out.

The digital display flips back and forth showing the temps of the two sensors attached to the system. One seats between the drive and the aluminum drive bay of the Cooling System, the other is long enough (approximately six inches) to reach well into a standard case. Antec suggests you use it to monitor the ambient temperature inside the case, the temperature of your CPU, whatever.

How Cool Is It?

We set the Cooling System up in one of our testbeds, running SiSoft's Sandra File System benchmark on the test drive. Without the Cooling System, the drive reached a temp of 90 degrees while running the benchmark. Mounted inside the HDSC, the drive temperature dropped between one and two degrees (88 to 89 degrees). Over time, the drive temp dropped to 86 degrees.

We weren't hugely impressed by that four-degree maximum temperature difference. It may be that the Seagate drive in our test bed simply doesn't run that hot. Or that the dual fans in the Cooling System don't draw much air, except over the very front edge of the drive. There doesn't seem to be much airflow drawn over the sides of the drive, or the aluminum heat sink.

If you're into temperature readouts, however, this is one way to get them, plus a degree or two of hard drive cooling.

Windows Tips

Automatic Update

Greg Melton

Microsoft regularly releases security patches, programs, language packs, and bug fixes through its Windows Update site.

Here's how to configure Windows XP to automatically download updates:

1. Click the Start menu, then Control Panel.
2. Click the Performance and Maintenance icon and the System icon.
3. On the System Properties dialog, click the Automatic Updates tab.
4. Click the radio button next to the text labeled Download the Updates Automatically and Notify Me When They Are Ready to Be Installed.
5. Click the Apply button.

The next time you're online and there's an available update, you'll be prompted to install it.

November

22

Internet Time Synchronization

Greg Melton

One of Windows' most legendary features has been its ability to lose track of time. Well, not anymore. Windows XP is now capable of synchronizing your computer's internal clock with an Internet time server.

1. Double-click Time on the taskbar to launch the Date and Time properties.

2. On the Date and Time tab, make sure it reads the correct date before continuing. If it doesn't, adjust the date and click Apply.

3. Click the Internet Time tab.

4. Select the time server you want to use.

5. Place a check next to the text that reads Automatically Synchronize with an Internet Time Server.

6. Click Update Now to begin synchronizing.

That's it. Your time display automatically synchronizes once a week. This means no more third-party applications if you rely on your PC to keep track of time.

If the update isn't successful, select a different time server and try again. Some firewall users might have trouble updating time via synchronization. If so, tweak your firewall settings to unblock time synchronization and try again.

Megan's Tips

Net Diagnostics

If you want Windows XP to give you detailed information about what's going on with your network connections, you can use a hidden utility.

1. Click the Start menu.

2. Open Accessories, System Tools, System Info.

3. From the Tools menu, click on Net diagnostics.

Download of the Day

PC Inspector File Recovery 3.0

Dan Mitchell

Pretend for a minute that you just deleted an extremely important spreadsheet instead of that animated dancing monkey GIF you've been spreading around the office. First reaction: panic. Then your phone rings, and the boss wants to see your work in 15 minutes. Do you tell the boss, take your lumps, and hope you don't get fired? Hell, no. You download PC Inspector File Recovery (www.pcinspector.de/file_recovery/uk) and pull that file from the brink of destruction.

Deleted data isn't really gone; it's sitting on your hard drive until Windows overwrites the area with new data. But to access it, you need a utility such as PC Inspector File Recovery.

Here's how it works.

Launch the program, choose the drive you want to search (usually your C: drive), and hit either Find File or Find Lost Data. Find File allows you to search for a file by name or type (.txt, .jpeg, etc.). Find Lost Data searches the drive, locating every deleted file. When you find the file you're looking for, right-click it and choose Save To from the options list. Pick a destination for the file, and you're done.

The program gives you a good amount of information about the deleted file, including the name (often vague or labeled as cluster), the size, the last date modified, the condition of the file, and the file type. There's more than enough information to find the file you're looking for.

Warning: Don't expect miracles. Run this program as soon as humanly possible after you've deleted a file. The longer you wait, the less likely you are to recover data. If a file has been overwritten, you're not getting it back.

Get Back Deleted Files

Call for Help **Staff**

The whole idea of the Recycle Bin is that it's just a temporary storage area on the way to the big bit bucket in the sky. Normally, when you want to remove a file from the Recycle Bin, you double-click the Recycle Bin and drag the file to your desktop.

How the Recycle Bin Works

After you've emptied the Recycle Bin, however, it's more difficult to recover deleted files. Windows doesn't actually delete the data when you hit Delete. It merely modifies the file's entry in the catalog (the file allocation table) and makes that space available for other programs or files to use.

If you delete a file and empty the Recycle Bin, but decide shortly thereafter that you need the file back, it's often possible to recover it when you use a file recovery utility.

FAT vs. NTFS

You need to use a file-recovery utility designed for your computer's file system. The two file systems used by Windows are FAT and NTFS. FAT stands for file allocation table and comes in two varieties: FAT16 and FAT32.

FAT32 is an updated version of FAT16. A computer running Windows 95, 98, or Me is capable of formatting a drive only using the FAT (16/32) file system.

NTFS stands for NT File System or New Technology File System. NTFS is found in Windows NT, 2000, and XP.

Here's how to find out which type of file system you have:

1. Double-click My Computer.
2. Right-click any hard drive, and choose Properties.
3. On the General tab, the file system is listed after File System.

The main Recycle Bin is probably on your C: drive. However, if you have more than one hard drive or partition, you might have separate Recycle Bins for each drive. Windows NT, 2000, or XP might have a combination of both.

File-Recovery Software

File Rescue ($30, `www.softwareshelf.com`), by Software Shelf, supports both FAT and NTFS. File Rescue searches for all the deleted files. Clicking Undelete recovers the deleted files.

Drive Rescue (`http://home.arcor.de/ christian_grau/rescue/index.html`), a great freeware solution by Christian Grau, supports FAT, but its NTFS support is incomplete. The interface is not as simple as File Rescue's; you have to specify what directory the deleted files are in. However, Drive Rescue is just as effective at recovering deleted files. Christian Grau's website also has a utility called Digital Image Recovery (`http:// home.arcor.de/ zchristian_grau/dir/index.html`) for recovering deleted files from digital camera media (CompactFlash, Memory Stick, SmartMedia).

Recovery Limitations and Tips

If the data has been overwritten, or the space has been reused, it's almost impossible to get the file back.

If only part of a text file has been overwritten, you might be able to recover the rest. If it's a picture or a word-processing document, however, recovering only a portion of the data probably isn't enough. Remember to back up (use a CD-R, Zip, or floppy) often. You'll save the headache of restoring your files.

General Recycle Bin Tips

Right-clicking on the Recycle Bin and selecting Properties lets you turn off the confirmation for deleting an item. It also lets you adjust the capacity and whether you want the Recycle Bin to work either by drive or globally. If you hold down Shift while deleting a file, it bypasses the Recycle Bin and automatically and permanently deletes the file. Be careful!

Thanksgiving Recipes Online

Alison Strahan and Cat Schwartz

Stuck for a new way to present your Thanksgiving turkey? Have a hankering to freshen up your mashed potatoes and squash? Here are my recipe choices to ensure that your Thanksgiving meal is delicious and mouthwatering. Epicurious, the premier gourmet presence on the web, has Thanksgiving recipes for vegetarians. It provides four complete menus ranging from a Mediterranean-inspired meal to a Mexican menu. The pumpkin roll cake with toffee cream filling and caramel sauce looks delicious.

The site also has menus from some of America's finest chefs. Each menu is inspired by the customs and produce of different states. For example, Charlie Trotter's Midwestern Thanksgiving includes peppercorn and thyme–roasted goose, while Jasper White's New England menu features lobster soup and roast Vermont turkey.

Try out Native American recipes at Adam Starchild's site (www.geocities.com/NapaValley/6312/indian.html). Recipes include mouthwatering chestnut cakes and a solid-sounding maple beer. This chef gets my vote—he's written an entire cookbook devoted to the banana.

The Williams-Sonoma site (http://williams-sonoma.com) also features a plethora of recipes for the holidays. This is where Cat's dad, Bob Schwartz, will be getting his recipes.

Trouble with Turkey

If you're having trouble figuring out how long to thaw or cook your turkey, get some help from Butterball. Aside from these handy turkey preparation tips (www.butterball.com), you can also call and talk to a live person.

Tako's Quick Cooking Tips at the 8Legged website (www.8legged.com) is also helpful and a lot of fun. The wacky animated instructions walk you through the steps of thawing, marinating, browning, and more. You can also play fun games with the animated characters.

Get the kids into the kitchen to help. ChildFun.com (www.childfun.com/menus/thanks.shtml) has creative craft ideas and recipes, including a turkey made from an apple and toothpicks that you can use as a centerpiece.

Download of the Day

Download Express

Craig Higdon

Like a mighty locomotive, Download Express (www.metaproducts.com) quickly gets you where you want to be. Even on broadband it effectively doubled my download rate.

Download Express collects chunks of the file you want to download from different places simultaneously. The result is the full file on your end without having to wait on a single server.

1. Download and install Download Express.

2. Restart Internet Explorer.

3. Start downloading. Download Express will pop up and ask you if you want to save it to disk or run it. Choose an option and start your download.

You'll see your basic download information on the Info tab, specifics about the download on the Progress tab, and a neat graphical representation of your download on the Map tab. The interface even gives you the option to open your file when the download completes.

I'm not one for tweaking, but Download Express has a bunch of options for you tweak types. Simply click the Advanced button to customize your connection.

Download Express is sweet, sweet juju, and it gets you your file a heck of a lot faster. If you're tired of wasting your youth while downloading our free files, get Download Express and rediscover your life.

Beat Five Windows Annoyances in Five Minutes

Call for Help **Staff**

Scream, slam your fists on your desk, throw your mouse out the window, or let us tell you how to eliminate five of your biggest computer frustrations in five minutes or less.

Kill Pop-Ups

Download and install our favorite free pop-up killer: EMS Free Surfer mk II (www.kolumbus.fi/eero.muhonen/ FS/fs.htm). Whenever you surf, you'll need to opt in to pop-ups. You'll get only the windows you want.

Associate Files with Programs

You can customize the programs you use for different types of files. For example, listen to your MP3s in Winamp or view your JPEGs in IrfanView. In general, here's how:

1. Hold down Shift and right-click the file.
2. Click Open With and select a program.
3. Check Always Use This Program to Open This Type of File. If you don't, this is a one-time solution.
4. Click OK.

Here's what to do if your initial file reassociation doesn't stick in Windows Media Player:

1. From the Tools menu choose Options.
2. Go to the File Types tab.
3. Select the file formats you want to play back in Windows Media Player.
4. Save your selections.

If you want to change Winamp's associations, do the following:

1. Right-click anywhere on the Winamp player not occupied by a button.
2. Click Options, choose Preferences.
3. Under the Setup heading, choose File Types.
4. To make Winamp the default player for an extension, toggle it on, or simply select All or None. Click Close.

Delete Without the Recycle Bin

Here's a great trick to delete files without emptying the Recycle Bin:

1. Select the file you want to delete.
2. Hold down Shift and press Delete.
3. Click Yes to confirm you want to delete the file. Voilá! The file is gone.

Extract Zip Files Quickly

This little trick reduces the time it takes to open a .zip file to mere seconds:

1. Make sure the unzip utility adds shell extensions to your right-click contextual menu when you install. You should have new Extract To and Extract to Folder options.
2. Save or copy the .zip file to your desktop.
3. Right-click the file and choose Extract to Folder to extract the files to a folder. To unzip multiple files, simply select them all and right-click.

Get Defrag to Finish

Defragging a hard drive takes as long as it takes, but make sure it finishes the first time around without entering Safe Mode.

Turn off all the applications running in the background. You shouldn't have any programs or scheduled system tasks sitting in your system tray. Turn off your screen saver.

Run the Disk Defragmenter to get the best results in Windows 9*x*:

1. Click Start, Programs, Accessories, System Tools, Disk Defragmenter.
2. Select the drive to defrag and click Settings.
3. Under Disk Defragmenter Settings, check Rearrange Program Files So My Programs Start Faster and Check Drive for Errors.
4. Click OK to go back to the first screen; click OK again to begin the process.

In Windows XP, Right-click My Computer and choose Manage. Click Defragment.

Energy-Efficient Office Equipment

Jim Chace

A typical desktop PC system comprises the computer (CPU or box), a monitor, and a printer. This typical system uses 110 to 300 watts of electricity or more. The worst-case scenario is that you run the computer 24 hours a day × 300 watts × 365 days a year × $0.12 per kilowatt-hour. This equals $300 per year, assuming $.12 per kWh.

Monitor Maintenance

A 15- to 17-inch color monitor uses 50 to 150 watts, proportionately more for larger monitors. Screen savers can save the phosphors in your monitor screen, but they do not save energy.

A monitor with a moving screen saver consumes as much electricity as it does when in active use. A blank screen saver is slightly better, but reduces energy consumption by only a few percent. The best screen saver is to simply turn off your monitor. This step also eliminates concern about exposure to any electromagnetic radiation emanating from the monitor. The next-best screen saver is your computer's power-management feature to shut down the monitor when you're not using it.

Monitors labeled Energy Star consume up to 90% less energy than models without power-management features. These monitors automatically power down to 15 watts or less and emit less heat than conventional monitors.

Save with Your CPU

Your CPU requires from 50 to 150 watts of electric power. You can save $7 to $52 per year by using Energy Star–labeled computers.

Energy Star–labeled computers power down to 30 watts or less when not in use and might actually last longer because they spend a large portion of time in a low-power sleep mode. These computers also generate less heat.

It's commonly believed that a computer's life is shortened by turning it on and off. But most experts agree that turning off PC equipment at night, or on and off a few times a day, will not appreciably affect its useful life. Modern drives are designed to operate reliably for thousands of hours, including thousands of on/off cycles.

Print with Less Power

Laser printers can consume as much as 100 watts or more when printing. It is much less if idling in sleep mode. Inkjet printers use 90% less energy than laser printers, because they use less heat in the printing process. Inkjet printers use about 12 watts while printing and 5 watts when idle. It's better to network and share printers when possible.

Energy Star–labeled printers cut a printer's electricity use by more than 65%. They automatically power down to less than 10 to 100 watts, depending on the pages per minute produced and the printer type (that is, standard-size, color, large/wide-format, or impact).

Using the power-management feature means your printer produces less heat. By generating less heat, your printer might last longer and be more reliable. A printer with a duplexing mode can save $30 a month in paper costs, which also helps to save trees.

Table Lamps Save Money

Most fluorescent light bulbs, often called compact fluorescents, use the same mineral powders (phosphors), to produce light as those used to manufacture CRTs. Fluorescent light bulbs, often disliked for their "bad color," are greatly improved. Most people cannot tell the difference between an incandescent light bulb and a fluorescent light bulb.

The Berkeley Lamp, developed at the Lawrence Berkeley National Laboratory in Berkeley, California uses an efficient fluorescent light bulb. This lamp, which can be dimmed, gives the user independent control of two light bulbs and uses about one quarter the energy of a typical incandescent lamp.

Secret TiVo Codes

Patrick Norton and Roman Loyola

The TiVo (www.TiVo.com) personal video recorder is a very handy device, but don't you wish you had more control over the unit? After searching the Internet for cool TiVo hacks, we found the TiVo Community Forum, with TiVo back-door codes (www.tivocommunity.com). These codes let you access the unit in back-door mode.

Important note: Some codes will work with certain versions of the TiVo software. Use these codes at your own risk. Using these codes might have the following consequences:

- Void the warranty
- Damage and render the TiVo unit useless if the codes are used improperly
- Cause a total loss of your TiVo's data
- Terminate your service contract with TiVo

TechTV is not responsible for any malfunction, damage, or loss of service due to the use of these codes.

Get the Codes

If you've considered the risks and you're convinced you want to use back-door mode, visit http://tivo.samba.org for a complete list of the codes.

The 30-Second Jump

Let's try something tame. We'll turn the button that advances to the end of a show (titled Advance or Skip to End) into a button that skips forward 30 seconds. It's a nifty way to zip through commercial blocks.

The TiVo operating system should be 2.5.1 or above. If your TiVo has not updated to the latest version, force a phone call, wait for the mega download, and restart the system. You need a of Select-Play-Select codes. We got our list from the Whole Hacking the TiVo FAQ (http://tivo.samba.org). This is an amazing source of TiVo hacks. Ready to hack?

1. Type in **Select-Play-Select-3-0-Select** to turn on the 30-second skip mode. You should hear a "ding-ding-ding" sound. That means you've made the change.

2. Don't like it? Type in **Select-Play-Select-3-0-Select** again and wait for your ding-ding-ding, and you're back skipping to the end of the program.

We're pretty sure you won't violate the warranty doing this, but, hey, don't blame us if this sets you off on the merry road of advanced TiVo hacking, and you kill your system. Don't tweak, modify, hack, or putter around with anything that you aren't willing to pay to replace if you kill it.

Purify Your Power

Robert Heron

Have you ever thought about the quality of the electricity flowing into your PC? Perhaps you should. Most electronic devices are designed to withstand small fluctuations in AC voltage. Over time, these power surges or sags can stress sensitive components, causing them to fail prematurely. In the case of PCs, irregular power can be the cause of all sorts of issues, including system lockups, application crashes, and physical damage to the PC. Surge protectors and uninterruptible power supplies tame less-than-clean power currents.

Surge Protectors

Surge protectors and suppressors are the gate-keepers of electrical current. They won't protect you from a complete outage or a sag in power, but they will stop spikes in electricity from reaching your electronic equipment.

Tripp Lite's premium Isotel8Ultra (www.tripplite.com) surge suppressor incorporates eight outlets as well as modem/fax protection. At $65, the Ultra differs from less expensive models by using several high-quality methods of noise and surge suppression. Each pair of outlets (four pairs total) is isolated to prevent your devices from interfering with each other. Equipped with all-metal housing, multiple warning lights, and a lifetime warranty, the Isotel8Ultra is a cheap but effective insurance policy against Mother Nature's bad days.

UPS (Not the Delivery People)

If you live in an area that suffers from brownouts and blackouts, consider adding an uninterruptible power supply (UPS) to your PC's arsenal. A UPS has a battery that can keep a system running long enough to shut down safely.

American Power Conversion (APC, www.apcc.com) manufacturers UPS devices for nearly any job. The $110 Back-UPS CS 500 and the $60 Back-UPS ES 500 are suited for the home or small office. Each model offers six outlets (three surge-only, three UPS-plus-surge) as well as modem/fax line protection. APC recently issued a recall on some CS models.

Back-UPS CS 500

The main difference between consumer UPS devices that cost $70 and those that cost $300 or more (such as APC's Back-UPS Pro models) isn't always obvious. Typically, a more expensive UPS includes better electronics for reconstituting raw power into its ideal form. Battery usage also makes a difference.

A value-priced UPS typically engages the battery whenever there's any problem with the flow of power. A more expensive UPS engages the battery only when there's a complete power failure. For brownouts or sags in power, a higher-quality UPS relies on internal capacitors for smoothing out the current, while a less expensive model would immediately switch to battery power until the situation passes. The more a UPS has to engage its battery, the shorter the battery's life span.

Summary

I swear by APC's Back-UPS Pro series and just about any Tripp Lite product. Over the past few years, my Back-UPS Pro 650 has kept my computers running smoothly, in spite of California's notorious power "shortages." My Back-UPS Pro also helps overcome the ancient wiring scheme of my apartment building here in San Francisco.

My entertainment center is routed through a Tripp Lite surge suppressor that also filters my cable TV feed. My protected gear has never given me one bit of trouble. A poorly made device can lull you into a false sense of protection. However, even a good UPS or surge suppressor may not save you from Mother Nature's absolute worst.

Turn Your PC into a ReplayTV Unit

Joshua Brentano

TiVo, shmeevo! If you have a ReplayTV (www.videolan.org/vlc/) unit, in my opinion, you have the best PVR on the market. Why? Because by using a simple piece of open-source software, you can connect your ReplayTV to your home network and turn your PC into a second ReplayTV unit. The steps are easy.

Step 1: Network the ReplayTV Unit

1. Turn on DHCP by using a router, a PC, or any other option.
2. Connect the ReplayTV unit to your network with a standard Ethernet cable.

If you have problems, the ReplayTV owner's manual can walk you through the steps.

Step 2: Choose Your Playback Software

Several programs can play back MPEG-2 videos, but I had problems with almost every one. Don't bother trying any program other than VideoLAN (www.videolan.org/vlc).

Step 3: Install Archive Software for Your Computer

1. Download and install DVArchive (http://dvarchive.sourceforge.net).
2. If you don't have Java installed, download it (http://java.sun.com/j2se/1.4.1/download.html).
3. Start DVArchive and choose a folder to store the ReplayTV files.
4. Click File and select DVArchive Properties.
   - Click the General tab.
   - Specify your video-playback software. Use VideoLAN for both MPEG Video Player and Streaming MPEG Video Player.
5. I recommend changing no other options except the Local Guide to suit your taste.

After you've installed the software, it automatically detects the ReplayTV unit. Give it a minute. To transfer shows to your PC, simply drag and drop. From your ReplayTV, you can set up scheduled tasks such as transferring shows.

Watch Shows from Your PC on Your ReplayTV

1. Start DVArchive on your PC.
2. Bring up the replay guide on the ReplayTV unit. In the upper-right corner, it says This ReplayTV. Move the cursor to these words and press left or right. This brings up the list of shows you've transferred to your PC.
3. Select the show you want to watch.

When watching a show stored on your PC, you won't be able to fast-forward and rewind as well as you should. But that's a small price to pay for the extra storage space.

Playback Tweaks

If the video playback across the network is choppy, you might need to tweak the MTU settings. I'd like to thank 1box from the Planet Replay forums (www.planetreplay.com). Here's his advice:

1. Change the MTU settings with DrTCP (www.dslreports.com/front/drtcp.html). Download and install, and run the software.
2. Make sure all settings are at default (or blank, where default isn't an option).
3. Change TCP Receive Window Size. This setting should be an even multiple of your MSS. (This setting is normally 1460 for a LAN or cable broadband.) Start with a number in the neighborhood of 20 and work your way up until you can successfully stream high-quality video. 1box used a setting of 64,240 (44×1,460).

December 2004

Leftovers

Megan Morrone

Having Thanksgiving dinner at someone else's house offers advantages. You're not responsible for cooking the bird or handling the seating assignments, and if your Aunt Lurlene comes down with botchulism from a bent can of yams, it's not your fault. But I'm willing to suffer the wrath (and the small claims suit) from Aunt Lurlene and have Thanksgiving at my house if it means that I'm left with a refrigerator full of Thanksgiving leftovers. If I'm very careful, they'll last through the end of December.

If you like leftovers as much as I do, then you'll love this last month of the almanac, where we collect all the tips and tricks that didn't fit into the other months and offer them up like a turkey and cranberry and green bean sandwich with gravy and mashed potato dressing.

In addition to the potluck of stories about making widgets in OS X, finding virtual magnifying glasses, and using speech-recognition technology, this month you'll also find all our best holiday stories, from decorating your PC with digital strings of colored lights to making your own cards on the computer. We offer you online travel tips and reviews of great gadget gifts, family software, and high-tech toys for kids.

As a child, the first of December for me always meant breaking out the cardboard advent calendar. Behind each of those days of the month lay a special surprise that was always worth waiting for. Think of this month as *The Screen Savers'* technology advent calendar. Turning the pages of each new day is like popping opening that little cardboard window on the calendar. Like the advent calendars of our childhood, these pages might even offer little pieces of chocolate or a gold coin, but not if Leo got there first.

Top Applications for New Computers

Leo Laporte and Patrick Norton

Leo's Bundle of Software

- **Ultimate Zip** (www.ultimatezip.com)
- **NoteTabPro** (www.notetab.com)
- **Download Accelerator** (www.downloadaccelerator.com)
- **AVG Antivirus** (www.grisoft.com)
- **Proxomitron** (www.spamblocked.com)

Pat's Apps

The first programs I install on a fresh PC? The list has gotten pretty short with Windows XP. It has a built-in file expander, so I don't need Stuffit Expander (www.stuffit.com) anymore. It's still good to have around for the more esoteric types of compressed files, though.

- First up: Install all the Windows security updates (see http://windowsupdate.microsoft.com). It's a good thing I have a DSL line; otherwise, downloading all the updates on a phone line would take a while.

- Next: Winamp (www.winamp.com) for playing MP3s.

- I also want Musicmatch (www.musicmatch.com) for ripping MP3s.

- AnalogX's Netstat Live (www.analogx.com) helps me figure out whether my network is behaving. (While you're up on AnalogX's site, get Atomic TimeSync if you really want to know what time it is.)

- I'm hidden behind a fairly solid hardware firewall. If I weren't, I would get Zone Alarm (www.zonealarm.com) or Tiny Personal Firewall (www.tinysoftware.com).

Corks for Dorks

Dave Roos

Ah, Las Vegas, city of tempered passions, where sobriety is the cardinal virtue, second only to frugality. You can imagine how surprised we were, then, when we heard about the wine-drenched excess occurring nightly at the Aureole Restaurant (www.aureolelv.com) in the otherwise staid and sedate Mandalay Bay Resort and Casino.

Aureole is the first restaurant to convert a tablet PC—in this case, the Compaq TC1000—into a portable repository of reviews, taste charts, and recommendations for all of Aureole's 4,000 wines. They call it the e-wine list. We call it fun!

Customers use a stylus to browse the menu and match the appropriate reds and whites with their veal and halibut. Curious eaters can even email the sommelier and chef to offer comments and ask questions. Wine-guy Andrew Bradbury says emailers usually receive responses by the next day.

The wines themselves are kept in Aureole's four-story "tower of wine," an eye-popping centerpiece supposedly inspired by a scene from Tom Cruise's *Mission Impossible*. A team of "wine angels" is hoisted by wires to retrieve bottles from their lofty perch.

Address: Site of the Night

Seamless City

Seamless City photographer Michael Koller has assembled one continuous digital picture of 30 miles of San Francisco streets: See www.seamlesscity.com.

Travel the World

Cat Schwartz

I like to imagine I'm an extremely adventurous person who likes to climb mountains, cross rivers by foot, commune with nature, and soak in every bit of obscure news from around the world. I'm actually the type of person who turns to the Net to find this sort of information and pass it on to my friend Kara, who knows her way around the world like it's the back of her hand. Here's a great site for all of us who like to sit at home imagining we're in other places doing other things.

The *National Geographic* website (www.nationalgeographic.com/index.html) is the perfect place to feed your fascination with the outside world. *National Geographic* is known for its exquisite photography and intense writing. The website won't disappoint on this front, but you'll also find a slew of other treasures here.

- Take a look at the latest magazines.
- Find out what's coming up on TV, and watch streaming video previews.
- Learn about exotic animals.
- Take a look at the swimsuit issue (http://magma.nationalgeographic.com/ngm/swimsuits/).

Take a trip to the Adventure section (www.nationalgeographic.com/explore/) to plan your trips of exploration. For example, you'll be able to find out how to visit the most active volcano in the world or find the best places for a back-country ski trip. It also offers step-by-step survival guides and maps.

This is a site worth exploring if you've ever been curious about the world.

Adam's and Morgan's Favorite Games

Adam Sessler and Morgan Webb

When it's your job to play games all day, it's hard to pick your favorites. But here they are, Adam Sessler's and Morgan Webb's top five (for now):

Adam's favorite games:

- **Legend of Zelda: The Wind Waker** (www.nintendo.com)
- **Sly Cooper and the Thevius Raccoonus** (www.us.playstation.com)
- **Metroid Prime** (www.nintendo.com)
- **Rise of Nations** (www.microsoft.com)
- **Battlefield 1942** (www.ea.com)

Morgan's favs:

- **Unreal Tournament** 2K3 (www.unrealtournament2003.com)
- **Golden Sun and Golden Sun 2: The Lost Age** (GBA, www.goldensun-games.com)
- **Mortal Kombat: Deadly Alliance** (http://pocket.ign.com)
- **Soul Calibur 2** (www.soulcalibur.com)
- **Castlevania: Aria of Sorrow** (GBA, http://pocket.ign.com)

Address: Site of the Night

Jeopardy Online: Techno-Files

Challenge geeks from around the world to this multiplayer version of your favorite quiz show at http://jeopardy.station.sony.com/play.jsp.

December
2

353

Festival of Volume Knobs

Patrick Norton

I like volume knobs. I hate clicking buttons to raise or lower the volume, whether it's a car stereo, PC, or boom box. When I saw the Griffin PowerMate ($45, www.griffintechnology.com) in an Apple store back in Jersey, I was fascinated.

It's a USB volume knob. It's burly and feels like it came off the 200-pound stereo my Dad had back in his day, right down to the brushed aluminum construction.

Yes, it's a $45 volume knob. Now quit laughing. The PowerMate was *MacAddict*'s 2002 input device of the year. Seriously. It works on PCs, too.

There's a reason I think it's cool, beyond the glowing blue base. It's supremely customizable for any application. It's a volume control for Winamp. You can use it to scroll text in Word. It makes a simple jog/shuttle control for your video-editing program (that's a control that lets you move video back and forth on the screen; you'll find one in every professional editing room). Press down on the PowerMate, and it acts like a big clickable button.

The Contour SpaceShuttle A/V (www.contouravs.com) was designed as a shuttle for video-editing applications. Neither as hefty nor as slickly designed as the PowerMate, the $50 tool includes five programmable buttons to the PowerMate's one. It's preprogrammed for heaps of video-editing applications, but like the PowerMate, you can customize it to work with any program.

"Ultimate volume controls," "alternative input devices," "video-editing essentials"—whatever you want to call these devices is up to you. I like both of them. I'm really stoked about having a proper volume knob to control my PC, but I may just have Yoshi hack a big hefty volume control into my keyboard just for my speakers.

24-Hour Computer Help

Cat Schwartz

We can't answer all your tech questions all the time, but I know where you can get help anytime you want. PCShowAndTell (www.pcshowandtell.com), is an awesome resource where you can watch and listen to tutorials and learn how to fix most software problems.

It's free to search through the site, but you need an account to view most of its material. Sign up for a free 14-day subscription to try it out. You must provide an email address and name, and you'll need to download the service's player.

1. Log on to the site.

2. Choose a subject from the list of products and programs on the left of the page. (You can also search by keyword.) Click a subject (Windows XP, for example) and keep cascading out topics (printing, for example) until you find what you want.

3. You can choose to watch, read, or email the results. If you select Watch, your newly installed player will pop up and start helping!

If you like what you see, buy the service. TechTV viewers get $10 off the $30 membership fee. To get your discount, enter the promo code TECHTV03. Pretty darn good for 24-hour PC help, if you ask me.

PCShowAndTell can also teach a company's workforce to use the unique technology in their office. Just register and enter **abc** as the promo code.

Holiday Icons

Nicole Carrico

Deck the halls with boughs of holly. Put up your tree and your twinkling lights, hang the stockings on the hearth, and get out that green and red sweater your Aunt Mabel knitted for you all those years ago. 'Tis the season for draping everything you own in holiday cheer. Why should your desktop be an exception?

Our first stop is Saho's Icon Room (http://saho.vis.ne.jp/index_e.html). Take a look in the Xmas folder to see seasonal choices for both Mac and PC. My personal favorite is the folder with the Santa hat. So cute! As a nondenominational option, don't miss the icon set called Snowy Town, which has an irresistible Winter Wonderland type of feel.

After you've stocked up at Saho's, cruise over to Debi's Wonderful World (www.debidawn.com/icons.htm). Debi has a huge assortment of goodies, including more holiday icons than you can shake a Yule log at. With a few quick clicks, your computer will be choked with holiday cheer.

Changing Icons in Windows XP

1. Right-click anywhere on your desktop.
2. Choose Properties.
3. Click Desktop.
4. Click Customize Desktop.

Changing Icons in Windows 98

1. Right-click anywhere on your desktop.
2. Choose Properties.
3. Choose Effects.
4. Select the icon you want to change.
5. Click Change Icon.
6. Browse for the new icon.

Download of the Day

Freevo

Roman Loyola

If there's one thing everyone on *The Screen Savers* loves, it's free stuff. We can't get enough free stuff, except for America Online CDs. (You need only so many coasters.)

We also love TiVo, especially the Home Media Option that turns your TiVo into a multimedia center. Problem is, TiVo costs money.

Patrick found what may be the coolest free application you can run on your PC. It's called Freevo (http://freevo.sourceforge.net/), and it combines our two favorite things, TiVo-like functionality and no price tag.

Freevo does more than just record video. Here's what you can do with Freevo:

- Watch TV with TV Guide (using XMLTV)
- Record TV in immediate mode or as a background task
- Play AVI, MPEG, and DVD movies
- Play MP3 or Ogg Vorbis files
- Play audio CDs (has CDDB support)
- View photos and pictures

Freevo also has these cool features:

- Skinnable user interface using XML files
- Movie and music file info using XML files
- Preliminary Mame support
- Web CGI interface for TV recording

To run Freevo on your PC, you need to run Linux.

Freevo is an open-source application, which means you can access the source code and make your own modifications (if you have the skills).

December

4

Leo's Pick: Konfabulator

Leo Laporte

In 1987, a program named HyperCard helped change the face of computing. This software for the Macintosh made it possible for even non-programmers to create their own simple applications, called stacks, and distribute them to the world.

Fast-forward to today, and Mac OS X. Konfabulator is a shareware program that's putting the same kind of power into users' hands. Konfabulator's creators, Arlo Rose and Perry Clarke, call their program "a JavaScript runtime engine for Mac OS X." Users call it a cool way to put widgets on their Mac desktop. Even better, Konfabulator lets people with limited programming skills create their own widgets. Konfabulator fulfills the promise that Microsoft's Active Desktop (www.microsoft.com) never delivered on, and it does it on the Mac.

Rose created the Macintosh shareware classic Kaleidoscope (www.kaleidoscope.net). Clarke is an engineer at Sun Microsystems. Together they've written one of those rare shareware programs that people have to have as soon as they see it. I paid the $25 shareware fee within minutes of downloading it. It's well worth the money. Within two weeks of its release, more than 100 widgets were contributed to the Konfabulator gallery, and more appear every day.

Konfabulator widgets are described in simple XML files. Their features are programmed in JavaScript. The JavaScript code can call shell commands, AppleScript, Perl, and other scripting languages. There's very little you can't do with Konfabulator.

There are many available free widgets, including weather forecasts, interesting clocks, Slashdot and other newsfeed readers, batteries, network activity and CPU monitors, and more.

The best way to understand Konfabulator is to try Konfabulator. Download and try it for free at www.konfabulator.com.

Family Software

Roman Loyola and David Prager

These ideas for some family-oriented software come from some brainstorming among *The Screen Savers* staff.

- **Monopoly** (www.us.infogrames.com). The popular board game has several different digital versions. It's $19.

- **Family Tree Maker** (www.genealogy.com). Trace the roots of your relatives. You might be surprised to find out who's in your family. It's $29 for the basic package.

- **You Don't Know Jack** (www.jellyvision.com). This game has been discontinued by Sierra, but you can still find copies of it on the Internet auction sites.

Download of the Day

Desktop Holiday Lights

Megan Morrone

It's time to start decking the halls and your monitor with holiday cheer. Unless you work with a bunch of Scrooges, you've probably seen some form of holiday desktop lights in Christmases past. But like most of your favorite ornaments, virtual holiday lights are often hidden beneath a year's worth of garbage in the attic or on your desktop.

How to Customize Holiday Lights

When you've downloaded the program, it couldn't be easier to customize. Click on the bulb icon in your system tray and select Holiday Lights Settings. There you can add different bulbs, adjust the flash rate, and choose the music.

Holiday Lights 5.2 (www.tigertech.com)

The lights are free trial versions from http://download.com. If you don't pay the $19.95 shareware price, you'll only get the basic set of lights and you'll get bugged about paying every time you start up your PC.

Browse by Object

Morgan Webb

You have more options than just the Find feature when you want to scan your Word document. You can perform what's known as an object search, where you hop between objects of a certain type until you land on the one you're looking for.

Spot That Magic Dot

To begin, open an object-heavy Word document and look to the far right of the screen. Beneath your scroll bar, near the bottom of your screen, should be a little 3D dot with up arrows above it and down arrows below. This inconspicuous morsel is your object search tool, and if you've passed it over a million times, it's because it doesn't look like much.

When you click on the dot you're given the option to browse by any number of item types. For example, you can browse by table, which will bring you jumping from table to table in your document until you find the one you're looking for. You can also browse for images, edits, footnotes, and tons of other options. Once you've chosen the item you want to search for, use the little double arrows above and below the magic dot to scan your document.

How easy was that? Word has plenty of little features you would never know existed unless you clicked every button, so have fun and explore!

Address: Site of the Night

Bilbanan

Design, build, and race slot cars on your own customized track at http://tv4.se/lattjo/kojan/bilbanan.asp.

Laporte Support

DVD Formats

Several DVD formats are out there:

- **DVD-RAM.** Not compatible with DVD-ROM drives and DVD players
- **DVD-R.** A nonrewriteable format; compatible with most DVD players and DVD-ROMs
- **DVD-RW.** A rewriteable format; compatible with most DVD players and DVD-ROMs
- **DVD+R.** A nonrewriteable format; compatible with most DVD players and DVD-ROMs
- **DVD+RW.** A rewriteable format; compatible with most DVD players and DVD-ROMs

The − and + formats are equally compatible. The R formats are a bit more compatible than the RW formats. The DVD drive manufacturers continue to battle it out. Microsoft recently announced support for the DVD+RW format. Pioneer and others support the − formats.

You're pretty safe with whatever format you choose. Make sure you get a newer burner, to ensure compatibility. Check out these links for more information:

- **DVD Demystified** (www.dvddemystified.com)
- **DVDR Help** (www.dvdrhelp.com)

Free Web-Based Photo Albums

Nicole Guilfoyle

Several services let you upload and share your photos. If you impress your friends with your photo prowess, they'll be able to order prints for a small fee. All you need is an Internet connection and web browser.

Ofoto (www.ofoto.com)

1. Sign up for a free account. You need to provide your first name and email address.

2. Sign into the site.

3. Click the Add Photos tab, click Create New Album icon.

4. Name, date, and describe your album. Click Next.

5. Select an upload option:
   - **Browser Upload:** Browse your hard drive for photos.
   - **Drag and Drop Upload:** Click and drag photos from your hard drive into the interface.
   - **Select Photos Upload:** Choose a file or multiple files from a folder on your hard drive.

6. Upload your photos and click Next.

7. Click Share This Album.

8. Enter your friends' email addresses and click Send. Your friends will receive an email with a link to your photos.

Shutterfly (www.shutterfly.com)

1. Sign up for a free account. You need to provide your name and email address.

2. Sign onto the site and click Add Pictures.

3. Name your album and click Next.

4. Install the Picture Upload plug-in.

5. Click Choose Pictures to browse for images, or drag and drop the images you want to share into the interface. When you're done adding pictures, click Next.

6. Click Share Online, select your album, and click Next.

7. Enter your friends' email addresses, specify whether you want them to enter a password or log on to Shutterfly to access the pictures, and click Send. Your friends will receive an email with a link to your photos and instructions about how to access them.

Snapfish (www.snapfish.com)

1. Sign up for a free account. You need to provide your first name and email address. Sign in.

2. Click Upload Photos.

3. Select a new album and name it. Click Choose This Album.

4. Drag and drop the photos you want to share onto the interface, or browse your hard drive for images. Click Upload Photos.

5. Click Share Photos. Enter your friends' email addresses and click Send. Your friends will receive an email with a link to your photos.

Yahoo! Photos (http://photos.yahoo.com)

1. Sign in with your Yahoo! ID (it's the same one you use for email and instant messaging) or register for a free account. Sign in.

2. Choose "Free: A Free Account gives you 30MB of storage to store up to 90 high-quality photos. The Upload Limit is 5MB." Select the type of album you want to create, enter the confirmation code (it's on the right), and click Submit.

3. Click Add Photos, select your album, and browse your hard drive for images. Click Upload.

4. Click Share Photos and specify whether you want to make your album public (open to everyone) or available to specific Yahoo! users. Save your preference.

5. Copy the link to your album and email it to your friends.

Free Web-Based Photo Albums (continued)

AOL's You've Got Pictures

AOL's You've Got Pictures is free for America Online members. Don't worry; anyone can view your albums—they don't have be a member.

1. Click Upload Pictures.

2. Use the Single Pictures Upload tool to upload individual images, or download the Multiple Picture Upload tool.

3. Locate the images on your hard drive.

4. Preview and click Upload.

5. You'll see thumbnail images when all the pictures are uploaded.

6. Click the tab containing the pictures you want to share—for example, Buddy Albums.

7. Click the radio button next to the roll or album you want to share. To select individual pictures, click View Pictures, and place a check mark next to your choices.

8. Click Share Pictures. Fill out the email information and click Send.

You can also upload and share your photos from any web browser.

1. Log on to You've Got Pictures online (http://aolsvc.pictures.aol.com).

2. Choose Create an Album or Find My Pictures.

3. Click the Pictures on My Computer tab, check the images you want to upload, and click Add to My Album.

4. Click My Albums on AOL, check the album you want to share, and click Share Album.

5. Fill out the email information and click Send.

6. Your friends will receive a direct link to your album. No sign-in is necessary.

If your friends like what they see, they can order prints on Kodak paper.

Home Inventory System

Greg Melton

Roger finally decided to inventory all his DVDs, comic books, and tech gadgets. Why, you ask? He wants an easy way to identify all his valuables in case he ever has to file an insurance claim.

He searched high and low to find a program that would track items in a database and that didn't cost a fortune. After reviewing Primasoft's Home Organizer Deluxe 1.9 (www.primasoft.com) and Down to Earth Software's Homewise (www.dtes.com)— he finally settled on the perfect solution: Frostbow's Home Inventory 4 (www.frostbow.com).

Home Inventory 4 boasts an easy-to-use interface and lets you enter information using 21 separate data entry fields. You can keep track of an item's name, manufacturer, make/model, serial number, category, location, date purchased, warranty, and more. It even includes a field to associate two different images with an item. The program features a section for creating detailed reports, bar graphs, and pie charts listing all the items you've inventoried.

Home Inventory creates a Zip file archive of the database, so you can keep a separate copy of the database in a different location (along with all the hard-copy reports it generates).

Free Alternative

My Stuff (www.contactplus.com) is a freeware program similar to Frostbow's Home Inventory 4. Although it is not as flexible, it does a great job of keeping track of your personal belongings. It features a simple interface and drop-down menus that let you access previously entered items.

As with Home Inventory 4, you can add graphic images as well as appreciating and depreciating amounts for each item.

December
8

Are You "Always On"?

Patrick Norton

Chances are, your Internet access at work is always on. Just launch your browser and go. It feels a lot different from firing up your modem, listening to it sing, and—has it been seconds or minutes?—finally getting online. It's one of the niftiest things about having broadband access: The Net is always on.

Well, at least Leo's old cable modem used to be always on. My DSL access to the Net takes a few seconds. I have to launch a dialer. That few seconds launches a PPPoE (Point to Point Protocol over Ethernet) connection to my ISP's server.

Rumor has it, some cable modem systems are implementing PPPoE, putting a similar dial-up box between you and the Net. But don't worry about that being a problem. The few seconds it takes to launch through a PPPoE aren't that painful.

Even if it isn't quite "always on," having fast access on tap changes the way you use the web. Leo uses Karelia's Watson (www.karelia.com/watson) to find movies with his Mac. I use Dictionary.com (www.dictionary.com), rather than plowing through my beat-up ol' book version.

Sound silly? Maybe. But broadband access doesn't just make for fast downloads. It makes accessing all kinds of information online a lot more practical than it would be with a dial-up connection.

Morgan's Tips

LED Holiday Decorations

Morgan Webb

My favorite Christmas ornaments of the season are simple, do-it-yourself kits that almost anyone can construct.

Take a look at them at Efston Science (www.e-sci.com/circuitT/0001/C9/ C9_400/ 13039.html) and HobbyTron.com (www.hobbytron.net/UK264.html). They boast full instructions for easy construction by even a novice, and they provide a perfect beginning to any electronics career or soldering hobbyist. A soldering iron and solder are required to construct each of these projects, and they usually require a 9-volt battery.

Grab your soldering iron and make your season bright!

Laporte Support

Play Old DOS Games

Can I run old DOS games in Windows 98?

If making a boot disk and running it from the DOS prompt doesn't work, check the game manufacturer's website to see if there are any known driver compatibility issues for your video card. If you don't know your system specs, use Belarc Advisor (www.belarc.com) to get them. You may also want to try using CD Anywhere (www.v-com.com) to put an image of the game on your hard drive.

SciTech Display Doctor (www.scitechsoft.com) might also help your computer display the game correctly.

Starter

Megan Morrone

Do you know what I can't stand? I can't stand programs that take it upon themselves to add themselves to my startup process. If I want to use a program every time I use my computer, I will add that program to my Start menu myself. Do you hear me?

You can customize your startup menu with a lot of digging around in Windows and a lot of dragging and dropping, or you can download a simple program called Starter (`http://codestuff.cjb.net`).

Download and install the program. During installation, Starter adds a shortcut to your desktop, your Start menu, and your Quick Launch bar, unless you tell it not to. Personally, I don't need all these shortcuts.

Double-click the lightning icon, and you're ready to customize your startup. Delete the programs you don't want to run at startup by unchecking the box.

If you'd like to add your email program, web browser, or other programs to the startup process, click the New button and browse for your program.

You might also want to take a look at Mike Lin's Startup Control Panel (`www.mlin.net/StartupCPL.shtml`).

Address: Site of the Day

Discoverykids.com

Cat Schwartz

It's hard to keep children amused. The kid-savvy site discoverykids.com (`http://kids.discovery.com`) can help you get the job done. Discovery does TV right, and its web programming doesn't disappoint, providing a fun yet educational haven for kids who want to play and learn online.

Had enough of the educational content? Head over to the fun and games area, where you and your little ones will learn without even knowing it.

There are enough tidbits on this site to keep the youngsters out of your hair for hours, including a search feature, a Cool Stuff section, and webcams.

Windows Tips

Create Document Scraps in Microsoft Word

David Prager

If you work with a lot of Microsoft Word and WordPad documents, here's a nifty little trick for creating scraps. A scrap is a file that immediately saves any selected portions of your document to the desktop. It's great for saving a few quick sentences for future reference or for removing important stuff from a longer document.

1. Highlight the passage you want to save.
2. Click and hold the highlighted portion. Drag it to a blank space on the desktop, and release the button.
3. A saved document is instantly created on your desktop starting with "Document scrap" and the first few words of your selected passage.

This feature seems to work well with just about any application that allows dragging and dropping of text.

December
10

Make Your TV Kid-Friendly

Nicole Guilfoyle

We all love watching TV. There are programs for adults, kids, teens, and the entire family. But there's little TV stations can do to make sure children don't watch adult-oriented programs containing strong language, violence, and sexual content. It's up to you to shield kids from adult content.

How Are Shows Rated?

Television shows are rated by content, using a rating code different from the movies'. Here's a quick guide to the ratings. You'll need to know them when you activate your V-Chip or TiVo parental controls so that you'll know which program you want to block.

- **TV-Y:** Appropriate for all children.
- **TV-Y7:** Appropriate for older children.
- **TV-G:** Appropriate for a general audience; it's family-friendly.
- **TV-PG:** Watch this program with your kids.
- **TV-14:** Some content is inappropriate for children younger than 14.
- **TV-MA:** Appropriate is for a mature audience.

TV-PG, TV-14, and TV-MA ratings may also be followed by a TV content rating. L indicates that the program contains strong language, S indicates sexual content, D stands for suggestive dialogue, and V tells you that the program contains violence. You can read more about TV ratings at The TV Parental Guidelines (www.tvguidelines.org).

Set V-Chip Controls

Television sets 13 inches and larger sold in the United States after January 2000 are equipped with a V-Chip. The V-Chip lets you block programs by rating. Although every TV has a different way of accessing V-Chip controls, most controls are located in your TV's menu options. When children try to access blocked programming, they get an error message on a blank screen.

Standalone TiVo

Here's how to set the parental controls on TiVo when you're not using the DirecTV satellite service.

1. From the parental control screen, select channel lock.
2. Enter your password.
3. A channel list appears with a padlock icon to the left of any locked channels. Highlight a channel and click Select to add or Remove a padlock icon.
4. When done, press the right or left arrow to return to the parental controls.

TiVo with DirecTV

These instructions help you set your parental controls. Scroll down to the next set of instructions if you're not using the DirecTV satellite service.

1. Go into Preferences and select Parental Controls.
2. Enter your four-digit password.
3. Set your parental controls.
   - Temporarily disable your parental controls, or turn them on or off.
   - Restrict content according to TV or MPAA ratings.
   - Lock and unlock channels.
   - Change your password.
4. Nobody will be able to watch restricted programs until you unlock the parental controls.

Make Your TV Kid-Friendly (continued)

More Help

TechTV Labs recently evaluated several products that can help you take control of what your kids watch. Here are a few favorites.

- **Weemote Children's Remote Control** (www.weemote.com) is a kid-friendly remote. You can preprogram up to six channels that your kids are allowed to watch.

- Some parents don't let their kids watch TV. But most of these kids can still rent videos and DVDs. **ClearPlay** (www.clearplay.com) and ProtecTV (www.protectv.com) bleep out profanity. A similar product, MovieMask (www.moviemask.com), should be out by the time you read this.

- **Fisher DVD-SL30 DVD Video Player** is a set-top DVD player that bleeps out profanity.

No matter how many new tech devices come out to help you moderate what your kids watch, there's no better strategy than sitting down to watch TV with your kids.

Web Tips

Learn Sign Online

Alison Strahan

If you're thinking about learning another language, why not try sign language? Deaf culture and the deaf community are thriving on the web. Sites such as ASLinfo.com (www.aslinfo.com) and Deaf Resource Library (www.deaflibrary.org) offer many resources, and HandSpeak (www.handspeak.com) lets you tap into a new form of expression: American Sign Language (ASL).

HandSpeak features videos that demonstrate popular sign words of the day, such as smile, sister, and love. When you learn the word of the day you can progress to sign a complete sentence. HandSpeak also has books in sign, a baby sign section, and a small section for international signs.

Create Your Own Holiday Card

James Kim

Do the right thing and create your own special card with your computer and inkjet printer. Here's what you need:

- Card stock (available where printers are sold).

- Card-creation program. I'm using Microsoft Word, but you can also use a program such as The Print Shop (www.broderbund.com) from Broderbund, or an image editor such as Adobe Photoshop (www.adobe.com).

- Digital photos.

- Creativity.

- Web access, if you want to use a premade Microsoft Word card template.

Here are the basics of creating your card in MS Word:

1. Find a template in Microsoft's Template Gallery (http:// search.officeupdate.microsoft.com/ TemplateGallery/ct113.asp). Using a template ensures that you'll be able to print correctly.

2. Use preset images or insert your own text and images. Click Insert, and choose Picture or Text Box.

3. Drag and drop your object, or mouse over the corner of the object to stretch and adjust the picture and text.

4. Finish the cover and inside of your card, stick your card stock into the printer, and print both sides of the card.

Windows Tips

Quickly change the case of letters in Microsoft Word. Place the cursor in the word you want to edit. Press Shift+F3 on your keyboard. The word will switch between capitalized, all caps, or not capitalized.

December

12

Toys for Twisted Tots

Dick DeBartolo
Ocean Explorer-1

Ocean Explorer-1 (www.megatech.com) is a crazy R/C submarine that can dive up to 6 feet. The manufacturer says it's the deepest-diving R/C sub on the market and the only one with built-in LED explorer lights and red/green running lights. (Okay, so I doubt that real subs have running lights, but they look neat on this miniature model!) Twin motors allow for precision movements. Price: $110 for the complete outfit, including the sub, a charger, a stand, an R/C unit, and spare props.

ColorCutter

ColorCutter (www.colorcutter.com/mainDefault.asp) is the strangest marker you'll ever see. It actually cuts the paper as it draws! Draw a circle, and it cuts out a circle. It's safe because it's done with pressure. I saw a guy run the marker over his wrist many times and came away unscathed. But it does cut paper when you press down on a flat surface, so kids should be supervised. It's from Gizmo Enterprises, which has nothing to do with the Giz Wiz! It's available in many colors. Price: $6 each.

Sister Discipline Bop Bean Bag

The Sister Discipline Bop Bean Bag (www.rocketusa.com/home.html) comes in 7-inch, 18-inch, and 24-inch versions. And if you've been screwed out of your pension, lost a ton on a stock, didn't get a raise, or got fired because of a dishonest boss, there's also the CEO Bop Bean Bag. Punch him out and save a bundle on therapy!

Teen Security Cam

The Teen Security Cam (www.itemfinders.com) is a bargain! It's a fake security camera with a blinking red light that senses motion and sounds an alarm. A recorded voice reads a warning when someone walks by, and the camera rotates. It's ideal for protecting a kid's room from snooping parents. And it costs only $10! This product is brand-new and is available from Item Finders.

The Special F/X Unit

It's like an indoor storm with lights flickering when you plug a lamp into the back of the unit and play the "stormy thunder" CD that's provided. The unit has a built-in microphone, so lights also flicker to your voice or your own music. Price: $30, available at Can You Imagine (www.cyi.net).

Cool Updates on Older Items

- **Litecubes** (www.litecubes.com). Everything else lights up, why not the ice in your drink? Freeze litecubes, turn 'em on, and then drop them into someone's drink. Talk about a conversation starter! These new cubes come in several colors and have better light distribution. Price: Four litecubes for $14.50.

- **Tireflys UV** (www.tireflys.com). These motion-activated lights attach to the "value stem" (the place where you inflate the tire) of bikes, motorcycles, or cars. The company released Tireflys UV for increased nighttime visibility. Price: Less than $10.

Megan's Tips

Animated GIFs can be huge bandwidth hogs. Here's how to disable them: Within Internet Explorer, click Tools, Internet Options; choose the Advanced tab, and scroll down to the Multimedia section; uncheck play animations.

TimeLeft

Mike Gadd

Whether you're working at the office or hanging out on your computer at home, the minutes can just fly by. TimeLeft (www.nestersoft.com/timeleft) is a great way for Windows users to keep track of those minutes and help you get the most out of every second of the day.

After you install it, a clock pops up in the upper-left corner of your screen. It has a What Time Is It Now window, as well as a Time Left to the New Year window so you can count off the days until that next big midnight bash. Synchronize TimeLeft's clock with atomic clock servers all over the world. Your clock will always be accurate, and you can keep track of the passing hours in far-off places.

You can also turn on the stopwatch feature to time how long you really spend playing games.

TimeLeft has tons of customization options:

- Right-click the different clock windows to select different fonts and colors to match your wallpaper.
- Select, download, or design your own skins to make the windows look just how you want them to look.
- Keep track of your busy schedule with the reminder tool. Type information about your appointments, and a desktop reminder will pop up before you're too late for that next meeting.

TimeLeft is easy to use, is fun to play with, and looks a whole lot more professional than Post-It notes all over your monitor.

Address: Site of the Day

PlanetSave.com

Imelda Jimenez

You do your best to toss empty soda cans and old newspapers into the recycling bin, but it's hard to figure out what else you can do to help preserve the Earth's resources. Go to PlanetSave.com (www.planetsave.com) to read about what governments and individuals around the globe are doing to help the environment. Visit the My Backyard section to find quick tips and read about the actions of environmentally conscious folks.

Share your thoughts on the site's message boards, or join the PlanetSave.com community to build your own free webpage dedicated to an issue close to your heart, including your pet or your garden. Building your webpage is quick and easy. The site provides a template. You don't need to know HTML.

1. Sign up for a free account.
2. Click the link to build a webpage.
3. Describe what your site is about and choose a username.
4. Fill in the blanks and post.

You can also donate to nonprofit organizations through the site (www.standardio.com/ps/). Do a quick search for an agency you like, or sort your options by state or topic. All proceeds go directly to the nonprofit.

Pay a visit to PlanetSave.com if you're an environmentalist who has something to say or if you just want to know what's going on with greenhouse gas emissions. Now if you'll excuse me, I'm off to see if anyone wants to carpool to work with me next week.

December

14

365

Techno Travel: Stay Entertained While You Fly

James Kim

The first hour of a typical flight is pleasant enough. But when hour two (of, say, five) kicks in, the world gets very boring. There's nothing to do except read *SkyMall* (again), take a nap, or watch an in-flight movie. It doesn't have to be that way. These tech goodies will make time zip by.

Gaming on the Go

Call me a sucker, but I bought the first-generation Nintendo Game Boy Advance long after TechTV Labs bashed it. It was even decent on planes because the overhead lamp lit the screen nicely. (I once played Tony Hawk nonstop from San Francisco to New York.) But in the end, like many others, I felt ripped off.

On the other hand, the $99 Game Boy Advance SP (www.gameboy.com) kicks butt and takes no prisoners. The wicked portable clamshell design closes to less than an inch thick, a 3.2-inch-by-3.2-inch square, and gets our tech mojo going.

The lithium-ion rechargeable battery (10 hours with the light on) and excellent ergonomics are nice, but the beautiful 2.9-inch side-lit display (same size and resolution as the original GBA) makes the SP enjoyable.

Available in platinum or cobalt, the 32-bit system has almost 500 titles and is backward-compatible with Game Boy and Game Boy Color Game Paks. The only thing missing is a headphone jack. Nintendo forces you to buy a special cable, which is still unavailable.

Watch Better Movies

In-flight movies usually stink. The $700 Panasonic PalmTheater DVD Audio/Video Player DVD-LA95 (www.prodcat.panasonic.com) offers a large, 9-inch-wide screen and is compatible with audio and MP3 CDs, video CDs, and DVD-audio, as well as DVD-R and DVD-RAM. The LA95 also features built-in Dolby Digital and DTS decoders, two virtual surround modes (16:9 and 4:3 mode), and a nice interface centered on a rounded blue jog controller.

The 500-plus horizontal line display looks nice enough, but it's not the nicest I've seen. Still, the 2.2-pound LA95 makes a great travel companion; its versatility makes it a great choice for home, too.

The included rechargeable battery pack lasts for about two and a half hours, good enough for most movies. The LA95 also ships with a remote control and AV cables.

Quiet Ride

Headphones dampen external noise. Noise-canceling headphones make ambient noise disappear—well, they try, anyway. Designed for use in airplanes (but useful elsewhere), the headphones have a chip that synthesizes an "antisound," canceling a lot of the hiss associated with airplane jets and ventilation systems.

- **Jensen's JNC50** (www.jensen.com) is a set of adjustable medium-size headphones that conveniently fold up for maximum portability. They operate on a single AAA battery and reduce the mid- and low-frequency tones of ambient noise by about half. You'll get a better listening environment, but the JNC50 doesn't cancel out all noise.

- I prefer the more portable and better-sounding $150 **Sony MDR-NC11** (www.sonystyle.com). The soft, silicon rubber earbuds are amazingly comfortable and conform to the ear canal to block out any noise. Power them on, and ambient noise fades away.

You'll notice a slight hiss and an increase in song volume with both of these models, leading us to believe that the best way to cancel noise is to increase the volume. Both models ship with an airline audio adapter for airline seats.

Celestia

Richard Statter and Roger Chang

Put the entire universe at your command with one simple free download called Celestia (www.shatters.net/celestia/). Anyone who's a bit curious about what's going on above us will love this well-designed space-simulation software. You can travel within our solar system, zooming in on the moon, the sun, and other planets.

Celestia is a 3D-based simulator. You need some sort of 3D acceleration video card and a relatively speedy computer to use it. The software is pretty involved. Read through the help and readme files to get the most out of the program. Here's what you'll find in Celestia's various menu options:

- **File.** Open the Celestia script, a file that has preplotted travel paths through our solar system. You can also save an image or record your virtual journey through our solar system and save the clip as an .avi file.

- **Navigation.** This is the meat of the program, where you can get Celestia to travel from, say, Mercury to Jupiter.
  1. Select a point of reference—the sun, for example. This is where you start your journey.
  2. Depending on your current view, the sun can be close in front of you or off in the distance. Center it on your screen with the solar system browser. This is probably the best way to navigate for your first dozen or so runs.
  3. Select a planet, moon, or satellite.
  4. Center the selection or go to it from your current location.
  5. As you progress, you can take "tours" through the solar system and view the real-time solar orbits of the planets and moons.

- **Time.** Here's where you speed up, slow down, or reverse time in Celestia. This is a great way to observe the planetary orbits over time.

- **Render.** Decide how you want Celestia to render the universe. You have control over the grid, the constellations, the stars, the asteroids, the lighting, and even the size of the screen.

- **View.** Choose how you want Celestia to present information. You can view multiple planetary objects. This setting is recommended for those of you with more muscle in your PCs.

- **Locations.** If you know where you want to begin your journeys, add more locations as navigation points.

Celestia lets you travel outside our solar system to more than 100,000 stars.

Download of the Day

Desktop Googles

Megan Morrone

I've talked about GoogleSearch Tool (www.frysianfools.com/ggsearch/download.asp), a program that lets you search Google from anywhere on your desktop. But Leo complained that the program was too big, especially in comparison to a similar program for the Mac.

Not surprisingly, our intrepid viewers sent me several programs that are just as efficient, smaller, and still free.

- **Desktop Google** (www.jeffloop.fcpages.com/DesktopGoogle.html)
- **SimpleGoogle** (www.davidyaw.com/SimpleGoogle)
- The all new **Google Search Tool** (www.nethugo.com)

If you use a Mac, check SockhoEasyFind (www.sockho-software.com/english/frame_sef.html), an alternative to Shadow Google (http://homepage.mac.com/stupidfish23/downloads.html).

Be a Good Gift Giver

Cat Schwartz

Do you remember how exciting it was to receive a toy as a young child? My aunt always used to bring my brothers and me gifts when she came to visit. But there was a problem: She just wasn't good at picking the right gifts. Regardless, we would get so excited about that entire extra suitcase full of gifts just for us. And we were always hoping that this year she would finally get it right and bring us the coolest gifts ever.

One year she had a boatload of small packages for me to open, and I thought that this had to be it—this was the time that Joan would get it right and make me the happiest kid in Happy Valley, California. Lo and behold, the ten small packages turned out to be a fake baking set that was good for nothing and smelled bad. To avoid becoming a lame toy giver like my Aunt Joan, visit these two sites.

Creative Toymaker, a group of stores in Connecticut, hit the bull's eye when it came up with the concept for Toys 2 Wish 4.com (www.toys2wish4.com). This company has searched nearly every toy store around the world to bring you the greatest range of top-quality toys on the market. The toys are organized into one extremely logical purchasing site. Here you can choose from 18 different categories, such as dolls, building, and science. Then you're directed to an even more specific menu of options within that genre of toy, which leads you to the goods and their details.

If you have no idea what to get a kid, Toys 2 Wish 4.com makes it easy for you with its Shop By Age options. You tell the site what age range you're shopping for and how much you want to spend; it provides you with a whole list of toys to choose from.

If the kid you're shopping for isn't really a kid, or if the kid is into strange or unusual action figures, anime, and toys, the site you want to shoot for is Raving Toy Maniac (www.toymania.com).

This online mag is one of the best places on the Net to find out about rare finds and to read full reviews that are extremely in-depth and informative. The site doesn't sell items, but it points you in the right direction in most cases by providing links and contacts.

Speaking of action figures, Sir Steve's Guide (www.sirstevesguide.com) is a great place to find *Star Wars* action figures.

Laporte Support

Phone Dialer in XP

Access the phone dialer in Windows XP. Here are the steps:

1. Click Start and choose Run.
2. Type **dialer** and click OK.
3. Click the Dial button.
4. Type the phone number in the Connect To box.
5. Choose to dial as a phone call, and click the Place Call button.

As long as the modem is connected to a phone line, you'll be able to make the call.

Software Basics

Tom Merritt

Software is a set of computer instructions that tells a computer what to do. As opposed to hardware, software doesn't exist in a tangible form.

Follow the Program

Programs make up almost all software. For instance, your Internet browser is software. It's made up of many programs that communicate with one another to make the browser work. Programmers create programs by writing in a programming language. This language is how the program talks to the computer.

What's an Installer?

The installer is a program that unpacks the programs and files that make your software work. Those programs and files are usually packed away in compressed files to save space and help prevent copying. The installer also tells your operating system that the software is installed and where to find it.

Where Do I Find It?

Some installers spring to life as soon as you put a CD-ROM in the drive, but only if you have autorun set up. If you turned off autorun, or if you're installing from floppy disks, you'll have to find the installer program. It's almost always called install.exe or setup.exe.

How Does an Installer Work?

When the installer is running, it looks in the directory of the install disk and uncompresses the files one by one. After it unpacks them, it moves them onto your hard drive or to wherever you told the installer to put them.

In the olden days, the installer copied over all the files. Now it not only copies them, but also tells your computer special information about them. Windows users may have heard of the Registry. The installer tells the Registry all kinds of special information to help your new software run smoothly.

The installer also cleans up after the install and often gives you a chance to read important information or register your new software.

If you're installing a new version of a software title, you don't need to uninstall the older version first. There shouldn't be a conflict.

How Do I Uninstall?

As the installer's job became more involved, so did the work of uninstalling software. Back in the dark early days of computing, you could delete a whole directory and be done with a program.

If you do that now, you get rid of the program, but you leave a whole mess of traces behind. Icons appear in your Start menu, shortcuts languish untended on your desktop and in your folders, and associated files wait for a program that no longer exists.

Today almost all decent programs deliver an uninstaller with the installer. The uninstaller works in reverse, deleting all the files, taking the information out of the Registry, and cleaning up all traces of the installed programs.

If you have the uninstaller, it's always better to use it. If you can't find or don't have an uninstaller, don't fret. Windows 95 and up, as well as third-party programs, provide ways to uninstall any program. Windows theoretically tracks all installs and provides a way to remove them in your control panel. The function is called Add/Remove.

Third-party programs such as Norton Utilities also claim to track all installs and help you uninstall them. None of these options works great, but they're better than deleting the programs by hand.

December
18

369

Get Safe with the "Giz Wiz"

Dick DeBartolo

Check out this wheelbarrow full of gadgets:

- **Lewis Locking Safety Knife.** Less than $10 (www.sealomatic.com/k710.html). This knife makes cutting open cardboard boxes much safer. It has a floating "guard" that protects your fingers from the blade. You must also hold down a button to cut. Release the button, and the safety guard locks in place again. Blades can be changed without tools.

- **Tire Minder.** $17.95 (www.garage-toys.com/tireminder.html). Proper tire pressure is very important. These valve caps come with color bars that indicate safe, caution, and dangerous tire pressure.

- **DocuDent.** Less than $18 (www.nov-8.com/docudent/docudent.htm). This kit includes everything you'll need to document a car accident: camera, ruler, whistle, and necessary forms.

- **Terrapin Safety Turtle.** $184 (www.safetyturtle.com). The Safety Turtle is worn by a child as a watch is. Whenever the child enters (or falls) into the pool, the receiver sounds an alarm that can be heard within 100 feet. An add-on unit can extend the distance to 400 feet. The receiver does not work in saltwater.

- **Elumina KidGuard Nightlight.** $8–10 (www.eluminalighting.com). This innovative nightlight has a shock guard to prevent accidents with partially plugged-in lights.

- **Streamlight Pro.** $25 (www.streamlight.com/led_propoly.htm). This LED flashlight is incredibly bright because it uses seven LEDs. Amazingly, it can run up to 155 hours on 4 AA batteries, about 20 times longer than a standard flashlight.

Download of the Day

Virtual Magnifying Glass v1.55

Megan Morrone

Virtual Magnifying Glass v1.55 (http://magnifier.sourceforge.net) is a free download that enlarges text on websites, word-processing documents, photographs, or any spot on your screen that requires a closer look.

Microsoft features a similar utility as part of its PowerToys pack (www.microsoft.com/windowsxp/pro/downloads/powertoys.asp) and as part of the accessibility features in Win98, but I like Magnifying Glass better. It's easier to use, and because it's an open-source program, we can expect more improvements in the future.

Using Virtual Magnifying Glass

- Download and unzip the program.
- Double-click the icon.
- Point your mouse to the area you want to magnify.
- When you're finished, click the left mouse button.

Magnifying Glass remains in your system tray. Just click it when you need it. You can also adjust the magnification by right-clicking the icon in the system tray.

Address: Site of the Night

Sales Circular

Compare product prices from big-name retailers at Sales Circular (www.salescircular.com).

Movie Mistakes

Cat Schwartz

Have you ever been watching a movie and noticed something wrong? I mean a camera operator in the background, an actor calling another actor by the person's real name, or someone coming out of a swimming pool bone dry? Movie industry people aren't always as smart as they make themselves out to be, and I've found a few sites that make them look downright dumb.

Eeggs.com (www.eeggs.com) helps you find hidden extras on DVDs, but it also helps you find movie blunders. Click the Movies link and use the slip-up finder to find the goofs.

Slipups.com (www.slipups.com) is the place to go to find slip-ups in movies, TV, books, and quotes. The mistakes are listed alphabetically.

Movie Mistakes (http://movie-mistakes.com) is a fantastic site filled with tons of cinematic blunders. The blooper archive contains a list of nearly every movie you have ever seen—or at least every movie I have seen.

Each movie title has a number next to it, indicating the number of mistakes that have been submitted for the film. Click on the title, and you're taken to a page filled with flubs. You can even vote for the mistake you feel was the worst of all time, or at least the ones that deserve to be recognized.

You may be surprised by some of the films included in the site's Top 20 Worst Movies. Because I want you all to visit the site, I'm not going to tell you the no. 1 movie.

The site is run by Jon Sandys, who is, needless to say, a movie buff with a keen eye. He welcomes your suggestions and posts the ones that seem to be legit, although he admits that he doesn't have time to verify each submission and mostly just trusts his audience.

Sandys also provides a chart of the most popular movies (http://movie-mistakes.com/charts.php) in theaters in the United States and the United Kingdom. Although it's not the most up-to-date chart, you can get a good idea of some new titles to check for silly mistakes.

Address: Site of the Day

World Wildlife Fund

Imelda Jimenez

The lions, tigers, and bears (oh my!) on the Discovery Channel are great, but a you can learn even more about the endangered species of the world at the World Wildlife Fund's website (www.wwf.org).

Start by selecting the country you want to focus on from the WWF's main page. Tabs along the top of each page will direct you to information about the organization, fun downloads, games, and information about how you can get involved.

Here are a couple must-visit stops on our tour of the WWF's United States site:

- **Take an exotic field trip** (www.worldwildlife.org/expeditions/). Expeditions in Conservation lets you track down scientists and find out what they're doing to help conserve exotic animals around the world. Yes, you'll learn the specifics of an expedition. Yes, you'll see amazing pictures of animals in the wild. But best of all, you can submit your questions about the trip.

- **Video gallery** (www.worldwildlife.org/videos/). If you have RealPlayer, you can watch videos about biodiversity, WWF lectures, and scientists in the field.

If you love the WWF and want to help its efforts to save endangered species and this big, blue planet or ours, become a member and support the organization.

Create and Remove Hyperlinks in Your Microsoft Office Applications

Nicole Guilfoyle

Hyperlinks organize the web, linking one part of a website to another webpage or part of a page so that you can quickly access new information. You can use hyperlinks in Microsoft Office applications to launch your browser and visit a website or open another file on your hard drive.

Create a Plain Hyperlink

1. Press Ctrl+K or choose Hyperlink from the Insert menu.
2. Type the URL in the Link to File or URL box.
3. Click OK.

Link a Picture or Text

1. Highlight the graphic or text you'd like to link.
2. Press Ctrl+K or choose Hyperlink from the Insert menu.
3. Type the URL in the Link to File or URL box or search for the file you'd like to link using the Browse button.
4. Click OK.

Remove a Hyperlink

1. Select the linked item and right-click it.
2. Click Hyperlink and choose Remove Hyperlink.

Download of the Day

Phatsoft TMR

Craig Higdon

This slick task manager can automate your life. Phatsoft TMR (www.phatsoft.net) lets you automate when your computer shows a message, plays a sound, opens a file, or shuts down. Here's how to use the simple intuitive interface:

1. Choose a date and time for your action, or set a countdown timer.
2. Choose which function you want to activate.
3. Write a message to yourself, set a sound to play, or open applications.
4. Schedule Shutdown, Restart, Logoff User, or Standby.

The manager also has a slick, built-in snooze feature similar to the one on your alarm clock. Push the task up to 120 minutes when the Phatsoft windows pops up.

It's a great, simple task automator and a handy reminder tool. Phatsoft deserves its name.

Megan's Tips

The frequently underrated Notepad is included with all versions of Windows. To access it, click Start, Programs, Accessories. Once Notepad is open, you can insert the date and time by pressing F5.

Info Angel

Dan Mitchell

No office? No job? No life? Fret not. You can still have a (digital) secretary. A wise man once told me that you can't plan your life on the back of a bar napkin. I'm not sure whether this was a warning about the dangers of alcohol or a plea for everyone to get a personal information manager (PIM). Two or three beers later, I downloaded Info Angel (www.angelicsoftware.com). It's a program that remembers everything so you don't have to.

A PIM is like a secretary, except it won't answer the phone or make you coffee. It keeps track of phone numbers, addresses, meetings, and important dates.

Info Angel has four parts:

- A notebook section where you can add text-based notes, recipes, directions, or anything you'd scribble in a notepad. The text editor lets you type or paste in text. You can even add photos and tables to documents.

- A contact book to keep track of all your friends, family, and business associates. You can add detailed information about each contact, including phone numbers, email addresses, and birthdays. Plus, you can add a photo to match the face with the name.

- An organizer complete with a calendar function to plan your schedule. Just pick a day, add an entry, and select a time. Info Angel pops up a reminder every time you're supposed to do something.

- A bookmark manager to keep track of all your favorite websites. Here's a quick tip: Info Angel comes with a built-in web browser in the side pane, but when you double-click one of your bookmarks, it launches a new IE window. To get it to open within the interface, click the bookmark once. The URL has been inserted into the address bar in the side pane. Now click the Refresh button. The site opens in Info Angel.

And here's another good feature: You can password-protect individual entries to keep your private information from prying eyes. Just right-click an entry, select Properties, click the Security tab, and enter a password.

Address: Site of the Night

YouDraw

Martin Sargent

For me, art is life. Whether I'm painting, drawing, pasteling, or sculpting, I'm happiest when I'm at my potter's wheel wearing a smock.

That's why I was ecstatic to find the site YouDraw (www.Youdraw.com). This site gives me a forum to show off my creations.

The YouDraw team is trying to amass 500,000 drawings that it will compile into a book and show in exhibits. Beyond just offering an entertaining diversion, the purpose of the site is to draw attention to the problem of world over-population. The idea? Collect 500,000 pictures of people around the world. Publish 12,000 books containing these images and create an exhibit. The result will be six billion stick people in one place at one time—an amount equal to the Earth's population in September 1999. To keep current, three books would need to be added a week, representing an additional 1.5 million people.

The drawing tool is crude, but people have managed to put together some pretty amazing works. Take a look at the contributions, or start working on your own masterpiece today!

Limit Internet Access

Greg Melton

We've shown you how to limit individual users from accessing programs or files in XP, but this question requires a different approach. You need to set up a filter. There are many different Internet filters. You can use a filter inside your browser, you can install specialty software, or you can import approved site templates into your browser or filtering software. Your Internet service provider (ISP) also might filter inappropriate content for you.

Filtering Rules

The platform for Internet content selection (PICS) is a standard that lets websites rate their content. For a site to comply with this standard, a webmaster must insert a piece of code into each webpage on the site. This code lets an Internet filter know what kind of content the site is displaying and then approve or disapprove of the content before serving it to your browser.

Most filtering software doesn't let you view sites that haven't been rated, but you'll be able to approve unrated sites if you deem them suitable for children.

Content Advisor

Content Advisor is built into Microsoft's Internet Explorer web browser (www.microsoft.com/windows/ie/evaluation/features/indepth/contentadv.asp). This feature lets parents use the PICS or other trusted organizations' rules, or specify their terms for approved or disapproved sites, no matter how a site rates itself.

To access the Content Advisor in Internet Explorer, follow these steps:

1. Open Internet Explorer.
2. Click Tools, Internet Option, and select the Content tab.
3. Under the Content Advisor section, click the Enable button.

Although the Content Advisor lets you set up a password to bypass disapproved sites, you need additional software to customize for different users on the same system.

ICRAfilter

The Internet Content Rating Association (www.icra.org) provides a free, downloadable filtering program. The main benefit of this program in Windows 2000/XP is that you can set up a different filter for each child.

Before you set up the ICRAfilter, you need to uninstall other Internet filters on your system and set up limited user accounts for each child. Just follow these steps:

1. Log on as an Administrator.
2. Single-click the Start menu, and select Control Panel.
3. Double-click the User Accounts icon.
4. Select the Create a New Account option.
5. Type a name for this new account and click the Next button.
6. Under Pick an Account Type, select the Limited option.
7. Click the Create Account button.

After you've created limited user accounts, install (www.icra.org/_en/filter/) the ICRAfilter. After it is installed, it appears in your system tray. Double-click the icon to configure the options.

Limit Internet Access (continued)

CyberPatrol

CyberPatrol (www.cyberpatrol.com), from SurfPatrol, lets you set up filtering profiles for different users, set the hours of the day that a user can access the Internet, and deny or allow users access to certain programs on your PC.

CyberPatrol also keeps an up-to-date CyberList (www.cyberpatrol.com/product/cyberlists.aspx) of approved and unapproved sites that you can import as templates. CyberPatrol is free to try for 14 days or $39 for a one-year subscription.

ISP Filtering

Some ISPs let you limit access to sites by setting up a special child account. For example, you can set—Kids Only, Young Adult, and so on—access levels in AOL. To find out which ISPs provide filtering services or software, visit the About.com Family Internet Section (http://familyinternet.about.com/cs/filteredisps/).

Speech Recognition

Morgan Webb

Speech recognition has long been the dream of the beleaguered typist. Why hunt and peck for that strangely located letter *R* when your wired friend can listen to you talk and take down every syllable? Here's the problem: You may think you talk just like everyone else, but the subtle differences in speech that seem insignificant to our organic brains are murderously complicated for our machines.

Despite the challenges, demand remains for functional speech-recognition software, and manufacturers are trying to comply. Unfortunately, consumer-friendly, off-the-shelf products are still a ways away. With that disclaimer in mind, let's take a look at the speech-recognition software that comes with Office XP.

First, you need to connect a microphone to your computer. When you have the microphone installed, open the Control Panel and choose

Speech. Then click the Speech Recognition tab (you must have Office XP to have this tab). Choose your profile and choose to train your profile, if this option is available. Spend as much time training as you can; the more training you do, the more accurate the tool will be. After you've trained your system, sit back and start chatting!

When you're done experimenting, make sure you turn off Speech Recognition. Leaving it running will cause havoc on your Office applications and IE, as your computer attempts to translate ambient noise into printed words. Please don't torture your machinery like this. It's isn't nice.

Download of the Day

Holiday Fonts

Megan Morrone

During this season of blatant commercialism, I'm glad some things are still free. Plus, I'm cheap. I don't like to spend a bunch of money on holiday cards, but I still like to keep in touch. That's why I always make my cards.

Everything you need to make beautiful cards can be found at the Dingbat pages (www.dingbatpages.com). This website offers dozens of free generic and religious-style fonts. Some of the dingbats are actual characters, and some are cute little images that can be enlarged and used as clip art for your cards.

Most of the fonts are freeware, although a few are shareware. When you get to the Dingbat pages, you can see the full character set by clicking on the small icon that looks like an eye. Enjoy!

- **Christmas Dingbats 1 and 2**
  www.dingbatpages.com/holiday/christmas.html
- **Ornament Dingbats**
  www.dingbatpages.com/ornament/ornament.html

December
24

Pat's Picks for Free and Legal Music Online

Patrick Norton

Apple's new Music Store offers 200,000 songs for download for $.99 each, but if you're anti-Apple you still have lots of choices for nonpirated music online.

- **MP3.com** (www.mp3.com) is the original source for free and legal MP3s. You'll find lots of bands you've never heard of, plus lots you'll be pleasantly surprised to find, such as The Mighty Mighty Bosstones (http://artists.mp3s.com/nn/artist/8/8866.html) and At The Drive-In (http://artists.mp3s.com/nn/artist/34/34431.html). You might also want to try Peoplesound.com (www.peoplesound.com), an MP3.com clone.

- **Emusic** (http://www.emusic.com) is one of my favorites (although I wish the sound quality was higher). You can try it out for free for 14 days and download 50 MP3s. After that, you pay $9.95 a month for 12 months, or $14.99 a month for 3 months. The site has artists from Matador, Epitaph, Lookout, Alternative Tentacles, and a ton of other labels. You'll find the bands Rancid, Flogging Molly, The Mighty Mighty Bosstones (yes, again), and oh so many more.

- **Music players.** Many media players offer free downloads and other links to free music. Try Winamp (www.winamp.com), Musicmatch (www.musicmatch.com), Windows Media Player (www.microsoft.com), and RealOne (www.real.com).

- **Bands.** Groups such as Pennywise (www.pennywisdom.com) often have MP3 downloads on their sites. Phish has an interesting version called Live Phish (www.livephish.com), where you can pay to download an entire concert. Choose the concert you want to hear, buy it, and download the audio in MP3 format or a new lossless audio format called FLAC http://flac.sourceforge.net. The band even provides cover art if you want to burn it to a CD.

Major Labels

- **Pressplay** (www.pressplay.com) uses secure Windows Media Audio format for its music files. It's $9.95 for unlimited downloads (that expire when your month-to-month subscription expires) and offers extra "packs" of Portable Downloads—$5.95 for the 5-pack, $9.95 for the 10-pack, and $18.95 for the 20-pack. As far as I know, you can only burn the Portable Downloads. Pressplay also lets you save your tracks on two separate computers, so you can enjoy your music at home and at work. Unfortunately, Pressplay offers no 95, NT, or Mac support. Of course, it does have The Clash.

- **MusicNet** (www.musicnet.com) is available only through AOL. It's $4.95 a month for 100 downloads and 100 streams of Microsoft's WMA 9 encoded files.

So start downloading that music legally, already!

Download of the Day

Santa Claus in Trouble

Santa Claus in Trouble (www.gamezone.com) is a free holiday game from Joymania Development and CDV Software Entertainment AG. Be careful, you will get addicted.

The object of the game is to collect the presents without letting Santa leap off into oblivion. Use your mouse to steer and your arrow keys to make Santa run.

Friendster

Sarah Lane

So I don't want to sound like I'm way too popular or anything, but sometimes I feel like I have too many friends. There aren't enough hours in the day to give lots of friends equal attention. I'm constantly feeling guilty about neglecting to call someone I should have called last week—or staying home instead of grabbing a drink with a buddy. Do you ever feel that way?

That's why I love Friendster (www.friendster.com). It's one of the most creative online ways I've found to keep in touch with friends while simultaneously introducing your friends to friends and making your social circle grander every day!

Here's How It Works

Sign up, fill out your profile, and add a nice little avatar for your pic. If you've been invited by someone, that person automatically becomes your friend. If not, you can ask to add someone as your friend, provided that that person is actually your friend. If not, that person has the option to reject your request to add him or her to your group. Of course, a real friend wouldn't do that, so you have nothing to worry about.

Here's Where It Gets Fun

After you've successfully added a friend, their friends become your friends. Well, not exactly your friends per se, but their information becomes available to you and they show up as New People in your network (kinda like acquaintances). And just like the real world, a few friends equals tons of acquaintances. For example, at the time of this writing, I have 5 friends and 23,207 people in my Personal Network. Wow!

Six Degrees from Sarah Lane

One fun game involves clicking on people in my Personal Network and figuring out how I'm loosely connected to them. Example: I know Maly, who knows Steven, who knows Grant, who knows Flank. I probably wouldn't know Flank unless I knew Maly. I now have the option to contact Flank directly or ask one of my connections to introduce me. Pretty civilized, huh?

Another feature I really like involves searching my Personal Network through keywords on my profile. Example: I love Hunter S. Thompson and say so in my Favorite Books section. If I click on that, Friendster searches my network and retrieves other profiles that mention HST. So not only do all these people know somebody who knows somebody I know, but we now have a common interest!

Friendster can be used for dating purposes, but it also has options for those in relationships who aren't looking for much more than activity partners and new buddies. I really like this site. You can play six degrees of Kevin Bacon with yourself.

Three Cool Spy Cams

Ray Weigel

When international super-spies need to video-tape people without being detected, they turn to small, hidden video cameras.

The lens of the camera can be set somewhere on your body: in a pen, eyeglasses, or a necktie, with a cord attached to a 12-volt power supply and wireless transmitter (about $300, sold separately) or mini-DV cam that you'd carry in your pocket to capture images.

The pen and necktie cameras delivered pretty clear pictures for the size of the hole needed to gather light into the lens, about 2mm across. Image quality was comparable to a standard black-and-white webcam, and with a little practice we learned to turn so we could capture images of specific people in the room without looking too unnatural.

Both cameras use CCDs (charged-coupled devices) and are very sensitive to light. However, they also consume a lot of power, so you need a 12V-power supply. Having to pocket the power supply, along with a DV camera or transmitter, makes them bulky and is a sure-fire way to blow your cover (the transmitter is about the size of a DV cam).

However, people are ingenious, and we're sure that if you absolutely have to videotape someone on the sly, you can find an unobtrusive place to conceal your camera.

Professional B/W Covert Pen Camera

This camera ($600, www.bolideco.com) fits in the breast pocket of a sport coat and has a small wire plug that connects to the power supply and camcorder or wireless transmitter. It looks like a real pen, and unless your subject wants to borrow your pen, you probably won't be found out.

Pros: Clear, crisp picture; tiny, tiny lens
Cons: Bulky transmitter; bulky power supply

Bolide International Covert Neck Tie

This camera ($260, www.bolideco.com) looks like a normal necktie but has a wire in the back and a lens housed below the knot of the tie. Like the pen cam, the wire on the Neck Tie cam is attached to a 12V-power supply and a DV cam or transmitter.

The tiny hole for the lens is harder to see than the lens of the pen camera, but because of the miniscule lens size, even the slightest bit of fabric can take up a lot of lens space.

Pros: Clear, crisp picture; tiny, tiny lens
Cons: Bulky transmitter; bulky power supply

Summary: Although these cameras deliver picture quality equivalent to that of a webcam, the large power supply and a bulky transmitter or DV camera makes them a little unwieldy for most super-spies.

BenQ 300mini

This camera ($99, www.benq.com) is not a wearable hidden camera, but we decided to include it, for a couple of reasons.

First of all, at 85mm × 40mm × 19.8mm, it's the smallest digital camera we've come across. Second, it's got a USB plug built into the camera, so you can plug it directly into your computer, bypassing the need for a cord and making it a snap to pull photos from the camera onto your hard drive.

The BenQ's 8MB of internal storage can hold 26 pictures at 640×480, or 107 pictures at 320×240. The image quality is decent but nowhere near a 3-megapixel camera. However, for the price, it's a great camera to snag quick snapshots with a minimal degree of fuss.

Bullfighter

Nicole Guilfoyle

At *The Screen Savers*, we often take meetings "off-line." Were these meetings ever "online"? Why is it so hard to say, "Hey, let's talk about this at my cube after the meeting"? You'd think we'd never had a conversation with people outside of work. Sound familiar? Bullfighter helps you keep phrases such as "corporate repository" and "paradigm shift" out of your vocabulary.

Jargon Alert! Jargon Alert!

Bullfighter (www.dc.com/insights/ bullfighter/downloads.asp) is a BS-detector for your Microsoft Word documents and PowerPoint presentations. It's the next best thing to having blinking lights and an alarm sound when you slip overused and unnecessarily complicated phrases into your writing.

1. Download and install the .exe program file. You'll need Windows NT, Windows 2000, or Windows XP with Microsoft Word and PowerPoint 2000.

2. Restart your computer.

3. Open the presentation or document you want to scan.

4. Click the Bullfighter icon on your toolbar.

5. Bullfighter scans your writing. When it finds jargon, it gives you a list of alternative phrases to insert.

6. Choose the phrase you want to use.

7. Click the Bull Index button to find out how much bull the tool found in your writing.

Reignite Your Relationship

We suggest plugging your personal email into Microsoft Word and running Bullfighter before you send another message to your significant other. You'll instantly make yourself more attractive.

If you like sounding like a corporate yes-man robot, keep on writing those convoluted jargon-filled speeches. If you want to start sounding like a normal human being again...

Download of the Day

Drempels

Roger Chang

I have a free file that'll have you pining for the free-love ambience of times long past. It's called Drempels (www.geisswerks.com/drempels/), and it adds a psychedelic kick to your screen saver and wallpaper. You heard me right—long hair. Experience the substance-enhanced euphoria of Wavy Gravy's train as your desktop wallpaper shimmers and flows like bad '60s pop art.

So what do you do when you get it? Simple. Install the thing and let it run. You have two options: Run it as a normal screen saver or run it as wallpaper. If you want to run it as a screen saver, select it from the screen saver list in the display properties. If you don't have a clue about what I'm referring to, follow these directions:

1. Right-click an empty area of your desktop and select Properties.

2. Go to the Screen Saver tab and select your screen saver.

3. Click OK.

If you want the lava lamp wallpaper effect, double-click the shortcut to Drempels. If you were somehow too hasty in cleaning your desktop and you accidentally deleted the shortcut, you'll find Drempels listed in your Start menu Programs list. Alter the rate of motion and size of the image by clicking the Drempels Config button.

Free love may be gone, but the Drempels freeware is available now.

Conquer the Universal Remote Control

Patrick Norton

It's time I admitted it: I have to clean up my coffee table mess.

- **RadioShack 6-in-1 Model 15-2133 Audio/Video Touchscreen** remote control's ($60, www.radioshack.com) glowing blue face changes icons depending on what device you're controlling. *The Screen Savers* segment producer Joshua Brentano swears by it. You can feel the button pad beneath the face. But why, oh why, can't it control the volume of my TV while in DVD mode?

- Harmony's latest remotes, **Model SST-748** ($200) and **Model SST-768** ($300, www.harmonyremote.com), are insanely priced (my DVD player cost less than these remotes) but have nifty features. They're small and considerably less button-saturated than most. They're configured via a webpage interface and a USB cable connected to your PC. Model SST-768 includes PVR controls, and both display TV listings right on the built-in LCD.

- **RadioShack 6-in-1 Model 15-2105** (www.radioshack.com). To balance things out, I paid a whopping $20 on the 6-in-1 Smart Remote Model 15-2104. It has four programmable Smart Keys that can do anything you want. For example, if your DVD player has a Step/Slow key to advance a single frame at a time, you can program one of the Smart Keys to be the Step/Slow key.

Tips for Universal Remote Users

There's an old saying that goes something like, "90% of the features in Microsoft Word aren't used by 90% of the users." That saying also applies to remotes.

- Don't obsess over needing the $300 LCD interface remote with an icon for your DVD remote's Angle key—unless you use that key.

- That said, the newer the design, the more likely it is to have buttons for the latest gadgets. Only the new and pricey Harmony controls offer a mode to control a PVR. With the $20 remote, the TiVo remote stays on the coffee table.

- Think twice before buying a supercheap remote that uses your current remote controls to program it. If you lose those remotes, you won't be able to reprogram the universal remote. You'll probably have to reprogram it when the batteries wear out.

- Some programmable remotes offer a "manual code search" that lets you try every code stored in the unit in the hope that one works on your device. It's time-consuming but worth a shot.

- Don't lose the manual. Many remotes require a code based on the manufacturer and the device.

- Look for a remote with programmable keys. It won't lose your favorite remote's features. Case in point: The 6-in-1 remote from RadioShack doesn't have an Eject key. I have to walk over and hit Eject?

- Got TiVo or Replay? You're probably not gonna find all those buttons on any universal remote. It might be easier to program your TiVo remote to fire up your TV and AV equipment (www.tivofaq.com).

- I have big hands, and I had trouble managing the larger remote controls. Take the remote out of the box and try it before you buy it.

- Remote Central (www.remotecentral.com) has an awesome array of reviews of universal remotes.

Answer Kids' Tough Questions

Cat Schwartz

Parents, you're expected to have the answers to all your kids' tough questions. But sometimes you don't know the answer, or how to say it, or where to get the most accurate information. And kids, sometimes you don't want to ask your parents because you're embarrassed, or you're a teenager who hates talking to your parents. I found some trustworthy sites that will help you.

TV to Your Desktop

The folks at Nick Jr. Parents (www.nickjr.com/grownups/parenting/) have a great page where you can find creative ways to interact with your children while talking about scary subjects. You can also find entertainment guides, expert advice, and parenting tips.

PBS Kids Parents' Pages (www.pbs.org/parents/) is full of articles about helping children deal with divorce, going to the doctor, handling imaginary friends, dealing with mad feelings, and more. You can also work with your kids to make their own TV show to explain their thoughts and feelings.

Sesame Street Parents has an Advice Finder (www.sesamestreet.org/parents/advice/) search engine that helps you find specific topics. Choose categories from its drop-down menus, or use the search box and sift through the results.

Tackle the Toughest Issues

Believe it or not, 8- to 12-year olds are ready to start having conversions about sex, violence, AIDS, and drinking. Talking with Kids About Tough Issues (www.talkingwithkids.org) is a national campaign by Children Now (www.childrennow.org/) and the Kaiser Family Foundation (www.kff.org). The site guides you through the process of tackling each subject in an open, honest, and age-appropriate manner.

Staying Healthy

KidsHealth (www.kidshealth.com) is produced by The Nemours Center for Children's Health Media and The Nemours Foundation (www.nemours.org/no/). It's separated into sections for Parents, Teens, and Kids. When you've selected your category, you're given a menu filled with issues. Find the issue you want and choose from a list of articles that are easy to read, easy to understand, and accurate.

I know that reading long articles can be a drag, but the site does an excellent job of making the articles interesting and fun.

The Parents section has 11 categories, including General Health, Emotions and Behavior (my mom could have used this one), Positive Parenting, and a constantly changing In The News article.

If you're a teen, you'll find the same layout, but the topics include Your Body, Sexual Health (this helps for things you don't want to ask your parents about), Drugs and Alcohol, Disease and Conditions, Staying Safe, and more.

Kids, you've lucked out. Along with the same easy-to-read articles (on topics like Dealing with Feelings, Growing Up, My Body, and more), you can play interactive games. There's a kid with clickable body parts and an interactive guide to how the body part works. My Journal lets you meet and learn all about children who are just like you, but who have health problems.

Another bonus: The site is also available in Spanish.

How Effective Are You?

You sat down and had "the talk." Now take the test at iVillage (http://quiz.ivillage.com/parentsoup/tests/teensex.htm). Answer a series of questions for an assessment of how you handled the situation. It also has advice about how to do better next time.

In my opinion, this is a great place to go before having the talk. You can get some solid advice on how you can better handle the real conversation when it comes.

December

30

Twenty Years of Goofy Gadgets

Dick DeBartolo

During my two decades as the "Giz Wiz," I've amassed an impressive collection of bizarre gadgets. When I told Leo about my secret cache, he flipped. "I'd love to see them," he said. So here they are:

- **Acclimator, The Jet Lag Watch** (www.jetlag.com). It should be called the anti–jet lag watch. You program it with the length of your flight and the direction you're flying. If you're flying east, the watch slowly speeds up so it's on local time when you land. Flying west, it slows down. The inventor believed that the very act of resetting your watch increased jet lag. It sells for $49.

- **Arm Alarm Sport Watch** (www.huntsmart.com), called "the watch with an attitude," because it has a built-in horn. It not only tells time, it also blasts a loud alert at the push of a button. Now you can give that old lady a warning before you bowl her over while you skateboard.

- **ShowerStar** (www.oryanindustries.com/showerstar/) is a great idea! The water pressure from the showerhead powers a built-in light. You can even buy bulbs of different colors so your shower hue can match your mood! It sells for $25 to $35.

- **Timex Data Link Watch** (www.timex.com/bin/detail.tmx?item=048148901308). The original Data Link came out in 1996. Newer models that let you beam information to and from your computer sell for $20 on eBay, but an original with the box (which I fortunately kept) sells for more than $50. I'm not selling mine! Data Link technology is going bye-bye because you need a special adapter to beam information from a flat screen or laptop.

- **Extend-A-Fork** (http://toodles.secure-shops.net/Merchant2/merchant.mv?Screen=PROD&Store_Code=TCS&Product_Code=P-EF). This novelty has somehow survived the years. It's a 7-inch fork that telescopes to nearly 18 inches. It's ideal for folks who like to sample food on other people's plates! It goes for $5.50.

Download of the Day

TypingMaster Pro

Craig Higdon

If you're like me, you have horrible handwriting. Hopefully you've made up for it by developing solid typing skills. If not, Brett has just the thing you need: a free download called TypingMaster Pro (www.typingmaster.com).

Budding typists will be challenged by TypingMaster Pro's array of tests and warm-up games. Here's how each type of exercise works.

Typing Tests

Copy excerpts from the text of famous works, such as "The Wizard of Oz" and poems by Rudyard Kipling. Set the timer and type like the wind in order to beat the clock. Make sure you type accurately; mistakes are counted against your words-per-minute score.

Warm-Up Games

The warm-up games test your ability to type while keeping your cool under pressure. The games are fairly similar. You're asked to type words or letters within a certain time limit. If you're doing well, the game speeds up, increasing the difficulty level.

TypingMaster Pro is sure to help you increase your typing skills and develop your finger finesse, as long as you already know the fundamentals of touch-typing. For a more in-depth tutorial, you need to buy the full version.

Index

D

T